# Classical Analysis of Real-Valued Functions

# Classical Analysis of
# Real-Valued
# Functions

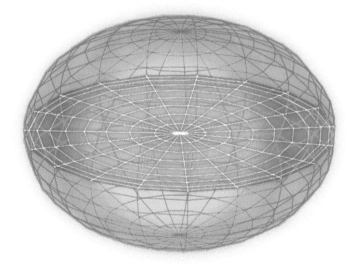

## V. S. Serov
### University of Oulu
### Oulu, Finland

Society for Industrial and Applied Mathematics
Philadelphia

| | |
|---|---|
| *Publications Director* | Kivmars H. Bowling |
| *Executive Editor* | Elizabeth Greenspan |
| *Acquisitions Editor* | Paula Callaghan |
| *Developmental Editor* | Rose Kolassiba |
| *Managing Editor* | Kelly Thomas |
| *Production Editor* | Lisa Briggeman |
| *Copy Editor* | Susan Fleshman |
| *Production Manager* | Donna Witzleben |
| *Production Coordinator* | Cally A. Shrader |
| *Compositor* | Cheryl Hufnagle |
| *Graphic Designer* | Doug Smock |

**Library of Congress Control Number 2023018600**

# Contents

# List of Figures

# Preface

The classical analysis of real-valued functions of one or more variables includes (along with other disciplines) elementary number theory, sequences and series, continuity and differentiability, proper and improper Riemann (Riemann–Stieltjes) integrals, elementary functions, investigation of graphs, implicit functions and dependence, uniform convergence, and integrals depending on a parameter. This book contains all these subjects and combines them based on a unified approach, starting with the theory of real numbers. In addition it contains Lebesgue measure and Lebesgue integration. The approach here is similar to Jordan measure and corresponding Riemann integration. Usually this material is not included in university courses for first- and second-year students, but we include it in this book on classical analysis due to the importance of Lebesgue's ideas and their connections with classical analysis.

The book consists of two parts: analysis of numbers and functions of one variable, including many classical inequalities and series, and analysis of multivariable functions, including all classical results of multidimensional integration. This part also includes (as mentioned earlier) Lebesgue measure and Lebesgue integration for one-dimensional and multidimensional cases and corresponds to some courses in functional analysis and function theory. But it encompasses classical mathematical analysis and its numerous applications in mathematical physics and applied mathematics. The second part covers the abstract approach of analysis for continuous functions in normed Banach spaces and establishes some connections with classical analysis. In addition, the abstract Banach fixed point theorem in Banach spaces is applied to nonlinear differential equations.

The material in this book corresponds to three-semester courses on mathematical analysis, including calculus, in classical Russian universities. Most of the material is devoted to a course of mathematical analysis for first-year students. A course of the same name was taught by the author at Lomonosov Moscow State University, Faculty of Computational Mathematics and Cybernetics from 1991 to 2001.

Each part of the book forms a self-contained text, although all parts are linked by a common approach and can be read independently. The book is designed to be an introduction to modern real analysis and may establish the connection with modern harmonic analysis and differential equations. But even in that case the book contains some real applications to differential geometry, Fourier series, differential equations, and other subjects.

The book contains more than 350 exercises and approximately 100 examples that are integral to the text. Some of the exercises are quite difficult and require much effort. But most of the exercises just clarify the theoretical considerations of the material. Each chapter contains its own collection of exercises and examples with their own numeration. They are not only integral to the book but also indispensable for the understanding of all parts whose collection is the content of this book. It can be expected that a careful reader will seriously consider and complete all these exercises and examples. But it can also be mentioned that the book cannot be considered as only a calculus text for students (in the usual understanding of this terminology) since all statements, theorems, lemmas, and propositions are proved and explained throughout. There is no doubt, however, that this book, especially its first part, can be used as a regular calculus text since it contains many exercises of different levels.

This book is intended for students in the first and second years of classical universities majoring in pure and applied mathematics, but even students of engineering disciplines may find here very useful information and material.

The crucial points of the first part of the book are the theorems of existence of supremum and infimum of bounded sets on the real line, and the Lagrange's formula for differentiable functions. Many applications of these two results are threaded throughout the whole text and are (from the author's point of view) crucial for classical mathematical analysis. We mention here the famous and very important Weierstrass approximation theorem and its real application to the summation by the trigonometric polynomials of continuous functions due to the regularization method of Tychonoff.

Concerning the second part of the book, the implicit function theorem plays a central and very important role. Another topic central to this material concerns the proof of the divergence theorem or the Gauss–Ostrogradskii formula and, as a consequence, surface integration. It must also be mentioned here that two fundamental results of classical real analysis, that is, the Heine–Borel lemma and the Ascoli–Arzelà theorem, are proved under quite general assumptions. Concerning Lebesgue measure and Lebesgue integration it can be mentioned that this part, along with Lebesgue's theory, itself contains the Lebesgue spaces $L^p$ and the Riesz theory on the representation of linear continuous functionals in these spaces. In particular, one of the most important theorems of one-dimensional classical analysis on the differentiability of monotone functions almost everywhere is proved here (Lebesgue's theorem). In addition, the one-dimensional indefinite Lebesgue integral is also presented in this part. Thus this book might be considered as an introduction to functional analysis and theory of $L^p$ spaces. The measure theory, both Jordan and Lebesgue, is important enough in itself, and not only for the introduction of the concept of an integral (Riemann or Lebesgue), and therefore deserves to be included in university courses on classical analysis. It should be noted that the presentation in this book, intended for first- and second-year students of Russian and possibly European universities, does not imply and in fact does not require consideration of metric (normed) spaces and their completeness, as is possibly assumed in American universities. This is the reason why the great theorems of functional analysis, namely the Banach–Steinhaus theorem, the Hahn–Banach theorem, the open mapping theorem, and the closed graph theorem, are left for Analysis III (Functional Analysis). The inclusion of the Lebesgue measure and Lebesgue integral in no way contradicts the basic principles of classical real analysis. Analysis of continuous functions in Banach spaces presented at the end of the book underlines only the importance of the classical approach.

In closing we note that this book is not as comprehensive as some known texts on classical mathematical analysis and functional analysis, but it can be considered as a good introduction to them. We have tried to collect the simplest proofs of classical well-known theorems and have given to each of them a special name in order to stress the main point of the results. Last but not least, we want to say that when writing the Lebesgue integration we were greatly influenced by the excellent book of Kolmogorov and Fomin [4]. Additional reading is recommended in the bibliography.

The present book could not have appeared at all without the strong participation, both in content and typesetting, of my colleague Adj. Prof. Markus Harju from the University of Oulu, Finland.

Oulu, Finland
March 2023                                                                                      Valery Serov

# Part I

# Analysis of numbers and functions of one variable

# Chapter 1

# Introduction

In this (preliminary) chapter we will prove the most important classical inequalities, along with the binomial formula of Newton; we assume that the reader has mastered operations with rational numbers. The main method applied here is the method of mathematical induction, or induction for short. Some operations on abstract sets (which are used later in the book) are also considered here.

We denote by $\mathbb{N}$ the set of all positive integer numbers, i.e., $\{1, 2, \ldots, n, \ldots\}$, and $\mathbb{N}_0 = \mathbb{N} \cup \{0\}$. By the symbol $\mathbb{Z}$ we denote the set of all integer numbers (positive, negative, and zero), i.e., $\{0, \pm 1, \pm 2, \ldots, \pm n, \ldots\}$. By the symbol $\mathbb{Q}$ we denote the set of all rational numbers, i.e., the set of all fractions of the form

$$q = \frac{m}{n}, \quad m \in \mathbb{Z}, n \in \mathbb{N}.$$

It is assumed that the arithmetic operations under rational numbers are known. More precisely,

$$q_1 \pm q_2 = \frac{m_1}{n_1} \pm \frac{m_2}{n_2} = \frac{m_1 n_2 \pm n_1 m_2}{n_1 n_2},$$

$$q_1 \cdot q_2 = \frac{m_1}{n_1} \cdot \frac{m_2}{n_2} = \frac{m_1 m_2}{n_1 n_2},$$

and

$$\frac{q_1}{q_2} = \frac{m_1/n_1}{m_2/n_2} = \frac{m_1 n_2}{n_1 m_2}, \quad m_2 \neq 0.$$

Along with these operations we assume that the $n$th root of the number $b > 0$ for $n \in \mathbb{N}$ is understood as the number $c := \sqrt[n]{b}$ for which $c^n = b$. Moreover, $b^\alpha$ with $\alpha = n_1/n_2, n_1, n_2 \in \mathbb{N}$ is understood as $b^\alpha = b^{n_1/n_2} = (\sqrt[n_2]{b})^{n_1}$. In addition, by $\log_a b, a > 0, b > 0$ we mean the number $c := \log_a b$ such that $a^c = b$, assuming (for the moment) that the values are rational. It is also assumed that the trigonometric quantities $\sin \alpha, \cos \alpha$, and others are well known from high school geometry courses.

We use the *method of mathematical induction* (MMI). This method can be explained as follows: if we want to prove some statement $S(n)$ depending on $n \in \mathbb{N}$ for $n \geq n_0 \geq 1$ then

1. we need first to prove (or to check) the validity of $S(n)$ for $n = n_0 \geq 1$, and

2. under the assumption that $S(k)$ is true (or valid) for $k \geq n_0$ we need to prove its validity for $n = k + 1$, i.e., to check the validity of $S(k + 1)$. In other words, we go step by step to the final result.

We demonstrate this method by proving some statements that play an important and necessary role in our later considerations and discussions. However, they have independent interest as well.

3

**Bernoulli inequality**   Let $a_1, a_2, \ldots, a_n$ be nonzero numbers of the same sign and all greater than $-1$. Then

$$(1 + a_1)(1 + a_2) \cdots (1 + a_n) \geq 1 + a_1 + a_2 + \cdots + a_n \qquad (1.1)$$

and the equality in (1.1) holds if and only if $n = 1$.

***Proof.*** Denoting by $S(n)$ the inequality (1.1) we see that $S(1)$ is obviously true. Next, assuming that $S(k)$ is true for $k \geq 1$, i.e.,

$$(1 + a_1)(1 + a_2) \cdots (1 + a_k) \geq 1 + a_1 + a_2 + \cdots + a_k,$$

let us prove that $S(k + 1)$ is also true. By the assumption of induction and by the fact that $(1 + a_{k+1}) > 0$ we have

$$(1 + a_1)(1 + a_2) \cdots (1 + a_k)(1 + a_{k+1}) \geq (1 + a_1 + a_2 + \cdots + a_k)(1 + a_{k+1})$$
$$= 1 + a_1 + a_2 + \cdots + a_k + a_{k+1} + a_{k+1}(a_1 + \cdots + a_k).$$

But the last term in the latter sum is strictly positive since $a_j \neq 0, j = 1, 2, \ldots, k$, and has the same sign. Hence, $S(k + 1)$ is true. Moreover, for $n > 1$, we have always strict inequality in (1.1).

**Corollary 1.1.** *If $h > -1$ then*

$$(1 + h)^n \geq 1 + nh,$$

*where equality holds if and only if either $n = 1$ or $h = 0$.*

**The inequalities for harmonic, geometric, arithmetic, and quadratic means**   Assume that $a_1, a_2, \ldots, a_n > 0$. Then

$$\frac{n}{1/a_1 + 1/a_2 + \cdots + 1/a_n} \leq \sqrt[n]{a_1 a_2 \cdots a_n}$$

$$\leq \frac{a_1 + a_2 + \cdots + a_n}{n} \leq \sqrt{\frac{a_1^2 + a_2^2 + \cdots + a_n^2}{n}}. \qquad (1.2)$$

The four terms in (1.2) are called *harmonic mean, geometric mean, arithmetic mean*, and *quadratic mean* of positive numbers $a_1, a_2, \ldots, a_n$, respectively. In addition, the equality in all inequalities of (1.2) holds if and only if $a_1 = a_2 = \cdots = a_n$.

We first prove an auxiliary assertion which is of independent interest.

**Proposition 1.2.** *Let $\alpha_1, \alpha_2, \ldots, \alpha_n > 0$ and $\alpha_1 \alpha_2 \cdots \alpha_n = 1$. Then*

$$\alpha_1 + \alpha_2 + \cdots + \alpha_n \geq n \qquad (1.3)$$

*and the equality in (1.3) holds if and only if $\alpha_1 = \alpha_2 = \cdots = \alpha_n = 1$.*

***Proof.*** Denoting the inequality (1.3) by $S(n)$ we see that $S(1)$ is clearly true. Assume that $S(k)$ is true for $k \geq 1$. Then we need to show that $S(k + 1)$ is also true. Indeed, if $\alpha_1 \alpha_2 \cdots \alpha_{k+1} = 1$ then by using the assumption of induction we obtain that

$$\alpha_1 + \alpha_2 + \cdots + \alpha_{k-1} + \alpha_k \alpha_{k+1} \geq k.$$

We first exclude the case when one (or all) of the numbers $\alpha_1, \alpha_2, \ldots, \alpha_k$ is equal to 1, since in this case the required inequality is trivially valid. Next, due to assumptions all these numbers cannot be greater than 1 or less than 1 simultaneously, i.e., there are at least two such that one is greater than 1 and one is less than 1.

Further, without loss of generality we may assume that $\alpha_k > 1$ and $\alpha_{k+1} < 1$ since otherwise the condition $\alpha_1 \alpha_2 \cdots \alpha_{k+1} = 1$ is not fulfilled. Thus, the latter inequality can be rewritten as

$$\alpha_1 + \alpha_2 + \cdots + \alpha_k + \alpha_{k+1}$$
$$\geq k + 1 + \alpha_k + \alpha_{k+1} - 1 - \alpha_k \alpha_{k+1} = (k+1) + (\alpha_k - 1)(1 - \alpha_{k+1}) > k + 1.$$

This proves also the condition for equality in (1.3).

Now let
$$\alpha_j := \frac{a_j}{\sqrt[n]{a_1 a_2 \cdots a_n}}, \quad j = 1, 2, \ldots, n.$$

Then obviously $\alpha_1 \alpha_2 \cdots \alpha_n = 1$, and by using Proposition 1.2 we obtain

$$\frac{a_1}{\sqrt[n]{a_1 a_2 \cdots a_n}} + \frac{a_2}{\sqrt[n]{a_1 a_2 \cdots a_n}} + \cdots + \frac{a_n}{\sqrt[n]{a_1 a_2 \cdots a_n}} \geq n.$$

This proves the second inequality in (1.2). It is clear also that equality here holds if and only if $a_1 = a_2 = \cdots = a_n$.

The first inequality in (1.2) is now a simple consequence of the previous one. Indeed, from the above we have

$$\sqrt[n]{\frac{1}{a_1} \frac{1}{a_2} \cdots \frac{1}{a_n}} \leq \frac{\frac{1}{a_1} + \frac{1}{a_2} + \cdots + \frac{1}{a_n}}{n}$$

or

$$\frac{n}{\frac{1}{a_1} + \frac{1}{a_2} + \cdots + \frac{1}{a_n}} \leq \sqrt[n]{a_1 a_2 \cdots a_n}$$

and still equality here holds if and only if $\frac{1}{a_1} = \frac{1}{a_2} = \cdots = \frac{1}{a_n}$, i.e., $a_1 = a_2 = \cdots = a_n$.

In order to prove the third inequality in (1.2) we prove the following proposition.

**Proposition 1.3 (Cauchy–Schwarz–Bunjakovskii).** *Let* $a_1, a_2 \ldots, a_n > 0$ *and* $b_1, b_2 \ldots, b_n > 0$. *Then*

$$\sum_{k=1}^{n} a_k b_k \leq \sqrt{\sum_{k=1}^{n} a_k^2} \sqrt{\sum_{k=1}^{n} b_k^2}. \tag{1.4}$$

*Proof.* Introducing a function $F(\lambda)$ of real variable $\lambda$ by

$$F(\lambda) := (a_1 + \lambda b_1)^2 + (a_2 + \lambda b_2)^2 + \cdots + (a_n + \lambda b_n)^2$$

we see that $F(\lambda) \geq 0$ for all $\lambda$. Rewriting $F(\lambda)$ as

$$F(\lambda) = \lambda^2 (b_1^2 + b_2^2 + \cdots + b_n^2) + 2\lambda(a_1 b_1 + a_2 b_2 + \cdots + a_n b_n) + (a_1^2 + a_2^2 + \cdots + a_n^2)$$

we may conclude that $F(\lambda) \geq 0$ for all real $\lambda$ if and only if the discriminant $D = \left(\sum_{k=1}^{n} a_k b_k\right)^2 - \left(\sum_{k=1}^{n} a_k^2\right)\left(\sum_{k=1}^{n} b_k^2\right) \leq 0$. This means that (1.4) is proved. It can be mentioned that equality in (1.4) holds if and only if $F(\lambda) = 0$ for some $\lambda = \lambda_0 \neq 0$, i.e., $b_j = -\lambda_0 a_j$ for all $j$.

The third inequality in (1.2) follows now as

$$\frac{a_1 + a_2 + \cdots + a_n}{n} = a_1\frac{1}{n} + a_2\frac{1}{n} + \cdots + a_n\frac{1}{n} \leq \sqrt{\sum_{k=1}^{n} a_k^2}\sqrt{\sum_{k=1}^{n}\frac{1}{n^2}}$$

$$= \sqrt{\frac{a_1^2 + a_2^2 + \cdots + a_n^2}{n}}$$

and equality here holds if and only if $a_j = -\lambda_0\frac{1}{n}$ for some $\lambda_0 \neq 0$ for all $j$ ($\lambda_0 < 0$ in this concrete case), i.e., $a_1 = a_2 = \cdots = a_n$. Thus, all inequalities in (1.2) are proved.

**Corollary 1.4.** *Under the conditions of Proposition* 1.3 *the inequality*

$$\sum_{k=1}^{n}\frac{b_k^2}{a_k} \geq \frac{\left(\sum_{k=1}^{n} b_k\right)^2}{\sum_{k=1}^{n} a_k}$$

*holds.*

**Corollary 1.5.** *For any* $n \in \mathbb{N}, n \geq 2$ *the inequality*

$$n! < \left(\frac{n+1}{2}\right)^n$$

*holds, where* $n! = 1 \cdot 2 \cdots n$.

**Proof.** Let $a_j = j$ for $j = 1, 2, \ldots, n$. Since $n \geq 2$ and $a_1 \neq a_2 \neq \cdots \neq a_n$, the second inequality in (1.2) leads to

$$\sqrt[n]{n!} = \sqrt[n]{1 \cdot 2 \cdots n} < \frac{1 + 2 + \cdots + n}{n} = \frac{n+1}{2},$$

which implies the claim.

**Exercise 1.6.** Using MMI prove that

1. $n! > \left(\frac{n}{1+1/2+\cdots+1/n}\right)^n$,

2. $(\sqrt{n})^n < n!$,

3. $a_1 a_2 \cdots a_n + (1 - a_1) \cdots (1 - a_n) \leq n!$ if $0 \leq a_k \leq k$,

4. $\frac{3n}{2n+1} < \sum_{k=1}^{n}\frac{1}{k^2} \leq \frac{5n}{3n+2}$,

5. $\sum_{k=1}^{n}\frac{1}{\sqrt{k}} > 2(\sqrt{n+1} - 1)$

for $n \geq 2$.

**Binomial theorem of Newton**   The following formula holds:

$$(a+b)^n = \sum_{j=0}^{n}\binom{n}{j}a^j b^{n-j}, \tag{1.5}$$

where $\binom{n}{j}$ denotes the *binomial coefficient*

$$\binom{n}{j} = \frac{n!}{j!(n-j)!} = \binom{n}{n-j}, \quad j = 0,1,\ldots,n, \quad 0! = 1. \tag{1.6}$$

**Proof.** Denoting the equality (1.5) by $S(n)$ we can easily check using (1.6) that $S(1)$ is valid. Let us assume that $S(k)$ is valid for $k \geq 1$. We will show that $S(k+1)$ is also valid. Indeed,

$$(a+b)^{k+1} = (a+b)\sum_{j=0}^{k}\binom{k}{j}a^j b^{k-j} = \sum_{j=0}^{k}\binom{k}{j}a^{j+1}b^{k-j} + \sum_{j=0}^{k}\binom{k}{j}a^j b^{k-j+1}$$

$$= \sum_{j=1}^{k+1}\binom{k}{j-1}a^j b^{k+1-j} + \sum_{j=0}^{k}\binom{k}{j}a^j b^{k+1-j}$$

$$= a^{k+1} + \sum_{j=1}^{k}\left[\binom{k}{j-1} + \binom{k}{j}\right]a^j b^{k+1-j} + b^{k+1}.$$

Since

$$\binom{k+1}{k+1} = \binom{k+1}{0} = 1,$$

it remains to show that

$$\binom{k}{j-1} + \binom{k}{j} = \binom{k+1}{j}, \quad j = 1,2,\ldots,k.$$

But this follows straightforwardly as

$$\binom{k}{j-1} + \binom{k}{j} = \frac{k!}{(j-1)!(k+1-j)!} + \frac{k!}{j!(k-j)!}$$

$$= \frac{k!}{(j-1)!(k-j)!}\left(\frac{1}{k+1-j} + \frac{1}{j}\right)$$

$$= \frac{k!}{(j-1)!(k-j)!}\cdot\frac{k+1}{j(k+1-j)} = \frac{(k+1)!}{j!(k+1-j)!} = \binom{k+1}{j}.$$

Next we consider some elements of set theory which are used in further considerations.

Some collection (finite or infinite) of objects is called a *set*, and these objects are called the elements of the set. We use the symbols $X, Y, Z, \ldots$ or $A, B, C, \ldots$ for denoting sets and the symbols $x, y, z, \ldots$ or $a, b, c, \ldots$ for denoting the elements of these sets, respectively. The fact that elements belong to sets will be denoted as

$$x \in X, y \in Y, z \in Z, \ldots, a \in A, b \in B, c \in C, \ldots.$$

**Assumption.** For any element $x$ and any set $X$ there are only two possibilities: either $x \in X$ or $x \notin X$, where the latter notation means that the element $x$ does not belong to the set $X$, i.e., it is not an element of $X$.

A set that does not contain any elements is called an *empty set* and is denoted as $\emptyset$. We will use the following shorthand symbols throughout the book:

$\forall$ "any," "for any," "all," "for all"

$\exists$ "exists," "there exists," "there is"

$\Rightarrow$ "follows in," "implies"

$\Leftarrow$ "follows back"

$\Leftrightarrow$ "if and only if," "is equivalent," "necessary and sufficient."

We list some properties and facts:

1. $X = Y \Leftrightarrow \forall x \in X \Rightarrow x \in Y$ and $\forall y \in Y \Rightarrow y \in X$.

2. $X \subset Y \Leftrightarrow \forall x \in X \Rightarrow x \in Y$. In particular, $X = Y \Leftrightarrow X \subset Y$ and $Y \subset X$.

3. $X \cup Y = \{x : x \in X \text{ or } x \in Y\} = Y \cup X$. Moreover, by induction we may define

$$\bigcup_{k=1}^{n} X_k, \quad \bigcup_{k=1}^{\infty} X_k.$$

   All these sets are called *union of sets.*

4. $X \cap Y = \{x : x \in X \text{ and } x \in Y\} = Y \cap X$. Again, by induction we may define

$$\bigcap_{k=1}^{n} X_k, \quad \bigcap_{k=1}^{\infty} X_k.$$

   These sets are called *intersection of sets.*

5. $X \cap Y = \emptyset \Leftrightarrow X$ and $Y$ have no common elements. In this case we say that $X$ and $Y$ are not intersecting (disjoint).

6. $X \setminus Y = \{x : x \in X \text{ and } x \notin Y\}$. This set is called the difference between $X$ and $Y$, and this difference is not symmetric, i.e., $X \setminus Y \neq Y \setminus X$ in general.

7. $(X \setminus Y) \cup (Y \setminus X)$ is said to be the *symmetric difference*, and it is denoted by $X \Delta Y = Y \Delta X$.

8. $X \times Y = \{(x; y) : x \in X, y \in Y\} = Y \cup X$ is called the *Cartesian product*. This product is not symmetric (in general) since this is a set of ordered pairs $(x; y)$.

**Exercise 1.7.** Show that if $X \setminus Y = \emptyset$ then $X \subset Y$.

**Exercise 1.8.** Show that $X \Delta Y = \emptyset \Leftrightarrow X = Y$.

**Exercise 1.9.** Prove the following:

1. $(X \cup Y) \cap Z = (X \cap Z) \cup (Y \cap Z)$.

2. $(X \cap Y) \cup Z = (X \cup Z) \cap (Y \cup Z)$.

3. $X \cup Y = X \Delta Y \cup (X \cap Y)$ or $X \Delta Y = (X \cup Y) \setminus (X \cap Y)$.

4. $X = (X \setminus Y) \cup (X \cap Y)$.

5. $X \Delta Y = (Z \setminus X) \Delta (Z \setminus Y)$ if $X, Y \subset Z$.

6. $Y = X \Delta (X \Delta Y)$.

7. $X \setminus (Y \setminus Z) = X \setminus (Y \cup Z)$.

8. $X \setminus (Y \cap Z) = (X \setminus Y) \cup (X \setminus Z)$.

9. $X \setminus (Y \cup Z) = (X \setminus Y) \cap (X \setminus Z)$.

10. $X \setminus Y = X \cap (Z \setminus Y)$ if $X, Y \subset Z$.

11. $(X \setminus Y) \cap Z = (X \cap Z) \setminus (Y \cap Z)$.

12. $(X \Delta Y) \cap Z = (X \cap Z) \Delta (Y \cap Z)$.

13. $(X \cup Y) \setminus Z = (X \setminus Z) \cup (Y \setminus Z)$.

14. $(X \cap Y) \setminus Z = (X \setminus Z) \cap (Y \setminus Z)$.

15. $(X \Delta Y) \setminus Z = (X \setminus Z) \Delta (Y \setminus Z)$.

**Exercise 1.10.** Verify the following statements:

1. $X \Delta Y \subset (X \Delta Z) \cup (Y \Delta Z)$,

2. $(X \cup Z) \Delta (Y \cup Z) = (X \Delta Y) \cup Z$,

3. $(X \cap Z) \Delta (Y \cap Z) = (X \Delta Y) \cap Z$,

4. $X \subset Y \cup (X \Delta Y)$,

5. $(X_1 \cup X_2) \Delta (Y_1 \cup Y_2) \subset (X_1 \Delta Y_1) \cup (X_2 \Delta Y_2)$.

**Exercise 1.11.**     1. Let $\{X_{k_j}\}_{k,j=1}^{\infty}$ be a family of sets numerated by two indices. Prove that

$$\bigcup_{k=1}^{\infty}\left(\bigcap_{j=1}^{\infty} X_{k_j}\right) \subset \bigcap_{j=1}^{\infty}\left(\bigcup_{k=1}^{\infty} X_{k_j}\right).$$

Show that the strict embedding here is possible.

2. Prove that if $X_j \subset X$ for $j = 1, 2, \ldots$ then

   (a) $X \setminus (\bigcup_{j=1}^{\infty} X_j) = \bigcap_{j=1}^{\infty}(X \setminus X_j)$,
   (b) $X \setminus (\bigcap_{j=1}^{\infty} X_j) = \bigcup_{j=1}^{\infty}(X \setminus X_j)$,
   (c) $\bigcap_{j=1}^{\infty} X_j = X \setminus \bigcup_{j=1}^{\infty}(X \setminus X_j)$,
   (d) $\bigcup_{j=1}^{\infty} X_j = X \setminus \bigcap_{j=1}^{\infty} X_j$.

# Chapter 2

# Real numbers

In this chapter we introduce the set of real numbers, in short "real line," and arithmetic operations on them. The approach here is quite constructive (compared with the abstract Dedekind method) and is based on the approximation by rational numbers. The most important result of one-dimensional classical analysis, the existence of supremum and infimum of bounded sets of real numbers, is also proved here.

Under a numerical *straight line*, denoted by $\mathbb{R}$, we mean a straight line on which the origin 0, a scale interval $\overrightarrow{0M}$ of length one, and a positive direction from 0 to $M$ are chosen such that $\overrightarrow{0M} = 1$.

Each point $A$ on $\mathbb{R}$ can be associated with an *infinite decimal fraction* (positive or negative), depending on whether $A$ is to the left or to the right of 0. For the points to the right of 0, decimals are positive and have the form

$$a_0, a_1 a_2 \ldots a_n \ldots, \tag{2.1}$$

where $a_0 \in \mathbb{N}_0$, and it shows how many times the scale interval fits in the interval $\overrightarrow{0A}$, and $a_1, a_2, \ldots \in \{0, 1, \ldots, 9\}$, and they show how many times the one-tenth part, one-hundredth part, and so on of the scale interval fit into the remainder, respectively. In other words, with any point $A \in \mathbb{R}$ to the right of 0 we can associate the sequence (process) of finite decimal fractions (rational numbers) of the form

$$a_0, \quad a_0, a_1 = a_0 + \frac{a_1}{10}, \quad a_0, a_1 a_2 = a_0 + \frac{a_1}{10} + \frac{a_2}{100}, \quad \ldots \quad ,$$

$$a_0, a_1 a_2 \cdots a_n = a_0 + \frac{a_1}{10} + \frac{a_2}{100} + \cdots + \frac{a_n}{10^n},$$

and so on. That's how we get an infinite decimal fraction (2.1). The converse is also true. Namely, each infinite decimal fraction can be associated with some point $A \in \mathbb{R}$ to the right of 0. Moreover, this correspondence will be one-to-one if we agree not to consider fractions ending in all 9's, i.e., for example, for the rational number 1/2 we will use the infinite decimal fraction $0,500 \cdots 0 \cdots$ but not the infinite decimal fraction $0,4999 \cdots 9 \cdots$.

The set of all positive infinite decimal fractions is denoted by $\mathbb{R}_+$. The set of all negative infinite decimal fractions can be obtained as $-\mathbb{R}_+ = \{y : y = -x, x \in \mathbb{R}_+\}$ and is denoted by $\mathbb{R}_-$. The set of all infinite decimal fractions is denoted by $\mathbb{R}$ (like the numerical straight line) such that

$$\mathbb{R} = \mathbb{R}_+ \cup \{0\} \cup \mathbb{R}_-,$$

where $0 = 0,00 \cdots 0 \cdots$. The following notations are also used:

$$\overline{\mathbb{R}_+} = \mathbb{R}_+ \cup \{0\}, \quad \overline{\mathbb{R}_-} = \mathbb{R}_- \cup \{0\}.$$

**Definition 2.1.** *Let $a \in \mathbb{R}$. The* modulus *of $a$, denoted by $|a|$, is defined as*

$$|a| = \begin{cases} a, & a \in \overline{\mathbb{R}_+}, \\ -a, & a \in \mathbb{R}_-. \end{cases}$$

**Definition 2.2.** *Let $a, b \in \overline{\mathbb{R}_+}$ such that*

$$a = a_0, a_1 a_2 \ldots a_n \ldots, \quad b = b_0, b_1 b_2 \ldots b_n \ldots.$$

*Then $a = b$ if and only if*

$$a_0 = b_0, \quad a_1 = b_1, \ldots, a_n = b_n, \ldots.$$

*If $a, b \in \overline{\mathbb{R}_-}$ then $a = b$ if and only if $|a| = |b|$.*

**Definition 2.3.** *Let $a, b \in \overline{\mathbb{R}_+}$ be as above. Then $a < b$ if and only if there exists $n_0 \in \mathbb{N}$ such that either $a_0 < b_0$ or $a_0 = b_0, a_1 = b_1, \ldots, a_{n_0-1} = b_{n_0-1}, a_{n_0} < b_{n_0}$. If $a, b \in \overline{\mathbb{R}_-}$ then $a < b$ if and only if $|a| > |b|$. If $a \in \mathbb{R}_-$ and $b \in \overline{\mathbb{R}_+}$ then $a < b$ by definition.*

**Definition 2.4.** *Let $X \subset \mathbb{R}$. Then $X$ is said to be*

1. bounded *if there exists $A > 0$ such that $|x| \leq A$ for any $x \in X$,*

2. unbounded *if for any $A > 0$ there exists $x_A \in X$ such that $|x_A| > A$.*

**Definition 2.5.** *A set $X \subset \mathbb{R}$ is said to be* bounded from above (from below) *if there exists $M$ such that for all $x \in X$ we have $x \leq M$ ($x \geq M$).*

**Exercise 2.6.** *Prove that $X \subset \mathbb{R}$ is bounded if and only if it is bounded from above and from below.*

**Definition 2.7.** *The* closed *and* open intervals *are defined as the sets*

$$[a, b] := \{x \in \mathbb{R} : a \leq x \leq b\}$$

*and*

$$(a, b) := \{x \in \mathbb{R} : a < x < b\},$$

*respectively.*

**Definition 2.8.** *A number $a \in \mathbb{R}$ is called the* supremum (infimum) *of a set $X \subset \mathbb{R}$, denoted $a = \sup X$ ($a = \inf X$), if*

1. $x \leq a$ ($x \geq a$) *for all $x \in X$,*

2. *for any $a' < a$ ($a' > a$) there exists $x' \in X$ such that $a' < x' \leq a$ ($a' > x' \geq a$).*

**Example 2.9.**   1. Let $X = \{1, 2, \ldots, n_0\}$ with $n_0 \in \mathbb{N}$. Then $\sup X = n_0$ and $\inf X = 1$.

2. Let $X = \{a_1, a_2, \ldots, a_{n_0}\}$ with $n_0 \in \mathbb{N}$. Then $\sup X = \max(a_1, a_2, \ldots, a_{n_0})$ and $\inf X = \min(a_1, a_2, \ldots, a_{n_0})$.

3. Let $X = \{\frac{1}{n} : n = 1, 2, \ldots\}$. Then $\sup X = 1$ and $\inf X = 0$.

**Exercise 2.10.**    1. Prove the latter two results from Example 2.9.

2. Prove that if $X' \subset X \subset \mathbb{R}$ then $\sup X' \leq \sup X$ and $\inf X' \geq \inf X$ if they exist.

3. Prove that if $X \subset \mathbb{R}$ then $\sup(-X) = -\inf X$ and $\inf(-X) = -\sup X$ if they exist, where the set $-X$ is defined as $-X = \{y : y = -x, x \in X\}$.

4. Let $X, Y \subset \mathbb{R}$. Prove that

$$\sup(X \cup Y) = \max(\sup X, \sup Y), \quad \inf(X \cup Y) = \min(\inf X, \inf Y)$$

if all quantities exist.

5. Let $X, Y \subset \mathbb{R}$. Prove that

$$\sup(X \cap Y) \leq \min(\sup X, \sup Y), \quad \inf(X \cap Y) \geq \max(\inf X, \inf Y)$$

if all quantities exist. Show that strict inequalities may occur here.

We are now in position to prove the main result in the theory of real numbers.

**Theorem 2.11 (Existence of sup and inf).** *Let $X \subset \mathbb{R}$ be nonempty and bounded. Then both $\sup X$ and $\inf X$ exist.*

***Proof.*** It is enough to prove the existence of $\sup X$ for the set which is bounded from above. Moreover, without loss of generality we may assume that $X$ is infinite and all its elements are positive (see part 3 of Exercise 2.10 for justification of this).

Next, by definition we have that there exists $A > 0$ such that $x \leq A$ for all $x \in X$. We denote the elements of $X$ by decimal fractions as

$$X = \{x : x = x_0, x_1 x_2 \ldots\}.$$

Since $x \leq A$, in particular $x_0 \leq A$. Thus, since $x_0 \in \mathbb{N}$, there is maximum among such $x_0$. Denote $a_0 := \max_{x \in X} x_0$. Consider now all elements from $X$ of the form

$$X_1 = \{x : x = a_0, x_1 x_2 \ldots x_n \ldots\}.$$

Let $a_1 := \max_{x \in X_1} x_1$. Consider all elements from $X_1$ of the form

$$X_2 = \{x \in X_1 : x = a_0, a_1 x_2 \ldots x_n \ldots\}$$

and choose $a_2 := \max_{x \in X_2} x_2$. This process can be continued to obtain

$$X_n = \{x \in X_{n-1} : x = a_0, a_1 a_2 \ldots a_{n-1} x_n \ldots\}.$$

Using this infinite process we obtain the following infinite decimal fraction:

$$a = a_0, a_1 a_2 \ldots a_n \ldots.$$

We will prove that $a = \sup X$. Indeed, by construction of $a$ we can easily see that $x \leq a$ for all $x \in X$. Let $a' < a$, i.e.,

$$a' = a_0', a_1' a_2' \ldots a_n' \ldots < a = a_0, a_1 a_2 \ldots a_n \ldots.$$

Therefore there is $n_0 \in \mathbb{N}$ such that $a_0' < a_0$ or $a_0' = a_0, \ldots, a_{n_0-1}' = a_{n_0-1}, a_{n_0}' < a_{n_0}$. Choose $x' \in X$ as

$$x' = a_0, a_1 a_2 \ldots a_{n_0} x_{n_0+1}' x_{n_0+2}' \ldots,$$

where $x' \in X_{n_0+1}$. Since $a_{n_0}' < a_{n_0}$, then $a' < x' \le a$ and the proof is finished.

This fundamental theorem allows us to introduce arithmetic operations for real numbers. Let $x$ be positive, i.e., $x \in \mathbb{R}_+$ such that

$$x = x_0, x_1 x_2 \ldots x_n \ldots.$$

Denote by $p_n$ and $q_n$ the decimal fractions

$$p_n = x_0, x_1 \ldots x_n 0 \ldots, \quad p_n \le x, \quad q_n = x_0, x_1 \ldots (x_n + 1) 0 \ldots, \quad q_n > x.$$

These fractions are called the *approximations of $x$ with deficiency* and *with excess*, respectively. Let us note that $p_n, q_n \in \mathbb{Q}$ and $q_n - p_n = 1/10^n$.

Next, let $x$ and $y$ be positive, and let

$$p' \le x < q', \quad p'' \le y < q'',$$

where $p', p''$ and $q', q''$ are arbitrary approximations of $x$ and $y$ with deficiency and with excess, respectively. For given $x$ and $y$ we consider the sets

$$X_1 = \{p' + p''\}, \quad X_2 = \{q' + q''\}.$$

It is clear that $X_1, X_2 \ne \emptyset$ and that any element of $X_1$ is strictly less than any element of $X_2$, i.e.,

$$p' + p'' < q' + q''.$$

This implies that $X_1$ is bounded from above by any element $q' + q''$ and $X_2$ is bounded from below by any element $p' + p''$. Theorem 2.11 implies that there exist

$$a := \sup X_1, \quad b := \inf X_2.$$

We can prove that $a = b$. Indeed, since $a \le b$, let us assume on the contrary that $a < b$, i.e.,

$$a = a_0, a_1 a_2 \ldots a_n \ldots < b = b_0, b_1 b_2 \ldots b_n \ldots.$$

Therefore, there is $k_0 \in \mathbb{N}$ such that either $a_0 < b_0$ or $a_0 = b_0, \ldots, a_{k_0-1} = b_{k_0-1}, a_{k_0} < b_{k_0}$. Let us construct the rational numbers $\overline{a}$ and $\overline{b}$ as

$$\overline{a} = a_0, \quad \overline{b} = a_0, 100 \ldots 0$$

if $a_0 < b_0$ or

$$\overline{a} = a_0, a_1 a_2 \ldots a_{k_0} \underbrace{99 \ldots 9}_{n_0} 00 \ldots,$$

$$\overline{b} = a_0, a_1 a_2 \ldots a_{k_0} \underbrace{99 \ldots 9}_{n_0} 10 \ldots,$$

where $n_0 \in \mathbb{N}$ indicates the number of successive 9's in the representation of $a$ after $k_0$. If $a_{k_0+1} < 9$ then we put $n_0 = 1$. Now we have that (in both cases)

$$a < \overline{a} < \overline{b} < b, \quad \overline{b} - \overline{a} = \frac{1}{10}$$

or

$$\bar{b} - \bar{a} = \frac{1}{10^{k_0+n_0+1}},$$

respectively. On the other hand, for any $n \in \mathbb{N}$ it follows from the definitions of $a$ and $b$ that

$$p'_n + p''_n \leq a < \bar{a} < \bar{b} < b < q'_n + q''_n.$$

This implies that either

$$0 < \bar{b} - \bar{a} = \frac{1}{10} < \frac{2}{10^n}$$

or

$$0 < \bar{b} - \bar{a} = \frac{1}{10^{k_0+n_0+1}} < \frac{2}{10^n}$$

with fixed $k_0$ and $n_0$, and arbitrary $n$. Taking, for example, $n = 2$ in the first case and $n = k_0 + n_0 + 2$ in the second case, we obtain the contradiction. Thus $a = b$.

**Definition 2.12.** *The sum of numbers $x, y \in \mathbb{R}_+$ is defined as the value*

$$x + y := \sup_{p' \leq x, p'' \leq y} \{p' + p''\} = \inf_{x < q', y < q''} \{q' + q''\}.$$

**Exercise 2.13.**    1. Define for given $x \in \mathbb{R}_-$ the approximations with deficiency and with excess, respectively.

2. Using these approximations, introduce the sum of two arbitrary numbers $x, y \in \mathbb{R}$.

3. Obtain the definition of the difference $x - y$ of two arbitrary numbers $x, y \in \mathbb{R}$.

Let $x, y$ be positive real numbers with the decimal representations

$$x = x_0.x_1x_2\ldots x_n \ldots, \quad y = y_0.y_1y_2\ldots y_n \ldots$$

and let $p', p''$ and $q', q''$ be their approximations with deficiency and with excess, respectively, i.e.,

$$0 < p' \leq x < q', \quad 0 < p'' \leq y < q''.$$

Note that

$$x_0 \leq p' < x_0 + 1, \quad y_0 \leq p'' < y_0 + 1, \quad x_0 < q' < x_0 + 1, \quad y_0 < q'' < y_0 + 1.$$

Consider the sets

$$X_1 = \{p' \cdot p''\}, \quad X_2 = \{q' \cdot q''\}.$$

Since $X_1$ is bounded from above by any element from $X_2$, and $X_2$ is bounded from below by any element from $X_1$, applying Theorem 2.11 we conclude that

$$a := \sup X_1, \quad b := \inf X_2$$

exist and that obviously $a \leq b$. Our aim is again to show that $a = b$.

Assuming on the contrary that $a < b$ and constructing $\bar{a} < \bar{b}$ as we did for the sum $x + y$, we obtain

$$p'_n p''_n \leq a < \bar{a} - \bar{b} < b < q'_n q''_n.$$

Now, either

$$0 < \bar{b} - \bar{a} = \frac{1}{10} < q_n'' q_n' - p_n'' p_n' = (q_n'' - p_n'')q_n' + (q_n' - p_n')p_n''$$

$$< \frac{x_0 + 1}{10^n} + \frac{y_0 + 1}{10^n} \le 2\max(x_0 + 1, y_0 + 1)\frac{1}{10^n}$$

or

$$0 < \bar{b} - \bar{a} = \frac{1}{10^{k_0 + n_0 + 1}} < 2\max(x_0 + 1, y_0 + 1)\frac{1}{10^n},$$

where positive integers $k_0, n_0, \max(x_0 + 1, y_0 + 1)$ are fixed but $n \in \mathbb{N}$ is arbitrary. Now choose $n = 1 + l$ or $n = k_0 + n_0 + 2 + l$ with integer $l$ such that $10^l > 2M$, where $M = \max(x_0 + 1, y_0 + 1)$. Then we obtain the contradiction. Thus $a = b$. This fact justifies the following definition.

**Definition 2.14.** *The* product *of numbers* $x, y \in \mathbb{R}_+$ *is defined as the value*

$$x \cdot y := \sup_{p' \le x, p'' \le y}\{p'p''\} = \inf_{x < q', y < q''}\{q'q''\}.$$

**Remark 2.15.** If $x, y \in \mathbb{R}_-$ then the product is defined as

$$x \cdot y := |x| \cdot |y|.$$

If $x \in \mathbb{R}_+$ and $y \in \mathbb{R}_-$ (or $x \in \mathbb{R}_-$ and $y \in \mathbb{R}_+$) then

$$x \cdot y := -x \cdot |y| \quad (\text{or } x \cdot y := -y \cdot |x|).$$

Let $x, y \in \mathbb{R}_+$. We want to define the *ratio* $\frac{x}{y}$ next. The idea is to represent this ratio as the product

$$\frac{x}{y} := x\frac{1}{y}.$$

So it suffices to define $\frac{1}{y}$ for any $y > 0$. Since

$$0 < p \le y < q,$$

where $p$ and $q$ are the approximations with deficiency and with excess, respectively, then

$$y = \sup_{p \le y}\{p\} = \inf_{y < q}\{q\}.$$

Consider the sets

$$X_1 = \left\{\frac{1}{q}\right\}, \quad X_2 = \left\{\frac{1}{p}\right\},$$

where $p$ and $q$ are from above. Using a similar procedure as for the sum and for the product, we may conclude that $\sup X_1$ and $\inf X_2$ exist and that

$$\sup X_1 = \inf X_2.$$

It can also be noticed that

$$\sup\left\{\frac{1}{q}\right\} = \frac{1}{\inf\{q\}} = \frac{1}{\sup\{p\}} = \inf\left\{\frac{1}{p}\right\}.$$

Therefore all these values and equalities uniquely determine the number $\frac{1}{y} > 0$. Hence the problem of defining $\frac{x}{y} = x\frac{1}{y}$ is reduced to the problem of defining the product of two real numbers $x$ and $\frac{1}{y}$, which was outlined above.

If $x, y \in \mathbb{R}_-$ then

$$\frac{x}{y} := \frac{|x|}{|y|}.$$

If $x \in \mathbb{R}_-$ and $y \in \mathbb{R}_+$ or $x \in \mathbb{R}_+$ and $y \in \mathbb{R}_-$ then in both cases

$$\frac{x}{y} := -\frac{|x|}{|y|}.$$

**Exercise 2.16.**    1. Show that if $x \in \mathbb{Q} \subset \mathbb{R}$ then $x$ is either a finite decimal fraction (ending with zeros) or an infinite periodic fraction (starting from a certain place after the comma).

2. Show that if $x, y \in \mathbb{R}$ and $x < y$ then there is $p \in \mathbb{Q}$ such that $x < p < y$ and there is $r \in \mathbb{R} \setminus \mathbb{Q}$ such that $x < r < y$.

**Exercise 2.17.** Prove that for any $a, b \in \mathbb{R}$

1. $|a + b| \le |a| + |b|$,

2. $|a + b| \ge |a| - |b|$,

3. $|a - b| \ge \big||a| - |b|\big|$,

and establish when strict inequalities occur in these statements.

After introducing real numbers and their arithmetic operations, we are in position to introduce functional dependence between sets of real numbers.

Let $X$ and $Y$ be two arbitrary sets from $\mathbb{R}$. Suppose that each element $x \in X$ is mapped, according to a certain law $f$, to only one element $y \in Y$. Then we say that on the set $X$ a *mapping* $f$ is defined with values in the set $Y$. We denote this as

$$f : X \to Y, \quad y = f(x).$$

The set $X$ is called the *domain* of $f$ and is denoted as $X = D(f)$. The set

$$f(X) := \{y \in Y : \text{there exists } x \in X \text{ such that } y = f(x)\}$$

is called the *range* of $f$ and is denoted as $f(X) = R(f)$. Sometimes $f(x)$ is said to be the *image* of $x$ under the mapping $f$, and $x$ is said to be the *preimage* of $f(x)$. If $f(X) = Y$ then $f$ is called a map onto, or *surjective mapping*.

**Definition 2.18.** *A map $f : X \to Y$ is called* bijective *(bijection) if*

1. *$f$ is surjective, i.e., $f(X) = Y$, and*

2. *$f$ is injective (one-to-one), i.e., for all $x_1, x_2 \in X, x_1 \ne x_2$ it holds that $y_1 = f(x_1) \ne y_2 = f(x_2)$.*

**Definition 2.19.** *If $f : X \to Y$ is bijective then there exists a mapping $g : Y \to X$ according to the following rule: for any $y \in Y$ there is $x \in X$ such that $x = g(y)$, with $y = f(x)$, i.e., $x = g(f(x))$. This map $g$ is called the* inverse *to $f$ and is denoted as $g = f^{-1}$.*

**Remark 2.20.** It is clear that $f^{-1}$ is also bijective and that $\left(f^{-1}\right)^{-1} = f$, i.e., $f^{-1}(f(x)) = x$ for any $x \in X$ and $f(f^{-1}(y)) = y$ for any $y \in Y$.

**Example 2.21.** Let us consider the map $f$ given by the rule $f(x) = x^2$. Then

1. $f : \mathbb{R} \to \mathbb{R}$ is not surjective since $f(x) \geq 0$,

2. $f : \mathbb{R} \to \overline{\mathbb{R}_+}$ is surjective since $R(f) = \overline{\mathbb{R}_+}$,

3. $f : \mathbb{R} \to \mathbb{R}$ is not injective since $f(x) = f(-x)$ for any $x \neq 0$,

4. $f : \overline{\mathbb{R}_+} \to \overline{\mathbb{R}_+}$ is bijective since it is surjective and injective. Moreover, the inverse $f^{-1}$ of $f$ is defined as
$$f^{-1}(y) = \sqrt{y}, \quad y \in \overline{\mathbb{R}_+}.$$

The concepts of functions and mappings can be effectively used to compare different sets of real numbers and, in particular, to introduce the basic concept of equivalence between sets.

**Definition 2.22.** *A set $A \subset \mathbb{R}$ is said to be* equivalent *to a set $B \subset \mathbb{R}$, denoted by $A \sim B$, if there exists a bijective mapping $f : A \to B$ (onto).*

**Remark 2.23.** This property is symmetric, i.e., $A \sim B$ if and only if $B \sim A$ since there is bijective $f^{-1} : B \to A$. In addition, if $A \sim B$ and $B \sim C$ then $A \sim C$.

**Example 2.24.** Let us show that $\mathbb{N} \sim \mathbb{Z}$. Indeed, we introduce $f$ on $\mathbb{N}$ as
$$f(n) = \begin{cases} n/2, & n = 2k, \\ -(n-1)/2, & n = 2k-1. \end{cases}$$

It follows that $f^{-1} : \mathbb{Z} \to \mathbb{N}$ with
$$f^{-1}(m) = \begin{cases} 2m, & m > 0, \\ -(2m-1), & m \leq 0. \end{cases}$$

**Definition 2.25.** *A set $A$ is called*

1. finite *if there is $n_0 \in \mathbb{N}$ such that $A \sim \{1, 2, \ldots, n_0\}$,*

2. infinite *if $A \neq \emptyset$ and $A \not\sim \{1, 2, \ldots, n\}$ for all $n \in \mathbb{N}$,*

3. countable *if $A \sim \mathbb{N}$,*

4. noncountable *if $A$ is infinite and $A \not\sim \mathbb{N}$,*

5. not more than countable *if $A$ is either finite or countable.*

**Exercise 2.26.**    1. Formulate the definition of the fact that $A \not\sim B$.

2. Let $X$ be countable, and let $X_1 \subset X$. Prove that if $X_1$ is infinite then $X_1$ is also countable.

**Proposition 2.27.** *Let $X_n$ be countable for any $n = 1, 2, \ldots$. Then*

$$X := \bigcup_{n=1}^{\infty} X_n$$

*is countable too.*

**Proof.** Let each $X_n$ be represented as

$$X_n = \{x_{n1}, x_{n2}, x_{n3}, \ldots, x_{nk}, \ldots\}.$$

Then $X$ is the union of

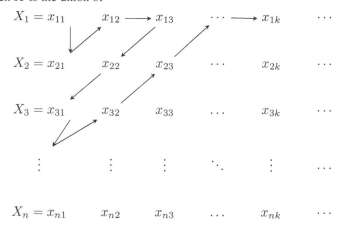

This diagram shows the algorithm of renumbering a countable union of countable sets. Obviously

$$\bigcup_{n=1}^{\infty} X_n \sim \mathbb{N}$$

by this algorithm.

**Corollary 2.28.** *The set $\mathbb{Q}$ of all rational numbers is countable.*

**Proof.** We define $\mathbb{Q}$ as the set of all irreducible fractions $\frac{m}{n}$, where $m \in \mathbb{Z}$ and $n \in \mathbb{N}$ with the convention that $0 = \frac{0}{1}$. Next, we set the height of the fraction $\frac{m}{n}$ as $h = |m| + n$, and $X_h$ is the set of all rational numbers of height $h$. Since

$$Q = \bigcup_{h=1}^{\infty} X_h,$$

Proposition 2.27 leads to the fact that $Q$ is countable.

**Proposition 2.29.** *The set of real numbers on $[0, 1] \subset \mathbb{R}$ is not countable.*

**Proof.** Since $(0, 1) \subset [0, 1]$, it suffices to show that $(0, 1)$ is not countable. Assume on the contrary that $(0, 1)$ is countable, i.e., $(0, 1)$ can be enumerated such that

$$(0, 1) = \{x_1, x_2, \ldots, x_n, \ldots\},$$

where each $x_j$ is a decimal fraction

$$x_j = 0,\alpha_{j1}\alpha_{j2}\ldots\alpha_{jn}\ldots.$$

Let us introduce the number

$$b = 0,\beta_1\beta_2\ldots\beta_n\ldots,$$

where $\beta_j$ are chosen such that

$$\beta_j \neq 0, 9, \alpha_{jj}.$$

It is easy to see that $b \in (0,1)$ and

$$b \notin \{x_1, x_2, \ldots, x_n, \ldots\}.$$

This contradiction proves the statement.

**Exercise 2.30.** Prove that

1. $\mathbb{R}_+, \mathbb{R}, \mathbb{R} \times \mathbb{R}, \underbrace{\mathbb{R} \times \mathbb{R} \times \cdots \times \mathbb{R}}_{m} \sim [0,1]$,

2. if $A \sim B' \subset B$ and $B \sim A' \subset A$ then $A \sim B$,

3. if $A \subset B \subset C$ and $A \sim C$ then $A \sim B$,

4. two finite sets are equivalent if and only if they have the same number of elements,

5. if $X$ is an arbitrary set and $X'$ is the set of all subsets of $X$ then $X \not\sim X'$,

6. the set of all *algebraic numbers*, i.e., the roots of polynomials with integer (positive or negative) coefficients, is countable.

**Definition 2.31.** *Any set $A \sim [0,1]$ is said to be the set of* continuum power.

# Chapter 3

# Theory of limits of real numbers

This chapter is devoted to the classical theory of limits of real numbers. The presentation here is not much different from all the known books on the theory of number limits. It should only be noted that Euler's constants e and $\gamma$ are obtained in a fairly clear and simple manner and with a fairly good approximation. In particular, it is shown that the harmonic sequence $1 + 1/2 + \cdots + 1/n$ diverges as $\log n$ (the natural logarithm).

**Definition 3.1.** *A set of enumerated real numbers* $\{x_n\}_{n=1}^{\infty} = \{x_1, x_2, \ldots, x_n, \ldots\}$ *is called a numerical sequence. Equivalently, there is a map* $f : \mathbb{N} \to \mathbb{R}$ *such that* $x_n = f(n), n = 1, 2, \ldots$.

For two numerical sequences $\{x_n\}_{n=1}^{\infty}$ and $\{y_n\}_{n=1}^{\infty}$ the following arithmetic operations are well-defined:

$$\{x_n \pm y_n\}_{n=1}^{\infty}, \quad \{x_n \cdot y_n\}_{n=1}^{\infty}, \quad \left\{\frac{x_n}{y_n}\right\}_{n=1}^{\infty}.$$

The ratio $\left\{\frac{x_n}{y_n}\right\}_{n=1}^{\infty}$ is well-defined if $y_n \neq 0$ for all $n \in \mathbb{N}$ (or starting from some number $n_0 \in \mathbb{N}$).

**Definition 3.2.** *A sequence* $\{x_n\}_{n=1}^{\infty}$ *is said to be*

1. bounded from above (from below) *if there is a constant* $M \in \mathbb{R}$ *such that* $x_n \leq M$ $(x_n \geq M)$ *for all* $n \in \mathbb{N}$,

2. not bounded from above (from below) *if for any* $M \in \mathbb{R}$ *there exists* $n_0 \in \mathbb{N}$ *such that* $x_{n_0} > M$ $(x_{n_0} < M)$.

**Definition 3.3.** *A sequence* $\{x_n\}_{n=1}^{\infty}$ *is said to be*

1. bounded *if there is a constant* $A > 0$ *such that* $|x_n| \leq A$ *for all* $n \in \mathbb{N}$,

2. not bounded (unbounded) *if for any* $A > 0$ *there exists* $n_0 \in \mathbb{N}$ *such that* $|x_{n_0}| > A$.

**Exercise 3.4.** Prove that a sequence $\{x_n\}_{n=1}^{\infty}$ is

1. bounded if and only if it is bounded from above and from below,

2. not bounded if and only if it is not bounded from above or from below.

**Example 3.5.**    1. The sequence $x_n = n^{(-1)^n}$ is not bounded since it is not bounded from above. But it is bounded from below.

2. The sequence $x_n = n/\sin(n)$ is not bounded. Note that $\sin(n) \neq 0$ for all $n \in \mathbb{N}$.

3. The sequence $x_n = n\sin(n)$ is not bounded.

**Definition 3.6.** *A sequence $\{x_n\}_{n=1}^\infty$ is called*

1. infinitely large *if for all $A > 0$ there exists $n_0 \in \mathbb{N}$ such that $|x_n| > A$ for all $n \geq n_0$, and in this case we write* $\lim_{n\to\infty} x_n = \infty$;

2. not infinitely large *if there exists $A > 0$ such that for any $n \in \mathbb{N}$ there exists $n_0 \geq n$ with $|x_{n_0}| \leq A$.*

It is clear from Definitions 3.3 and 3.6 that any infinitely large sequence is unbounded, but the converse is not true.

**Exercise 3.7.** Show that

1. $x_n = n^{(-1)^n}$ is not bounded and is not infinitely large,

2. $x_n = n/\sin(n)$ is infinitely large,

3. $x_n = n\sin(n)$ is not bounded and is not infinitely large,

4. $x_n = \log n$ is infinitely large.

**Definition 3.8.** *A sequence $\{x_n\}_{n=1}^\infty$ is called*

1. infinitely small *if for any $\varepsilon > 0$ there exists $n_0 \in \mathbb{N}$ such that $|x_n| < \varepsilon$ for all $n \geq n_0$, and in this case we write* $\lim_{n\to\infty} x_n = 0$;

2. not infinitely small *if there exists $\varepsilon_0 > 0$ such that for any $n \in \mathbb{N}$ there exists $n_0 \geq n$ with $|x_{n_0}| \geq \varepsilon_0$.*

**Example 3.9.** Let $x_n = q^n$. Then $\{x_n\}_{n=1}^\infty$ is infinitely small if $|q| < 1$, infinitely large if $|q| > 1$, and bounded if $|q| = 1$ (and not infinitely small in this case). Indeed, first let $|q| > 1$. Then $|q| = 1 + \delta$ with some $\delta > 0$. Using Bernoulli's inequality we have

$$|q^n| = |q|^n = (1+\delta)^n > 1 + n\delta > A$$

for $n > (A-1)/\delta$. Thus, considering any $A > 1$ and $n_0 = [(A-1)/\delta] + 1$, where $[x]$ denotes the *entire part* of $x$ (i.e., the largest integer less than or equal to $x$), we obtain that for arbitrary $A > 1$ and for all $n \geq n_0$ it is true that

$$|q^n| > 1 + n\delta \geq n_0\delta + 1 > \delta(A-1)/\delta + 1 = A$$

since $[x] + 1 > x$ always. So $q^n$ is infinitely large if $|q| > 1$.

If $|q| < 1$ (and $q \neq 0$) we need to show that for any $\varepsilon > 0$ there exists $n_0 \in \mathbb{N}$ such that $|q^n| < \varepsilon$ for all $n \geq n_0$. Equivalently, for any $A = 1/\varepsilon$ there exists $n_0 \in \mathbb{N}$ such that $|1/q|^n > A$ for all $n \geq n_0$. But since $|1/q| > 1$, we may apply the previous case. Thus, $q^n$ is infinitely small if $|q| < 1, q \neq 0$. For $q = 0$ this obviously holds too.

If $|q| = 1$ then $q^n$ is bounded since $|q^n| = |q|^n = 1$ and it is not infinitely small.

**Theorem 3.10 (The properties of infinitely small sequences).** *Let a sequence $\{x_n\}_{n=1}^{\infty}$ be infinitely small. Then*

1. *$\{x_n\}_{n=1}^{\infty}$ is bounded, but the converse is not true;*

2. *$\{x_n y_n\}_{n=1}^{\infty}$ is infinitely small if $\{y_n\}_{n=1}^{\infty}$ is bounded;*

3. *$\{x_n \pm y_n\}_{n=1}^{\infty}, \{x_n y_n\}_{n=1}^{\infty}$ is infinitely small if $\{y_n\}_{n=1}^{\infty}$ is infinitely small.*

*Proof.*

1. Since $\{x_n\}_{n=1}^{\infty}$ is infinitely small, for $\varepsilon = 1$ there is $n_0 \in \mathbb{N}$ such that $|x_n| < 1$ for all $n \geq n_0$. Let us denote

$$M := \max\{1, |x_1|, \ldots, |x_{n_0-1}|\} < \infty.$$

Then $|x_n| \leq M$ for all $n \geq 1$. So $\{x_n\}_{n=1}^{\infty}$ is bounded. The sequence $x_n = (-1)^n$ gives us an example of bounded but not infinitely small sequence.

2. If $\{y_n\}_{n=1}^{\infty}$ is bounded then there exists $A > 0$ such that $|y_n| \leq A$ for all $n \geq 1$. Since $\{x_n\}_{n=1}^{\infty}$ is infinitely small, for arbitrary $\varepsilon > 0$ we may choose $n_0 \in \mathbb{N}$ such that $|x_n| < \varepsilon/A$ for all $n \geq n_0$. This implies that for any $\varepsilon > 0$ there exists $n_0 \in \mathbb{N}$ such that

$$|x_n y_n| = |x_n||y_n| < (\varepsilon/A)A = \varepsilon$$

for all $n \geq n_0$. Hence $\{x_n y_n\}_{n=1}^{\infty}$ is infinitely small.

3. If $\{x_n\}_{n=1}^{\infty}$ and $\{y_n\}_{n=1}^{\infty}$ are infinitely small then for any $\varepsilon > 0$ there exist $n_0', n_0'' \in \mathbb{N}$ such that

$$|x_n| < \varepsilon/2, \quad n \geq n_0',$$

and

$$|y_n| < \varepsilon/2, \quad n \geq n_0''.$$

Choosing $n_0 := \max\{n_0', n_0''\}$ we obtain

$$|x_n \pm y_n| \leq |x_n| + |y_n| < \varepsilon$$

for all $n \geq n_0$. For $\{x_n y_n\}_{n=1}^{\infty}$ the claim follows immediately from parts 1 and 2. Hence this theorem is completely proved.

**Remark 3.11.** If $\{x_n\}_{n=1}^{\infty}$ and $\{y_n\}_{n=1}^{\infty}$ are both infinitely small and $y_n \neq 0, n \in \mathbb{N}$ then the ratio $\{x_n/y_n\}_{n=1}^{\infty}$ is well-defined, but it might be arbitrary in the following sense:

1. $x_n = (-1)^n/n, y_n = 1/n$ gives $x_n/y_n = (-1)^n$ which is only bounded, not infinitely small;

2. $x_n = 1/n, y_n = 1/n^2$ gives $x_n/y_n = n$ which is infinitely large;

3. $x_n = 1/n^2, y_n = 1/n$ gives $x_n/y_n = 1/n$ which is infinitely small.

**Corollary 3.12.**

1. *The finite sum of infinitely small sequences is infinitely small.*

2. *The finite product of infinitely small sequences is infinitely small.*

**Exercise 3.13.**     1. Let $\{x_n^{(j)}\}_{n=1}^\infty, j = 1, 2, \ldots$, be given by

$$x_n^{(1)} = \{1, 1/2, 1/3, \ldots\}, \quad x_n^{(2)} = \{0, 1/2, 1/3, \ldots\}$$

and

$$x_n^{(j)} = \{\underbrace{0, \ldots, 0}_{j-1}, 1/j, 1/(j+1), \ldots\}.$$

Show that $\{x_n^{(1)} + x_n^{(2)} + \cdots + x_n^{(n)}\}_{n=1}^\infty$ is not infinitely small although $\{x_n^{(j)}\}_{n=1}^\infty$ is infinitely small for each $j = 1, 2, \ldots$.

2. What can we say about the infinite product of arbitrary infinitely small sequences?

**Theorem 3.14 (The correspondence between infinitely small and infinitely large sequences).**
*A sequence $\{x_n\}_{n=1}^\infty$ is infinitely large if and only if $\{1/x_n\}_{n=1}^\infty$ is infinitely small.*

**Proof.** Let $\{x_n\}_{n=1}^\infty$ be infinitely large. Then for any $A > 0$ there exists $n_0 \in \mathbb{N}$ such that $|x_n| > A$ for all $n \geq n_0$. But this means that $\{1/x_n\}_{n=1}^\infty$ is well-defined (at least starting from some index), and for any $\varepsilon = 1/A > 0$ there is $n_0 \in \mathbb{N}$ such that $|1/x_n| < \varepsilon$ for all $n \geq n_0$.

Conversely, if $\{1/x_n\}_{n=1}^\infty$ is infinitely small then for any $\varepsilon > 0$ there exists $n_0 \in \mathbb{N}$ such that $|1/x_n| < \varepsilon$ for all $n \geq n_0$. But then $|x_n| > 1/\varepsilon = A$, where $A$ is arbitrary since $\varepsilon > 0$ is arbitrary. Hence $\{x_n\}_{n=1}^\infty$ is infinitely large.

**Example 3.15.** Let us show that the sequence

$$x_n = \sqrt[n]{n} - 1$$

is infinitely small. Indeed, $x_n > 0$ for $n = 2, 3, \ldots$ and $(1 + x_n)^n = n$. By Newton's binomial theorem we have

$$(1 + x_n)^n = 1 + nx_n + \frac{n(n-1)}{2}x_n^2 + \cdots + x_n^n = n.$$

Since $x_n > 0$, for $n = 2, 3, \ldots$ we get

$$\frac{n(n-1)}{2}x_n^2 < n$$

or

$$0 < x_n < \sqrt{\frac{2}{n-1}}.$$

Now

$$\sqrt{\frac{2}{n-1}} < \varepsilon$$

if and only if $n > 2/\varepsilon^2 + 1$. Thus, choosing $n_0 := [2/\varepsilon^2] + 2$ we obtain that $0 < x_n < \varepsilon$ for all $n \geq n_0$. This means that $x_n = \sqrt[n]{n} - 1$ is infinitely small.

**Exercise 3.16.** Prove that the sequence

$$x_n = n^k q^n$$

is infinitely small for $|q| < 1$ and any $k > 0$.

**Exercise 3.17.**     1. What can one conclude about the sequences

$$\{x_n \pm y_n\}_{n=1}^{\infty}, \quad \{x_n y_n\}_{n=1}^{\infty}, \quad \{x_n/y_n\}_{n=1}^{\infty}$$

if

(a) $\{x_n\}_{n=1}^{\infty}$ and $\{y_n\}_{n=1}^{\infty}$ are unbounded,

(b) $\{x_n\}_{n=1}^{\infty}$ and $\{y_n\}_{n=1}^{\infty}$ are infinitely large,

(c) $\{x_n\}_{n=1}^{\infty}$ is infinitely large and $\{y_n\}_{n=1}^{\infty}$ is unbounded?

2. Prove that $x_n = 1 + 1/\sqrt{2} + \cdots + 1/\sqrt{n}$ is infinitely large. Hint: Show first by MMI that $\sqrt{n} < 1 + 1/\sqrt{2} + \cdots + 1/\sqrt{n} < 2\sqrt{n}$ for $n \geq 2$. See also Exercise 1.6.

3. Prove that $x_n = n^{n+1}/(n+1)^{n-1}$ is infinitely large. Hint: Show first by MMI that $n^{n+1} > (n+1)^n$ for $n \geq 3$.

Having the concepts of infinitely large and infinitely small sequences at hand we can develop the theory of limits of arbitrary number sequences.

**Definition 3.18.** *A number $a \in \mathbb{R}$ is*

1. *said to be the* limit *of sequence $\{x_n\}_{n=1}^{\infty}$, denoted by $a = \lim_{n\to\infty} x_n$, if for any $\varepsilon > 0$ there exists $n_0 \in \mathbb{N}$ such that $|x_n - a| < \varepsilon$ for all $n \geq n_0$, which is equivalent to the fact that $\{x_n - a\}_{n=1}^{\infty}$ is an infinitely small sequence;*

2. *not a limit of the sequence $\{x_n\}_{n=1}^{\infty}$, written $a \neq \lim_{n\to\infty} x_n$, if there exists $\varepsilon_0 > 0$ such that for any $n \in \mathbb{N}$ there is $n_0 \geq n$ with $|x_{n_0} - a| \geq \varepsilon_0$.*

**Definition 3.19.** *A sequence $\{x_n\}_{n=1}^{\infty}$ is*

1. *called* convergent *if there exists $a \in \mathbb{R}$ such that $a = \lim_{n\to\infty} x_n$, i.e., there exists $a \in \mathbb{R}$ such that for any $\varepsilon > 0$ there is $n_0 \in \mathbb{N}$ such that $|x_n - a| < \varepsilon$ for all $n \geq n_0$;*

2. *not convergent (is* divergent*) if for any $a \in \mathbb{R}$ it holds that $a \neq \lim_{n\to\infty} x_n$, i.e., for any $a \in \mathbb{R}$ there exists $\varepsilon_0 > 0$ such that for any $n \in \mathbb{N}$ there is $n_0 \geq n$ with $|x_{n_0} - a| \geq \varepsilon_0$.*

**Theorem 3.20 (The properties of convergent sequences).**

1. *The limit $\lim_{n\to\infty} x_n$ is unique if it exists.*

2. *Let $\{x_n\}_{n=1}^{\infty}$ be convergent. Then it is bounded, but the converse is not true.*

3. *Let $\{x_n\}_{n=1}^{\infty}$ and $\{y_n\}_{n=1}^{\infty}$ be convergent sequences. Then*

$$\{x_n \pm y_n\}_{n=1}^{\infty}, \quad \{x_n y_n\}_{n=1}^{\infty}, \quad \{x_n/y_n\}_{n=1}^{\infty}$$

*provided that $\lim_{n\to\infty} y_n \neq 0$ in the last claim. Moreover,*

$$\lim_{n\to\infty} (x_n \pm y_n) = \lim_{n\to\infty} x_n \pm \lim_{n\to\infty} y_n,$$

$$\lim_{n\to\infty} (x_n y_n) = (\lim_{n\to\infty} x_n)(\lim_{n\to\infty} y_n),$$

$$\lim_{n\to\infty} (x_n/y_n) = \frac{\lim_{n\to\infty} x_n}{\lim_{n\to\infty} y_n}.$$

*Proof.*

1.  Let $a_1 = \lim_{n \to \infty} x_n$ and $a_2 = \lim_{n \to \infty} x_n$ with $a_1 \neq a_2$. Then $\alpha_n := x_n - a_1$ and $\beta_n := x_n - a_2$ are infinitely small. Hence $a_2 - a_1 = \alpha_n - \beta_n$ is also infinitely small. But $a_2 - a_1 \neq 0$ is a fixed number. This contradiction proves the claim.

2.  If $\{x_n\}_{n=1}^{\infty}$ is convergent then there exists $a \in \mathbb{R}$ such that $a = \lim_{n \to \infty} x_n$. So $\{x_n - a\}_{n=1}^{\infty}$ is infinitely small. By Theorem 3.10 it is bounded. Hence for any $A > 0$ we have $|x_n - a| < A$ for all $n \in \mathbb{N}$. It follows that $|x_n| \leq |a| + A$.

3.  Let $a = \lim_{n \to \infty} x_n$ and $b = \lim_{n \to \infty} y_n$. Then $\alpha_n := x_n - a$ and $\beta_n := y_n - b$ are infinitely small. Thus,

$$x_n \pm y_n = (a \pm b) + (\alpha_n \pm \beta_n) = a \pm b + \gamma_n^{\pm}$$

and

$$x_n y_n = ab + b\alpha_n + a\beta_n + \alpha_n \beta_n = ab + \gamma_n,$$

where $\gamma_n^{\pm}$ and $\gamma_n$ are infinitely small by Theorem 3.10. Hence we may conclude (using Theorem 3.10 again) that $x_n \pm y_n, x_n y_n$ are convergent and $\lim_{n \to \infty}(x_n \pm y_n) = a \pm b$ and $\lim_{n \to \infty}(x_n y_n) = ab$.

To finish the proof we first prove the following lemma.

**Lemma 3.21.** *If $\{y_n\}_{n=1}^{\infty}$ is convergent and $\lim_{n \to \infty} y_n \neq 0$ then $\{1/y_n\}_{n=1}^{\infty}$ is well-defined (at least starting from some index) and bounded.*

**Proof.** Let $\lim_{n \to \infty} y_n = b \neq 0$. Then for $\varepsilon = |b|/2 > 0$ there is $n_0 \in \mathbb{N}$ such that $|y_n - b| < |b|/2$ for all $n \geq n_0$. This implies that $|y_n| > |b|/2$ or $|1/y_n| < 2/|b|$. This proves the lemma.

Now let $\lim_{n \to \infty} x_n = a$ and $\lim_{n \to \infty} y_n = b \neq 0$. Then due to Lemma 3.21, $\{x_n/y_n\}_{n=1}^{\infty}$ is well-defined, and for $\alpha_n = x_n - a$ and $\beta_n = y_n - b$ we have

$$\frac{x_n}{y_n} = \frac{a}{b} + \frac{b\alpha_n - a\beta_n}{by_n} = \frac{a}{b} + \frac{1}{y_n}\frac{b\alpha_n - a\beta_n}{b} = \frac{a}{b} + \frac{1}{y_n}\gamma_n,$$

where $\{1/y_n\}$ is bounded by Lemma 3.21 and $\{\gamma_n\}$ infinitely small by Theorem 3.10. Thus, $\{\gamma_n/y_n\}$ is infinitely small and therefore

$$\lim_{n \to \infty} \frac{x_n}{y_n} = \frac{a}{b} = \frac{\lim_{n \to \infty} x_n}{\lim_{n \to \infty} y_n}.$$

**Exercise 3.22.**    1.  Prove that $\lim_{n \to \infty} \sin n$ does not exist.

2.  Show that the converse statements of parts 2 and 3 of Theorem 3.20 are not true, in general.

3.  Show that if $\{x_n\}_{n=1}^{\infty}$ is convergent and $\{y_n\}_{n=1}^{\infty}$ is divergent then $\{x_n \pm y_n\}_{n=1}^{\infty}$ is necessarily divergent. What can be concluded about the sequences $\{x_n y_n\}_{n=1}^{\infty}$ and $\{x_n/y_n\}_{n=1}^{\infty}$ in that case?

**Theorem 3.23 (Limit passage in inequalities).** *Suppose $\lim_{n \to \infty} x_n = a$ and $\lim_{n \to \infty} y_n = b$ and $a < b$. Then for all $c$ such that $0 < c < b - a$ there exists $n_0 \in \mathbb{N}$ such that $y_n - x_n > c$ for all $n \geq n_0$.*

**Proof.** Put $\varepsilon := (b - a - c)/2$. Then there exist $n_1, n_2 \in \mathbb{N}$ such that $|x_n - a| < (b - a - c)/2$ for all $n \geq n_1$ and $|y_n - b| < (b - a - c)/2$ for all $n \geq n_2$. Denoting $n_0 := \max(n_1, n_2)$ we have for all $n \geq n_0$ that

$$\frac{2a - b - c}{2} < x_n < \frac{a + b - c}{2}, \quad \frac{a + b + c}{2} < y_n < \frac{3b - a - c}{2}.$$

It follows that

$$y_n - x_n > \frac{a + b + c}{2} - \frac{a + b - c}{2} = c.$$

**Corollary 3.24.** *Let* $\lim_{n \to \infty} x_n = a$ *and* $\lim_{n \to \infty} y_n = b$. *If there is* $n_0 \in \mathbb{N}$ *such that* $x_n > y_n$ *or* $x_n \geq y_n$ *for all* $n \geq n_0$ *then* $a \geq b$.

**Proof.** Assume on the contrary that $a < b$. Then by Theorem 3.23, for any $c, 0 < c < b - a$ there is $n_1 \in \mathbb{N}$ such that $y_n - x_n > c > 0$ for all $n \geq n_1$. It follows that $y_n - x_n > c > 0$ for all $n \geq \max(n_0, n_1)$ too. This contradiction proves the statement.

**Remark 3.25.** The sequences $x_n = 1/n$ and $y_n = 1/(n + 1)$ show that the strict inequality $x_n > y_n$ does not imply the strict inequality for their limits.

**Theorem 3.26 (About two policemen).** *Let* $\lim_{n \to \infty} x_n = \lim_{n \to \infty} y_n = a$, *and let* $n_0' \in \mathbb{N}$ *be such that* $x_n \leq z_n \leq y_n$ *for all* $n \geq n_0'$. *Then* $\{z_n\}_{n=1}^{\infty}$ *is convergent and* $\lim_{n \to \infty} z_n = a$.

**Proof.** By the condition of this theorem, for any $\varepsilon > 0$ there exist $n_1, n_2 \in \mathbb{N}$ such that $|x_n - a| < \varepsilon$ for all $n \geq n_1$ and $|y_n - a| < \varepsilon$ for all $n \geq n_2$. Choosing $n_0 := \max(n_0', n_1, n_2)$ we obtain

$$a - \varepsilon < x_n \leq z_n \leq y_n < a + \varepsilon, \quad n \geq n_0.$$

So $|z_n - a| < \varepsilon$ for all $n \geq n_0$, i.e., $\{z_n\}_{n=1}^{\infty}$ is convergent and $\lim_{n \to \infty} z_n = a$.

**Exercise 3.27.** Prove that

1. the sequence $x_n = (-1)^n$ is not convergent,

2. for sequences $x_n = -1, y_n = 1, z_n = (-1)^n$, Theorem 3.26 does not hold. Explain the reason for this.

**Definition 3.28 (Monotone sequences).** *A sequence* $\{x_n\}_{n=1}^{\infty}$ *is called*

1. increasing (decreasing) *if* $x_n < x_{n+1}$ ($x_n > x_{n+1}$) *for all* $n \geq 1$,

2. nondecreasing (nonincreasing) *if* $x_n \leq x_{n+1}$ ($x_n \geq x_{n+1}$) *for all* $n \geq 1$.

**Theorem 3.29 (Sufficient condition of convergence for monotone sequences).** *Let* $\{x_n\}_{n=1}^{\infty}$ *be nondecreasing (nonincreasing). If* $\{x_n\}_{n=1}^{\infty}$ *is bounded from above (from below) then it is convergent and*

$$\lim_{n \to \infty} x_n = \sup_n x_n \quad (\inf_n x_n).$$

**Proof.** Let $\{x_n\}_{n=1}^{\infty}$ be nondecreasing and bounded from above. Then there exists $A \in \mathbb{R}$ such that $x_n \leq x_{n+1} \leq A$ for $n \geq 1$. By Theorem 2.11 we conclude that $a := \sup_n x_n$ exists. Let us prove that $a = \lim_{n \to \infty} x_n$. Indeed, by the definition of supremum, for any $a' < a$ there is $x_{n_0}$

such that $a' < x_{n_0} \leq a$. Setting $a' := a - \varepsilon$ for arbitrary $\varepsilon > 0$ we obtain (due to monotonicity)

$$a - \varepsilon < x_{n_0} \leq x_n \leq a$$

for all $n \geq n_0$. So $|x_n - a| < \varepsilon$ for all $n \geq n_0$. The proof for nonincreasing sequence is the same with $a = \inf_n x_n$.

**Exercise 3.30.** Prove that a monotone sequence is convergent if and only if it is bounded.

**Definition 3.31.** *The set $\{[a_n, b_n]\}_{n=1}^{\infty}$ of closed intervals is called* contracting segments of system *(collapsible segments of system) if*

1. $[a_{n+1}, b_{n+1}] \subset [a_n, b_n], n = 1, 2, \ldots,$ *and*

2. $\lim_{n \to \infty}(b_n - a_n) = 0.$

**Theorem 3.32 (On contracting segments of system).** *Let $\{[a_n, b_n]\}_{n=1}^{\infty}$ be contracting segments of system. Then there exists a unique number $c$ such that*

$$c = \bigcap_{n=1}^{\infty}[a_n, b_n].$$

*Proof.* Since $[a_{n+1}, b_{n+1}] \subset [a_n, b_n]$ then for any $n \geq 1$ we have

$$a_{n+1} \geq a_n, \quad b_{n+1} \leq b_n.$$

In addition,

$$a_n \leq b_1, \quad b_n \geq a_1$$

for all $n \geq 1$. By Theorem 3.29 there exist $\lim_{n \to \infty} a_n$ and $\lim_{n \to \infty} b_n$. Since $\lim_{n \to \infty}(b_n - a_n) = 0$ then

$$c := \lim_{n \to \infty} a_n = \lim_{n \to \infty} b_n.$$

Due to monotonicity we have $c \in [a_n, b_n]$ for all $n \geq 1$ and hence

$$c \in \bigcap_{n=1}^{\infty}[a_n, b_n].$$

It remains to show that $c$ is the only element of

$$\bigcap_{n=1}^{\infty}[a_n, b_n].$$

If we assume on the contrary that there is another element $c_1 \neq c$ such that

$$c_1 \in \bigcap_{n=1}^{\infty}[a_n, b_n]$$

then $a_n \leq c_1 \leq b_n$ for all $n \geq 1$. This implies

$$c_1 = \lim_{n \to \infty} a_n = \lim_{n \to \infty} b_n = c.$$

This contradiction proves the theorem.

**Example 3.33.**     1. *The number* e. Let us consider two sequences

$$x_n = (1 + 1/n)^n, \quad y_n = (1 + 1/n)^{n+1}.$$

We show first that $\{x_n\}_{n=1}^{\infty}$ is increasing and $\{y_n\}_{n=1}^{\infty}$ is decreasing. Indeed,

$$
\begin{aligned}
\frac{x_{n+1}}{x_n} &= \left(\frac{n+2}{n+1}\right)^{n+1} \left(\frac{n}{n+1}\right)^n = \frac{n+2}{n+1} \left(\frac{n^2 + 2n}{n^2 + 2n + 1}\right)^n \\
&= \frac{n+2}{n+1} \left(1 - \frac{1}{(n+1)^2}\right)^n > \frac{n+2}{n+1} \left(1 - \frac{n}{(n+1)^2}\right) \\
&= \frac{n+2}{n+1} \frac{n^2 + n + 1}{n^2 + 2n + 1} = \frac{n^3 + 3n^2 + 3n + 2}{n^3 + 3n^2 + 3n + 1} > 1,
\end{aligned}
$$

where we have made use of Bernoulli's inequality. Hence $\{x_n\}_{n=1}^{\infty}$ is increasing. For $\{y_n\}_{n=1}^{\infty}$ we have

$$
\begin{aligned}
\frac{y_n}{y_{n+1}} &= \frac{n+1}{n+2} \left(\frac{n^2 + 2n + 1}{n^2 + 2n}\right)^{n+1} \\
&= \frac{n+1}{n+2} \left(1 + \frac{1}{n^2 + 2n}\right)^{n+1} > \frac{n+1}{n+2} \left(1 + \frac{n+1}{n^2 + 2n}\right) \\
&= \frac{n+1}{n+2} \frac{n^2 + 3n + 1}{n^2 + 2n} = \frac{n^3 + 4n^2 + 4n + 1}{n^3 + 4n^2 + 4n} > 1
\end{aligned}
$$

again by Bernoulli's inequality. So $\{y_n\}_{n=1}^{\infty}$ is decreasing.

Next we show that $y_n > 2$ and $x_n < 3$ for all $n \geq 1$. Obviously

$$
\begin{aligned}
y_n &= (1 + 1/n)^n (1 + 1/n) > (1 + 1/n)^n \\
&= 1 + n \frac{1}{n} + \frac{n(n-1)}{2} \frac{1}{n^2} + \cdots + \left(\frac{1}{n}\right)^n \geq 2.
\end{aligned}
$$

Using $n! \geq 2^{n-1}$ we have

$$
\begin{aligned}
x_n = (1 + 1/n)^n &= 1 + n \frac{1}{n} + \frac{n(n-1)}{2} \frac{1}{n^2} + \cdots + \frac{n(n-1)(n-2)\cdots 1}{2 \cdot 3 \cdots n} \frac{1}{n^n} \\
&< 2 + \frac{1}{2!} + \frac{1}{3!} + \cdots \frac{1}{n!} \leq 2 + \frac{1}{2} + \frac{1}{4} + \cdots \frac{1}{2^{n-1}} = 2 + \frac{1}{2} \frac{1 - (1/2)^n}{1 - 1/2} \\
&= 2 + 1 - (1/2)^n < 3.
\end{aligned}
$$

That's why $\{x_n\}_{n=1}^{\infty}$ is increasing and bounded from above by 3. Hence the limits

$$\lim_{n \to \infty} (1 + 1/n)^n, \quad \lim_{n \to \infty} (1 + 1/n)^{n+1}$$

exist and they are equal since

$$\lim_{n \to \infty} (1 + 1/n)^{n+1} = \lim_{n \to \infty} (1 + 1/n)^n \lim_{n \to \infty} (1 + 1/n) = \lim_{n \to \infty} (1 + 1/n)^n.$$

These facts justify the following definition.

**Definition 3.34.** *The special number* e, *called the* Euler's number, *is defined as*

$$\mathrm{e} := \lim_{n \to \infty} (1 + 1/n)^n = \lim_{n \to \infty} (1 + 1/n)^{n+1}.$$

**Remark 3.35.** It follows from above that $2 \leq e \leq 3$ and

$$(1 + 1/n)^n < e < (1 + 1/n)^{n+1}$$

for all $n \geq 1$. This implies the double inequality

$$\frac{1}{n+1} < \log(1 + 1/n) < \frac{1}{n}. \tag{3.1}$$

2. *Harmonic sequence*. Let

$$x_n = 1 + \frac{1}{2} + \cdots + \frac{1}{n}, \quad n \geq 1.$$

Clearly $\{x_n\}_{n=1}^{\infty}$ is increasing. We want to show that $\{x_n\}_{n=1}^{\infty}$ is infinitely large, i.e.,

$$\lim_{n \to \infty} \left( 1 + \frac{1}{2} + \cdots + \frac{1}{n} \right) = \infty.$$

Assume on the contrary that $\{x_n\}_{n=1}^{\infty}$ is bounded from above. Then there exists $A > 0$ such that

$$1 + \frac{1}{2} + \cdots + \frac{1}{n} \leq A, \quad n \geq 1.$$

Using (3.1) we obtain

$$A \geq 1 + \frac{1}{2} + \cdots + \frac{1}{n} > \log 2 + \log \frac{3}{2} + \cdots + \log \frac{n+1}{n}$$
$$= \log \left( 2 \cdot \frac{3}{2} \cdot \frac{4}{3} \cdots \frac{n+1}{n} \right) = \log(1 + n).$$

This contradicts the fact that log is increasing to infinity for large argument. Thus

$$\lim_{n \to \infty} \left( 1 + \frac{1}{2} + \cdots + \frac{1}{n} \right) = \infty.$$

Moreover, using again (3.1) we have

$$1 + \frac{1}{2} + \cdots + \frac{1}{n} < 1 + \log 2 + \log \frac{3}{2} + \cdots + \log \frac{n}{n-1} = 1 + \log n.$$

Therefore we have the double inequality for harmonic sequence

$$\log(1 + n) < 1 + \frac{1}{2} + \cdots + \frac{1}{n} < 1 + \log n$$

or

$$1 < \frac{\log(1 + n)}{\log n} < \frac{1 + \frac{1}{2} + \cdots + \frac{1}{n}}{\log n} < 1 + \frac{1}{\log n}.$$

By Theorem 3.26 we get

$$\lim_{n \to \infty} \frac{1 + \frac{1}{2} + \cdots + \frac{1}{n}}{\log n} = 1$$

or

$$1 + \frac{1}{2} + \cdots + \frac{1}{n} \sim \log n$$

for large $n$.

Moreover, the limit

$$\lim_{n\to\infty}\left(1+\frac{1}{2}+\cdots+\frac{1}{n}-\log n\right)=:\gamma$$

exists. This number $\gamma$ is called *Euler's constant*. Indeed, we know from above that

$$0<1+\frac{1}{2}+\cdots+\frac{1}{n}-\log n<1$$

and

$$\left(1+\frac{1}{2}+\cdots+\frac{1}{n+1}-\log(n+1)\right)-\left(1+\frac{1}{2}+\cdots+\frac{1}{n}-\log n\right)$$
$$=\frac{1}{n+1}-\log(1+1/n)<0,$$

i.e., the sequence in question is decreasing and bounded. Thus it converges.

3. *Binary partition.* Let $a_n\ge a_{n+1}$ and $a_n\ge 0$. Put

$$x_n:=a_1+a_2+\cdots+a_n,\quad y_n:=a_1+2a_2+\cdots 2^n a_{2^n}.$$

Then the sequences $\{x_n\}_{n=1}^\infty$ and $\{y_n\}_{n=1}^\infty$ converge or diverge simultaneously. Since these sequences are increasing, it suffices to show that they are bounded (from above) or unbounded simultaneously. Indeed, if $2^m\ge n$ then

$$x_n=a_1+\cdots+a_n\le a_1+\cdots+a_{2^m}=\sum_{j=0}^{m-1}\sum_{2^j\le n<2^{j+1}}a_n+a_{2^m}$$

$$\le\sum_{j=0}^{m-1}a_{2^j}\sum_{2^j\le n<2^{j+1}}1+a_{2^m}=\sum_{j=0}^{m-1}a_{2^j}2^j+a_{2^m}$$

$$=y_{m-1}+a_{2^m}\le y_{m-1}+2^m a_{2^m}=y_m.$$

For $2^m\le n$ we have

$$x_n=a_1+\cdots+a_n\ge a_1+\cdots+a_{2^m}=\sum_{j=0}^{m-1}\sum_{2^j\le n<2^{j+1}}a_n+a_{2^m}$$

$$>\sum_{j=0}^{m-1}2^j a_{2^{j+1}}+a_{2^m}=\frac{1}{2}\sum_{j=0}^{m-1}a_{2^{j+1}}2^{j+1}+a_{2^m}=\frac{1}{2}\sum_{j=0}^{m}a_{2^j}2^j+a_{2^m}$$

$$=\frac{1}{2}y_m-\frac{1}{2}a_1+a_{2^m}\ge\frac{1}{2}y_m-\frac{1}{2}a_1.$$

Hence these two sequences converge or diverge simultaneously.

**Exercise 3.36.** Prove that

1. $\lim_{n\to\infty}(2+\frac{1}{2!}+\cdots+\frac{1}{n!})=\mathrm{e}$,

2. $\lim_{n\to\infty}\frac{n}{\sqrt[n]{n!}}=\mathrm{e}$,

3. $\lim_{n\to\infty}(\frac{1}{np+1}+\cdots+\frac{1}{nq})=\log(q/p)$ for $q,p\in\mathbb{N},q>p$,

4. $\lim_{n\to\infty}(1 + \frac{1}{2^\alpha} + \cdots + \frac{1}{n^\alpha})$ exists if and only if $\alpha > 1$,

5. $\lim_{n\to\infty}(1 + \frac{1}{2(\log 2)^\beta} + \cdots + \frac{1}{n(\log n)^\beta})$ exists if and only if $\beta > 1$,

6. e is an irrational number.

In the case when it is necessary to prove only the existence of a limit of a sequence (without calculating it or if we have difficulties in calculating it) the concept of Cauchy sequence is the most essential and sometimes the only possibility.

**Definition 3.37.** *A sequence $\{x_n\}_{n=1}^\infty$ is said to be a* Cauchy sequence *if for any $\varepsilon > 0$ there exists $n_0 \in \mathbb{N}$ such that $|x_n - x_m| < \varepsilon$ for all $n, m \geq n_0$.*

**Exercise 3.38.**    1.  Prove that Definition 3.37 is equivalent to the following two statements:

   (a) For any $\varepsilon > 0$ there exists $n_0 \in \mathbb{N}$ such that $|x_{n+p} - x_n| < \varepsilon$ for all $n \geq n_0$ and for all $p \in \mathbb{N}$.

   (b) The sequence $r_n := \sup_{p\in\mathbb{N}} |x_{n+p} - x_n|$ is infinitely small.

2. Show that $\{x_n\}_{n=1}^\infty$ is not a Cauchy sequence if there exists $\varepsilon_0 > 0$ such that for any $n \in \mathbb{N}$ there are $n_0, m_0 \geq n$ with $|x_{n_0} - x_{m_0}| \geq \varepsilon_0$.

3. Show that any Cauchy sequence is bounded but the converse is not true.

4. Let $x_n = \log(n+1) - \log n$. Show that $\{x_n\}_{n=1}^\infty$ is infinitely small, but $y_n = \log n$ is not a Cauchy sequence.

**Theorem 3.39 (Cauchy criterion).**   *A sequence $\{x_n\}_{n=1}^\infty$ is convergent if and only if it is a Cauchy sequence.*

**Proof.** Let us assume that $\{x_n\}_{n=1}^\infty$ is convergent. Then there exists $a \in \mathbb{R}$ such that $\lim_{n\to\infty} x_n = a$, i.e., for any $\varepsilon > 0$ there is $n_0 \in \mathbb{N}$ such that $|x_n - a| < \varepsilon/2$ for all $n \geq n_0$. It follows that

$$|x_n - x_m| \leq |x_n - a| + |x_m - a| < \varepsilon/2 + \varepsilon/2 = \varepsilon, \quad n, m \geq n_0.$$

This means that $\{x_n\}_{n=1}^\infty$ is a Cauchy sequence.

Conversely, let $\{x_n\}_{n=1}^\infty$ be a Cauchy sequence. Then $\{x_n\}_{n=1}^\infty$ is bounded (Exercise 3.38). This fact allows us to consider the sequences

$$a_k := \inf_{n\geq k} x_n, \quad b_k := \sup_{n\geq k} x_n.$$

It is easy to see that $\{a_k\}_{k=1}^\infty$ is nondecreasing and $\{b_k\}_{k=1}^\infty$ is nonincreasing and $a_k \leq b_k$. Thus $\{[a_k, b_k]\}_{k=1}^\infty$ is a contracting segments of system. Indeed, without loss of generality we may assume $a_k < b_k$ (since otherwise $\{x_n\}_{n=1}^\infty$ is a constant sequence). Next, for arbitrary $\varepsilon > 0$ there exists $n_0 \in \mathbb{N}$ such that

$$x_{n_0} - \varepsilon/2 \leq \inf_{n\geq k\geq n_0} x_n = a_k < b_k = \sup_{n\geq k\geq n_0} x_n \leq x_{n_0} + \varepsilon/2.$$

It follows that $0 < b_k - a_k \leq \varepsilon$ for any $k \geq n_0$. Applying Theorem 3.32 we obtain that there is only one point

$$c = \bigcap_{k=1}^\infty [a_k, b_k]$$

and $c = \lim_{k\to\infty} a_k = \lim_{k\to\infty} b_k$. We will prove that actually $c = \lim_{n\to\infty} x_n$.

Now

$$a_k = \inf_{n \geq k \geq n_0} x_n \leq x_n \leq \sup_{n \geq k \geq n_0} x_n = b_k$$

for all $n \geq n_0$. It implies that $a_k - c \leq x_n - c \leq b_k - c$ for $n \geq k \geq n_0$. Thus,

$$|x_n - c| \leq \max(b_k - c, c - a_k) \to 0$$

as $k \to \infty$ (and for $n \to \infty, n \geq k$). This completes the proof.

**Definition 3.40.** *An open interval* $(a - \delta, a + \delta), \delta > 0$ *is called a* neighborhood of the point $a$, *denoted by* $U_\delta(a)$. *By* $U'_\delta(a)$ *we denote the set* $U_\delta(a) \setminus \{a\}$ *and call it the* deleted neighborhood *of* $a$.

**Definition 3.41.** *Let* $\{x_n\}_{n=1}^\infty$ *be an arbitrary sequence of real numbers, and let* $k_n$ *be an increasing sequence of positive integers, i.e.,* $k_n \in \mathbb{N}$ *and* $k_{n+1} > k_n$. *Then* $\{x_{k_n}\}_{n=1}^\infty \subset \{x_n\}_{n=1}^\infty$ *is said to be a* subsequence *of the sequence* $\{x_n\}_{n=1}^\infty$.

**Remark 3.42.** It follows that $k_n \geq n$ for $n = 1, 2, \dots$.

**Theorem 3.43 (On convergent subsequence).** *Assume that* $\{x_n\}_{n=1}^\infty$ *is a convergent sequence and* $\lim_{n \to \infty} x_n = a$. *Then for any subsequence* $\{x_{k_n}\}_{n=1}^\infty$ *of this sequence we have that* $\lim_{n \to \infty} x_{k_n} = a$.

***Proof.*** If $\lim_{n \to \infty} x_n = a$ then for any $\varepsilon > 0$ there exists $n_0 \in \mathbb{N}$ such that $|x_n - a| < \varepsilon$ for all $n \geq n_0$. Since $k_n \geq n$ then $|x_{k_n} - a| < \varepsilon$. Hence $\lim_{n \to \infty} x_{k_n} = a$.

**Exercise 3.44.** Assume that for any proper subsequence $\{x_{k_n}\}_{n=1}^\infty$ of a sequence $\{x_n\}_{n=1}^\infty$ we have that $\lim_{n \to \infty} x_{k_n} = a$ (same for all subsequences). Prove that $\{x_n\}_{n=1}^\infty$ is convergent and $\lim_{n \to \infty} x_n = a$.

**Definition 3.45.** *A number* $a \in \mathbb{R}$ *is said to be a* limiting point *of a sequence* $\{x_n\}_{n=1}^\infty$ *if there is a subsequence* $\{x_{k_n}\}_{n=1}^\infty \subset \{x_n\}_{n=1}^\infty$ *such that* $\lim_{n \to \infty} x_{k_n} = a$. *This is equivalent to the fact that for any* $\delta > 0$ *there are infinitely many elements of* $\{x_n\}_{n=1}^\infty$ *in* $U_\delta(a)$. *The set of all limiting points of* $\{x_n\}_{n=1}^\infty$ *is denoted by* $S(x_n)$.

**Exercise 3.46.** Prove that these two definitions of a limiting point are equivalent.

**Example 3.47.**     1. Let $x_n = (-1)^n$. Then $S(x_n) = \{-1, 1\}$.

2. Let $x_n = n^{(-1)^n}$. Then $S(x_n) = \{0\}$.

3. Let $x_n = \sin \sqrt{n}$. Then $S(x_n) = [-1, 1]$.

4. Let $\{x_n\}_{n=1}^\infty$ be the sequence of all rational numbers. Then $S(x_n) = \mathbb{R}$. This fact follows from the possibility of approximating any real number by rational numbers with deficiency and by excess such that

$$p_n \leq a < q_n, \quad p_n, q_n \in \mathbb{Q}, \quad q_n - p_n = 2/10^n.$$

**Exercise 3.48.** Prove part 3 of Example 3.47.

**Theorem 3.49 (Bolzano–Weierstrass).** *Let a sequence $\{x_n\}_{n=1}^{\infty}$ be bounded. Then $S(x_n) \neq \emptyset$, i.e., every bounded sequence contains a convergent subsequence.*

**Proof.** Since $\{x_n\}_{n=1}^{\infty}$ is bounded, there exists $A > 0$ such that $|x_n| \leq A$ for all $n \geq 1$. Denote $[a_1, b_1] = [-A, A]$ and then by $[a_2, b_2]$ one of the segments $[-A, 0]$ or $[0, A]$, where infinitely many elements of $\{x_n\}_{n=1}^{\infty}$ exist. By induction, we denote by $[a_{n+1}, b_{n+1}]$ one of the half segments of $[a_n, b_n]$, where infinitely many elements of $\{x_n\}_{n=1}^{\infty}$ exist. This process may be continued infinitely many times to obtain the sequence

$$\{[a_n, b_n]\}_{n=1}^{\infty}, \quad [a_{n+1}, b_{n+1}] \subset [a_n, b_n], \quad b_n - a_n = 2A/2^{n-1}, \quad n = 1, 2, \ldots.$$

Thus, this sequence is a contracting segments of system. Hence, Theorem 3.32 leads to

$$c = \bigcap_{n=1}^{\infty} [a_n, b_n] = \lim_{n \to \infty} a_n = \lim_{n \to \infty} b_n.$$

Let us show that $c \in S(x_n)$. Indeed, $a_n \leq c \leq b_n$ for any $n \geq 1$, and for any $\varepsilon > 0$ there exist $n_0 \in \mathbb{N}$ such that $0 \leq c - a_n, b_n - c < \varepsilon$ for all $n \geq n_0$. Therefore $[a_n, b_n] \subset U_\varepsilon(c)$. So $c \in S(x_n)$ because any segment $[a_n, b_n]$ contains infinitely many elements of $\{x_n\}_{n=1}^{\infty}$ by construction.

**Definition 3.50.**

1. *Let a sequence $\{x_n\}_{n=1}^{\infty}$ be bounded. The values*

$$\sup S(x_n) := \overline{\lim_{n \to \infty}} \, x_n, \quad \inf S(x_n) := \underline{\lim_{n \to \infty}} \, x_n$$

   *are called the* upper limit *and* lower limit *of $\{x_n\}_{n=1}^{\infty}$, respectively.*

2. *Let a sequence $\{x_n\}_{n=1}^{\infty}$ be bounded from above (below) but not from below (above). Then we put by definition*

$$\underline{\lim_{n \to \infty}} \, x_n = -\infty \quad \left( \overline{\lim_{n \to \infty}} \, x_n = \infty \right).$$

3. *Let a sequence $\{x_n\}_{n=1}^{\infty}$ be unbounded from above and below. Then we put by definition*

$$\underline{\lim_{n \to \infty}} \, x_n = -\infty, \quad \overline{\lim_{n \to \infty}} \, x_n = \infty.$$

**Exercise 3.51.** Prove that

1. if a sequence $\{x_n\}_{n=1}^{\infty}$ is infinitely large then either $\underline{\lim}_{n \to \infty} x_n = -\infty$ or $\overline{\lim}_{n \to \infty} x_n = \infty$ or both;

2. if a sequence $\{x_n\}_{n=1}^{\infty}$ is not bounded and is not infinitely large then there are two subsequences $\{x'_{k_n}\}_{n=1}^{\infty}$ and $\{x''_{k_n}\}_{n=1}^{\infty}$ of $\{x_n\}_{n=1}^{\infty}$ such that $\{x'_{k_n}\}_{n=1}^{\infty}$ is infinitely large and $\{x''_{k_n}\}_{n=1}^{\infty}$ is bounded, and therefore $S(x_n) \neq \emptyset$ in this case;

3. if a sequence $\{x_n\}_{n=1}^{\infty}$ is bounded then $S(x_n)$ is bounded and closed, i.e., $S(x_n)$ contains all its limiting points.

**Theorem 3.52 (Criterion of convergence II).** *A sequence $\{x_n\}_{n=1}^{\infty}$ is convergent if and only if $\{x_n\}_{n=1}^{\infty}$ is bounded and $S(x_n)$ contains only one limiting point which is a limit of $\{x_n\}_{n=1}^{\infty}$, i.e.,*

$$\underline{\lim_{n \to \infty}} \, x_n = \overline{\lim_{n \to \infty}} \, x_n = \lim_{n \to \infty} x_n.$$

**Proof.** Let $\{x_n\}_{n=1}^{\infty}$ be convergent. Then $\{x_n\}_{n=1}^{\infty}$ is bounded and $S(x_n) = \{a\}$, where $a = \lim_{n \to \infty} x_n$ (see Theorems 3.20 and 3.43).

Conversely, let $\{x_n\}_{n=1}^{\infty}$ be bounded, and let $S(x_n) = \{a\}$ such that $a = \underline{\lim}_{n \to \infty} x_n = \overline{\lim}_{n \to \infty} x_n$. We show that actually $a = \lim_{n \to \infty} x_n$. Let us assume on the contrary that $a \neq \lim_{n \to \infty} x_n$. Then there exists $\varepsilon_0 > 0$ such that for any $n \in \mathbb{N}$ there is $k_n \geq n$ with $|x_{k_n} - a| \geq \varepsilon_0$. Hence $x_{k_n} - a \geq \varepsilon_0$ or $x_{k_n} - a \leq -\varepsilon_0$. Thus, there are infinitely many elements of $\{x_{k_n}\}_{n=1}^{\infty}$ that satisfy one or both of these inequalities. Denoting these infinitely many elements as $\{x_n'\}_{n=1}^{\infty}$ we obtain a subsequence of the original sequence $\{x_n\}_{n=1}^{\infty}$. Since $\{x_n\}_{n=1}^{\infty}$ is bounded then so is $\{x_{k_n}'\}_{n=1}^{\infty}$. By the Bolzano–Weierstrass theorem we may conclude that there is a limiting point of this subsequence. But

$$x_{k_n}' \geq a + \varepsilon_0 \quad \text{or} \quad x_{k_n}' \leq a - \varepsilon_0$$

with fixed $\varepsilon_0 > 0$. This implies that the limiting point $a'$ mentioned above must satisfy

$$a' \geq a + \varepsilon_0 \quad \text{or} \quad a' \leq a - \varepsilon_0.$$

This contradicts the fact $S(x_n) = \{a\}$ or $a = \underline{\lim}_{n \to \infty} x_n = \overline{\lim}_{n \to \infty} x_n$. Hence this theorem is proved.

**Exercise 3.53.**     1. Show that if $a = \lim_{n \to \infty} x_n$ then

$$\lim_{n \to \infty} \frac{x_1 + x_2 + \cdots + x_n}{n} = a$$

but the converse is not true.

2. Let $\{x_n\}_{n=1}^{\infty}$ be infinitely large. What can be said about the sequence

$$\left\{ \frac{x_1 + x_2 + \cdots + x_n}{n} \right\}_{n=1}^{\infty} ?$$

Hint: Consider the sequence $n(-1)^n$.

3. Show that if $a = \lim_{n \to \infty} x_n$ and $x_n > 0$ then $\lim_{n \to \infty} \sqrt[n]{x_1 x_2 \cdots x_n} = a$. Is the converse statement true?

4. Show that if $\{x_n\}_{n=1}^{\infty}$ is infinitely large and $x_n > 0$ then

$$\lim_{n \to \infty} \frac{x_1 + x_2 + \cdots + x_n}{n} = +\infty.$$

5. Let $x_n > 0$ and $a = \lim_{n \to \infty} \sqrt[n]{x_n}$. Prove that

$$\lim_{n \to \infty} \frac{x_{n+1}}{x_n} = a.$$

Show that the converse is not true.

6. Construct a sequence $\{x_n\}_{n=1}^{\infty}$ such that

   (a) $\{x_n\}_{n=1}^{\infty}$ is bounded,
   (b) $\lim_{n \to \infty} (x_{n+1} - x_n) = 0$,
   (c) $\{x_n\}_{n=1}^{\infty}$ is not convergent.

7. Let a sequence $\{x_n\}_{n=1}^{\infty}$ satisfy

    (a) $\{x_n\}_{n=1}^{\infty}$ is bounded,
    (b) $\lim_{n\to\infty}(x_{n+1} - x_n) = 0$.

    Prove that $S(x_n) = [l, L]$, where $l = \underline{\lim}_{n\to\infty} x_n$ and $L = \overline{\lim}_{n\to\infty} x_n$. Compare this with part 3 of Example 3.47.

8. Prove that if $\{x_n\}_{n=1}^{\infty}$ is a sequence then

$$\underline{\lim_{n\to\infty}} x_n = \lim_{n\to\infty} \varphi_n, \quad \overline{\lim_{n\to\infty}} x_n = \lim_{n\to\infty} \psi_n,$$

    where

$$\varphi_n := \inf_{k\geq n} x_k, \quad \psi_n := \sup_{k\geq n} x_k.$$

9. Let a sequence $\{x_n\}_{n=1}^{\infty}$ be defined by

$$x_n := x_{n-1}(1 - x_{n-1}), \quad n = 1, 2, \ldots, \quad x_0 \in (0, 1).$$

    Prove that $\lim_{n\to\infty} n x_n = 1$.

10. Let a sequence $\{x_n\}_{n=1}^{\infty}$ be defined by

$$x_n := \sin(\cos x_{n-1}), \quad n = 1, 2, \ldots, \quad x_0 \in \mathbb{R}.$$

    Prove that $\{x_n\}_{n=1}^{\infty}$ is convergent.

11. Prove the *Stolz theorem*: Let $\{x_n\}_{n=1}^{\infty}$ be an increasing sequence of positive numbers such that $\lim_{n\to\infty} x_n = \infty$. Let $\{y_n\}_{n=1}^{\infty}$ be an arbitrary sequence, and suppose that

$$a = \lim_{n\to\infty} \frac{y_n - y_{n-1}}{x_n - x_{n-1}}$$

    is finite or infinite. Then $a = \lim_{n\to\infty} y_n/x_n$.

12. Using the Stolz theorem prove that

    (a)
$$\lim_{n\to\infty} \frac{1^p + 2^p + \cdots + n^p}{n^{p+1}} = \frac{1}{p+1}, \quad p > 0,$$

    (b)
$$\lim_{n\to\infty} \left( \frac{1^p + 2^p + \cdots + n^p}{n^p} - \frac{n}{p+1} \right) = \frac{1}{2}, \quad p > 0.$$

13. Evaluate the limits

    (a)
$$\lim_{n\to\infty} \sum_{k=1}^{n} \frac{1}{n + k^\alpha},$$

    (b)
$$\lim_{n\to\infty} n^\alpha \left( \frac{\sqrt[n+1]{(n+1)!}}{n+1} - \frac{\sqrt[n]{n!}}{n} \right),$$

    (c)
$$\lim_{n\to\infty} \sum_{k=1}^{n} \left( \frac{k}{n} \right)^{\alpha k},$$

    where $\alpha > 0$.

# Chapter 4

# Series and infinite products of real numbers

This chapter discusses the convergence of number series, including power series and double series. Along with widespread convergence criteria, such as d'Alembert, Cauchy, Raabe, Leibniz, Dirichlet, and Abel, we also consider the universal Gauss criterion, the deep Riemann theorem on rearrangements of conditionally convergent series, and the Mertens theorem on double series. In addition, the principles of infinite products make it possible to introduce (by an equivalent and rather simple method) Euler's Gamma function and treat many of its properties.

Let $\{a_k\}_{k=1}^{\infty}$ be an arbitrary sequence of real numbers. Then the notation

$$\sum_{k=1}^{\infty} a_k = a_1 + a_2 + \cdots + a_n + \cdots \tag{4.1}$$

denotes *formal infinite series*, and $a_k$ are called the terms of series (4.1). The partial sums of the series (4.1) are denoted as

$$S_n := \sum_{k=1}^{n} a_k.$$

**Definition 4.1.** *Finite or infinite limit of the sequence* $\{S_n\}_{n=1}^{\infty}$, *i.e.,*

$$S := \lim_{n \to \infty} S_n,$$

*is said to be the* sum *of series (4.1), denoted by*

$$S = \sum_{k=1}^{\infty} a_k.$$

*If* $S \neq \pm\infty$ *then series (4.1) is called* convergent. *Otherwise, i.e., if* $S = \pm\infty$ *or* $\lim_{n \to \infty} S_n$ *does not exist, series (4.1) is called* divergent.

**Remark 4.2.** Since the question of convergence of series (4.1) is equivalent to the convergence of the sequence of partial sums, then all theorems of Chapter 3 can be applied here also.

**Example 4.3.**     1. Let us consider the *sum of geometric progression*, i.e., the sum of the form

$$\sum_{k=1}^{\infty} q^{k-1}.$$

37

Let $|q| < 1$. Then

$$S_n = \sum_{k=1}^{n} q^{k-1}$$

and so

$$qS_n = \sum_{k=1}^{n} q^k.$$

It follows that $S_n - qS_n = 1 - q^n$ or

$$S_n = \frac{1 - q^n}{1 - q}.$$

Since $|q| < 1$,

$$\lim_{n \to \infty} S_n = \frac{1 - \lim_{n \to \infty} q^n}{1 - q} = \frac{1}{1 - q}.$$

Hence

$$\sum_{k=1}^{\infty} q^{k-1} = \frac{1}{1 - q}, \quad \sum_{k=1}^{\infty} q^k = \frac{q}{1 - q}.$$

2. Let $\alpha \notin \mathbb{Z} \setminus \mathbb{N}_0$. Then, for $p \in \mathbb{N}$ it holds that

$$\sum_{k=1}^{\infty} \frac{1}{(\alpha + k)(\alpha + k + 1) \cdots (\alpha + k + p)} = \frac{1}{p(\alpha + 1) \cdots (\alpha + p)}.$$

Indeed,

$$S_n = \sum_{k=1}^{n} \frac{1}{(\alpha + k)(\alpha + k + 1) \cdots (\alpha + k + p)}$$

$$= \frac{1}{p} \sum_{k=1}^{n} \left( \frac{1}{(\alpha + k)(\alpha + k + 1) \cdots (\alpha + k + p - 1)} \right.$$

$$\left. - \frac{1}{(\alpha + k + 1)(\alpha + k + 2) \cdots (\alpha + k + p)} \right)$$

$$= \frac{1}{p(\alpha + 1) \cdots (\alpha + p)} - \frac{1}{p(\alpha + 2) \cdots (\alpha + p + 1)}$$

$$+ \frac{1}{p(\alpha + 2) \cdots (\alpha + p + 1)} - \frac{1}{p(\alpha + 3) \cdots (\alpha + p + 2)}$$

$$+ \cdots + \frac{1}{p(\alpha + n) \cdots (\alpha + n + p)} - \frac{1}{p(\alpha + n + 1) \cdots (\alpha + n + p + 1)}$$

$$= \frac{1}{p(\alpha + 1) \cdots (\alpha + p)} - \frac{1}{p(\alpha + n + 1) \cdots (\alpha + n + p + 1)}.$$

So

$$\lim_{n \to \infty} S_n = \frac{1}{p(\alpha + 1) \cdots (\alpha + p)}.$$

3. The number e can be represented as

$$e = \sum_{k=0}^{\infty} \frac{1}{k!}, \quad 0! = 1,$$

as can be checked using part 1 of Exercise 3.36.

Applying the Cauchy criterion to the sequence of partial sums $S_n$ of series (4.1) we obtain that the series (4.1) converges if and only if for any $\varepsilon > 0$ there exists $n_0 \in \mathbb{N}$ such that $|S_n - S_m| < \varepsilon$ for all $n, m \geq n_0$. This means that

$$\left| \sum_{k=n+1}^{m} a_k \right| < \varepsilon, \quad m > n,$$

or

$$\left| \sum_{k=n+1}^{\infty} a_k \right| < \varepsilon,$$

i.e., the tail of the series can be made as small as we want.

Consequently, if two series $\sum_{k=1}^{\infty} a_k$ and $\sum_{k=1}^{\infty} b_k$ converge then the series $\sum_{k=1}^{\infty} (a_k \pm b_k)$ converges also and

$$\sum_{k=1}^{\infty} (a_k \pm b_k) = \sum_{k=1}^{\infty} a_k \pm \sum_{k=1}^{\infty} b_k.$$

It is clear that the converse statement does not hold.

There is one more important consequence. Namely, if the series $\sum_{k=1}^{\infty} a_k$ converges then necessarily

$$\lim_{k \to \infty} a_k = 0. \tag{4.2}$$

Indeed, by the Cauchy criterion we have for any $\varepsilon > 0$ that there exists $n_0 \in \mathbb{N}$ such that $|a_{n+1}| = |S_n - S_{n+1}| < \varepsilon$ for all $n \geq n_0$. However, this condition is not sufficient for given series to converge. For example, if we consider the harmonic series $\sum_{k=1}^{\infty} \frac{1}{k}$ then $\lim_{k \to \infty} \frac{1}{k} = 0$, but by Example 3.33

$$\sum_{k=1}^{n} \frac{1}{k} \sim \log n, \quad n \to \infty,$$

and so

$$\sum_{k=1}^{\infty} \frac{1}{k} = \infty,$$

i.e., the harmonic series diverges. This series is called harmonic since

$$\frac{1}{k} = \frac{2}{k-1+k+1}, \quad k = 2, 3, \dots,$$

i.e., every term of harmonic series (starting from the second term) is equal to the harmonic mean of two neighboring terms.

## 4.1 ▪ Series with positive terms

**Theorem 4.4 (Convergence of the series with positive and monotone terms).** *Let $a_k > 0$ and $a_{k+1} \leq a_k$. Then the series*

$$\sum_{k=1}^{\infty} a_k \quad and \quad \sum_{k=0}^{\infty} 2^k a_{2^k}$$

*converge and diverge simultaneously.*

*Proof.* The proof follows immediately from Example 3.33.

**Exercise 4.5.** Prove that

1. the series $\sum_{k=1}^{\infty} \frac{1}{k^s}$ converges if and only if $s > 1$,

2. the series $\sum_{k=2}^{\infty} \frac{1}{k(\log k)^t}$ converges if and only if $t > 1$.

**Theorem 4.6 (Comparison of series with positive terms).** *Let $\sum_{k=1}^{\infty} a_k$ and $\sum_{k=1}^{\infty} b_k$ be two series with positive terms. If there is a number $k_0 \in \mathbb{N}$ such that $a_k \leq b_k$ for all $k \geq k_0$ then the convergence of the second series implies the convergence of the first series, and the divergence of the first series implies the divergence of the second series.*

*Proof.* We may assume without loss of generality that the inequality for the terms holds for all $k \geq 1$. Thus $S_n \leq S_n'$, where $S_n$ and $S_n'$ are the partial sums of the first and second series, respectively. Hence, boundedness of $S_n'$ implies boundedness of $S_n$ and unboundedness of $S_n$ implies unboundedness of $S_n'$. Since $S_n$ and $S_n'$ are increasing, the convergence of $S_n'$ implies the convergence of $S_n$ and divergence of $S_n$ implies divergence of $S_n'$ (see Theorem 3.32).

**Corollary 4.7.** *Under the conditions of Theorem 4.6 suppose that there is the limit*

$$\lim_{k \to \infty} a_k/b_k = c, \quad b_k \neq 0.$$

*Then for $0 < c < \infty$ convergence of the series $\sum_{k=1}^{\infty} b_k$ implies the convergence of the series $\sum_{k=1}^{\infty} a_k$, and divergence of $\sum_{k=1}^{\infty} a_k$ implies the divergence of $\sum_{k=1}^{\infty} b_k$.*

*Proof.* If $0 < c < \infty$ then there is a number $k_0 \in \mathbb{N}$ such that

$$0 < a_k/b_k < c + 1$$

or $0 < a_k < (c+1)b_k$ for all $k \geq k_0$. The claim now follows directly from Theorem 4.6.

**Corollary 4.8.** *If there exists $k_0 \in \mathbb{N}$ such that*

$$\frac{a_{k+1}}{a_k} \leq \frac{b_{k+1}}{b_k}, \quad a_k, b_k > 0,$$

*for all $k \geq k_0$ then the statement of Theorem 4.6 also holds.*

*Proof.* We may assume without loss of generality that $k_0 = 1$. Then

$$\frac{a_2}{a_1} \leq \frac{b_2}{b_1}, \quad \frac{a_3}{a_2} \leq \frac{b_3}{b_2}, \dots, \frac{a_k}{a_{k-1}} \leq \frac{b_k}{b_{k-1}}.$$

Multiplying these inequalities we obtain

$$\frac{a_k}{a_1} = \frac{a_2}{a_1}\frac{a_3}{a_2}\cdots\frac{a_k}{a_{k-1}} \leq \frac{b_2}{b_1}\frac{b_3}{b_2}\cdots\frac{b_k}{b_{k-1}} = \frac{b_k}{b_1}$$

or $a_k \leq (a_1/b_1)b_k$ for $k \geq 1$. This proves the corollary.

**Example 4.9.**     1. Let us consider the series

$$\sum_{k=1}^{\infty} \frac{1}{1+a^k}$$

for $a \geq 0$. If $0 \leq a \leq 1$ then the series does not converge since the necessary condition (4.2) is not satisfied. If $a > 1$ then

$$\frac{1}{1+a^k} < \frac{1}{a^k}.$$

But the series

$$\sum_{k=1}^{\infty} \frac{1}{a^k} = \sum_{k=1}^{\infty} \left(\frac{1}{a}\right)^k$$

is a geometric series, and it converges since $0 < 1/a < 1$. Therefore the series

$$\sum_{k=1}^{\infty} \frac{1}{1+a^k}$$

converges too.

2. The series

$$\sum_{k=1}^{\infty} \frac{(k!)^2}{(2k)!}$$

converges since

$$\frac{(k!)^2}{(2k)!} = \frac{k!}{(k+1)\cdots(2k)} < \frac{1}{2^k}, \quad k \geq 2,$$

where the latter inequality can be easily proved using MMI.

3. The series

$$\sum_{n=1}^{\infty} \frac{n!}{n^n}$$

converges since

$$\frac{n!}{n^n} < \frac{((n+1)/2)^n}{n^n} = \left(\frac{n+1}{2n}\right)^n \leq \left(\frac{2}{3}\right)^n, \quad n \geq 3.$$

4. The series

$$\sum_{n=1}^{\infty} \frac{1}{n\sqrt[n]{n}}$$

diverges. Indeed, we know from Example 3.15 that

$$\lim_{n\to\infty} \sqrt[n]{n} = 1.$$

Thus

$$\lim_{n \to \infty} \frac{1/(n \sqrt[n]{n})}{1/n} = 1.$$

The result follows now from Corollary 4.7.

**Exercise 4.10.**    1. Prove that the series

$$\sum_{k=1}^{\infty} \left(1 - \frac{\log k}{k}\right)^k$$

diverges.

2. Prove that the series

$$\sum_{k=1}^{\infty} \left(\frac{1}{k} - \log\left(1 + \frac{1}{k}\right)\right)$$

converges.

3. Prove that

$$\sum_{n=1}^{\infty} \left(n \log \frac{2n+1}{2n-1} - 1\right) = \frac{1}{2}(1 - \log 2).$$

**Theorem 4.11 (Cauchy test).** *Let* $a_k > 0$, *and suppose that the limit*

$$q := \lim_{k \to \infty} \sqrt[k]{a_k}$$

*exists. Then the series* $\sum_{k=1}^{\infty} a_k$ *converges if* $0 \le q < 1$ *and diverges if* $q > 1$.

**Proof.** Let $0 \le q < 1$. Then for any $\varepsilon > 0$ there exists $k_0 \in \mathbb{N}$ such that

$$|\sqrt[k]{a_k} - q| < \varepsilon, \quad k \ge k_0.$$

It follows that $a_k < (q + \varepsilon)^k$. Choosing now $\varepsilon > 0$ such that $q + \varepsilon \le q_1 < 1$ (it is possible since $0 \le q < 1$) we obtain that there is $k_0 \in \mathbb{N}$ such that

$$0 < a_k < q_1^k, \quad k \ge k_0.$$

Due to Theorem 4.6 the series $\sum_{k=1}^{\infty} a_k$ converges.

Now let $q > 1$. As above we have $a_k > (q - \varepsilon)^k$. Choosing $\varepsilon > 0$ such that $q - \varepsilon \ge q_1 > 1$ we obtain that there is $k_0 \in \mathbb{N}$ such that $a_k > q_1^k$ for all $k \ge k_0$. By Theorem 4.6 the series $\sum_{k=1}^{\infty} a_k$ diverges.

**Remark 4.12.** Theorem 4.11 holds if there is $k_0 \in \mathbb{N}$ such that either $\sqrt[k]{a_k} \le q < 1$ or $\sqrt[k]{a_k} \ge q > 1$ for all $k \ge k_0$.

**Theorem 4.13 (d'Alembert test).** *Let* $a_k > 0$ *and suppose that the limit*

$$q := \lim_{k \to \infty} \frac{a_{k+1}}{a_k}$$

*exists. Then the series* $\sum_{k=1}^{\infty} a_k$ *converges if* $0 \le q < 1$ *and diverges if* $q > 1$.

**Proof.** Let $0 \le q < 1$. Then for any $\varepsilon > 0$ there exists $k_0 \in \mathbb{N}$ such that $|a_{k+1}/a_k - q| < \varepsilon$ for all $k \ge k_0$. So $a_{k+1} < (q + \varepsilon)a_k$ for all $k \ge k_0$. Choosing $\varepsilon > 0$ so that $q + \varepsilon \le q_1 < 1$ we obtain for any $k \ge k_0$ that

$$a_{k+1} < q_1 a_k < q_1^2 a_{k-1} < \cdots < q_1^{k+1-k_0} a_{k_0}.$$

Since $0 < q_1 < 1$ and $k_0$ is fixed we may conclude from Theorem 4.6 that the series $\sum_{k=1}^{\infty} a_k$ converges.

Let now $q > 1$. Then $a_{k+1} > (q - \varepsilon)a_k$. Choosing $q - \varepsilon \ge q_1 > 1$ we have $a_{k+1} > q_1 a_k$ for $k \ge k_0$. Next,

$$a_{k+1} > q_1 a_k > q_1^2 a_{k-1} > \cdots > q_1^{k+1-k_0} a_{k_0}.$$

As above we conclude that the series $\sum_{k=1}^{\infty} a_k$ diverges.

**Corollary 4.14.** *Let $a_k > 0$. Suppose that there is $k_0 \in \mathbb{N}$ such that either $a_{k+1}/a_k \le q < 1$ or $a_{k+1}/a_k \ge q > 1$ for all $k \ge k_0$. Then the statement of Theorem 4.13 also holds.*

**Remark 4.15.** The Cauchy test and the d'Alembert test do not provide answers to the question of convergence or divergence in the case $q = 1$. In addition, since the existence of

$$q = \lim_{k \to \infty} \frac{a_{k+1}}{a_k}$$

implies the existence (and equality) of

$$q = \lim_{k \to \infty} \sqrt[k]{a_k}$$

(but not vice versa), the Cauchy test is stronger than the d'Alembert test in the sense that the range of application is wider.

**Exercise 4.16.** Construct a positive sequence $\{a_k\}_{k=1}^{\infty}$ such that the limit $\lim_{k \to \infty} \sqrt[k]{a_k}$ exists but the limit $\lim_{k \to \infty} \frac{a_{k+1}}{a_k}$ does not.

**Exercise 4.17.** Consider the convergent series

$$\sum_{k=1}^{\infty} \frac{1}{k^s}, \quad s > 1.$$

1. Show that the Cauchy test cannot be applied.

2. Show that the d'Alembert test cannot be applied.

**Exercise 4.18.** Consider the divergent series

$$\sum_{k=1}^{\infty} \frac{1}{k}.$$

1. Show that the Cauchy test cannot be applied.

2. Show that the d'Alembert test cannot be applied.

Exercises 4.17 and 4.18 show that in the case $q = 1$ the Cauchy and d'Alembert tests cannot be applied. Thus we need to find more precise tests for convergence of corresponding series.

**Theorem 4.19 (Raabe test).** *Let $a_k > 0$ and suppose that the limit*

$$r := \lim_{k \to \infty} k \left( \frac{a_k}{a_{k+1}} - 1 \right)$$

*exists. Then the series $\sum_{k=1}^{\infty} a_k$ converges if $r > 1$ and this series does not converge if $r < 1$.*

**Proof.** Let $r > 1$. Then for any $\varepsilon > 0$ there exists $k_0 \in \mathbb{N}$ such that $|k(\frac{a_k}{a_{k+1}} - 1) - r| < \varepsilon$ for all $k \geq k_0$. So $k(\frac{a_k}{a_{k+1}} - 1) > r - \varepsilon \geq r_1$ where $\varepsilon > 0$ can be chosen such that $r_1 > 1$. This implies that

$$\frac{a_k}{a_{k+1}} \geq 1 + r_1/k, \quad k \geq k_0, \quad r_1 > 1.$$

We choose $s > 1$ such that

$$1 + r_1/k > (1 + 1/k)^s, \quad k \geq k_0.$$

This is possible since

$$\lim_{k \to \infty} (1 + 1/k)^{1+1/k} = \lim_{k \to \infty} (1 + 1/k) \lim_{k \to \infty} \frac{\sqrt[k]{k+1}}{\sqrt[k]{k}} = 1.$$

Hence, for all $k \geq k_0$,

$$\frac{a_{k+1}}{a_k} < \frac{1/(k+1)^s}{1/k^s} = \frac{b_{k+1}}{b_k}, \quad b_k = 1/k^s.$$

But the series $\sum_{k=1}^{\infty} \frac{1}{k^s}$ converges for $s > 1$. Therefore, using Corollary 4.8 we may conclude that $\sum_{k=1}^{\infty} a_k$ converges also.

For $r < 1$ similar considerations imply that the series $\sum_{k=1}^{\infty} a_k$ diverges. $\blacksquare$

The most general test is due to Gauss.

**Theorem 4.20 (Gauss test).** *Let $a_k > 0$, and suppose that*

$$\frac{a_k}{a_{k+1}} = \lambda + \frac{\mu}{k} + \frac{\theta_k}{k^2},$$

*where a sequence $\{\theta_k\}_{k=1}^{\infty}$ is bounded. Then for $\lambda > 1$ or $\lambda = 1$ and $\mu > 1$ the series $\sum_{k=1}^{\infty} a_k$ converges, and for $\lambda < 1$ or $\lambda = 1$ and $\mu \leq 1$ the series $\sum_{k=1}^{\infty} a_k$ diverges.*

**Exercise 4.21.**    1. Prove the Gauss test.

2. Using the Raabe and Gauss tests investigate the convergence (or divergence) of the series

(a)

$$\frac{a}{b} + \sum_{k=1}^{\infty} \frac{a(a+d)\cdots(a+kd)}{b(b+d)\cdots(b+kd)}, \quad a, b, d > 0,$$

(b)

$$\sum_{k=1}^{\infty} \frac{k!}{k^p q(q+1)\cdots(q+k)},$$

(c)
$$\sum_{k=1}^{\infty} \frac{k!a^k}{(a+a_1)(2a+a_2)\cdots(ka+a_k)},$$
where $a > 0$, $a_k > 0$, and $a = \lim_{k\to\infty} a_k$.

3. Prove the *logarithm test*: the series $\sum_{k=1}^{\infty} a_k$, $a_k > 0$ converges if there is $\alpha > 0$ such that
$$\frac{\log(1/a_k)}{\log k} \geq 1 + \alpha, \quad k \geq k_0,$$
and diverges if
$$\frac{\log(1/a_k)}{\log k} \leq 1, \quad k \geq k_0.$$

4. Let $a_k > 0$ and $p > 0$. Prove that the convergence of the series $\sum_{k=1}^{\infty} k^p a_k$ and $\sum_{k=1}^{\infty} (a_k - a_{k+1}) k^{p+1}$ implies the convergence of the series $\sum_{k=1}^{\infty} a_k$ and $\lim_{k\to\infty} a_k k^{1+p} = 0$.

5. Let the series $\sum_{k=1}^{\infty} a_k$ converge, and assume that the limit
$$\lim_{k\to\infty} \left( b_k \sum_{j=k}^{\infty} a_j \right)$$
exists. Prove that the series $\sum_{k=1}^{\infty} a_k b_k$ and $\sum_{k=1}^{\infty} \left[ (b_k - b_{k+1}) \sum_{j=k}^{\infty} a_j \right]$ converge or diverge simultaneously.

**Definition 4.22.** *The series $\sum_{k=1}^{\infty} a_k$ is said to be* absolutely convergent *if the series $\sum_{k=1}^{\infty} |a_k|$ converges.*

**Proposition 4.23.** *If the series $\sum_{k=1}^{\infty} a_k$ converges absolutely then it converges. The converse statement is false in general.*

**Proof.** Since the series $\sum_{k=1}^{\infty} |a_k|$ converges, by the Cauchy criterion we obtain that for any $\varepsilon > 0$ there exists $n_0 \in \mathbb{N}$ such that
$$\sum_{k=n}^{m} |a_k| < \varepsilon$$
for all $m \geq n \geq n_0$. Hence
$$\left| \sum_{k=n}^{m} a_k \right| \leq \sum_{k=n}^{m} |a_k| < \varepsilon.$$
This means that the series $\sum_{k=n}^{m} a_k$ converges.

In order to see that the converse statement does not hold we consider the series $\sum_{k=1}^{\infty} \frac{(-1)^{k-1}}{k}$. This series does not converge absolutely since the harmonic series diverges. But the partial sums become
$$S_n = \sum_{k=1}^{n} \frac{(-1)^{k-1}}{k} = 1 - \frac{1}{2} + \frac{1}{3} - \frac{1}{4} + \frac{1}{5} - \frac{1}{6} + \cdots + \frac{(-1)^{n-2}}{n-1} + \frac{(-1)^{n-1}}{n}$$
$$= \frac{1}{2} + \frac{1}{12} + \frac{1}{30} + \cdots + (-1)^{n-2} \frac{1}{n(n-1)}$$
$$= \begin{cases} \sum_{k=1}^{n} \frac{1}{k(k+1)}, & n = 2l, \\ \sum_{k=1}^{n} \frac{1}{k(k+1)} + \frac{1}{n+1}, & l = 2n-1, \quad l = 1, 2, \ldots. \end{cases}$$

That's why the limit

$$\lim_{n \to \infty} S_n = \sum_{k=1}^{\infty} \frac{1}{k(k+1)} < \infty$$

exists, i.e., the series $\sum_{k=1}^{\infty} \frac{(-1)^{k-1}}{k}$ converges.

**Exercise 4.24.**    1. Evaluate the series

$$\sum_{k=1}^{\infty} \frac{1}{k^s(k+1)}, \quad \sum_{k=1}^{\infty} \frac{1}{k(k+1)^s}$$

for $s = 1, 2, 3, \ldots$.

   2. Prove that

$$\sum_{k=1}^{\infty} \frac{1}{k(k+1)\cdots(k+n)} = \frac{1}{n!n}.$$

There is one special and very important class of series for which the principles of absolute convergence can be applied effectively.

**Definition 4.25.** *A series of the form*

$$\sum_{k=0}^{\infty} a_k(x - x_0)^k \tag{4.3}$$

*is said to be a* power series *centered at the point $x_0$ with coefficients $a_k$, $k = 0, 1, 2, \ldots$.*

**Proposition 4.26.** *If the series (4.3) converges for some $x_1 \neq x_0$ then it converges absolutely for all $x$ such that $|x - x_0| < |x_1 - x_0|$.*

**Proof.** The convergence of (4.3) at $x_1$ implies that

$$\lim_{k \to \infty} a_k(x_1 - x_0)^k = 0.$$

Therefore there exists $M > 0$ such that

$$|a_k(x_1 - x_0)^k| \le M, \quad k \ge 1.$$

Hence

$$|a_k(x - x_0)^k| = |a_k(x_1 - x_0)^k| \left| \frac{x - x_0}{x_1 - x_0} \right|^k \le M \left| \frac{x - x_0}{x_1 - x_0} \right|^k =: Mq^k, \quad q < 1.$$

The convergence of (4.3) for $|x - x_0| < |x_1 - x_0|$ follows from Theorem 4.6.

This proposition justifies the following definition.

**Definition 4.27.** *Let us define the number*

$$R := \sup_x |x - x_0|,$$

*where the supremum is taken over all such $x$ for which the series (4.3) converges. A region of convergence of (4.3) is defined as $\{x : |x - x_0| < R\}$, and $R$ is said to be a* radius of convergence.

**Remark 4.28.** Proposition 4.26 and Definition 4.27 say that a power series converges absolutely for all $|x - x_0| < R$ and diverges for all $|x - x_0| > R$ if $R \neq \infty$. For $|x - x_0| = R$ the convergence of (4.3) must be investigated separately.

**Theorem 4.29 (Cauchy–Hadamard).** *The radius of convergence $R$ of (4.3) can be calculated as*

$$R = \frac{1}{\overline{\lim}_{k \to \infty} \sqrt[k]{|a_k|}} = \lim_{k \to \infty} \frac{1}{\sqrt[k]{|a_k|}},$$

*where $R = 0$ if $\overline{\lim}_{k \to \infty} \sqrt[k]{|a_k|} = \infty$ and $R = \infty$ if $\overline{\lim}_{k \to \infty} \sqrt[k]{|a_k|} = 0$.*

**Proof.** Let first $\overline{\lim}_{k \to \infty} \sqrt[k]{|a_k|} = 0$. It is equivalent to $\lim_{k \to \infty} \sqrt[k]{|a_k|} = 0$. Then the Cauchy test gives that for $x \in \mathbb{R}$,

$$\lim_{k \to \infty} \sqrt[k]{|a_k||x - x_0|^k} = |x - x_0| \lim_{k \to \infty} \sqrt[k]{|a_k|} = 0.$$

Hence the series (4.3) converges (even absolutely) for any $x \in \mathbb{R}$, i.e., $R = \infty$.

If $\overline{\lim}_{k \to \infty} \sqrt[k]{|a_k|} = \infty$ then there exists a subsequence $\{a_{k_n}\}_{n=1}^{\infty}$ such that

$$\lim_{n \to \infty} \sqrt[k_n]{|a_{k_n}|} = \infty.$$

Hence, for any $x \neq x_0$ we have that there exists $n_0 \in \mathbb{N}$ such that

$$\sqrt[k_n]{|a_{k_n}|} > \frac{1}{|x - x_0|}, \quad n \geq n_0,$$

or

$$|a_{k_n}||x - x_0|^{k_n} > 1, \quad n \geq n_0,$$

i.e., the general term of the series (4.3) does not vanish. It means that the necessary condition of convergence is not satisfied. Therefore $R = 0$ in this case.

Now let $0 < \overline{\lim}_{k \to \infty} \sqrt[k]{|a_k|} < \infty$. Take arbitrary $x$ such that

$$|x - x_0| < \frac{1}{\overline{\lim}_{k \to \infty} \sqrt[k]{|a_k|}} = R.$$

We may choose $\varepsilon > 0$ so small that

$$|x - x_0| < \frac{R}{1 + \varepsilon R}.$$

Since $1/R = \overline{\lim}_{k \to \infty} \sqrt[k]{|a_k|}$, we may find for this $\varepsilon > 0$ a number $k_0 \in \mathbb{N}$ such that

$$\sqrt[k]{|a_k|} < \frac{1}{R} + \varepsilon, \quad k \geq k_0.$$

Thus we have

$$\sqrt[k]{|a_k||x - x_0|^k} = |x - x_0| \sqrt[k]{|a_k|} < \frac{R}{1 + \varepsilon R}(1/R + \varepsilon) = 1.$$

By the Cauchy test the series (4.3) converges (even absolutely) for any $x$ such that $|x - x_0| < R$.

Finally, let us take $x$ such that $|x - x_0| > R$. Then we may choose $\varepsilon > 0$ so small that for this $x$ we have

$$|x - x_0| > \frac{1}{1/R - \varepsilon} = \frac{R}{1 - \varepsilon R} > 0.$$

Since $1/R = \overline{\lim}_{k\to\infty} \sqrt[k]{|a_k|}$ we may find for this $\varepsilon > 0$ a number $k_0 \in \mathbb{N}$ such that

$$\sqrt[k]{|a_k|} > 1/R - \varepsilon, \quad k \geq k_0.$$

It follows that

$$\sqrt[k]{|a_k||x-x_0|^k} = |x - x_0|\sqrt[k]{|a_k|} > \frac{R}{1 - \varepsilon R}(1/R - \varepsilon) = 1.$$

Consequently, the Cauchy test implies that the series (4.3) diverges for this $x$.

**Corollary 4.30.** *Let the limit*

$$\rho := \lim_{k\to\infty}\left|\frac{a_{k+1}}{a_k}\right|$$

*exist (finite or infinite). Then the radius of convergence of (4.3) is $R = 1/\rho$.*

**Proof.** The proof follows from the Cauchy–Hadamard theorem and from the fact that

$$\rho = \lim_{k\to\infty}\left|\frac{a_{k+1}}{a_k}\right|$$

implies $\lim_{k\to\infty}\sqrt[k]{|a_k|} = \rho$.

**Example 4.31.**     1. The power series $\sum_{k=0}^{\infty} k!x^k$ converges only at $x = 0$, i.e., the radius of convergence is $R = 0$. Indeed, the latter corollary implies that

$$\lim_{k\to\infty}\left|\frac{a_{k+1}}{a_k}\right| = \lim_{k\to\infty}(k+1) = \infty.$$

2. The power series $\sum_{k=0}^{\infty}\frac{(-1)^k x^{2k+1}}{2k+1}$ converges for all $|x| < 1$. Indeed, it is easy to see that

$$\overline{\lim_{k\to\infty}}\sqrt[k]{|a_k|} = 1,$$

i.e., $R = 1$. Moreover, this series converges if $x = \pm 1$ (see Proposition 4.26).

3. Consider the *hypergeometric series*

$$F(\alpha, \beta, \gamma; x) = 1 + \sum_{k=1}^{\infty}\frac{\alpha(\alpha+1)\cdots(\alpha+k+1)\beta(\beta+1)\cdots(\beta+k+1)}{k!\gamma(\gamma+1)\cdots(\gamma+k+1)}x^k,$$

where $\alpha, \beta, \gamma \notin \overline{\mathbb{Z}_-}$. Then the d'Alembert test shows that

$$\overline{\lim_{k\to\infty}}\left|\frac{a_{k+1}}{a_k}\right| = \lim_{k\to\infty}\frac{(\alpha+k)(\beta+k)}{(\gamma+k)(k+1)} = 1.$$

Thus, this series converges for all $|x| < 1$. If $x = 1$ then applying the Gauss test gives us that

$$\frac{a_k}{a_{k+1}} = \frac{(\gamma+k)(k+1)}{(\alpha+k)(\beta+k)} = \frac{k^2 + (\gamma+1)k + \gamma}{k^2 + (\alpha+\beta)k + \alpha\beta} = 1 + \frac{\gamma - \alpha - \beta + 1}{k} + \frac{\theta_k}{k^2}$$

with a bounded sequence $\{\theta_k\}_{k=1}^{\infty}$. Hence, for $\gamma > \alpha + \beta$ this series converges and for $\gamma \leq \alpha + \beta$ it diverges.

**Exercise 4.32.**    1. Investigate using the Gauss test the convergence of the hypergeometric series at the point $x = -1$.

2. Prove that if the series (4.3) diverges at some point $x_1 > x_0$ then it diverges at any point $x' > x_1$.

3. Prove that if two power series $\sum_{k=0}^{\infty} a_k(x - x_0)^k$ and $\sum_{k=0}^{\infty} b_k(x - x_0)^k$ have radius of convergences $R_1$ and $R_2$, respectively, then the series

$$\sum_{k=0}^{\infty} (a_k \pm b_k)(x - x_0)^k$$

has a radius of convergence $R = \min(R_1, R_2)$.

4. Let $\sum_{k=0}^{\infty} a_k(x - x_0)^k$ and $\sum_{j=0}^{\infty} b_j(x - x_0)^j$ be two power series with radius of convergence $R_1 > 0$ and $R_2 > 0$, respectively. Prove that their product $\sum_{k=0}^{\infty} a_k(x - x_0)^k \sum_{j=0}^{\infty} b_j(x - x_0)^j$ is a power series $\sum_{k=0}^{\infty} c_k(x - x_0)^k$ too with $c_k = \sum_{j=0}^{k} a_j b_{k-j}$. This product is called the *Cauchy product of power series*. Prove also that its radius of convergence is $R \geq R_1 R_2$.

5. Prove that the radius of convergence of the series

$$\sum_{k=0}^{\infty} \frac{x^{3k}}{(3k)!}$$

is equal to $\infty$.

6. Determine the radius of convergence of the power series

$$\sum_{k=0}^{\infty} \frac{x^{2k+1}}{(2k+1)!!},$$

where $(2k+1)!! = 1 \cdot 3 \cdot 5 \cdots (2k+1)$.

## 4.2 ▪ Series with terms of any sign

**Theorem 4.33 (Leibniz).** *Let*

$$\sum_{k=1}^{\infty} (-1)^{k-1} c_k, \quad c_k > 0,$$

*be an* alternating series. *If* $\{c_k\}_{k=1}^{\infty}$ *is decreasing and* $\lim_{k \to \infty} c_k = 0$ *then this series converges (possibly not absolutely).*

***Proof.*** The conditions of the theorem imply that

$$0 < S_{2n} = \sum_{k=1}^{2n} (-1)^{k-1} c_k = c_1 - (c_2 - c_3) - \cdots - (c_{2n-2} - c_{2n-1}) - c_{2n} < c_1.$$

It is also easy to see that $S_{2n}$ is increasing. Thus, the limit

$$S = \lim_{n \to \infty} S_{2n}$$

exists. On the other hand, $S_{2n+1} = S_{2n} + c_{2n+1}$, and since $\lim_{n\to\infty} c_{2n+1} = 0$, we obtain

$$S = \lim_{n\to\infty} S_{2n+1}.$$

Consequently,

$$\sum_{k=1}^{\infty} (-1)^{k-1} c_k = S$$

and the theorem is proved.

**Corollary 4.34.** *Under the condition of Theorem* 4.33 *it holds that*

$$|S_n - S| < c_{n+1},$$

*i.e., the error of approximating $S$ by the partial sums $S_n$ is equal to $c_{n+1}$.*

**Proof.** Since the series in question converges,

$$|S - S_n| = \left| \sum_{k=n+1}^{\infty} (-1)^{k-1} c_k \right| = c_{n+1} - (c_{n+2} - c_{n+3}) - (c_{n+4} - c_{n+5}) - \cdots < c_{n+1}.$$

Here we have used the fact that $c_{n+j} - c_{n+j+1} > 0$ and $c_{n+1} > 0$.

**Example 4.35.**  1.  The series $\sum_{k=1}^{\infty} \frac{(-1)^{k-1}}{k}$ converges due to the Leibniz theorem but not absolutely since the harmonic series diverges.

2. The series $1 + \sum_{k=2}^{\infty} \frac{(-1)^{k-1}}{\log k}$ converges (but not absolutely) due to the Leibniz theorem and

$$\left| \sum_{k=n+1}^{\infty} \frac{(-1)^{k-1}}{\log k} \right| < \frac{1}{\log(n+1)}$$

since $\lim_{n\to\infty} \log(n+1) = \infty$.

3. It is true that

$$\sum_{k=1}^{\infty} \frac{(-1)^{k-1}}{k} = \log 2.$$

Indeed,

$$
\begin{aligned}
S_{2n} &= 1 - \frac{1}{2} + \frac{1}{3} - \frac{1}{4} - \cdots - \frac{1}{2n} \\
&= 1 + \frac{1}{3} + \frac{1}{5} + \cdots + \frac{1}{2n-1} - \left( \frac{1}{2} + \frac{1}{4} + \cdots + \frac{1}{2n} \right) \\
&= 1 + \frac{1}{2} + \frac{1}{3} + \cdots + \frac{1}{2n} - 2 \left( \frac{1}{2} + \frac{1}{4} + \cdots + \frac{1}{2n} \right) \\
&= \log(2n) + \gamma + \alpha_n - (\log n + \gamma + \beta_n) = \log 2 + \gamma_n,
\end{aligned}
$$

where $\alpha_n$, $\beta_n$, and $\gamma_n$ are infinitely small, and $\gamma$ is the Euler's constant (see Example 3.33).

**Proposition 4.36 (Abel's transform).** *The following formula, called* summation by parts *or* Abel's transform, *is valid:*

$$\sum_{k=m+1}^{n} a_k(b_k - b_{k-1}) = a_n b_n - a_m b_m - \sum_{k=m+1}^{n} b_{k-1}(a_k - a_{k-1}), \quad n > m.$$

*Proof.* If $n > m$ then

$$\sum_{k=m+1}^{n} a_k(b_k - b_{k-1}) = \sum_{k=m+1}^{n} a_k b_k - \sum_{k=m+1}^{n} a_k b_{k-1}$$

$$= \sum_{k=m+2}^{n+1} a_{k-1} b_{k-1} - \sum_{k=m+1}^{n} a_k b_{k-1}$$

$$= a_n b_n + \sum_{k=m+2}^{n} a_{k-1} b_{k-1} - \sum_{k=m+1}^{n} a_k b_{k-1}$$

$$= a_n b_n - a_m b_m + \sum_{k=m+1}^{n} a_{k-1} b_{k-1} - \sum_{k=m+1}^{n} a_k b_{k-1}$$

$$= a_n b_n - a_m b_m - \sum_{k=m+1}^{n} b_{k-1}(a_k - a_{k-1}).$$

**Theorem 4.37 (Abel).** *Let the series $\sum_{k=1}^{\infty} b_k$ be convergent, and let the sequence $\{a_k\}_{k=1}^{\infty}$ be monotone (increasing or decreasing) and bounded. Then the series $\sum_{k=1}^{\infty} a_k b_k$ converges.*

*Proof.* Since the series $\sum_{k=1}^{\infty} b_k$ converges, by the Cauchy criterion we have that for any $\varepsilon > 0$ there exists $k_0 \in \mathbb{N}$ such that

$$\left| \sum_{k=m+1}^{n} b_k \right| < \varepsilon, \quad n > m \geq k_0.$$

Denoting $B_k := \sum_{j=m+1}^{k} b_j, k > m$, and applying Abel's transform we obtain

$$\left| \sum_{k=m+1}^{n} a_k b_k \right| = \left| \sum_{k=m+1}^{n} a_k(B_k - B_{k-1}) \right|$$

$$= \left| a_n B_n - a_m B_m - \sum_{k=m+1}^{n} B_{k-1}(a_k - a_{k-1}) \right|$$

$$\leq |a_n||B_n| + |a_m||B_m| + \sum_{k=m+1}^{n} |B_{k-1}|(a_k - a_{k-1})$$

$$\leq 2M\varepsilon + \varepsilon \sum_{k=m+1}^{n} (a_k - a_{k-1}) = 2M\varepsilon + \varepsilon(a_n - a_m) \leq 4M\varepsilon,$$

where $|a_n| \leq M$, and we have assumed $a_k > a_{k-1}$ for definiteness.

**Theorem 4.38 (Dirichlet).** *Let the sequence $\{\sum_{k=1}^{n} b_k\}_{n=1}^{\infty}$ be bounded, and let the sequence $\{a_k\}_{k=1}^{\infty}$ be monotone (increasing or decreasing) and $\lim_{k\to\infty} a_k = 0$. Then the series $\sum_{k=1}^{\infty} a_k b_k$ converges.*

***Proof.*** We assume without loss of generality that $\{a_k\}_{k=1}^{\infty}$ is increasing. Since $\lim_{k\to\infty} a_k = 0$, for any $\varepsilon > 0$ there exists $k_0 \in \mathbb{N}$ such that $|a_k| < \varepsilon$ for any $k \geq k_0$. Denoting $B_k := \sum_{j=1}^{k} b_j$, $k > m$, and applying Abel's transform we obtain, for $n > m \geq k_0$, that

$$\left| \sum_{k=m+1}^{n} a_k b_k \right| = \left| a_n B_n - a_m B_m - \sum_{k=m+1}^{n} B_{k-1}(a_k - a_{k-1}) \right|$$

$$\leq 2M\varepsilon + \sum_{k=m+1}^{n} |B_{k-1}|(a_k - a_{k-1})$$

$$\leq 2M\varepsilon + M \sum_{k=m+1}^{n} (a_k - a_{k-1}) = 2M\varepsilon + M(a_n - a_m) \leq 4M\varepsilon,$$

where $M > 0$ limits the sequence $\{B_k\}_{k=1}^{\infty}$ from above.

**Remark 4.39.** It is clear from these proofs that the theorems of Leibniz and Abel follow from the theorem of Dirichlet. This is due to the equality

$$\sum_{k=1}^{\infty} a_k b_k = \sum_{k=1}^{\infty} (a_k - a) b_k + a \sum_{k=1}^{\infty} b_k.$$

**Example 4.40.**    1. The series

$$\sum_{k=1}^{\infty} a_k \sin(kx), \quad \sum_{k=1}^{\infty} a_k \cos(kx)$$

both converge for every $x \neq 2\pi m$, $m = 0, \pm 1, \ldots$, whenever $a_k$ is monotone and $\lim_{k\to\infty} a_k = 0$. Indeed, due to the theorem of Dirichlet it suffices to show that the sequences

$$\left\{ \sum_{k=1}^{n} \sin(kx) \right\}_{n=1}^{\infty}, \quad \left\{ \sum_{k=1}^{n} \cos(kx) \right\}_{n=1}^{\infty}$$

are bounded for every $x \neq 2\pi m$, $m = 0, \pm 1, \ldots$. Next, it is easy to check by MMI that for these $x$ we have

$$\sum_{k=1}^{n} \sin(kx) = \frac{\cos(x/2) - \cos(n+1/2)x}{2\sin(x/2)},$$

$$\sum_{k=1}^{n} \cos(kx) = \frac{\sin(n+1/2)x - \sin(x/2)}{2\sin(x/2)}.$$

Hence

$$\left| \sum_{k=1}^{n} \sin(kx) \right|, \left| \sum_{k=1}^{n} \cos(kx) \right| \leq \frac{2}{2|\sin(x/2)|} = \frac{1}{|\sin(x/2)|}.$$

Thus, the claim follows. It is also easy to see that the first series converges for all $x \in \mathbb{R}$.

2. The two power series

$$\sum_{k=1}^{\infty} a_k x^k, \quad \sum_{k=1}^{\infty} a_k \frac{x^k}{1-x^k}, \quad x \neq \pm 1$$

(the latter series being called the *Lambert series*), converge or diverge simultaneously for $|x| < 1$.

Let $\sum_{k=1}^{\infty} a_k x^k$ converge for $|x| < 1$. Then by the theorem of Abel the two series

$$\sum_{k=1}^{\infty} a_k x^k \frac{1}{1 - x^{2k}}, \quad \sum_{k=1}^{\infty} a_k x^{2k} \frac{1}{1 - x^{2k}}$$

converge since the sequence $\{1/(1 - x^{2k})\}_{k=1}^{\infty}$ is monotone increasing for every $|x| < 1$. Consequently, the Lambert series

$$\sum_{k=1}^{\infty} a_k \frac{x^k}{1 - x^k} = \sum_{k=1}^{\infty} a_k x^k \frac{1}{1 - x^{2k}} + \sum_{k=1}^{\infty} a_k x^k \frac{x^k}{1 - x^{2k}}$$

converges also.

Conversely, if the Lambert series converges for $|x| < 1$ then

$$\sum_{k=1}^{\infty} a_k x^k = \sum_{k=1}^{\infty} a_k \frac{x^k}{1 - x^k} - \sum_{k=1}^{\infty} a_k x^k \frac{x^k}{1 - x^k}$$

converges also due to Abel's theorem.

3. We consider the latter two series for $|x| > 1$. There are two possibilities: the series $\sum_{k=1}^{\infty} a_k$ either diverges or converges. In the first case the series

$$\sum_{k=1}^{\infty} a_k x^k$$

obviously diverges for $|x| > 1$. If we assume that the Lambert series converges then the series

$$\sum_{k=1}^{\infty} a_k = \sum_{k=1}^{\infty} a_k \frac{1}{1 - (1/x)^k} - \sum_{k=1}^{\infty} a_k \frac{(1/x)^k}{1 - (1/x)^k}$$

must be convergent also since both series on the right-hand side converge (by our considerations for $|x| < 1$). This contradiction shows that the Lambert series is also divergent.

In the second case we have that

$$\sum_{k=1}^{\infty} a_k \frac{x^k}{1 - x^k} = -\sum_{k=1}^{\infty} a_k \frac{1}{1 - (1/x)^k} = -\sum_{k=1}^{\infty} \left( a_k + a_k \frac{(1/x)^k}{1 - (1/x)^k} \right).$$

This means that the Lambert series converges for $|x| > 1$ if $\sum_{k=1}^{\infty} a_k$ converges. But this power series will be convergent only for $|x| < R$, where $R$ is the radius of convergence, i.e., the behavior of these two series in the second case is equivalent if $R = \infty$.

4. Let the radius of convergence of the power series

$$\sum_{k=0}^{\infty} a_k x^k$$

be $R \leq 1$. Then the following equality holds:

$$\sum_{k=0}^{\infty} a_k x^k = (1 - x) \sum_{n=0}^{\infty} S_n x^n, \quad |x| < R,$$

where $S_n = \sum_{k=0}^{n} a_k$. Indeed, putting $S_{-1} = 0$ we have

$$\sum_{k=0}^{n} a_k x^k = \sum_{k=0}^{n} (S_k - S_{k-1}) x^k = \sum_{k=0}^{n} S_k x^k - \sum_{k=0}^{n} S_{k-1} x^k$$

$$= \sum_{k=0}^{n} S_k x^k - \sum_{k=0}^{n-1} S_k x^{k+1} = (1-x) \sum_{k=0}^{n} S_k x^k + S_n x^{n+1}.$$

The needed equality will be shown if we show that $\lim_{n\to\infty} S_n x^{n+1} = 0$ for $|x| < R$. If $|x| < R$ then there is $r$ such that $|x| < r < R \le 1$. Since

$$\sum_{k=1}^{\infty} |a_k| r^k$$

converges, there is $M > 0$ such that

$$|a_k| r^k \le M, \quad k = 0, 1, \dots.$$

Therefore,

$$\begin{aligned}
|S_n x^{n+1}| &\le |x|(|a_0| + |a_1| + \cdots |a_n|)|x|^n \\
&\le |x|(M + M/r + \cdots + M/r^n)|x|^n \\
&\le rM(1 + 1/r + \cdots + 1/r^n)|x|^n \\
&= rM|x|^n \frac{(1/r)^{n+1} - 1}{1/r - 1} \le rM|x|^n \frac{r}{1-r} \left(\frac{1}{r}\right)^{n+1} \\
&= rM \left(\frac{|x|}{r}\right)^n \frac{1}{1-r} = M \left(\frac{|x|}{r}\right)^n \frac{r}{1-r}.
\end{aligned}$$

Since $|x|/r < 1$ and $r < 1$, $\lim_{n\to\infty} S_n x^{n+1} = 0$.

**Definition 4.41.** *If a series converges but does not converge absolutely then it is called a* conditionally convergent series.

**Exercise 4.42.**    1. Let the series

$$\sum_{k=1}^{\infty} a_k, \quad a_k \ne 0,$$

converge, and let $\lim_{k\to\infty} \frac{b_k}{a_k} = 1$. Is it true that the series $\sum_{k=1}^{\infty} b_k$ converges?

2. Let the series

$$\sum_{k=1}^{\infty} a_k$$

converge conditionally. Prove that there is a sequence $\{b_k\}_{k=1}^{\infty}$ such that $\lim_{k\to\infty} b_k = 0$ but $\sum_{k=1}^{\infty} a_k b_k$ diverges.

3. Let a sequence $\{a_k\}_{k=1}^{\infty}$ be such that $\lim_{k\to\infty} a_k = 0$. Prove that there exists a sequence $\{b_k\}_{k=1}^{\infty}$ such that $b_k \ge b_{k+1} \ge 0$, the series $\sum_{k=1}^{\infty} b_k$ diverges, but the series $\sum_{k=1}^{\infty} a_k b_k$ converges absolutely.

**Theorem 4.43 (Riemann).** *Let the series $\sum_{k=1}^{\infty} a_k$ converge absolutely. Then the series obtained from the original series by any permutation of its terms is convergent and to the same value.*

***Proof.*** Let us first assume that $a_k > 0, k = 1, 2, \ldots$, and let $\sum_{k=1}^{\infty} a_k'$ be the series obtained by permutation of the terms of the original series $\sum_{k=1}^{\infty} a_k$. Since

$$\sum_{k=1}^{n} a_k' = \sum_{k=1}^{n} a_{j_k}, \quad a_{j_k} > 0,$$

then we evidently have the inequality

$$\sum_{k=1}^{n} a_k' \leq \sum_{k=1}^{j_n} a_k.$$

But due to the fact that $\sum_{k=1}^{\infty} a_k = A < \infty$ and $a_k > 0$, we have

$$\sum_{k=1}^{n} a_k' \leq A.$$

The monotonicity of $\sum_{k=1}^{n} a_k'$ with respect to $n$ leads to the existence of the limit

$$A' := \lim_{n \to \infty} \sum_{k=1}^{n} a_k' \leq A.$$

Similarly, the series $\sum_{k=1}^{\infty} a_k$ can be considered as some permutation of the terms of the series $\sum_{k=1}^{\infty} a_k'$. Therefore we have also that $A \leq A'$. So actually $A = A'$.

Assume, second, that the series $\sum_{k=1}^{\infty} a_k$ is an arbitrary (with respect to sign of its terms) absolutely convergent series, and let

$$\sum_{k=1}^{\infty} a_k = A.$$

We may assume without loss of generality that this series has infinitely many positive terms and infinitely many negative terms. Thus, we can represent a partial sum as

$$S_n = \sum_{k=1}^{n} a_k = \sum_{k=1}^{n_1} p_k - \sum_{k=1}^{n_2} q_k,$$

where $n = n_1 + n_2$ and $p_k, q_k > 0$. Since the series $\sum_{k=1}^{\infty} |a_k|$ converges, both series $\sum_{k=1}^{\infty} p_k$ and $\sum_{k=1}^{\infty} q_k$ converge to the sums $P$ and $Q$, respectively, and $A = P - Q$. The series $\sum_{k=1}^{\infty} a_k'$ obtained by permutation of the terms of the series $\sum_{k=1}^{\infty} a_k$ can be represented as

$$\lim_{n \to \infty} \sum_{k=1}^{n} a_k' = \lim_{n_1, n_2 \to \infty} \left( \sum_{k=1}^{n_1} p_k' - \sum_{k=1}^{n_2} q_k' \right)$$

so that the series $\sum_{k=1}^{\infty} p_k'$ and $\sum_{k=1}^{\infty} q_k'$ are obtained by permutation of the terms of the series $\sum_{k=1}^{\infty} p_k$ and $\sum_{k=1}^{\infty} q_k$, respectively. As it was proved above,

$$\sum_{k=1}^{\infty} p_k' = P, \quad \sum_{k=1}^{\infty} q_k' = Q.$$

Hence

$$\sum_{k=1}^{\infty} a_k' = P - Q = A,$$

and the proof is finished.

**Remark 4.44.** If the series $\sum_{k=1}^{\infty} a_k$ converges conditionally then the situation is completely different. Namely, if we write formally that

$$\sum_{k=1}^{\infty} a_k = \sum_{k=1}^{\infty} p_k - \sum_{k=1}^{\infty} q_k,$$

where $p_k, q_k > 0$, then $\lim_{k\to\infty} a_k = 0$ implies $\lim_{k\to\infty} p_k = \lim_{k\to\infty} q_k = 0$ but both series on the right-hand side are divergent. Indeed, since

$$\sum_{k=1}^{\infty} |a_k|$$

diverges and since

$$\sum_{k=1}^{\infty} |a_k| = \sum_{k=1}^{\infty} p_k + \sum_{k=1}^{\infty} q_k,$$

it follows that

$$\sum_{k=1}^{\infty} p_k = \sum_{k=1}^{\infty} q_k = \infty.$$

The behavior of conditionally convergent series is characterized by the following famous theorem of Riemann.

**Theorem 4.45 (Riemann).** *If the series $\sum_{k=1}^{\infty} a_k$ converges conditionally then for any $B \in \overline{\mathbb{R}} := \mathbb{R} \cup \{\infty\}$ there is a permutation $\sum_{k=1}^{\infty} a_k'$ of the original series such that*

$$\sum_{k=1}^{\infty} a_k' = B.$$

***Proof.*** Let first $B \in \mathbb{R}$. Since $\sum_{k=1}^{\infty} p_k = \infty$ (see Remark 4.44 above), there is $j_1 \in \mathbb{N}$ such that

$$\sum_{k=1}^{j_1} p_k > B.$$

Since $\sum_{k=1}^{\infty} q_k = \infty$ also, there is $l_1 \in \mathbb{N}$ such that

$$\sum_{k=1}^{j_1} p_k - \sum_{k=1}^{l_1} q_k < B.$$

Repeating this procedure, there are $j_2 > j_1$ and $l_2 > l_1$ such that

$$\sum_{k=1}^{j_1} p_k + \sum_{k=j_1+1}^{j_2} p_k - \sum_{k=1}^{l_1} q_k > B$$

and

$$B - q_{l_2} < \sum_{k=1}^{j_2} p_k - \sum_{k=1}^{l_1} q_k - \sum_{k=l_1+1}^{l_2} q_k < B.$$

This process can be continued as long as we need to obtain

$$B - q_{l_m} < \sum_{k=1}^{j_m} p_k - \sum_{k=1}^{l_m} q_k < B$$

and

$$B + p_{j_m} > \sum_{k=1}^{j_m} p_k - \sum_{k=1}^{l_{m-1}} q_k > B.$$

Since $p_{j_m} \to 0$ and $q_{l_m} \to 0$ as $j_m, l_m \to \infty$, we obtain that

$$\sum_{k=1}^{\infty} a_k' := \lim_{j_m, l_m \to \infty} \left( \sum_{k=1}^{j_m} p_k - \sum_{k=1}^{l_m} q_k \right) = B.$$

If $B = \infty$ then we find a sequence $B_k \to \infty$ monotonically, so that repeating the above procedure leads to

$$\sum_{k=1}^{j_1} p_k > B_1, \quad \sum_{k=1}^{j_1} p_k - \sum_{k=1}^{l_1} q_k < B_1$$

and

$$\sum_{k=1}^{j_1} p_k + \sum_{k=j_1+1}^{j_2} p_k - \sum_{k=1}^{l_1} q_k > B_2$$

and

$$\sum_{k=1}^{j_2} p_k - \sum_{k=1}^{l_1} q_k - \sum_{k=l_1+1}^{l_2} q_k < B_2$$

and so on. Since $\lim_{k \to \infty} B_k = \infty$, we obtain the needed result. Similar considerations work for $B = -\infty$.

Let the two series

$$\sum_{k=1}^{\infty} a_k, \quad \sum_{k=1}^{\infty} b_k$$

be convergent, and let

$$\begin{pmatrix} a_1 b_1 & a_2 b_1 & a_3 b_1 & \cdots & a_k b_1 & \cdots \\ a_1 b_2 & a_2 b_2 & a_3 b_2 & \cdots & a_k b_2 & \cdots \\ \vdots & \vdots & \vdots & \ddots & \vdots & \\ a_1 b_k & a_2 b_k & a_3 b_k & \cdots & a_k b_k & \cdots \\ \vdots & \vdots & \vdots & & \vdots & \end{pmatrix}$$

be an infinite matrix with elements $\{a_j b_k\}_{j,k=1}^{\infty}$.

In the case of absolute convergence of these series the following theorem holds.

**Theorem 4.46 (Cauchy).** *Let the series $\sum_{k=1}^{\infty} a_k$ and $\sum_{k=1}^{\infty} b_k$ be absolutely convergent. Then the series*

$$\sum_{k,j=1}^{\infty} a_k b_j$$

*converges absolutely to the product*

$$\left(\sum_{k=1}^{\infty} a_k\right)\left(\sum_{k=1}^{\infty} b_k\right).$$

***Proof.*** Let us numerate the elements of this infinite matrix by some law as $c_m = a_k b_j, m = 1, 2, \ldots$. Then

$$\left|\sum_{m=1}^{n} c_m\right| \leq \sum_{m=1}^{n} |c_m| \leq \sum_{k=1}^{n_1} |a_k| \sum_{j=1}^{n_2} |b_j|.$$

Since the given series converge absolutely, by using the Cauchy criterion we may conclude that

$$\sum_{m=1}^{\infty} |c_m| < \infty$$

under any numeration of all elements of this infinite matrix. Hence the limit

$$\lim_{n,m\to\infty} \sum_{k,j=1}^{n,m} a_k b_j = \lim_{n\to\infty} \sum_{k=1}^{n} a_k \lim_{m\to\infty} \sum_{j=1}^{m} b_j = \left(\sum_{k=1}^{\infty} a_k\right)\left(\sum_{k=1}^{\infty} b_k\right)$$

exists.

**Example 4.47.** By the Cauchy product (see Exercise 4.32) we have, for $|x| < 1$,

$$\left(\frac{1}{1-x}\right)^2 = \sum_{k=0}^{\infty} x^k \sum_{j=0}^{\infty} x^j = \sum_{m=0}^{\infty} (m+1)x^m$$

and

$$\left(\frac{1}{1-x}\right)\left(\frac{1}{1+x}\right) = \sum_{k=0}^{\infty} x^k \sum_{j=0}^{\infty} (-1)^j x^j = \sum_{m=0}^{\infty} x^{2m}$$

since

$$\sum_{j=0}^{m} (-1)^j = \begin{cases} 1, & m = 2l, \\ 0, & m = 2l+1. \end{cases}$$

**Exercise 4.48.**     1. Assume that $\lim_{k\to\infty} x_k = \lim_{k\to\infty} y_k = 0$ and the sequence $\{\sum_{k=1}^{n} |y_k|\}_{n=1}^{\infty}$ is bounded. Prove that

$$\lim_{n\to\infty} \sum_{k=1}^{n} x_k y_{n-k} = 0.$$

2. How can the latter result be generalized if one assumes that $\lim_{k\to\infty} x_k = a$ and $\lim_{k\to\infty} y_k = b$?

**Theorem 4.49 (Mertens).** *Suppose that the series*

$$\sum_{k=1}^{\infty} a_k, \quad \sum_{k=1}^{\infty} b_k$$

*converge and one or both of them converge absolutely. Then the series*

$$\sum_{m=1}^{\infty} \sum_{k=1}^{m} a_k b_{m+1-k}$$

*converges and*

$$\sum_{m=1}^{\infty} \sum_{k=1}^{m} a_k b_{m+1-k} = \sum_{k=1}^{\infty} a_k \sum_{k=1}^{\infty} b_k.$$

*Proof.* Let

$$A = \sum_{k=1}^{\infty} a_k, \quad B = \sum_{k=1}^{\infty} b_k.$$

Then it suffices to show that the limit

$$\lim_{n \to \infty} \sum_{m=1}^{n} \sum_{k=1}^{m} a_k b_{m+1-k}$$

exists and equals $AB$. Denoting $B_l := \sum_{j=1}^{l} b_j$ we may rewrite the required double sum as

$$\sum_{m=1}^{n} \sum_{k=1}^{m} a_k b_{m+1-k} = \sum_{k=1}^{n} a_k \sum_{m=k}^{n} b_{m+1-k} = \sum_{k=1}^{n} a_k \sum_{j=1}^{n+1-k} b_j = \sum_{k=1}^{n} a_k B_{n+1-k}.$$

Assuming $\sum_{k=1}^{\infty} |a_k| < \infty$ we obtain that

$$\sum_{k=1}^{n} a_k B_{n+1-k} = \sum_{k=1}^{n} a_k (B - \beta_{n-k}) = B \sum_{k=1}^{n} a_k - \sum_{k=1}^{n} a_k \beta_{n-k},$$

where $\beta_{n-k} = \sum_{j=n-k+2}^{\infty} b_j$. So it suffices to show that

$$\lim_{n \to \infty} \sum_{k=1}^{n} a_k \beta_{n-k} = 0.$$

To this end we write

$$\left| \sum_{k=1}^{n} a_k \beta_{n-k} \right| \leq \sum_{k=1}^{n} |a_k||\beta_{n-k}| = \sum_{k=1}^{[n/2]} |a_k||\beta_{n-k}| + \sum_{k=[n/2]+1}^{n} |a_k||\beta_{n-k}| =: I_1 + I_2.$$

Since $\sum_{j=1}^{\infty} b_j$ converges, $\{\beta_{n-k}\}$ is bounded, i.e., $|\beta_{n-k}| \leq c_0$ for all $n, k$ such that $n - k \geq 1$. Thus

$$|I_2| \leq c_0 \sum_{k=[n/2]+1}^{n} |a_k| \to 0, \quad n \to \infty,$$

by the Cauchy criterion. For the estimation of $I_1$ we note that $\lim_{l\to\infty}\beta_l = 0$ as the tail of the convergent series. That's why for any $\varepsilon > 0$ there exists $l_0 \in \mathbb{N}$ such that $|\beta_l| < \varepsilon$ for $l \geq l_0$. But for $I_1$ we have $l = n - k$, where $k = 1, 2, \ldots, [n/2]$. Therefore

$$n - k \geq n - [n/2] > n/2 - 1 \geq l_0$$

or $n \geq 2l_0 + 2$. This condition guarantees for such choice of $n$ that

$$I_1 = \sum_{k=1}^{[n/2]} |a_k||\beta_{n-k}| < \varepsilon \sum_{k=1}^{[n/2]} |a_k| \leq \varepsilon \sum_{k=1}^{\infty} |a_k|,$$

i.e., $\lim_{n\to\infty} I_1 = 0$. This completes the proof.

**Remark 4.50.** This theorem does not hold if both series converge conditionally (not absolutely). Indeed, let us consider the series

$$\sum_{k=1}^{\infty} \frac{(-1)^{k-1}}{\sqrt{k}}, \quad \sum_{k=1}^{\infty} \frac{(-1)^{k-1}}{\sqrt{k}}.$$

Then

$$\sum_{m=1}^{\infty}\sum_{k=1}^{m} a_k b_{m+1-k}$$

$$= \sum_{m=1}^{\infty}\sum_{k=1}^{m} \frac{(-1)^{k-1}}{\sqrt{k}}\frac{(-1)^{m+1-k}}{\sqrt{m+1-k}} = \sum_{m=1}^{\infty}(-1)^m \sum_{k=1}^{m}\frac{1}{\sqrt{k}\sqrt{m+1-k}}.$$

It is easy to prove by MMI that

$$\sqrt{k}\sqrt{m+1-k} \leq m, \quad k \geq 1.$$

This fact implies that

$$\sum_{k=1}^{m}\frac{1}{\sqrt{k}\sqrt{m+1-k}} \geq \sum_{k=1}^{m}\frac{1}{m} = 1.$$

This means that the necessary condition of the convergence of the latter series does not hold, and therefore this series does not converge.

**Corollary 4.51 (Abel's theorem).** *Let the series*

$$A = \sum_{k=1}^{\infty} a_k, \quad B = \sum_{k=1}^{\infty} b_k, \quad C = \sum_{m=1}^{\infty}\sum_{k=1}^{m} a_k b_{m+1-k}$$

*converge. Then $C = AB$.*

***Proof.*** Let us denote

$$c_m = \sum_{k=1}^{m} a_k b_{m+1-k}, \quad C_n = \sum_{m=1}^{n} c_m.$$

Since $\lim_{n\to\infty} C_n = C$,

$$\lim_{n\to\infty} \frac{C_1 + C_2 + \cdots + C_n}{n} = C.$$

Next,

$$\sum_{j=1}^{n} C_j = \sum_{j=1}^{n}\sum_{m=1}^{j} c_m = \sum_{j=1}^{n}\sum_{m=1}^{j}\sum_{k=1}^{m} a_k b_{m+1-k}$$

$$= \sum_{j=1}^{n}\left(\sum_{k=1}^{j} a_k \sum_{m=k}^{j} b_{m+1-k}\right) = \sum_{j=1}^{n}\left(\sum_{k=1}^{j} a_k \sum_{l=1}^{j-k+1} b_l\right).$$

It follows that

$$\frac{1}{n}\sum_{j=1}^{n} C_j = \frac{1}{n}\sum_{j=1}^{n}\left(\sum_{k=1}^{j} a_k B_{j-k+1}\right).$$

Hence

$$C = \lim_{n\to\infty}\frac{1}{n}\sum_{j=1}^{n} C_j = \lim_{n\to\infty}\frac{1}{n}\sum_{j=1}^{n}\left(\sum_{k=1}^{j} a_k B_{j-k+1}\right) = AB,$$

since $A = \sum_{j=1}^{\infty} a_j$ and $\lim_{j\to\infty} B_j = B$.

## 4.3 ▪ Infinite products

**Definition 4.52.** *Let $\{p_k\}_{k=1}^{\infty}$ be a sequence of real numbers. The symbol*

$$\prod_{k=1}^{\infty} p_k = p_1 p_2 \cdots p_k \cdots$$

*denotes a (formal)* infinite product. *If there is a limit (finite of infinite)*

$$\lim_{n\to\infty}\prod_{k=1}^{n} p_k = P$$

*then this limit is said to be a value for this infinite product, i.e.,*

$$P = \prod_{k=1}^{\infty} p_k.$$

*If $P \neq \pm\infty$ then the infinite product is called* convergent. *Otherwise it* diverges.

**Remark 4.53.** If one of the terms $p_k$ is zero then trivially

$$\prod_{k=1}^{\infty} p_k = 0.$$

That's why we will assume in what follows that $p_k \neq 0$ for all $k \in \mathbb{N}$.

**Example 4.54.**    1. The formula

$$\prod_{k=1}^{\infty}\left(1 - \frac{1}{(k+1)^2}\right) = \frac{1}{2}$$

holds. Indeed, we have

$$\prod_{k=1}^{n}\left(1 - \frac{1}{(k+1)^2}\right) = \prod_{k=1}^{n}\frac{k(k+2)}{(k+1)^2}$$

$$= \frac{3}{4}\frac{8}{9}\frac{15}{16}\cdots\frac{(n-1)(n+1)}{n^2}\frac{n(n+2)}{(n+1)^2} = \frac{1}{2}\frac{n+2}{n+1},$$

and the result follows by taking the limit $n \to \infty$.

2. The *Wallis formula* reads as

$$\frac{\pi}{2} = 2 \prod_{k=1}^{\infty} \left(1 - \frac{1}{(2k+1)^2}\right) = 8 \prod_{k=1}^{\infty} \frac{k(k+1)}{(2k+1)^2}.$$

3. If $|x| < 1$ then

$$\prod_{k=0}^{\infty} \left(1 + x^{2^k}\right) = \frac{1}{1-x}.$$

It is easy to see that

$$(1-x) \prod_{k=0}^{n} \left(1 + x^{2^k}\right) = (1-x)(1+x)(1+x^2) \cdots (1+x^{2^n})$$

$$= (1-x^2)(1+x^2)(1+x^4) \cdots (1+x^{2^n})$$

$$= (1-x^4)(1+x^4) \cdots (1+x^{2^n}) = 1 - x^{2^{n+1}}.$$

Hence

$$(1-x) \prod_{k=0}^{\infty} \left(1 + x^{2^k}\right) = \lim_{n \to \infty} (1 - x^{2^{n+1}}) = 1, \quad |x| < 1.$$

4.

$$\prod_{k=1}^{\infty} \cos \frac{\varphi}{2^k} = \frac{\sin \varphi}{\varphi}.$$

This fact follows from

$$\sin \varphi = 2 \sin \frac{\varphi}{2} \cos \frac{\varphi}{2} = 4 \sin \frac{\varphi}{4} \cos \frac{\varphi}{4} \cos \frac{\varphi}{2} = \cdots = 2^n \sin \frac{\varphi}{2^n} \prod_{k=1}^{n} \cos \frac{\varphi}{2^k}.$$

Hence

$$\prod_{k=1}^{n} \cos \frac{\varphi}{2^k} = \frac{\sin \varphi}{2^n \sin(\varphi/2^n)},$$

and the formula follows by taking the limit $n \to \infty$.

5.

$$\prod_{k=1}^{\infty} \frac{e^{1/k}}{1 + 1/k} = e^{\gamma},$$

where $\gamma = \lim_{n \to \infty} (1 + 1/2 + \cdots + 1/n - \log n)$ is the Euler's constant. Indeed,

$$\prod_{k=1}^{n} \frac{e^{1/k}}{1 + 1/k} = \frac{e^{1+1/2+\cdots+1/n}}{1+n} = \frac{e^{\gamma + \log n + \alpha_n}}{1+n} = e^{\gamma} \frac{n}{n+1} e^{\alpha_n},$$

where $\alpha_n$ is infinitely small. Again the result follows by taking the limit.

**Theorem 4.55 (Necessary condition of convergence of product).** *If the product*

$$\prod_{k=1}^{\infty} p_k = P$$

*converges, i.e., $P \neq \pm\infty$ and $P \neq 0$, then $\lim_{n \to \infty} p_n = 1$.*

**Proof.** Since

$$\prod_{k=1}^{n+1} p_k = p_{n+1} \prod_{k=1}^{n} p_k,$$

we have

$$p_{n+1} = \frac{\prod_{k=1}^{n+1} p_k}{\prod_{k=1}^{n} p_k}.$$

Therefore

$$\lim_{n\to\infty} p_{n+1} = \frac{\lim_{n\to\infty}\prod_{k=1}^{n+1} p_k}{\lim_{n\to\infty}\prod_{k=1}^{n} p_k} = P/P = 1.$$

**Remark 4.56.** Since $\lim_{k\to\infty} p_k = 1$ (if the product converges), $p_k > 0$ at least starting from some $k_0 \geq 1$. Thus we may assume without loss of generality that in this case $p_k > 0$ for all $k \geq 1$.

**Theorem 4.57 (Comparison with logarithm series).** *The product $\prod_{k=1}^{\infty} p_k$ converges if and only if the series $\sum_{k=1}^{\infty} \log p_k$ converges.*

**Proof.** In order to prove this fact let us first prove the following lemma, which also is of independent interest.

**Lemma 4.58.** *For any $1 < p < 2$ we have*

$$\frac{p-1}{2p-1} < \log p < \frac{p-1}{2-p}.$$

**Proof.** We will use the following facts:

1. $\log x_1 > \log x_2$ if $x_1 > x_2 > 1$.

2. $1/(n+1) < \log(1+1/n) < 1/n$ for all $n \in \mathbb{N}$.

If $0 < x < 1$ then

$$\log(1+x) = \log\left(1+\frac{1}{1/x}\right) \leq \log\left(1+\frac{1}{[1/x]}\right) < \frac{1}{[1/x]} < \frac{1}{1/x-1} = \frac{x}{1-x}$$

and

$$\log(1+x) = \log\left(1+\frac{1}{1/x}\right) > \log\left(1+\frac{1}{[1/x]+1}\right)$$
$$> \frac{1}{[1/x]+2} > \frac{1}{1/x+2} = \frac{x}{1+2x}.$$

We have used here the fact that

$$[1/x] \leq \frac{1}{x} < [1/x]+1, \quad 0 < x < 1.$$

Substituting $x = p - 1$ we obtain the needed double inequality.

In order to prove Theorem 4.57 let

$$P = \prod_{k=1}^{\infty} p_k \neq 0.$$

This can be rewritten as

$$\lim_{n\to\infty} \frac{\prod_{k=1}^n p_k}{P} = 1$$

or

$$\lim_{n\to\infty} g_n = 1,$$

where

$$g_n = \frac{\prod_{k=1}^n p_k}{P}.$$

Without loss of generality we may assume that $g_n > 1$ for all $n \in \mathbb{N}$. Indeed, if $g_n < 1$ then we may use the limit

$$\lim_{n\to\infty} \frac{P}{\prod_{k=1}^n p_k} = 1,$$

or if there are infinitely many elements $g_n < 1$ and $g_n > 1$ then we may consider a subsequence with needed properties.

Further,

$$\log g_n = \log \frac{\prod_{k=1}^n p_k}{P} = \sum_{k=1}^n \log p_k - \log P.$$

Applying Lemma 4.58 we obtain

$$\frac{g_n - 1}{2g_n - 1} < \sum_{k=1}^n \log p_k - \log P < \frac{g_n - 1}{2 - g_n}.$$

Since $\lim_{n\to\infty} g_n = 1$,

$$\lim_{n\to\infty} \sum_{k=1}^n \log p_k = \log P.$$

Conversely, if $\sum_{k=1}^\infty \log p_k$ converges then $\lim_{n\to\infty} g_n = 1$, i.e., $\prod_{k=1}^\infty p_k$ converges.

**Corollary 4.59.** *Let us assume that $p_k > 1$ or $p_k < 1$ for all $k \geq 1$. The product $\prod_{k=1}^\infty p_k$ converges if and only if the series $\sum_{k=1}^\infty (p_k - 1)$ converges.*

**Proof.** The proof follows immediately from Lemma 4.58 and Theorem 4.57.

**Corollary 4.60.** *Let us assume that the series $\sum_{k=1}^\infty (p_k - 1)$ and $\sum_{k=1}^\infty (p_k - 1)^2$ both converge. Then $\prod_{k=1}^\infty p_k$ converges.*

**Example 4.61.**     1. The product

$$\prod_{k=1}^\infty \left(1 + \frac{1}{k^x}\right)$$

converges for all $x > 1$ and diverges for all $x \leq 1$. This is a consequence of Corollary 4.59 since all $p_k = 1 + 1/k^x > 1$ and the series

$$\sum_{k=1}^\infty \frac{1}{k^x}$$

converges for $x > 1$ and diverges for $x \leq 1$.

2. The product

$$\prod_{k=1}^{\infty} \left( 1 - \frac{1}{k^x} \right)$$

converges for $x > 1$ and diverges for $x \le 1$ since $p_k < 1$; see Corollary 4.59.

3. The product

$$\prod_{k=1}^{\infty} \left( 1 + \frac{(-1)^{k-1}}{k^x} \right)$$

converges for $x > 1/2$ due to Corollary 4.60. Another argument is as follows: let us consider the products

$$\prod_{k=1}^{\infty} \left( 1 + \frac{(-1)^{k-1}}{k^x} \right), \quad \prod_{k=1}^{\infty} \left( 1 + \frac{(-1)^{k}}{k^x} \right).$$

It is clear that they converge or diverge simultaneously. Thus their product converges or diverges at the same time. But

$$\prod_{k=1}^{\infty} \left( 1 + \frac{(-1)^{k-1}}{k^x} \right) \prod_{k=1}^{\infty} \left( 1 + \frac{(-1)^{k}}{k^x} \right) = \prod_{k=1}^{\infty} \left( 1 - \frac{1}{k^{2x}} \right),$$

and the latter product converges for $x > 1/2$.

4. The product

$$\prod_{k=1}^{\infty} \left( 1 - \frac{x^2}{k^2 \pi^2} \right)$$

converges for all $x \in \mathbb{R}$. Actually, it is possible to prove that

$$\prod_{k=1}^{\infty} \left( 1 - \frac{x^2}{k^2 \pi^2} \right) = \frac{\sin x}{x}.$$

**Exercise 4.62.**  1. Prove Corollary 4.60.

2. Prove that the products

$$\prod_{k=1}^{\infty} \cos x_k, \quad \prod_{k=1}^{\infty} \frac{\sin x_k}{x_k}$$

converge if and only if $\sum_{k=1}^{\infty} x_k^2$ converges.

3. Using the method of infinite products prove the following Abel's theorem: The series $\sum_{k=1}^{\infty} a_k, a_k > 0$, converges or diverges simultaneously with the series $\sum_{k=1}^{\infty} \frac{a_k}{A_k}$, where $A_k = \sum_{j=1}^{k} a_j$.

4. Using the Wallis formula evaluate the product

$$\prod_{k=1}^{\infty} \left( 1 - \frac{1}{(2k)^2} \right).$$

## 4.4 ▪ Gamma function of Euler

Let $x \in \mathbb{R} \setminus \{0, -1, -2, \ldots\}$. The *Gamma function of Euler* for such $x$ is defined as

$$\Gamma(x) := \frac{1}{x} \prod_{n=1}^{\infty} \frac{(1+1/n)^x}{1+x/n}. \tag{4.4}$$

For

$$p_n := \frac{(1+1/n)^x}{1+x/n}$$

we have

$$
\begin{aligned}
p_n - 1 &= \frac{(1+1/n)^x - (1+x/n)}{1+x/n} \\
&= ((1+1/n)^x - (1+x/n))(1 - x/n - x^2/n^2 + \cdots) \\
&= ((1+1/n)^x - (1+x/n))(1 - x/n + \alpha_n/n) \\
&= \frac{x(x-1)}{2n^2} + \widetilde{\alpha_n}/n^2,
\end{aligned}
$$

where $\alpha_n$ and $\widetilde{\alpha_n}$ are infinitely small.

**Exercise 4.63.** Prove the latter formula.

Using this exercise we may conclude that for any fixed $x \in \mathbb{R} \setminus \{0, -1, -2, \ldots\}$ and for all $n$ large enough, $p_n > 1$ if $x > 1$ or $x < 0$, and $p_n < 1$ if $0 < x < 1$. Hence the infinite product $\prod_{n=1}^{\infty} p_n$ converges.

It can be easily rewritten as

$$\Gamma(x) = \lim_{n \to \infty} \frac{n! n^x}{x(x+1) \cdots (x+n)}.$$

This fact implies that

$$
\begin{aligned}
\frac{\Gamma(x+1)}{\Gamma(x)} &= \frac{\lim_{n\to\infty} \frac{n! n^{x+1}}{(x+1)\cdots(x+n+1)}}{\lim_{n\to\infty} \frac{n! n^x}{x(x+1)\cdots(x+n)}} \\
&= \lim_{n\to\infty} \frac{\frac{n! n^{x+1}}{(x+1)\cdots(x+n+1)}}{\frac{n! n^x}{x(x+1)\cdots(x+n)}} = \lim_{n\to\infty} \frac{nx}{x+1+n} = x.
\end{aligned}
$$

It leads to the following fundamental property of the Gamma function of Euler:

$$\Gamma(x+1) = x\Gamma(x). \tag{4.5}$$

In particular, $\Gamma(n+1) = n!$ for all $n \in \mathbb{N}$.

Recall that we have proved that

$$\prod_{n=1}^{\infty} \frac{e^{1/n}}{1+1/n} = e^{\gamma},$$

where $\gamma = \lim_{n\to\infty}(1 + 1/2 + \cdots + 1/n - \log n)$ is the Euler's constant. Then

$$\prod_{n=1}^{\infty} \frac{e^{x/n}}{(1+1/n)^x} = e^{x\gamma}$$

or, using $\Gamma(x+1) = x\Gamma(x)$,

$$e^{x\gamma}\Gamma(x+1) = \prod_{n=1}^{\infty} \frac{e^{x/n}}{(1+1/n)^x} \prod_{n=1}^{\infty} \frac{(1+1/n)^x}{1+x/n} = \prod_{n=1}^{\infty} \frac{e^{x/n}}{1+x/n}$$

or

$$\frac{1}{\Gamma(x+1)} = e^{\gamma x} \prod_{n=1}^{\infty} \frac{1+x/n}{e^{x/n}}. \tag{4.6}$$

This formula is called the *Weierstrass formula* for the Gamma function of Euler.

The Weierstrass formula (4.6) shows that $\Gamma(x) \neq 0$ for all $x \in \mathbb{R} \setminus \{0, -1, -2, \ldots\}$. Moreover, it can be seen that

$$\frac{1}{\Gamma(x+1)} = 0$$

for $x = -1, -2, \ldots$. Indeed, letting $x \neq -n$, $n = 0, 1, 2, \ldots$, we have that (4.5) leads to

$$\Gamma(x+n) = (x+n-1)\Gamma(x+n-1) = \cdots = (x+n-1)(x+n-2)\cdots x\Gamma(x).$$

This implies that

$$(x+n)\Gamma(x) = \frac{(x+n)\Gamma(x+n)}{(x+n-1)\cdots x} = \frac{\Gamma(x+n+1)}{(x+n)\cdots x}.$$

Taking $x \to -n$ in the latter equality we obtain

$$\lim_{x\to -n}(x+n)\Gamma(x) = \frac{\Gamma(1)}{(-1)(-2)\cdots(-n)} = \frac{(-1)^n}{n!}. \tag{4.7}$$

It means that

$$\Gamma(x) \sim \frac{(-1)^n}{n!(x+n)}, \quad x \to -n, \quad \Gamma(-n) := \infty.$$

Thus $\frac{1}{\Gamma(x)}$ is now well-defined for all $x \in \mathbb{R}$ and is equal to zero only for $x = 0, -1, -2, \ldots$.

Using the Gamma function one may prove the *Stirling's formula*

$$n! \sim \sqrt{2\pi n}\left(\frac{n}{e}\right)^n, \quad n \to \infty.$$

A more advanced fact is connected to the so-called $\zeta$-function of Riemann. Let us enumerate the prime numbers

$$p_1 = 2, \quad p_2 = 3, \quad p_3 = 5, \ldots.$$

Then for $x > 1$ we have that

$$\prod_{k=1}^{\infty} \frac{1}{1-1/p_k^x} = \sum_{n=1}^{\infty} \frac{1}{n^x} =: \zeta(x).$$

Indeed, using the geometric progression

$$\frac{1}{1-1/p_k^x} = 1 + \frac{1}{p_k^x} + \frac{1}{(p_k^x)^2} + \cdots + \frac{1}{(p_k^x)^m} + \cdots$$

we obtain the equality

$$P_x^{(N)} := \prod_{p_k \leq N} \frac{1}{1 - 1/p_k^x}$$

$$= \left( 1 + \frac{1}{2^x} + \frac{1}{4^x} + \cdots + \frac{1}{(2^m)^x} + \cdots \right)$$

$$\cdot \left( 1 + \frac{1}{3^x} + \frac{1}{9^x} + \cdots + \frac{1}{(3^m)^x} + \cdots \right) \cdots$$

$$\cdot \left( 1 + \frac{1}{p_l^x} + \frac{1}{(p_l^2)^x} + \cdots + \frac{1}{(p_l^m)^x} + \cdots \right),$$

where $p_l$ is the biggest prime number satisfying $p_l \leq N$. Then it follows that

$$P_x^{(N)} = \sideset{}{'}\sum_{n=1}^{\infty} \frac{1}{n^x} = \sum_{n=1}^{N} \frac{1}{n^x} + \sideset{}{'}\sum_{n=N+1}^{\infty} \frac{1}{n^x},$$

where the sums $\sum'$ denote the summation over such $n \in \mathbb{N}$ ($n = 1$ is clearly included) and includes the multipliers $p_1, p_2, \ldots, p_l$ ($p_l \leq N$). Moreover, we have

$$0 < P_x^{(N)} - \sum_{n=1}^{N} \frac{1}{n^x} < \sum_{n=N+1}^{\infty} \frac{1}{n^x}.$$

Since for $x > 1$ the latter series converges, we have finally

$$\zeta(x) = \sum_{n=1}^{\infty} \frac{1}{n^x} = \prod_{k=1}^{\infty} \frac{1}{1 - 1/p_k^x}.$$

**Corollary 4.64** ($x = 1$). *Since formally the latter equality holds for $x = 1$ also,*

$$\sum_{k=1}^{\infty} \frac{1}{p_k} = \infty.$$

*Proof.* Indeed,

$$\infty = \sum_{n=1}^{\infty} \frac{1}{n} = \prod_{k=1}^{\infty} \frac{1}{1 - 1/p_k}$$

is equivalent to

$$\prod_{k=1}^{\infty} (1 - 1/p_k) = 0$$

or

$$\sum_{k=1}^{\infty} \frac{1}{p_k} = \infty.$$

**Remark 4.65.** The latter fact is much stronger than

$$\sum_{n=1}^{\infty} \frac{1}{n} = \infty$$

since $p_k$ is a sequence of prime numbers.

# Chapter 5

# Continuity of one-variable functions

In this chapter the main local and global properties of continuous functions are considered based on the limit of functions. Moreover, the fundamental theorems of Weierstrass and Cantor are proved. It is also proved that only monotone continuous functions can have inverse. This fundamental result and continuity criterion for monotone functions, together with remarkable limits, make it possible to correctly define most of the elementary functions and their properties. An important part of this chapter is devoted to functions of bounded variation. In particular, it is shown that any such function is the difference of two monotone increasing functions. A classification of discontinuity points is given, including their more thorough study for monotone functions.

## 5.1 ▪ Limit of functions

We consider the mappings $f$ from $X \subset \mathbb{R}$ to the real line $\mathbb{R}$ such that

$$f : X \subset \mathbb{R} \to \mathbb{R},$$

where $X = D(f)$ is called the *domain* of $f$ and the *image* of $X$, $R(f) := f(X)$ is called the range of $f$. We say that two functions $f$ and $g$ are equal if and only if $D(f) = D(g)$ and $f(x) = g(x)$ for all $x \in D(f)$.

**Example 5.1.**   1. The function defined by

$$H(x) = \begin{cases} 1, & x \geq 0, \\ 0, & x < 0, \end{cases}$$

is said to be the *Heaviside function* or the *step function*.

2. The function

$$\mathcal{D}(x) = \begin{cases} 1, & x \in \mathbb{Q}, \\ 0, & x \in \mathbb{R} \setminus \mathbb{Q}, \end{cases}$$

is called the *Dirichlet function*.

3. The function given by

$$\mathrm{sgn}(x) = \begin{cases} 1, & x > 0, \\ 0, & x = 0, \\ -1, & x < 0, \end{cases}$$

is said to be the *signum* of $x$. It is easy to see that

$$\text{sgn}(x) = H(x) - H(-x), \quad \text{sgn}(x) = \frac{|x|}{x}, \quad x \neq 0.$$

4. The *entire part* of $x \in \mathbb{R}$ is the function

$$[x] = \max\{n \in \mathbb{Z} : n \leq x\}.$$

It is clear that this maximum exists and that, moreover,

(a) $[x] = x$ if $x \in \mathbb{Z}$,

(b) $[x] \leq x < [x] + 1$ if $x \in \mathbb{R}$,

(c) $0 \leq \{x\} < 1$, where $\{x\} := x - [x]$ is said to be the *fractional part* of $x$.

5. Let $E \subset \mathbb{R}$ be an arbitrary set. Then the function

$$\chi_E(x) = \begin{cases} 1, & x \in E, \\ 0, & x \notin E, \end{cases}$$

is said to be the *characteristic function* of the set $E$. For example, $\mathcal{D}(x) = \chi_{\mathbb{Q}}(x)$.

6. The *Riemann function* is defined as

$$R(x) = \begin{cases} 1/n, & x = m/n, m \in \mathbb{Z}, n \in \mathbb{N}, \\ 0, & x \in \mathbb{R} \setminus \mathbb{Q}, \end{cases}$$

where $m/n$ is irreducible fraction.

**Definition 5.2.** *Let $X$ be a set in $\mathbb{R}$. A number $a \in \mathbb{R}$ is called a* limiting point *of $X$ if for any $\delta > 0$ it holds that*

$$U'_\delta(a) \cap X \neq \emptyset,$$

*where $U'_\delta(a) = U_\delta(a) \setminus \{a\}$ is the* deleted neighborhood *of $a$, i.e.,*

$$U_\delta(a) = \{x \in \mathbb{R} : |x - a| < \delta\}, \quad U'_\delta(a) = \{x \in \mathbb{R} : 0 < |x - a| < \delta\}.$$

*The set of all limiting points of $X$ is denoted as $X'$.*

**Exercise 5.3.** Prove that $a$ is a limiting point of $X$ if and only if there exists $\{x_n\}_{n=1}^\infty \subset X$ such that $x_n \neq a$ and $\lim_{n\to\infty} x_n = a$.

**Definition 5.4.** *A point $a \in X \subset \mathbb{R}$ is said to be an* isolated point *if there exists $\delta > 0$ such that $U_\delta(a) \cap X = \{a\}$, i.e., $U'_\delta(a) \cap X = \emptyset$.*

**Definition 5.5 (Cauchy).** *Let $f : X \subset \mathbb{R} \to \mathbb{R}$ be a function on $X$ and let $a \in X'$. Then $b \in \mathbb{R}$ is called the* limit *of $f$ as $x$ tends to $a$, denoted $b = \lim_{x\to a} f(x)$, if for any $\varepsilon > 0$ there exists $\delta(\varepsilon, a) > 0$ such that $|f(x) - b| < \varepsilon$ for all $x \in X$ with $0 < |x - a| < \delta$ (i.e., for all $x \in U'_\delta(a) \cap X$).*

**Exercise 5.6.** Prove that this definition of Cauchy is equivalent to the definition of Heine: for any $\{x_n\}_{n=1}^\infty \subset X$ such that $x_n \neq a$ and $\lim_{n\to\infty} x_n = a$ it follows that $\lim_{n\to\infty} f(x_n) = b$.

**Exercise 5.7.** Formulate the statement $b \neq \lim_{x \to a} f(x)$ by Cauchy and Heine, respectively.

**Example 5.8.** 1. We show by definitions of Cauchy and Heine that

$$\lim_{x \to 0} x \sin(1/x) = 0.$$

Indeed, if $x_n \neq 0, \lim_{n \to \infty} x_n = 0$ then

$$\left| x_n \sin \frac{1}{x_n} \right| \leq |x_n|.$$

Since $\lim_{n \to \infty} |x_n| = 0$, the theorem of two policemen (Theorem 3.26) leads to

$$\lim_{n \to \infty} x_n \sin \frac{1}{x_n} = 0.$$

It is equivalent to the following: for any $\varepsilon > 0$ there exists $\delta(\varepsilon) = \varepsilon$ such that

$$\left| x \sin \frac{1}{x} \right| \leq |x| < \delta = \varepsilon$$

for all $0 < |x| < \delta$.

2. We show that

$$\lim_{x \to 0} |x|^\alpha \sin \frac{1}{|x|^\beta} = 0$$

for any $\alpha > 0$ and $\beta \geq 0$. Indeed, if $0 < |x| < \delta$ then

$$\left| |x|^\alpha \sin \frac{1}{|x|^\beta} \right| \leq |x|^\alpha < \delta^\alpha = \varepsilon, \quad \delta = \varepsilon^{1/\alpha}.$$

3. We show that $\lim_{x \to 0} \sin(1/x)$ does not exist. To this end let us consider two sequences:

$$x_n' = \frac{1}{2\pi n}, \quad x_n'' = \frac{1}{\pi/2 + 2\pi n}.$$

Then $\lim_{n \to \infty} x_n' = \lim_{n \to \infty} x_n'' = 0$ and $x_n' \neq 0, x_n'' \neq 0$ but

$$\lim_{n \to \infty} \sin \frac{1}{x_n'} = \lim_{n \to \infty} \sin(2\pi n) = 0$$

and

$$\lim_{n \to \infty} \sin \frac{1}{x_n''} = \lim_{n \to \infty} \sin(\pi/2 + 2\pi n) = 1.$$

4. It is clear that $\lim_{x \to 0} \text{sgn}(x)$ does not exist but $\lim_{x \to 0} |\text{sgn}(x)| = 1$.

5. It is also clear that $\lim_{x \to a} f(x) = b$ if and only if $f(x) = b + \beta(x)$ with $\lim_{x \to a} \beta(x) = 0$.

All these examples justify the following definition.

**Definition 5.9.** *The limit* $\lim_{x \to a} f(x)$ *exists or, equivalently, a function $f$ has a limit as $x$ tends to $a$ if and only if there is a number $b \in \mathbb{R}$ such that $b = \lim_{x \to a} f(x)$.*

**Definition 5.10.** *A function f has* one-sided limit *at the point a, denoted*

$$f(a \pm 0) := \lim_{x \to a \pm 0} f(x)$$

*if for any $\varepsilon > 0$ there exists $\delta(\varepsilon, a) > 0$ such that $|f(x) - b| < \varepsilon$ for any $x \in X$ with $0 < x - a < \delta$ ($0 < a - x < \delta$). Equivalently, $\lim_{n \to \infty} f(x_n) = b$ for any $\{x_n\}_{n=1}^{\infty} \subset X$ with $\lim_{n \to \infty} x_n = a$ and $x_n > a$ ($x_n < a$).*

**Definition 5.11.** *A function $f : X \subset \mathbb{R} \to \mathbb{R}$ is said to be*

1. bounded *on X if there exists $M > 0$ such that $|f(x)| \leq M$ for all $x \in X$,*

2. *bounded at $x_0 \in X$ if there exists $\delta > 0$ such that f is bounded on $X \cap U_\delta(x_0)$,*

3. *bounded at $x_0 \in X'$ if there exists $\delta > 0$ such that f is bounded on $X \cap U_\delta'(x_0)$.*

**Definition 5.12.** *A function f is said to be* bounded at infinity *if there exists $A > 0$ such that f is bounded on the set $X \cap \{x \in \mathbb{R} : |x| > A\}$ which is nonempty.*

**Exercise 5.13.** *Let $f : [a, b] \to \mathbb{R}$ be bounded at every point on $[a, b]$. Prove that f is bounded on $[a, b]$. Show that this statement does not hold for open interval $(a, b)$.*

**Theorem 5.14 (Properties of a function having limit).** *Let $f : X \subset \mathbb{R} \to \mathbb{R}$ and $a \in X'$. Then*

1. *if $\lim_{x \to a} f(x)$ exists then it is unique,*

2. *if $\lim_{x \to a} f(x)$ exists then f is bounded at $x = a$,*

3. *$\lim_{x \to a} f(x)$ exists if and only if $f(a \pm 0)$ exist and they are equal.*

*Proof.*

1. Let us assume on the contrary that there are numbers $b_1 \neq b_2$ such that

$$b_1 = \lim_{x \to a} f(x), \quad b_2 = \lim_{x \to a} f(x).$$

Choosing $\varepsilon = |b_1 - b_2|/2 > 0$ we may find $\delta_1 > 0$ and $\delta_2 > 0$ such that

$$|f(x) - b_1| < \frac{|b_1 - b_2|}{2}, \quad x \in U_{\delta_1}'(a) \cap X,$$

and

$$|f(x) - b_2| < \frac{|b_1 - b_2|}{2}, \quad x \in U_{\delta_2}'(a) \cap X.$$

But for $\delta = \min(\delta_1, \delta_2) > 0$ we have

$$|b_1 - b_2| \leq |f(x) - b_1| + |f(x) - b_2| < |b_1 - b_2|$$

for all $x \in U_\delta'(a) \cap X$. This contradiction proves the claim.

2. If $\lim_{x \to a} f(x)$ exists then there is a number $b \in \mathbb{R}$ such that $\lim_{x \to a} f(x) = b$. It means that for any $\varepsilon > 0$ there is $\delta(\varepsilon, a) > 0$ such that $|f(x) - b| < \varepsilon$ for all $x \in U_\delta'(a) \cap X$. It implies $|f(x)| < |b| + \varepsilon$. Fixing $\varepsilon > 0$ we obtain the boundedness of f at a.

3. It is clear that if $\lim_{x\to a} f(x)$ exists then $\lim_{x\to a\pm 0} f(x)$ exist too and they are equal to each other.

Conversely, if

$$b = \lim_{x\to a+0} f(x) = \lim_{x\to a-0} f(x)$$

then for any $\varepsilon > 0$ there exist $\delta_1(\varepsilon, a) > 0$ and $\delta_2(\varepsilon, a) > 0$ such that

$$|f(x) - b| < \varepsilon, \quad x \in X, \quad 0 < x - a < \delta_1,$$

and

$$|f(x) - b| < \varepsilon, \quad x \in X, \quad 0 < a - x < \delta_2.$$

Choosing $\delta = \min(\delta_1, \delta_2) > 0$ we obtain that

$$|f(x) - b| < \varepsilon, \quad x \in X, \quad 0 < |x - a| < \delta.$$

This finishes the proof.

**Exercise 5.15.** Prove that the function

$$\widetilde{R}(x) = \begin{cases} n, & x = m/n, m \in \mathbb{Z}, n \in \mathbb{N}, \\ 0, & x \in \mathbb{R} \setminus \mathbb{Q}, \end{cases}$$

is unbounded at any point from $\mathbb{R}$ although it takes finite value at any point. Explain this fact.

**Definition 5.16.** *Let a function $f$ be defined on an unbounded set $X \subset \mathbb{R}$. A number $b \in \mathbb{R}$ is said to be a limit*

$$\lim_{x\to\infty} f(x) = b \quad \left( \lim_{x\to\pm\infty} f(x) = b \right)$$

*if for any $\varepsilon > 0$ there exists $A(\varepsilon) > 0$ such that $|f(x) - b| < \varepsilon$ for all $x \in X$ and $|x| > A$ ($x > A$ or $x < -A$).*

**Remark 5.17.** It is easy to see that Theorem 5.14 holds also for limits at infinity.

**Exercise 5.18.** Prove that Definition 5.16 is equivalent to the following: for any $\{x_n\}_{n=1}^{\infty} \subset X$ such that $\lim_{n\to\infty} x_n = \infty$ or $\lim_{n\to\infty} x_n = \pm\infty$, respectively, $\lim_{n\to\infty} f(x_n) = b$.

**Example 5.19.** 1. The limits

$$\lim_{x\to\infty} \sin x, \quad \lim_{x\to\infty} x \sin x$$

do not exist. Indeed, let us consider the sequences

$$x'_n = \pi/2 + 2\pi n, \quad x''_n = 2\pi n.$$

Then

$$\lim_{n\to\infty} \sin x'_n = 1, \quad \lim_{n\to\infty} \sin x''_n = 0$$

and

$$\lim_{n\to\infty} x'_n \sin x'_n = \infty, \quad \lim_{n\to\infty} x''_n \sin x''_n = 0.$$

Since both sequences $\{x'_n\}_{n=1}^{\infty}$ and $\{x''_n\}_{n=1}^{\infty}$ tend to infinity, due to uniqueness of the limit we obtain that given limits do not exist.

2. We have
$$\lim_{x \to \infty} \frac{[x]}{x} = 1.$$

Indeed, since $[x] \leq x < [x] + 1$,
$$1 - \frac{1}{x} < \frac{[x]}{x} \leq 1, \quad x > 0,$$

and
$$1 \leq \frac{[x]}{x} \leq 1 - \frac{1}{x}, \quad x < 0.$$

Using $\lim_{x \to \infty} \frac{1}{x} = 0$ we obtain
$$\lim_{x \to \pm\infty} \frac{[x]}{x} = 1$$

and hence
$$\lim_{x \to \infty} \frac{[x]}{x} = 1.$$

3. It is easy to check that
$$\lim_{x \to +\infty} H(x) = 1, \qquad \lim_{x \to -\infty} H(x) = 0$$

but
$$\lim_{x \to \infty} H(x)$$

does not exist.

**Exercise 5.20.**     1.  Show that $\lim_{x \to 0} [x]/x$ does not exist.

2. Show that $\lim_{x \to \pm\infty} \sin x$ does not exist.

3. Show that if $f$ is periodic then $\lim_{x \to \pm\infty} f(x)$ do not exist.

4. Show that
$$\lim_{x \to 0} \frac{x}{a} \left[ \frac{b}{x} \right] = \frac{b}{a}$$

for any $a, b > 0$.

5. Show that $\lim_{x \to a} x \mathcal{D}(x)$ exists if and only if $a = 0$.

**Theorem 5.21 (Arithmetic operations for functions having limits).** *Let $f, g : X \subset \mathbb{R} \to \mathbb{R}$ and $a \in X'$ (in the case $a = \infty$ the set $X$ is unbounded). If the limits*
$$\lim_{x \to a} f(x) = b_1, \quad \lim_{x \to a} g(x) = b_2$$

*exist then*
$$\lim_{x \to a} (f(x) \pm g(x)) = b_1 \pm b_2,$$
$$\lim_{x \to a} (f(x) g(x)) = b_1 b_2,$$

*and*
$$\lim_{x \to a} \frac{f(x)}{g(x)} = \frac{b_1}{b_2}$$

*for $b_2 \neq 0$.*

**Exercise 5.22.** Prove Theorem 5.21.

**Theorem 5.23 (The limit of superposition).** *Let* $f : X \subset \mathbb{R} \to \mathbb{R}$ *and* $\varphi : f(X) \to \mathbb{R}$. *Suppose that*

$$b = \lim_{x \to a} f(x), \quad B = \lim_{y \to b} \varphi(y),$$

*where* $a \in X'$ *($X$ is unbounded for $a = \infty$) and* $b \in f(X)'$. *Then the limit*

$$\lim_{x \to a} h(x) = B$$

*exists, where* $h = \varphi \circ f$ *is the superposition of $f$ and $\varphi$ defined by* $h(x) = \varphi(f(x))$.

*Proof.* Under the assumptions of this theorem the superposition $h = \varphi \circ f$ is well-defined. Furthermore, for any $\delta > 0$ there exists $\mu(\delta, a)$ (or there exists $A > 0$ when $a = \infty$) such that $|f(x) - b| < \delta$ for all $x \in X$ and $0 < |x - a| < \mu$ (or $|x| > A$). It means that $f(x) \in U_\delta(b)$ for these values of $x$. Thus, for any $\varepsilon > 0$ there exists $\delta(\varepsilon, b) > 0$ such that $|\varphi(y) - B| < \varepsilon$ for all $y \in f(X)$ and $0 < |y - b| = |f(x) - b| < \delta$. It follows that $y = f(x)$ and $0 < |f(x) - b| < \delta$ for all $x \in X$ and $0 < |x - a| < \mu$ (or $|x| > A$ for $a = \infty$). So $|\varphi(f(x)) - B| = |h(x) - B| < \varepsilon$, and the theorem is proved.

**Theorem 5.24 (Limit passage in inequalities for functions with limits).**

1. *Let*

$$\lim_{x \to a} f(x) = b_1, \quad \lim_{x \to a} g(x) = b_2,$$

*where* $a \in X'$ *or $X$ is unbounded if $a = \infty$, and let* $b_1 < b_2$. *Then for any $b$ such that* $0 < b < b_2 - b_1$ *there exists* $\delta(b) > 0$ *such that*

$$g(x) - f(x) > b > 0$$

*for all $x \in X$ and* $0 < |x - a| < \delta$ *($|x| > A$ if $a = \infty$).*

2. *Let* $f, g : X \subset \mathbb{R} \to \mathbb{R}$ *be functions such that*

$$f(x) > g(x) \quad or \quad f(x) \geq g(x)$$

*for all $x \in X$ and* $0 < |x - a| < \delta$ *($|x| > A$ for $a = \infty$) with some $\delta > 0$ ($A > 0$). If*

$$b_1 = \lim_{x \to a} f(x), \quad b_2 = \lim_{x \to a} g(x),$$

*then necessarily* $b_1 \geq b_2$ *(strict inequality for functions does not guarantee strict inequality for limits).*

*Proof.*

1. By hypotheses we have that for any $\varepsilon > 0$ there exists $\delta_1(\varepsilon), \delta_2(\varepsilon) > 0$ (or $A_1, A_2 > 0$) such that $b_1 - \varepsilon < f(x) < b_1 + \varepsilon$ for all $x \in X$ and $0 < |x - a| < \delta_1$ (or $|x| > A_1$), and $b_2 - \varepsilon < g(x) < b_2 + \varepsilon$ for all $x \in X$ and $0 < |x - a| < \delta_2$ (or $|x| > A_2$). If we choose $\varepsilon = (b_2 - b_1 - b)/2$ and $\delta = \min(\delta_1, \delta_2)$ (or $A = \max(A_1, A_2)$) then we have

$$f(x) < b_1 + \varepsilon < b_2 - \varepsilon < g(x)$$

for all $x \in X$ and $0 < |x - a| < \delta$ (or $|x| > A$). For such $x$ we obtain

$$g(x) - f(x) > b_2 - b_1 - 2\varepsilon = b,$$

and the claim follows.

2. This follows from part 1 using proof by contradiction.

**Corollary 5.25 (About two policemen).** *Let $f, g, h : X \subset \mathbb{R} \to \mathbb{R}$ and $a \in X'$ ($a = \infty$ if $X$ is unbounded). Suppose in addition that there exists $\delta > 0$ (or $A > 0$) such that*

$$f(x) \leq h(x) \leq g(x)$$

*for all $x \in X$ and $0 < |x - a| < \delta$ (or $|x| > A$). If*

$$\lim_{x \to a} f(x) = \lim_{x \to a} g(x) = b$$

*then*

$$\lim_{x \to a} h(x) = b.$$

**Proof.** By hypotheses, for any $\varepsilon > 0$ there exist $\delta_1(\varepsilon), \delta_2(\varepsilon) > 0$ (or $A_1, A_2 > 0$) such that

$$|f(x) - b| < \varepsilon$$

for all $x \in X$ and $0 < |x - a| < \delta_1$ (or $|x| > A_1$), and

$$|g(x) - b| < \varepsilon$$

for all $x \in X$ and $0 < |x - a| < \delta_2$ (or $|x| > A_2$). Choosing $\delta = \min(\delta_1, \delta_2)$ we obtain

$$b - \varepsilon < f(x) \leq h(x) \leq g(x) < b + \varepsilon,$$

which implies $|h(x) - b| < \varepsilon$.

**Definition 5.26.** *Let $f : X \subset \mathbb{R} \to \mathbb{R}$ and $a \in X'$ ($a = \infty$ if $X$ is unbounded). Then $f$ is said to satisfy the* Cauchy criterion *at $a$ if for any $\varepsilon > 0$ there exists $\delta(\varepsilon) > 0$ (or $A > 0$) such that*

$$|f(x') - f(x'')| < \varepsilon$$

*for all $x', x'' \in X$ and $0 < |x' - a| < \delta$ and $0 < |x'' - a| < \delta$ (or $|x'|, |x''| > A$).*

**Theorem 5.27 (Cauchy criterion).** *The limit $\lim_{x \to a} f(x)$ exists if and only if $f$ satisfies the Cauchy criterion at $a$.*

**Proof.** Suppose first that the limit $\lim_{x \to a} f(x)$ exists, i.e., there is a number $b \in \mathbb{R}$ such that

$$b = \lim_{x \to a} f(x).$$

So there exists $b \in \mathbb{R}$ such that for any $\varepsilon > 0$ there exists $\delta > 0$ (or $A > 0$) such that $|f(x) - b| < \varepsilon/2$ for all $x \in X$ and $0 < |x - a| < \delta$ (or $|x| > A$). It follows that

$$|f(x') - f(x'')| \leq |f(x') - b| + |f(x'') - b| < \varepsilon$$

for all $x', x'' \in X$ and $0 < |x' - a| < \delta$ and $0 < |x'' - a| < \delta$ (or $|x'|, |x''| > A$).

Let us assume now that $f$ satisfies the Cauchy criterion at $a$. Let $\{x_n\}_{n=1}^{\infty} \subset X, x_n \neq a$, and $\lim_{n \to \infty} x_n = a$ (or $\lim_{n \to \infty} x_n = \infty$). By the Cauchy criterion, for $\delta > 0$ (or $A > 0$) we may find $n_0 \in \mathbb{N}$ such that

$$|f(x_n) - f(x_m)| < \varepsilon, \quad n, m \geq n_0$$

whenever $0 < |x_n - a| < \delta$ (or $|x_n| > A$) for $n \geq n_0$. But this means that $\{f(x_n)\}_{n=1}^{\infty}$ is a Cauchy sequence, and therefore it has a limit (see the Cauchy criterion for sequences). It remains to show that all these sequences $\{f(x_n)\}_{n=1}^{\infty}$ converge to the same number $b$ (which will be a limit of $f$ at $a$ in that case). Indeed, let us assume on the contrary that there are two sequences $\{x_n'\}_{n=1}^{\infty}$ and $\{x_n''\}_{n=1}^{\infty}$ with $x_n' \neq a, x_n'' \neq a$ and

$$\lim_{n \to \infty} x_n' = \lim_{n \to \infty} x_n'' = a$$

or $(\lim_{n \to \infty} x_n' = \lim_{n \to \infty} x_n'' = \infty)$ but

$$\lim_{n \to \infty} f(x_n') = b' \neq b'' = \lim_{n \to \infty} f(x_n'').$$

Let us construct a new sequence

$$\{x_n\}_{n=1}^{\infty} = \{x_n'\}_{n=1}^{\infty} \cup \{x_n''\}_{n=1}^{\infty} = \{x_1', x_1'', x_2', x_2'', \ldots\}.$$

Obviously, $\{x_n\}_{n=1}^{\infty} \subset X, x_n \neq a$ and $\lim_{n \to \infty} x_n = a$ (or $\lim_{n \to \infty} x_n = \infty$). By what has been proved for any such sequence, $\{f(x_n)\}_{n=1}^{\infty}$ must be a Cauchy sequence and $b'$ must equal $b''$. This contradiction proves the theorem.

The concepts of infinitely large and infinitely small sequences are very useful and can be easily transferred to the case of limits of functions.

**Definition 5.28.**

1. *A function $\alpha(x)$ is said to be* infinitely small *at $a$ (at infinity) if $\lim_{x \to a} \alpha(x) = 0$ (or $\lim_{x \to \infty} \alpha(x) = 0$).*

2. *A function $A(x)$ is said to be* infinitely large *at $a$ (at infinity) if $\lim_{x \to a} A(x) = \infty$ (or $\lim_{x \to \infty} A(x) = \infty$). It means that for any $M > 0$ there exists $\delta > 0$ (or $B > 0$) such that*

$$|A(x)| > M$$

*for all $x \in X \cap U_\delta'(a)$ (or $x \in X \cap \{|x| > B\}$). If in this case $A(x) > 0$ or $A(x) < 0$ then we write $\lim_{x \to a} A(x) = +\infty$ or $\lim_{x \to a} A(x) = -\infty$ (or $\lim_{x \to \infty} A(x) = +\infty, \lim_{x \to \infty} A(x) = -\infty$), respectively.*

**Exercise 5.29.** Prove that $\lim_{x \to a} f(x)$ (or $\lim_{x \to \infty} f(x)$) exists if and only if there is $b \in \mathbb{R}$ such that

$$f(x) = b + \alpha(x),$$

where $\alpha(x)$ is infinitely small at $a$ (at infinity).

**Exercise 5.30.** Prove that $\alpha(x)$ is infinitely small at $a$ (at infinity) if and only if $\alpha(x) \neq 0$ and $1/\alpha(x)$ is infinitely large at $a$ (at infinity).

It is useful to compare infinitely small and infinitely large functions, respectively.

**Definition 5.31.** *Let $\alpha(x)$ and $\beta(x)$ be infinitely small at $a$ (at infinity). Then we have as follows:*

1. *$\alpha(x)$ is said to be* infinitely small of higher order of smallness *than $\beta(x)$ at $a$ (at infinity) if there is infinitely small $\gamma(x)$ at $a$ (at infinity) such that*

$$\alpha(x) = \gamma(x)\beta(x).$$

*If in addition $\beta(x) \neq 0$ then it is equivalent to*

$$\lim_{x \to a(x \to \infty)} \frac{\alpha(x)}{\beta(x)} = 0.$$

*This fact will be denoted as*

$$\alpha(x) = o(\beta(x)), \quad x \to a \quad (x \to \infty).$$

2. *$\alpha(x)$ and $\beta(x)$ are said to be* infinitely small of the same order of smallness *if*

$$\lim_{x \to a(x \to \infty)} \frac{\alpha(x)}{\beta(x)} = K, \quad K \neq 0.$$

*This fact will be denoted as*

$$\alpha(x) = O^*(\beta(x)), \quad x \to a \quad (x \to \infty).$$

3. *If $K = 1$ above then we say that $\alpha(x)$ and $\beta(x)$ are* equivalent, *and we denote this fact as*

$$\alpha(x) \sim \beta(x), \quad x \to a \quad (x \to \infty).$$

**Definition 5.32.** *Let $A(x)$ and $B(x)$ be infinitely large at $a$ (at infinity). Then we have as follows:*

1. *$A(x)$ is said to be* infinitely large of higher order of growth *than $B(x)$ at $a$ (at infinity) if*

$$\lim_{x \to a(x \to \infty)} \frac{A(x)}{B(x)} = \infty$$

*or*

$$\lim_{x \to a(x \to \infty)} \frac{B(x)}{A(x)} = 0.$$

*This fact will be denoted as*

$$B(x) = o(A(x)), \quad x \to a \quad (x \to \infty).$$

2. *$A(x)$ and $B(x)$ are said to be* infinitely large of the same order of growth *if*

$$\lim_{x \to a(x \to \infty)} \frac{A(x)}{B(x)} = K, \quad K \neq 0.$$

*This fact will be denoted as*

$$A(x) = O^*(B(x)), \quad x \to a \quad (x \to \infty)$$

*or*

$$B(x) = O^*(A(x)), \quad x \to a \quad (x \to \infty).$$

3. *If $K = 1$ above then we say that $A(x)$ and $B(x)$ are* equivalent, *and we denote this fact as*

$$A(x) \sim B(x), \quad x \to a \quad (x \to \infty).$$

**Example 5.33.** 1. $x \sin(1/x) = o(|x|^\gamma)$ as $x \to 0$ for any $0 < \gamma < 1$. Indeed,

$$\left| \frac{x \sin(1/x)}{|x|^\gamma} \right| \leq |x|^{1-\gamma} \to 0$$

as $x \to 0$ for such $\gamma$.

2. $x \sin(1/x) \neq O^*(x)$ as $x \to 0$. This follows from the fact that

$$\lim_{x \to 0} \frac{x \sin(1/x)}{x} = \lim_{x \to 0} \sin(1/x)$$

does not exist.

3. $|x|^\gamma = o(x/\sin x)$ as $x \to \infty$ for any $0 < \gamma < 1$. Indeed,

$$\left| \frac{x/\sin x}{|x|^\gamma} \right| = \frac{|x|^{1-\gamma}}{|\sin x|} \geq |x|^{1-\gamma} \to \infty$$

as $x \to \infty$.

**Definition 5.34.** *If there is a constant $K > 0$ such that*

$$|f(x)| \leq K|g(x)|$$

*for all $x \in X$ (or $x \to a$ or $x \to \infty$) then we denote this fact as*

$$f(x) = O(g(x)), \quad x \in X \quad (or\, x \to a\, or\, x \to \infty).$$

**Exercise 5.35.** Prove that for $x \to a$ (or $x \to \infty$)

1. $o(o(f)) = o(f)$,

2. $o(O(f)) = O(o(f)) = o(f)$,

3. $o(f)O(g) = o(fg)$,

4. $O(O(f)) = O(f)$,

5. $g = O^*(f)$ implies $g = O(f)$ and $f = O(g)$ but not vice versa.

**Exercise 5.36.** What can we say about the following?

1. $o(f) + o(g)$,

2. $o(f) + O(g)$,

3. $O(f) + O(g)$.

## 5.2 ▪ Remarkable limits

**Proposition 5.37 (First remarkable limit).**

$$\lim_{x \to 0} \frac{\sin x}{x} = 1.$$

**Proof.** Since $\frac{\sin x}{x}$ is even, it suffices to consider this limit when $x \to +0$. Let $0 < x < \pi/2$. Then the following inequalities hold:

$$\cos x < \frac{\sin x}{x} < 1.$$

These facts are based on the geometric observation shown in Figure 5.1.

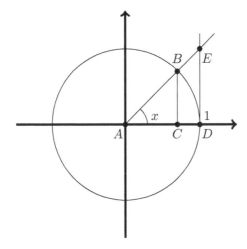

**Figure 5.1.** *Geometric justification of a trigonometric inequality.*

It is clear that $\sin x = |BC|$. But the arc length $\overset{\frown}{BD}$ is bigger than $|BC|$ so $\sin x < x$. Considering now the triangle $AED$ we obtain that its area is

$$S_\Delta = \frac{\tan x}{2}.$$

The area of the sector $\overset{\frown}{ABD}$ is equal to

$$S_s = \frac{x}{2}.$$

Since $S_\Delta$ is bigger than $S_s$ we get

$$x < \tan x.$$

Therefore

$$\sin x < x < \tan x$$

or

$$\cos x < \frac{\sin x}{x} < 1$$

for $0 < x < \pi/2$. Since $\sin x < x$ for $0 < x < \pi/2$, we obtain

$$0 < 1 - \cos x = 2\sin^2(x/2) < x^2/2.$$

Hence

$$\lim_{x \to 0} \cos x = 1$$

and consequently

$$\lim_{x \to 0} \frac{\sin x}{x} = 1$$

(see Corollary 5.25).

**Remark 5.38.** We have the useful inequalities

$$|\sin x| < |x|, \quad 0 < |x| \le 1,$$

and

$$|\sin x| \le 1, \quad |x| > 1.$$

**Proposition 5.39 (Second remarkable limit).**

$$\lim_{x \to 0} (1 + x)^{1/x} = e = \lim_{y \to \infty} (1 + 1/y)^y.$$

**Proof.** First let $x > 0$. Consider a monotone increasing sequence $\{y_n\}_{n=1}^{\infty}$ such that $\lim_{n \to \infty} y_n = +\infty$. Then $k_n := [y_n] \in \mathbb{N}$ is also monotone increasing. This fact implies that

$$\left(1 + \frac{1}{k_n + 1}\right)^{k_n} < \left(1 + \frac{1}{y_n}\right)^{y_n} < \left(1 + \frac{1}{k_n}\right)^{k_n + 1}.$$

Since

$$e = \lim_{n \to \infty} (1 + 1/n)^n = \lim_{n \to \infty} (1 + 1/n)^{n+1},$$

we obtain from the latter double inequality that

$$e = \lim_{n \to \infty} (1 + 1/y_n)^{y_n}.$$

We have used here the fact that $k_n$ is a subsequence of $n$.

If a sequence $\{y_n\}_{n=1}^{\infty}$ is not monotone increasing but $\lim_{n \to \infty} y_n = +\infty$ then we may find two monotone increasing sequences $\{y_n'\}_{n=1}^{\infty}$ and $\{y_n''\}_{n=1}^{\infty}$ such that

$$\lim_{n \to \infty} y_n' = \lim_{n \to \infty} y_n'' = +\infty, \quad y_n' \le y_n \le y_n''.$$

In that case

$$\left(1 + \frac{1}{y_n''}\right)^{y_n'} \le \left(1 + \frac{1}{y_n}\right)^{y_n} \le \left(1 + \frac{1}{y_n'}\right)^{y_n''}.$$

Choosing $y_n'' - y_n'$ to be bounded we obtain

$$e = \lim_{n \to \infty} (1 + 1/y_n)^{y_n}.$$

This is equivalent to

$$e = \lim_{y \to \infty} (1 + 1/y)^y$$

or

$$e = \lim_{x \to +0} (1 + x)^{1/x}.$$

If $x < 0$ then we may proceed as follows. Introducing $z := -x/(1+x) > 0$ for small $x$ we obtain

$$1 + z = \frac{1}{1+x}.$$

Then

$$(1+x)^{1/x} = (1+z)^{-1/x} = (1+z)^{1+1/z} = (1+z)(1+z)^{1/z}.$$

Hence

$$\lim_{x \to -0}(1+x)^{1/x} = \lim_{z \to +0}(1+z)(1+z)^{1/z} = \lim_{z \to +0}(1+z)\lim_{z \to +0}(1+z)^{1/z} = \mathrm{e}.$$

**Corollary 5.40.** *The following remarkable limits hold:*

1. $\lim_{x \to 0}(a^x - 1)/x = \log a, a > 0$.

2. $\lim_{x \to 0} \frac{\log(1+x)}{x} = 1$.

3. $\lim_{x \to 0} \frac{(1+x)^\alpha - 1}{x} = \alpha, \alpha \in \mathbb{R}$.

**Exercise 5.41.** Prove the latter corollary using Proposition 5.39.

**Exercise 5.42.** Let $a$ be positive. Evaluate the limit

$$\lim_{n \to \infty}\left(\mathrm{e}^{\frac{1}{a} + \frac{1}{a+1} + \cdots + \frac{1}{a+n}} - \mathrm{e}^{\frac{1}{a} + \frac{1}{a+1} + \cdots + \frac{1}{a+n-1}}\right).$$

## 5.3 ▪ Local properties of continuous functions

**Definition 5.43.** *Let $f : X \subset \mathbb{R} \to \mathbb{R}$ and $a \in X$. Then $f$ is said to be* continuous *at $a$ if for any $\varepsilon > 0$ there exists $\delta > 0$ such that*

$$|f(x) - f(a)| < \varepsilon$$

*for all $x \in X \cap U_\delta(a)$.*

This definition assumes two different possibilities:

1. If $a \in X$ is an isolated point of $X$, i.e., $a \notin X'$, then there is $\delta_0 > 0$ such that $X \cap U_{\delta_0}(a) = \{a\}$, and the criterion of continuity at $a$ is automatically satisfied. Hence any function is continuous at an isolated point.

2. If $a \in X$ and $a \in X'$, i.e., $a$ is a limiting point of $X$, then $f$ is continuous at $a$ if and only if

$$\lim_{x \to a} f(x) = f(a).$$

**Definition 5.44.** *Let $f : X \subset \mathbb{R} \to \mathbb{R}$. Then $f$ is called* continuous *on $X$ if $f$ is continuous at any point of $X$. This will be denoted as $f \in C(X)$.*

**Definition 5.45.** *The points of $X$, where $f$ is not continuous, are called* breakpoints.

**Definition 5.46.** *Let $f : X \subset \mathbb{R} \to \mathbb{R}$ and $a \in X$. Then $f$ is said to be* continuous from right (left) *at $a$ if for any $\varepsilon > 0$ there exists $\delta > 0$ such that*

$$|f(x) - f(a)| < \varepsilon$$

*for all $x \in X$ and $0 \le x - a < \delta$ ($0 \le a - x < \delta$). In the case when $a \in X'$ this is equivalent to*

$$\lim_{x \to a \pm 0} f(x) = f(a).$$

**Exercise 5.47.** Prove that $f$ is continuous at $a$ if and only if it is continuous from right and left at $a$.

**Example 5.48.**　　1. The Heaviside function is continuous from right at $x = 0$ but not from left. Thus it is not continuous at $x = 0$.

2. A function $f \in C[a, b]$ is continuous on the interval $(a, b)$ and is continuous from right at $a$ and from left at $b$.

3. Let $f(x) = xD(x)$, where $D(x)$ is the Dirichlet function. Then $f$ is continuous at $x = 0$ and is not continuous at any point $x \ne 0$. Indeed, if $x_0 \ne 0$ then $\lim_{x \to x_0} xD(x)$ does not exist since we can find two different sequences $\{x'_n\}_{n=1}^{\infty}$ and $\{x''_n\}_{n=1}^{\infty}$ such that

$$\lim_{n \to \infty} x'_n = \lim_{n \to \infty} x''_n = x_0,$$

and $x'_n \in \mathbb{Q}$ but $x''_n \in \mathbb{R} \setminus \mathbb{Q}$. In that case,

$$\lim_{n \to \infty} x'_n D(x'_n) = \lim_{n \to \infty} x'_n = x_0 \ne 0$$

while

$$\lim_{n \to \infty} x''_n D(x''_n) = \lim_{n \to \infty} 0 = 0.$$

By Heine's definition, $\lim_{x \to x_0} xD(x)$ does not exist. If $x_0 = 0$ then

$$\lim_{x \to 0} xD(x) = 0 = f(0)$$

so $f$ is continuous at $x = 0$.

4. Let $R(x)$ be the Riemann function. Then $R$ is continuous at any $x \in \mathbb{R} \setminus \mathbb{Q}$ but is not continuous at any $x \in \mathbb{Q}$. Indeed, let $x_0 = m_0/n_0 \in \mathbb{Q}$, and let $\{x'_n\}_{n=1}^{\infty} \subset \mathbb{R} \setminus \mathbb{Q}$ with

$$\lim_{n \to \infty} x'_n = \frac{m_0}{n_0}$$

and

$$x''_n = \frac{nm_0}{nn_0 + 1}$$

assuming that this fraction is irreducible. Then

$$\lim_{n \to \infty} x''_n = \frac{m_0}{n_0}$$

also. But

$$\lim_{n \to \infty} R(x'_n) = \lim_{n \to \infty} R(x''_n) = \lim_{n \to \infty} 0 = 0$$

and

$$R(x_0) = R(m_0/n_0) = \frac{1}{n_0} \neq 0.$$

Hence $R$ cannot be continuous at $x_0 = m_0/n_0$.

If $x_0 \in \mathbb{R} \setminus \mathbb{Q}$ then $R(x_0) = 0$ by definition. Furthermore, without loss of generality we consider two arbitrary sequences

$$\{x_n'\}_{n=1}^\infty \subset \mathbb{Q}, \quad \{x_n''\}_{n=1}^\infty \subset \mathbb{R} \setminus \mathbb{Q}$$

such that $\lim_{n\to\infty} x_n' = \lim_{n\to\infty} x_n'' = x_0$. The denominators of the first sequence $\{x_n'\}_{n=1}^\infty$ necessarily converge to $+\infty$; otherwise only finitely many such fractions occur. Thus $\lim_{n\to\infty} R(x_n') = 0$. But $\lim_{n\to\infty} R(x_n'') = \lim_{n\to\infty} 0 = 0$ and therefore the Riemann function is continuous at any irrational point.

**Theorem 5.49 (Local properties of continuous functions).** *Let $f : X \subset \mathbb{R} \to \mathbb{R}$ be continuous at $a \in X$. Then*

1. *$f$ is bounded in the neighborhood of $a$,*

2. *if $f(a) \neq 0$ then there is $U_\delta(a)$ such that $\operatorname{sgn} f(x) = \operatorname{sgn} f(a)$ for all $x \in X \cap U_\delta(a)$,*

3. *the functions $f \pm g$, $fg$, and $f/g$ ($g(a) \neq 0$) are continuous at $a$ if $f$ and $g$ are,*

4. *if $h(x) := \varphi(f(x))$ and $\varphi$ is continuous at $f(a)$ then $h$ is also continuous at $a$.*

**Proof.** We may assume without loss of generality that $a \in X'$. Then parts 1, 3, and 4 follow immediately from the corresponding properties of functions which have limits. It remains to consider part 2.

For any $\varepsilon > 0$ there is $\delta > 0$ such that

$$|f(x) - f(a)| < \varepsilon$$

for all $x \in X \cap U_\delta(a)$. Choosing $\varepsilon = |f(a)|/2 > 0$ we obtain

$$f(a) - |f(a)|/2 < f(x) < f(a) + |f(a)|/2.$$

For $f(a) > 0$ this reads

$$f(a)/2 < f(x) < 3f(a)/2.$$

For $f(a) < 0$ we have

$$3f(a)/2 < f(x) < f(a)/2.$$

So $\operatorname{sgn} f(x) = \operatorname{sgn} f(a)$ for all $x \in X \cap U_\delta(a)$.

**Remark 5.50.** The latter property can be reformulated in a clearer form. Namely, if $f(a) > 0$ then

$$f(x) > f(a)/2 > 0$$

for all $x \in X \cap U_\delta(a)$. If $f(a) < 0$ then

$$f(x) < f(a)/2 < 0$$

for all $x \in X \cap U_\delta(a)$.

**Definition 5.51.** *Let* $f : X \subset \mathbb{R} \to \mathbb{R}$. *Then* $f$ *is said to be* increasing (decreasing) *on* $X$ *if* $f(x_1) < f(x_2)$ $(f(x_1) > f(x_2))$ *for any* $x_1, x_2 \in X$ *with* $x_1 < x_2$.

*If* $f(x_1) \leq f(x_2)$ $(f(x_1) \geq f(x_2))$ *then* $f$ *is said to be* nondecreasing (nonincreasing). *These functions are called* strictly monotone *and* nonstrictly monotone, *respectively, and all such functions are called* monotone.

**Remark 5.52.** If $f$ is increasing or decreasing on $X$ then $f$ is injective on $X$ since $f(x_1) \neq f(x_2)$ for any $x_1, x_2 \in X$ with $x_1 \neq x_2$. Hence, $y = f(x)$ has an inverse $x = f^{-1}(y)$ on $Y := f(X)$ and $f^{-1}$ is increasing or decreasing, respectively.

**Example 5.53.** Let $X = [0, 1]$ and

$$f(x) = \begin{cases} x, & x \in [0, 1] \cap \mathbb{Q}, \\ 1 - x, & x \in [0, 1] \cap (\mathbb{R} \setminus \mathbb{Q}). \end{cases}$$

Then $Y = f(X) = [0, 1]$ and $f$ has an inverse

$$x = f^{-1}(y) = \begin{cases} y, & y \in [0, 1] \cap \mathbb{Q}, \\ 1 - y, & y \in [0, 1] \cap (\mathbb{R} \setminus \mathbb{Q}). \end{cases}$$

But it is easy to see that $y = f(x)$, as well as $x = f^{-1}(y)$, is not monotone at all.

**Theorem 5.54 (Continuity criteria for monotone functions).** *Let* $f : [a, b] \to \mathbb{R}$ *be increasing* (decreasing). *Let also* $\alpha = f(a)$ *and* $\beta = f(b)$. *Then* $f$ *is continuous on* $[a, b]$ *if and only if for any* $\gamma \in [\alpha, \beta]$ $([\beta, \alpha])$ *there exists* $c \in [a, b]$ *such that* $\gamma = f(c)$.

***Proof.*** We may assume for definiteness and without loss of generality that $f$ is increasing. Let $f \in C[a, b]$ and let $\gamma \in (\alpha, \beta)$. Bisecting $[a, b]$ we obtain two intervals $[a, (a + b)/2]$ and $[(a + b)/2, b]$. If $f((a + b)/2) = \gamma$ then $c = (a + b)/2$, and the result is proved. If not, then for $f((a+b)/2) > \gamma$ we take the interval $[a, (a+b)/2]$, and for $f((a+b)/2) < \gamma$ we take the interval $[(a + b)/2, b]$. The resulting interval is again divided in half and we select the desired interval by the algorithm described above. Hence we obtain the sequence $\{[a_n, b_n]\}_{n=1}^{\infty}$ (otherwise we stop at some point with respect to $n$ if $f(a_n)$ or $f(b_n)$ is equal to $\gamma$) which satisfies the following conditions:

1. $f(a_n) < \gamma < f(b_n)$,

2. $[a_n, b_n] \supset [a_{n+1}, b_{n+1}]$,

3. $\lim_{n \to \infty}(b_n - a_n) = \lim_{n \to \infty}(b - a)/2^n = 0$.

Thus, $\{[a_n, b_n]\}_{n=1}^{\infty}$ is a contracting system of segments, and therefore Theorem 3.32 leads to the fact that there is a unique $c$ such that

$$c = \bigcap_{n=1}^{\infty} [a_n, b_n], \quad c = \lim_{n \to \infty} a_n = \lim_{n \to \infty} b_n.$$

The continuity of $f$ implies that

$$\lim_{n \to \infty} f(a_n) = f(c) \leq \gamma \leq f(c) = \lim_{n \to \infty} f(b_n),$$

i.e., $\gamma = f(c)$.

Conversely, assume that for any $\gamma \in [\alpha, \beta]$ there is $c \in [a, b]$ such that $\gamma = f(c)$. It suffices to prove that $f$ is continuous from the right and from the left at any point $x \in [a, b]$. For these purposes we need a special lemma, which also is of very important independent interest.

**Lemma 5.55.** *Let $f : [a, b] \to \mathbb{R}$ be monotone. Then the limits*

$$\lim_{x \to a+0} f(x), \quad \lim_{x \to b-0} f(x), \quad \lim_{x \to x_0 \pm 0} f(x), \quad a < x_0 < b,$$

*exist.*

**Proof.** The nature of monotonicity does not matter in this lemma. Indeed, we assume without loss of generality that $f$ is nondecreasing, and we will prove that the limit

$$\lim_{x \to x_0+0} f(x), \quad a \le x_0 < b,$$

exists. Introducing the set

$$Y_{x_0} := \{y = f(x) : x_0 < x \le b\}$$

we can easily see that $Y_{x_0} \ne \emptyset$ (since $\beta = f(b) \in Y_{x_0}$) and $Y_{x_0} \subset [\alpha, \beta]$. Hence there is

$$\inf Y_{x_0} =: \gamma.$$

We shall actually prove that $\gamma = \lim_{x \to x_0+0} f(x)$. Indeed, due to the definition of infimum we have that

1. for any $y \in Y_{x_0}$ we have $\gamma \le f(x)$ with any $x_0 < x \le b$,

2. for any $\gamma' > \gamma$ there exists $y' \in Y_{x_0}$ such that $\gamma \le y < \gamma'$, i.e., there is $x' \in [a, b]$ such that $x_0 < x' \le b$ and $\gamma \le f(x') < \gamma'$.

This implies that for any $\varepsilon > 0$ ($\gamma' = \gamma + \varepsilon$) there is $\delta > 0$ ($\delta = x' - x_0 > 0$) such that

$$\gamma + \varepsilon > f(x') \ge f(x) \ge \gamma$$

or

$$0 \le f(x) - \gamma < \varepsilon$$

for all $0 < x - x_0 < \delta$. So $\gamma = \lim_{x \to x_0+0} f(x)$, and the lemma is proved.

To end the proof of the theorem it remains to show that the limit from the lemma is equal to $f(x_0)$. If we assume on the contrary that $\lim_{x \to x_0+0} f(x) \ne f(x_0)$ then due to monotonicity (nondecreasing) of $f$ we have that $\lim_{x \to x_0+0} f(x) > f(x_0)$. But then we have for $a \le x \le x_0$ that $\alpha = f(a) \le f(x) \le f(b) = \beta$, where the latter inequality holds for $x_0 < x \le b$, i.e., for $\gamma$ from the interval $(f(x_0), \lim_{x \to x_0+0} f(x))$ there is no $x'$ such that $\gamma = f(x')$ since the image of a monotone function is empty. This contradiction proves the theorem. ∎

**Corollary 5.56.** *Let $f \in C[a, b]$ be increasing (decreasing) and let $\alpha = f(a)$ and $\beta = f(b)$. Then on the interval $[\alpha, \beta]$ ($[\beta, \alpha]$) there exists an inverse function $f^{-1}$ which is continuous on $[\alpha, \beta]$ ($[\beta, \alpha]$) and also increasing (decreasing) there.*

**Proof.** Since $f$ is increasing (decreasing), $f$ is injective. Hence the inverse of $f$ exists. Let us prove that $f^{-1}$ is increasing (decreasing) and continuous on $[\alpha, \beta]$ ($[\beta, \alpha]$).

Indeed, for $y_1 := f(x_1) < y_2 := f(x_2)$ let us assume on the contrary that $x_1 \geq x_2$ ($x_1 \leq x_2$). Then it follows that $f(x_2) \leq f(x_1)$ ($f(x_2) \geq f(x_1)$) and this contradicts the fact that $f$ is increasing (decreasing).

The last step in the proof is that due to Theorem 5.54 $f$ maps $[a, b]$ onto $[\alpha, \beta]$ ($[\beta, \alpha]$) and is one-to-one, i.e., injective. Hence $f^{-1}$ maps $[\alpha, \beta]$ ($[\beta, \alpha]$) onto $[a, b]$ and is also injective. Applying again Theorem 5.54 we obtain that $f^{-1}$ is continuous on $[\alpha, \beta]$ ($[\beta, \alpha]$). Thus this corollary is completely proved.

**Remark 5.57.** In the class of continuous functions the inverse function exists only for increasing or decreasing functions. This fact will be proved later in the text.

## 5.4 ▪ Elementary functions

### Power function

We first define function $y = x^n$ for $n \in \mathbb{N}$ and $x \in \overline{\mathbb{R}_+}$. In this case $x^n$ is defined as follows:

$$x^n := \underbrace{x \cdot x \cdots x}_{n \text{ times}}.$$

We have the following properties:

1. $y = x^n$ is increasing on $\overline{\mathbb{R}_+}$. Indeed, if $0 \leq x_1 < x_2$ then $x_1^n - x_2^n = (x_1 - x_2)(x_1^{n-1} + x_1^{n-2}x_2 + \cdots + x_2^{n-1}) < 0$ since the value in the second parentheses is positive.

2. $y = x^n$ is continuous on $\overline{\mathbb{R}_+}$. Indeed, let first $x_0 = 0$. Then for any $\varepsilon > 0$ there is $\delta = \sqrt[n]{\varepsilon} > 0$ such that

$$|x^n - x_0^n| = x^n < \delta^n = \varepsilon$$

for any $x \in \overline{\mathbb{R}_+} \cap U_\delta(0)$. Here $\sqrt[n]{\varepsilon}$ is defined as the value for which $(\sqrt[n]{\varepsilon})^n = \varepsilon$. If $x_0 > 0$ then

$$|x^n - x_0^n| = |(x_0 + (x - x_0))^n - x_0^n| = \left| \sum_{k=0}^{n} \binom{n}{k}(x - x_0)^k x_0^{n-k} - x_0^n \right|$$

$$= \left| \sum_{k=1}^{n} \binom{n}{k}(x - x_0)^k x_0^{n-k} \right| \leq |x - x_0| \sum_{k=1}^{n} \binom{n}{k}|x - x_0|^{k-1} x_0^{n-k}$$

$$\leq |x - x_0| \sum_{k=1}^{n} \binom{n}{k} x_0^{n-k} \leq |x - x_0| \sum_{k=0}^{n} \binom{n}{k} x_0^{n-k}$$

$$= |x - x_0|(1 + x_0)^n < \delta(1 + x_0)^n = \varepsilon, \quad |x - x_0| < \delta \leq 1.$$

So $\delta = \varepsilon/(1 + x_0)^n$. This proves that $y = x^n$ is continuous on $\overline{\mathbb{R}_+} = [0, \infty)$.

Applying now Corollary 5.56 to the function $y = x^n$ on the interval $[0, A]$ for any $A > 0$ we obtain that there is an inverse function $x = \sqrt[n]{y}$ which is increasing and defined on $[0, A^n]$ and continuous there.

The property of continuity holds also for an algebraic polynomial of order $n$, i.e., for the function

$$P_n(x) := a_0 x^n + a_1 x^{n-1} + \cdots + a_n, \quad a_0 \neq 0, a_j \in \mathbb{R}.$$

## Exponential function

This function is formally defined as

$$y = a^x, \quad a > 0, \quad a \neq 1, \quad x \in \mathbb{R}.$$

The definition is made precise in the following steps:

1. $a^0 = 1$ by definition.

2. $a^{-x} := 1/a^x, x \geq 0$, i.e., it is enough to consider only $x > 0$.

3. If $x = n \in \mathbb{N}$ then
$$a^n := \underbrace{a \cdot a \cdots a}_{n \text{ times}}.$$

4. If $x > 0$ and $x \in \mathbb{Q}$ then $x = m/n, m, n \in \mathbb{N}$ and
$$a^x = a^{m/n} := (a^m)^{1/n} = \sqrt[n]{a^m}.$$

   Thus $a^x$ is now well-defined for all $x \in \mathbb{Q}$.

5. If $x > 0$ and $x \in \mathbb{R} \setminus \mathbb{Q}$ then we use rational approximations for $x$, namely $p, q \in \mathbb{Q}$ and
$$0 < p \leq x < q.$$

Now we consider two sets

$$X_1 = \{a^p : p \leq x\}, \quad X_2 = \{a^q : x < q\}.$$

Let us assume for definiteness that $a > 1$. In that case both these sets are bounded (from both sides) and therefore there exist

$$\sup X_1, \quad \inf X_2.$$

We will show that $\sup X_1 = \inf X_2$. For this purpose it suffices to show that for any $\varepsilon > 0$ there is $p \leq x$ and $q > x$ such that

$$0 < a^{q-p} - 1 < \varepsilon.$$

Let $0 < p_n \leq x < q_n, p_n, q_n \in \mathbb{Q}$, and $z_n := q_n - p_n = 1/10^n$ with $\lim_{n \to \infty} p_n = \lim_{n \to \infty} q_n = x$. Since $\lim_{n \to \infty} z_n = 0$, we have $\lim_{n \to \infty} 1/z_n = +\infty$. Denoting $k_n := [1/z_n]$ we have that $k_n \in \mathbb{N}$ and $\lim_{n \to \infty} k_n = +\infty$. Now

$$0 < a^{q_n - p_n} - 1 = a^{z_n} - 1 =: r_n$$

implies that

$$a = (1 + r_n)^{1/z_n} \geq (1 + r_n)^{k_n} > k_n r_n.$$

Hence $0 < r_n < a/k_n$ and so $\lim_{n \to \infty} r_n = 0$. This justifies that for any $\varepsilon > 0$ there exist $0 < p \leq x < q$ such that

$$0 < a^{q-p} - 1 < \varepsilon$$

or $\sup X_1 = \inf X_2$. This implies the definition

$$a^x := \sup_{p \leq x} a^p = \inf_{q > x} a^q.$$

This function satisfies the following properties:

1. We have
$$a^{x_1+x_2} = a^{x_1}a^{x_2}, \quad a^{x_1-x_2} = a^{x_1}/a^{x_2}, \quad a^{x_1}a^{x_2} = (a^{x_1})^{x_2} = (a^{x_2})^{x_1},$$
since these equalities hold for rational numbers.

2. The function $y = a^x$ is increasing for $a > 1$ and decreasing for $0 < a < 1$. Indeed, let $x_1 < x_2$. Then
$$a^{x_2} - a^{x_1} = a^{x_1}(a^{x_2-x_1} - 1)$$
and it suffices to show that $a^h > 1$ ($a^h < 1$) for $h > 0$. Since $a^h = \sup_{0<p\leq h} a^p$ and $a^p > 1$ ($a^p < 1$) for any positive rational $p$, we obtain immediately that $a^h > 1$ when $a > 1$ and $a^h < 1$ when $0 < a < 1$ for $h > 0$.

3. It holds that
$$\lim_{x\to+\infty} a^x = +\infty, \quad \lim_{x\to-\infty} a^x = 0, \quad a > 1,$$
and
$$\lim_{x\to+\infty} a^x = 0, \quad \lim_{x\to-\infty} a^x = +\infty, \quad 0 < a < 1.$$
Since $a^x = 1/a^{-x}$, it suffices only to show that
$$\lim_{x\to+\infty} a^x = +\infty, \quad a > 1.$$
Indeed, for $a > 1$ we have $a = 1 + \delta, \delta > 0$. Let $\lim_{n\to\infty} x_n = +\infty$. Then
$$a^{x_n} \geq a^{[x_n]} = (1+\delta)^{[x_n]} > \delta[x_n]$$
by Bernoulli's inequality. That's why
$$\lim_{n\to\infty} a^{x_n} \geq \lim_{n\to\infty} \delta[x_n] = +\infty.$$

4. The continuity of $y = a^x$ can be provided in the same manner. Let $x_0 \in \mathbb{R}$ be an arbitrary point, and our task is to show that
$$\lim_{x\to x_0} (a^x - a^{x_0}) = \lim_{x\to x_0} a^{x_0}(a^{x-x_0} - 1) = 0$$
or
$$\lim_{h\to\pm 0} a^h = 1.$$
If $\lim_{n\to\infty} h_n = 0, h_n > 0$ then $k_n := [1/h_n] \in \mathbb{N}$ and $\lim_{n\to\infty} k_n = +\infty$. Denoting
$$r_n := a^{h_n} - 1 > 0$$
we obtain
$$a = (1 + r_n)^{1/h_n} \geq (1 + r_n)^{k_n} > 1 + k_n r_n.$$
Therefore $0 < r_n < a/k_n$ and moreover
$$\lim_{n\to\infty} r_n = 0$$
or
$$\lim_{h\to+0} a^h = 1.$$
If $h < 0$ and $h \to 0$ then we use the property
$$a^h = \frac{1}{a^{-h}},$$
which implies that
$$\lim_{h\to-0} a^h = 1.$$

## Logarithmic function

This function is denoted as

$$y = \log_a x, \quad a > 0, a \neq 1, x \in \mathbb{R}_+.$$

The exponential function $y = a^x$ is continuous and increasing if $a > 1$ and decreasing if $0 < a < 1$ on the interval $[-A, A]$ for any $A > 0$. Corollary 5.56 implies that on the interval $[a^{-A}, a^A]$ if $a > 1$ and on the interval $[a^A, a^{-A}]$ if $0 < a < 1$ there is an inverse of exponential function which is also monotone and continuous. This inverse function is called a logarithmic function and is denoted as

$$x = \log_a y, \quad y \in \mathbb{R}_+.$$

The following properties follow from the corresponding properties of the exponential function:

1.
$$\log_a(x_1 x_2) = \begin{cases} \log_a x_1 + \log_a x_2, & x_1, x_2 \in \mathbb{R}_+, \\ \log_a |x_1| + \log_a |x_2|, & x_1, x_2 \in \mathbb{R}_-. \end{cases}$$

2.
$$\log_a x^\alpha = \alpha \log_a x, \quad \alpha \in \mathbb{Q}, x \in \mathbb{R}_+.$$

3.
$$\lim_{x \to +\infty} \log_a x = \begin{cases} +\infty, & a > 1, \\ -\infty, & 0 < a < 1, \end{cases}$$

and

$$\lim_{x \to +0} \log_a x = \begin{cases} -\infty, & a > 1, \\ +\infty, & 0 < a < 1. \end{cases}$$

4. $\log_a 1 = 0$ for any $a > 0, a \neq 1$.

## The general power function

Let $\alpha \in \mathbb{R}$ and $x \in \mathbb{R}_+$. Then the general power function $x^\alpha$ is defined as

$$x^\alpha := a^{\alpha \log_a x}, \quad a > 0, a \neq 1,$$

i.e., the general power function is considered as a superposition of functions defined above. We note that the definition is independent on $a$.

This definition implies the following properties:

1. If $a > 1$ then $x^\alpha$ is continuous and increasing for $\alpha > 0$ and decreasing for $\alpha < 0$. If $0 < a < 1$ then $x^\alpha$ is continuous and decreasing for $\alpha > 0$ and increasing for $\alpha < 0$.

2.
$$x^{\alpha_1 + \alpha_2} = a^{(\alpha_1 + \alpha_2)\log_a x} = a^{\alpha_1 \log_a x} a^{\alpha_2 \log_a x} = x^{\alpha_1} x^{\alpha_2}$$

and

$$x^{\alpha_1 \alpha_2} = (x^{\alpha_1})^{\alpha_2} = \left(a^{\alpha_1 \log_a x}\right)^{\alpha_2} = \left(a^{\alpha_2 \log_a x}\right)^{\alpha_1} = (x^{\alpha_2})^{\alpha_1}.$$

3.

$$\lim_{x \to +0} x^\alpha = \begin{cases} 0, & \alpha > 0, \\ +\infty, & \alpha < 0, \end{cases}$$

and

$$\lim_{x \to +\infty} x^\alpha = \begin{cases} +\infty, & \alpha > 0, \\ 0, & \alpha < 0. \end{cases}$$

4. If $\alpha$ is rational, i.e., $\alpha = m/n$, and $n$ is odd then

$$x^\alpha := \begin{cases} |x|^\alpha, & m \text{ even}, \\ -|x|^\alpha, & m \text{ odd}, \end{cases}$$

for $x \in \mathbb{R}_-, x \neq 0$. So the general power function can be defined for all nonzero arguments in the case when $\alpha$ is rational with odd denominator.

## Trigonometric functions

We introduce the trigonometric functions sin and cos axiomatically. Namely, let $f(x)$ and $g(x)$ be two functions defined for all $x \in \mathbb{R}$ satisfying the following conditions (axioms) for $x_1, x_2 \in \mathbb{R}$:

1. $f(x_1 + x_2) = f(x_1)g(x_2) + f(x_2)g(x_1)$,

2. $g(x_1 + x_2) = g(x_1)g(x_2) - f(x_1)f(x_2)$,

3. $f^2(x) + g^2(x) = 1$ for all $x \in \mathbb{R}$,

4. $f(\pi/2) = 1, g(0) = 1$,

5. $0 < f(x) < x < f(x)/g(x)$ for all $0 < x < \pi/2$.

One can prove that there exist only one pair of $f$ and $g$ which satisfies conditions 1–5.

**Definition 5.58.** *Function $f(x)$ is called* $\sin x$ *and function $g(x)$ is called* $\cos x$.

Let us prove that the continuity of $\sin x$ and $\cos x$ is provided by 1–5. Indeed,

$$\begin{aligned} |\sin(x_0 + h) - \sin x_0| &= |\sin x_0 \cos h + \sin h \cos x_0 - \sin x_0| \\ &\leq |\sin x_0||\cos h - 1| + |\sin h||\cos x_0| \\ &\leq (1 - \cos^2 h) + |h| = \sin^2 h + |h| \leq h^2 + |h|. \end{aligned}$$

Similarly,

$$|\cos(x_0 + h) - \cos x_0| \leq |\cos x_0|(1 - \cos^2 h) + |\sin h||\sin x_0| \leq h^2 + |h|.$$

Therefore

$$\lim_{h \to 0} |\sin(x_0 + h) - \sin x_0| = \lim_{h \to 0} |\cos(x_0 + h) - \cos x_0| = 0.$$

The periodicity with period $2\pi$ also follows from 1–5.

The other trigonometric functions are defined as

$$\tan x := \frac{\sin x}{\cos x}, \quad x \neq \pi/2 + \pi k, k \in \mathbb{Z},$$

$$\cot x := \frac{\cos x}{\sin x}, \quad x \neq \pi k, k \in \mathbb{Z}.$$

The functions $\arcsin x$, $\arccos x$, $\arctan x$, and $\operatorname{arccot} x$ are defined as the inverse functions of $\sin x$, $\cos x$, $\tan x$, and $\cot x$, respectively, on the intervals where they are monotone increasing or decreasing. For example, $\sin x$ is increasing on the interval $[-\pi/2, \pi/2]$ from $-1$ to $1$. Hence, $\arcsin x$ is a well-defined and increasing function on the interval $[-1, 1]$. Moreover, all these inverse functions are continuous. In particular we have the identities

$$\arcsin(\sin x) = x, \quad x \in [-\pi/2, \pi/2],$$

$$\sin(\arcsin y) = y, \quad y \in [-1, 1].$$

**Exercise 5.59.** Show the periodicity of trigonometric functions using axioms 1–5.

### Hyperbolic functions

These functions are defined as

$$\sinh x := \frac{e^x - e^{-x}}{2}, \quad \cosh x := \frac{e^x + e^{-x}}{2},$$

$$\tanh x := \frac{e^x - e^{-x}}{e^x + e^{-x}}, \quad \coth x := \frac{e^x + e^{-x}}{e^x - e^{-x}}.$$

It follows that

$$\cosh^2 x - \sinh^2 x = 1, \quad \cosh x > \sinh x,$$

$$e^x = \cosh x + \sinh x, \quad e^{-x} = \cosh x - \sinh x$$

for all $x \in \mathbb{R}$.

## 5.5 ▪ Classification of breakpoints

The points where the function is not continuous are called breakpoints (see Definition 5.45). These points can be classified as follows.

**Definition 5.60.** *Let $f : X \subset \mathbb{R} \to \mathbb{R}$ and $a \in X'$. Point $a$ is called*

1. *a removable singularity if $\lim_{x \to a} f(x)$ exists and either $f$ is not defined at $a$ or $\lim_{x \to a} f(x) \neq f(a)$;*

2. *a breakpoint of the first kind if both $\lim_{x \to a \pm 0} f(x)$ exist but $\lim_{x \to a+0} f(x) \neq \lim_{x \to a-0} f(x)$; in this case it does not matter if $a \in X$ or $a \notin X$;*

3. *a breakpoint of the second kind if at least one of the limits $\lim_{x \to a \pm 0} f(x)$ does not exist.*

**Example 5.61.**   1. For the function $y = |\operatorname{sgn} x|$ the point $x = 0$ is a removable singularity since

$$\lim_{x \to 0} |\operatorname{sgn} x| = 1 \neq |\operatorname{sgn} 0| = 0.$$

For the function $y = \operatorname{sgn} x$ the point $x = 0$ is a breakpoint of the first kind since

$$\lim_{x \to 0+} \operatorname{sgn} x = 1 \neq \lim_{x \to 0-} \operatorname{sgn} x = -1.$$

2. For the function $y = \mathcal{D}(x)$ any point $x_0 \in \mathbb{R}$ is a breakpoint of the second kind since $\lim_{x \to x_0 \pm 0} \mathcal{D}(x)$ do not exist.

3. For the function

$$y = \begin{cases} \frac{\sin x}{|x|^\alpha}, & x \neq 0, \\ 1, & x = 0, \end{cases}$$

the point $x = 0$ is a removable singularity if $\alpha < 1$, a breakpoint of the first kind if $\alpha = 1$, and a breakpoint of the second kind if $\alpha > 1$.

**Exercise 5.62.** Show that

1. $x = 0$ is a breakpoint of the second kind for the function $f(x) = e^{-1/x}, x \neq 0$,

2. any $x \in \mathbb{Q}$ is a removable singularity for the Riemann function $R(x)$.

**Definition 5.63.** *A function* $f : [a, b] \to \mathbb{R}$ *is said to be* piecewise continuous *if there are points* $x_0, x_1, \ldots, x_n$ *such that*

1. $a = x_0 < x_1 < \cdots < x_{n-1} < x_n = b$,

2. $f \in C(x_{j-1}, x_j)$ *for* $j = 1, 2, \ldots, n$,

3. *the limits*

$$\lim_{x \to a+0} f(x), \quad \lim_{x \to b-0} f(x), \quad \lim_{x \to x_j \pm 0} f(x), j = 1, 2, \ldots, n-1,$$

*exist.*

**Example 5.64.** The function $f(x) = x - [x]$ is piecewise continuous on any interval containing integers.

**Theorem 5.65 (Breakpoints of monotone functions).** *Let* $f : [a, b] \to \mathbb{R}$ *be a monotone function. Then it may have only breakpoints of the first kind, and their quantity is at most countable.*

*Proof.* Lemma 5.55 shows that for any monotone function (regardless of the character of monotonicity) at any point $x_0 \in [a, b]$ the limits

$$\lim_{x \to x_0 \pm 0} f(x)$$

exist. Hence, this function may not have breakpoints of the second kind. There are no removable singularities either since $f$ is monotone and defined everywhere on $[a, b]$.

Next, for each jump interval

$$\left[ \lim_{x \to x_0 - 0} f(x), \lim_{x \to x_0 + 0} f(x) \right]$$

or

$$\left[ \lim_{x \to x_0 + 0} f(x), \lim_{x \to x_0 - 0} f(x) \right]$$

we assign a rational number from inside this interval. These numbers are obviously different due to monotonicity of $f$. This fact implies that the quantity of breakpoints is at most countable.

**Exercise 5.66.** Let $\{c_n\}_{n=1}^{\infty} \subset \mathbb{R}_+$ be a sequence such that $\sum_{n=1}^{\infty} c_n < \infty$. Let $f$ be defined for $x \in [a, b]$ as

$$f(x) := \sum_{x_n < x} c_n, \quad f(b) := \sum_{n=1}^{\infty} c_n,$$

where $\{x_n\}_{n=1}^{\infty}$ is monotone increasing sequence from $[a, b]$. Show that

1. $f$ is nondecreasing on $[a, b]$,

2. $\lim_{x \to x_n + 0} f(x) - \lim_{x \to x_n - 0} f(x) = c_n$ and $x_n$ are the breakpoints of the first kind for $f$,

3. there are no other breakpoints of $f$ on $[a, b]$.

**Functions of bounded variation**   To study integration according to Riemann–Stieltjes or Lebesgue (see Chapters 9 and 16) it is necessary to consider functions of bounded variation (not strongly oscillating) although their study is also of independent interest in classical mathematical analysis.

**Definition 5.67.** *A function $f$ is said to be of* bounded variation *on the interval $[a, b]$, denoted by $f \in BV[a, b]$, if there is a constant $C_0 \geq 0$ such that for any partition $P = \{x_0, x_1, \ldots, x_n\}$ of the interval $[a, b]$ with*

$$a = x_0 < x_1 < x_2 < \cdots < x_n = b$$

*it holds that*

$$V(P, f) := \sum_{j=1}^{n} |f(x_j) - f(x_{j-1})| \leq C_0.$$

*The number*

$$V_a^b(f) := \sup_P V(P, f)$$

*is called the* full variation *of $f$ on the interval $[a, b]$.*

It is clear that any function of bounded variation is bounded. Indeed, if $f \in BV[a, b]$ then for the partition $P = \{a, x, b\}, x \in (a, b)$, we have

$$2|f(x)| = |f(x) - f(a) + f(x) - f(b) + f(a) + f(b)|$$
$$\leq |f(x) - f(a)| + |f(b) - f(x)| + |f(a) + f(b)|$$

and hence

$$|f(x)| \leq \frac{1}{2} V_a^b(f) + \frac{1}{2} |f(a) + f(b)|.$$

The statement does not hold in the opposite direction. To see this we consider the Dirichlet function $\mathcal{D}(x)$. Then for partition $P$ of the interval $[a, b]$ of the form

$$P = \{x_0, x_1, \ldots, x_n\}, \quad x_0 = a, \quad x_n = b,$$

where $x_1 \in \mathbb{Q}, x_2 \in \mathbb{R} \setminus \mathbb{Q}, x_3 \in \mathbb{Q}, \ldots$, we have

$$V_a^b(\mathcal{D}) \geq \sum_{j=2}^{n-1} |\mathcal{D}(x_j) - \mathcal{D}(x_{j-1})| = n - 2 \to \infty.$$

This means that $V_a^b(\mathcal{D}) = +\infty$. It is also clear that $V_a^b(f) = 0$ if and only if $f$ is constant.

**Theorem 5.68 (Properties of full variation).** *Let $f$ be a function of bounded variation on the interval $[a, b]$. Then for any $x, a < x \le b$ we have $f \in BV[a, x]$, and $V_a^x(f)$ is nondecreasing in $x$. Moreover, for any $c \in [a, b]$ we have that*

$$V_a^b(f) = V_a^c(f) + V_c^b(f).$$

*Proof.* Let $a < x \le b$. Then for any partition $P$ of the interval $[a, x]$ we have

$$V(P, f) \le V(P', f),$$

where $P' = P \cup \{b\}$ is a partition of the interval $[a, b]$. Hence

$$V(P, f) \le V_a^b(f)$$

and thus $f \in BV[a, x]$. Next, for any $x$ and $y$ such that $a < x < y \le b$ and for any partition $P$ of the interval $[a, x]$ we have that

$$V(P, f) \le V(P, f) + |f(y) - f(x)| = V(P', f) \le V_a^y(f),$$

where $P' = P \cup \{y\}$ is a partition of the interval $[a, y]$. Taking the supremum of the first term with respect to partitions of $[a, x]$ we obtain

$$V_a^x(f) \le V_a^y(f),$$

i.e., $V_a^x(f)$ is a nondecreasing function.

Now let $a < c < b$. Then for partition $P$ of the interval $[a, b]$ of the form $P = P_1 \cup P_2$, where $P_1$ is a partition of $[a, c]$ and $P_2$ is a partition of $[c, b]$, we have that

$$V(P, f) = V(P_1, f) + V(P_2, f).$$

This implies that

$$V_a^b(f) \ge \sup_{P = P_1 \cup P_2} V(P, f) = \sup_{P_1} V(P_1, f) + \sup_{P_2} V(P_2, f) = V_a^c(f) + V_c^b(f).$$

To obtain the opposite inequality one can note that for any partition $P$ of the interval $[a, b]$ it holds that $P' := P \cup \{c\} \supset P$. That's why $P' = P_1 \cup P_2$, where $P_1$ and $P_2$ are partitions of the intervals $[a, c]$ and $[c, b]$, respectively. This implies that

$$V(P, f) \le V(P', f) = V(P_1, f) + V(P_2, f) \le V_a^c(f) + V_c^b(f).$$

Thus,

$$V_a^b(f) \le V_a^c(f) + V_c^b(f)$$

and this finishes the proof.

**Corollary 5.69.** *Let $f$ be a real-valued function of bounded variation on the interval $[a, b]$. Then $f$ can be represented as the difference of two nondecreasing functions.*

*Proof.* We will first prove that if $f$ is real-valued then $V_a^x(f) - f(x)$ is nondecreasing. Indeed, for any $h > 0$ small enough we have

$$(V_a^{x+h}(f) - f(x + h)) - (V_a^x(f) - f(x))$$
$$= (V_a^{x+h}(f) - V_a^x(f)) - (f(x + h) - f(x)) = V_x^{x+h}(f) - (f(x + h) - f(x))$$
$$\ge V_x^{x+h}(f) - |f(x + h) - f(x)| \ge 0.$$

Now the equality
$$f(x) = V_a^x(f) - (V_a^x(f) - f(x))$$
gives the needed representation.

**Corollary 5.70.** *Let $f$ be a real-valued function of bounded variation. Then it may have only breakpoints of the first kind, and their quantity is at most countable.*

*Proof.* This follows immediately from Corollary 5.69 and Theorem 5.65.

The latter theorem and its corollaries can be used for consideration of Riemann–Stieltjes integration with respect to functions of bounded variation (see Chapter 9).

**Exercise 5.71.**    1. Prove that any piecewise constant function on any interval is of bounded variation.

2. Show that the function
$$f(x) = \begin{cases} x \sin \frac{1}{x}, & x \in (0,1], \\ 0, & x = 0, \end{cases}$$
which is continuous on the interval $[0,1]$, is not of bounded variation on $[0,1]$.

3. Show that the continuous function
$$f(x) = \begin{cases} x\sqrt{x} \cos \frac{1}{x}, & x \in (0,1], \\ 0, & x = 0, \end{cases}$$
is of bounded variation on $[0,1]$.

4. Prove that any monotone function $f : [a,b] \to \mathbb{R}$ is of bounded variation with
$$V_a^b(f) = |f(b) - f(a)|.$$

5. Let $f$ satisfy the condition
$$|f(x) - f(y)| \le M|x - y|, \quad M > 0,$$
for all $x, y \in [a,b]$. Prove that $f$ is of bounded variation with
$$V_a^b(f) \le M(b - a).$$

6. Prove that a linear combination of functions of bounded variation is again a function of bounded variation with
$$V_a^b(f + g) \le V_a^b(f) + V_a^b(g), \quad V_a^b(cf) = |c|V_a^b(f).$$

7. Prove that the product of functions of bounded variation is again a function of bounded variation with
$$V_a^b(fg) \le \sup_{x \in [a,b]} |f(x)| V_a^b(g) + \sup_{x \in [a,b]} |g(x)| V_a^b(f).$$

8. Prove that if $f$ is of bounded variation on the interval $[a,b]$ and $f$ is continuous at some point $x_0 \in [a,b]$ then $V_a^x(f)$ is also continuous at $x_0$.

## 5.6 ▪ Global properties of continuous functions

**Definition 5.72.** *A function $f : X \subset \mathbb{R} \to \mathbb{R}$ is said to be bounded on $X$ if there exists $M > 0$ such that $|f(x)| \leq M$ for all $x \in X$.*

**Remark 5.73.** A function $f$ is not bounded on a set $X$ if there is a sequence $\{x_n\}_{n=1}^{\infty} \subset X$ such that $\lim_{n \to \infty} f(x_n) = \infty$.

**Theorem 5.74 (Passing through zero).** *Let $f : [a, b] \to \mathbb{R}$ be continuous and let $f(a)f(b) < 0$. Then there exists a point (possibly not unique) $c \in (a, b)$ such that $f(c) = 0$.*

*Proof.* Dividing an interval in half and taking the ends of the intervals so that the value of $f$ at the ends has different signs we obtain a sequence of intervals $\{[a_n, b_n]\}_{n=1}^{\infty}$ (if this process does not stop at some step) such that $[a_{n+1}, b_{n+1}] \subset [a_n, b_n]$ and $b_n - a_n = (b - a)/2^n$. Due to Theorem 3.32 there is a unique $c = \bigcap_{n=1}^{\infty} [a_n, b_n]$ with

$$c = \lim_{n \to \infty} a_n = \lim_{n \to \infty} b_n.$$

Continuity of $f$ and the condition $f(a_n)f(b_n) < 0$ imply that

$$0 \leq \lim_{n \to \infty} f(a_n) = f(c) = \lim_{n \to \infty} f(b_n) \leq 0$$

or

$$0 \leq \lim_{n \to \infty} f(b_n) = f(c) = \lim_{n \to \infty} f(a_n) \leq 0.$$

In any case, $f(c) = 0$ follows. The fact that $c \in (a, b)$ follows from the process.

**Corollary 5.75.** *Let $f \in C[a, b]$ and $\alpha = f(a), \beta = f(b)$. Then for any $\gamma \in [\alpha, \beta]$ (or $\gamma \in [\beta, \alpha]$) there is $c \in (a, b)$ (possibly not unique) such that $\gamma = f(c)$.*

*Proof.* Without loss of generality we assume that $\alpha \neq \beta$. Let $F(x) := f(x) - \gamma$ with $\alpha < \gamma < \beta$. Then $F(a) = \alpha - \gamma < 0$ and $F(b) = \beta - \gamma > 0$, i.e., $F(a)F(b) < 0$. Similarly, this holds for $\beta < \gamma < \alpha$. Applying Theorem 5.74 to $F$ we obtain that there is $c \in (a, b)$ such that $F(c) = 0$ or $f(c) = \gamma$.

**Exercise 5.76.** Let $f \in C[a, b]$ and $f : [a, b] \to [a, b]$. Prove that there is a point $x_0 \in [a, b]$ such that $f(x_0) = x_0$. These points are said to be *fixed points* of $f$.

**Theorem 5.77 (On monotonicity of a continuous function which has an inverse).** *Let $f \in C[a, b]$ have an inverse. Then $f$ is either increasing or decreasing on $[a, b]$.*

*Proof.* Let us assume on the contrary that $f$ is not monotone. Then there are at least three points $x_1 < x_2 < x_3$ such that $f(x_1) < f(x_2)$ but $f(x_2) > f(x_3)$. Let $d := \max(f(x_1), f(x_3))$. Then for $\gamma \in (d, f(x_2))$ there exist two points $c_1 \in (x_1, x_2)$ and $c_2 \in (x_2, x_3)$ such that $\gamma = f(c_1) = f(c_2)$. Since $c_1 \neq c_2$ this contradicts the existence of the inverse (see Figure 5.2).

**Theorem 5.78 (Weierstrass I).** *Let $f \in C[a, b]$. Then $f$ is bounded on $[a, b]$.*

*Proof.* This statement is a simple consequence of Exercise 5.13. But for the continuous function there is a simple and clear proof. Indeed, let us assume on the contrary that $f$ is not bounded on $[a, b]$. Then there is a sequence $\{x_n\}_{n=1}^{\infty} \subset [a, b]$ such that $\lim_{n \to \infty} f(x_n) = \infty$. Since

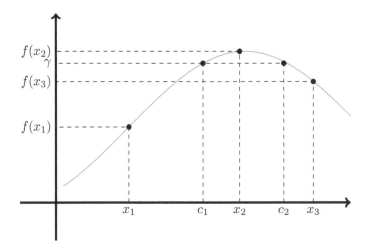

**Figure 5.2.** *Graphical illustration of a nonmonotone function.*

$\{x_n\}_{n=1}^{\infty}$ is bounded, the Bolzano–Weierstrass principle implies that there exists a subsequence $\{x_{k_n}\}_{n=1}^{\infty}$ of $\{x_n\}_{n=1}^{\infty}$ such that

$$\lim_{n\to\infty} x_{k_n} = c, \quad c \in [a, b].$$

Continuity of $f$ yields

$$\lim_{n\to\infty} f(x_{k_n}) = f(c).$$

But $\{f(x_{k_n})\}_{n=1}^{\infty}$ is a subsequence of infinitely large sequence. This contradiction proves the theorem.

**Remark 5.79.** Let $f(x) = 1/x$ on $(0, 1)$. Then $f$ is continuous on open interval $(0, 1)$ but not bounded there.

Let $f : X \subset \mathbb{R} \to \mathbb{R}$ be bounded. Then there are the finite numbers

$$M := \sup_{x \in X} f(x), \quad m := \inf_{x \in X} f(x)$$

such that

1. $m \le f(x) \le M$ for all $x \in X$,

2. for all $M' < M$ and all $m' > m$ there exist $x_1', x_2' \in X$ such that

$$M' < f(x_1') \le M, \quad m \le f(x_2') < m'.$$

**Theorem 5.80 (Weierstrass II).** *Let $f \in C[a, b]$. Then there are two points $x_1, x_2 \in [a, b]$ such that $f(x_1) = \sup_{x \in [a,b]} f(x)$ and $f(x_2) = \inf_{x \in [a,b]} f(x)$.*

***Proof.*** Due to Theorem 5.78

$$M = \sup_{x \in [a,b]} f(x), \quad m = \inf_{x \in [a,b]} f(x)$$

exist and are finite. Let us assume on the contrary that there are no $x_1, x_2 \in [a, b]$ such that $f(x_1) = M$ or $f(x_2) = m$, i.e., for all $x \in [a, b]$ we have $f(x) < M$ (or $f(x) > m$). This implies that the function

$$F(x) := \frac{1}{M - f(x)}$$

or

$$F(x) := \frac{1}{f(x) - m}$$

is continuous on $[a, b]$. By Theorem 5.78 there exists $A > 0$ such that

$$0 < \frac{1}{M - f(x)} \le A$$

or

$$0 < \frac{1}{f(x) - m} \le A$$

for all $x \in [a, b]$. Thus

$$f(x) \le M - 1/A$$

or

$$f(x) \ge m + 1/A$$

for all $x \in [a, b]$. It means that $M$ (or $m$) is not a supremum (an infimum) of $f$ on $[a, b]$. This contradiction proves the theorem.

**Remark 5.81.** In the framework of Theorem 5.80 we denote

$$M := \max_{x \in [a,b]} f(x) = f(x_1), \quad m := \min_{x \in [a,b]} f(x) = f(x_2).$$

**Exercise 5.82.** Let $f : X \subset \mathbb{R} \to \mathbb{R}$ be bounded on $X$. The value (which exists)

$$\omega_f(\delta) := \sup_{x', x'' \in X, |x' - x''| < \delta} |f(x') - f(x'')|$$

is called the *modulus of continuity* of $f$ on $X$. Prove that if $f \in C[a, b]$ then $\omega_f(\delta)$ satisfies

1. $\omega_f(\delta) \ge 0$,

2. $\lim_{\delta \to +0} \omega_f(\delta) = 0$,

3. $\omega_f(\delta)$ is a nondecreasing function,

4. $\omega_f(\delta_1 + \delta_2) \le \omega_f(\delta_1) + \omega_f(\delta_2)$.

**Exercise 5.83.** Evaluate $\omega_f(\delta)$ for the functions

1. $f(x) = x^2, x \in [0, 1]$,

2. $f(x) = \sin(1/x), x \in (0, 1)$,

3. $f(x) = \sin(x^2), x \in \mathbb{R}$.

**Definition 5.84.** *A function $f : X \subset \mathbb{R} \to \mathbb{R}$ is said to be* uniformly continuous *on $X$ if for every $\varepsilon > 0$ there exists $\delta > 0$ such that*

$$|f(x') - f(x'')| < \varepsilon$$

*for any $x', x'' \in X$ and $|x' - x''| < \delta$.*

**Remark 5.85.** The latter definition shows that any uniformly continuous function on $X$ is certainly continuous on $X$ since it is continuous at any point from $X$. The question now is, When is the statement true in the opposite direction?

**Example 5.86.**      1.  $f(x) = \sin(1/x)$ is not uniformly continuous on $X = (0,1)$. Indeed, let $x'_n = 1/(2\pi n)$ and $x''_n = 1/(\pi/2 + 2\pi n)$. Then

$$\lim_{n \to \infty} |x'_n - x''_n| = 0$$

but

$$|f(x'_n) - f(x''_n)| = |\sin(2\pi n) - \sin(\pi/2 + 2\pi n)| = 1.$$

2.  $f(x) = \sin(x^2)$ is not uniformly continuous on $X = \mathbb{R}$. Indeed, let

$$x'_n = \sqrt{2\pi n}, \quad x''_n = \sqrt{\pi/2 + 2\pi n}.$$

Then

$$\lim_{n \to \infty} |\sqrt{2\pi n} - \sqrt{\pi/2 + 2\pi n}| = \lim_{n \to \infty} \frac{\pi/2}{\sqrt{2\pi n} + \sqrt{\pi/2 + 2\pi n}} = 0$$

but

$$\lim_{n \to \infty} |\sin(x'_n)^2 - \sin(x''_n)^2| = \lim_{n \to \infty} |\sin(2\pi n) - \sin(\pi/2 + 2\pi n)| = 1.$$

3.  $f(x) = x^\alpha$ is uniformly continuous on $X = [1, \infty)$ if $\alpha \le 1$ and is not uniformly continuous on $X$ if $\alpha > 1$. First let $\alpha > 1$. Then choosing

$$x'_n = (n + 1)^{1/\alpha}, \quad x''_n = n^{1/\alpha}$$

we obtain

$$x'_n - x''_n = (n + 1)^{1/\alpha} - n^{1/\alpha} = n^{1/\alpha}[(1 + 1/n)^{1/\alpha} - 1]$$
$$= n^{1/\alpha - 1} \frac{(1 + 1/n)^{1/\alpha} - 1}{1/n}$$

so that

$$\lim_{n \to \infty} |x'_n - x''_n| = \lim_{n \to \infty} n^{1/\alpha - 1} \lim_{n \to \infty} \frac{(1 + 1/n)^{1/\alpha} - 1}{1/n} = 0 \cdot \frac{1}{\alpha} = 0$$

since $\alpha > 1$. But

$$|f(x'_n) - f(x''_n)| = 1.$$

Now if $\alpha \le 1$ then

$$|x_1^\alpha - x_2^\alpha| = \frac{|x_2|^\alpha |(1 + \frac{x_1 - x_2}{x_2})^\alpha - 1|}{|\frac{x_1 - x_2}{x_2}|} \left| \frac{x_1 - x_2}{x_2} \right| \le c_0 |x_2|^{\alpha - 1} |x_1 - x_2|,$$

where we have employed the bound

$$\left| \frac{(1 + \frac{x_1 - x_2}{x_2})^\alpha - 1}{\frac{x_1 - x_2}{x_2}} \right| \le c_0 < \infty.$$

This latter bound follows from the limit

$$\lim_{z \to 0} \frac{(1 + z)^\alpha - 1}{z} = \alpha.$$

Thus, finally we have

$$|x_1^\alpha - x_2^\alpha| \le c_0 |x_2|^{\alpha - 1} |x_1 - x_2| \le c_0 |x_1 - x_2| < c_0 \delta = \varepsilon, \quad \delta = \varepsilon / c_0,$$

since $\alpha \le 1$ and $x_1, x_2 \ge 1$.

**Exercise 5.87.** Investigate the uniform continuity of $f(x) = \sin(x^\alpha)$ on $X = [1, \infty)$.

**Theorem 5.88 (Cantor).** *Let $f \in C[a, b]$. Then $f$ is uniformly continuous on $[a, b]$.*

*Proof.* In order to prove this theorem we assume on the contrary that $f$ is not uniformly continuous on $[a, b]$. It means that there exists $\varepsilon_0 > 0$ such that for any $\delta > 0$ there exist $x', x'' \in [a, b]$ with $|x' - x''| < \delta$ and $|f(x') - f(x'')| \ge \varepsilon_0$. Let $\delta_n = 1/n$. Then there are $x_n', x_n'' \in [a, b]$ and $|x_n' - x_n''| < 1/n$ but

$$|f(x_n') - f(x_n'')| \ge \varepsilon_0.$$

Since $x_n', x_n''$ are bounded, the Bolzano–Weierstrass theorem implies that there is a subsequence $x_{k_n}'$ such that $\lim_{n \to \infty} x_{k_n}' = \xi$ and $\lim_{n \to \infty} x_{k_n}'' = \xi$ also. Since $x_{k_n}', x_{k_n}'' \in [a, b]$, $\xi \in [a, b]$. Continuity of $f$ at $\xi$ leads to

$$\lim_{n \to \infty} f(x_{k_n}') = f(\xi) = \lim_{n \to \infty} f(x_{k_n}'').$$

So

$$\lim_{n \to \infty} |f(x_{k_n}') - f(x_{k_n}'')| = 0.$$

This contradicts

$$|f(x_{k_n}') - f(x_{k_n}'')| \ge \varepsilon_0 > 0$$

and proves the theorem.

**Exercise 5.89.** Prove that $f$ is uniformly continuous on $X$ if and only if

$$\lim_{\delta \to +0} \omega_f(\delta) = 0.$$

**Exercise 5.90.** Prove that Theorems 5.78, 5.80, and 5.88 hold for any *compact set* $K \subset \mathbb{R}$, i.e., for any set $K$ which is closed (meaning that it contains all its limiting points) and bounded.

**Exercise 5.91.** Let $f \in C[a, \infty)$. Assume that $\lim_{x \to +\infty} f(x)$ exists. Prove that $f$ is uniformly continuous on $[a, \infty)$.

# Chapter 6

# Differentiation

The cornerstone of this chapter, as well as of the whole one-dimensional classical analysis of differentiable functions, is the Lagrange formula or the mean value formula. It allows one to obtain nontrivial consequences such as a criterion for monotonicity of differentiable functions, l'Hôpital's rules for calculating limits, sufficient conditions for the uniform continuity of functions, the passage of a derivative through an intermediate value, and a characterization of the discontinuity points of the derivative. The results of this chapter precede Taylor's formula and the application of the concept of convexity to the proofs of many classical inequalities.

## 6.1 ▪ The concept of differentiability

**Definition 6.1.** *Let $f : X \subset \mathbb{R} \to \mathbb{R}, x_0 \in X \cap X'$, and $h \neq 0$ such that $x_0 + h \in X$. Then the limit (if it exists)*

$$\lim_{h \to 0} \frac{f(x_0 + h) - f(x_0)}{h} =: f'(x_0)$$

*is called the* derivative *of $f$ at the point $x_0$.*

**Definition 6.2.** *The limits (if they exist)*

$$\lim_{h \to \pm 0} \frac{f(x_0 + h) - f(x_0)}{h} =: f'_\pm(x_0)$$

*are called the* right and left derivatives *of $f$ at the point $x_0$.*

**Remark 6.3.** Obviously, $f'(x_0)$ exists if and only if $f'_\pm(x_0)$ exists and $f'_+(x_0) = f'_-(x_0)$.

**Example 6.4.**   1. Let $f(x) = |x|$ and $x_0 = 0$. Then $f'(0)$ does not exist since $f'_+(0) = 1$ and $f'_-(0) = -1$.

2. Let

$$f(x) = \begin{cases} |x|^\alpha \cos(1/x), & x \neq 0, \\ 0, & x = 0, \end{cases}$$

and $x_0 = 0$. Then $f'(0) = 0$ if $\alpha > 1$, and $f'(0)$ does not exist if $\alpha \leq 1$. Indeed, for $\alpha > 1$ we have

$$\lim_{h \to 0} \frac{|h|^\alpha \cos(1/h) - 0}{h} = \lim_{h \to 0} |h|^{\alpha - 1} \frac{|h|}{h} \cos(1/h) = 0$$

since

$$\left| \frac{|h|}{h} \cos(1/h) \right| \leq 1.$$

Now, if $\alpha \leq 1$ then both $f'_{\pm}(0)$ do not exist. This follows from the following considerations. Let $h_n = 1/(2\pi n)$. Then

$$\frac{|h_n|^{\alpha} \cos(1/h_n)}{h_n} = (2\pi n)^{1-\alpha} \to +\infty, \quad n \to \infty,$$

if $\alpha < 1$. If $\alpha = 1$ then

$$\lim_{h \to \pm 0} \frac{|h|}{h} \cos(1/h) = \pm \lim_{h \to 0} \cos(1/h),$$

which do not exist, as we know from Chapter 5.

3. Let

$$f(x) = \begin{cases} \log(x + \sqrt{x^2 - 1}), & x \geq 1, \\ 0, & x < 1, \end{cases}$$

and $x_0 = 1$. It is easy to check that $f$ is continuous everywhere. But

$$f'_-(1) = \lim_{h \to -0} \frac{f(1+h) - f(1)}{h} = 0$$

and

$$\begin{aligned} f'_+(1) &= \lim_{h \to +0} \frac{f(1+h) - f(1)}{h} = \lim_{h \to +0} \frac{\log(1 + h + \sqrt{h^2 + 2h})}{h} \\ &= \lim_{h \to +0} \frac{\log(1 + h + \sqrt{h^2 + 2h})}{h + \sqrt{h^2 + 2h}} \frac{h + \sqrt{h^2 + 2h}}{h} \\ &= \lim_{z \to +0} \frac{\log(1 + z)}{z} \lim_{h \to +0} \frac{h + \sqrt{h^2 + 2h}}{h} \\ &= \lim_{h \to +0} \frac{h + \sqrt{h^2 + 2h}}{h} = \lim_{h \to +0} \frac{-2h}{h(h - \sqrt{h^2 + 2h})} \\ &= -2 \lim_{h \to +0} \frac{1}{h(1 - \sqrt{1 + 2/h})} = +\infty. \end{aligned}$$

**Exercise 6.5.** Let

$$f(x) = \begin{cases} 1/\log(1/x), & x > 0, \\ 0, & x = 0, \end{cases}$$

and $x_0 = 0$. Prove that $f$ is continuous from the right at $x_0$ but $f'_+(0) = +\infty$.

**Theorem 6.6 (Continuity of function having the derivative).** *If $f'(x_0)$ exists then $f$ is continuous at $x_0$.*

*Proof.* From

$$\lim_{h \to 0} \frac{f(x_0 + h) - f(x_0)}{h} = f'(x_0)$$

we may conclude that $f(x_0 + h) - f(x_0) = hf'(x_0) + o(h) \to 0$ as $h \to 0$. Hence $f$ is continuous at $x_0$.

**Corollary 6.7.** *If both $f'_{\pm}(x_0)$ exist (but are not necessarily equal) then $f$ is continuous at $x_0$.*

**Exercise 6.8.** Prove the latter corollary.

**Remark 6.9.** The opposite statement of Theorem 6.6 (or Corollary 6.7) is not true; see part 1 of Example 6.4.

**Theorem 6.10 (Properties of derivatives).** *Let $f'(x_0)$ and $g'(x_0)$ exist. Then the following derivatives exist also and the equalities hold:*

1. $(f \pm g)'(x_0) = f'(x_0) + g'(x_0)$,

2. $(f \cdot g)'(x_0) = f'(x_0)g(x_0) + f(x_0)g'(x_0)$,

3.
$$\left(\frac{f}{g}\right)'(x_0) = \frac{f'(x_0)g(x_0) - f(x_0)g'(x_0)}{g(x_0)^2}$$

*provided that $g(x_0) \neq 0$.*

**Proof.** We will prove only the last part since the proofs of the first two parts are similar (and even simpler).

By hypothesis, $g$ is continuous at $x_0$ and $g(x_0 + h) \neq 0$ for all $h$ small enough. Next,

$$\frac{\frac{f(x_0+h)}{g(x_0+h)} - \frac{f(x_0)}{g(x_0)}}{h} = \frac{f(x_0 + h)g(x_0) - f(x_0)g(x_0 + h)}{hg(x_0)g(x_0 + h)}$$

$$= \frac{\frac{f(x_0+h)-f(x_0)}{h}g(x_0) - \frac{g(x_0+h)-g(x_0)}{h}f(x_0)}{g(x_0)g(x_0 + h)}.$$

Hence

$$\lim_{h \to 0} \frac{\frac{f(x_0+h)}{g(x_0+h)} - \frac{f(x_0)}{g(x_0)}}{h} = \frac{\lim_{h \to 0}\frac{f(x_0+h)-f(x_0)}{h}g(x_0) - \lim_{h \to 0}\frac{g(x_0+h)-g(x_0)}{h}f(x_0)}{g(x_0)\lim_{h \to 0}g(x_0 + h)}$$

$$= \frac{f'(x_0)g(x_0) - g'(x_0)f(x_0)}{g(x_0)^2}$$

since all latter limits exist and $g(x_0) \neq 0$.

**Example 6.11.**  1. Let $f(x) = |x|$ and $g(x) = -|x|$ and $x_0 = 0$. Then $f(x) + g(x) \equiv 0$ and therefore $(f + g)'(0) = 0$, but $f'(0)$ and $g'(0)$ do not exist.

2. Let $f(x) = |x|$ and $g(x) = -|x|$ and $x_0 = 0$. Then $f(x)g(x) = -x^2$ and therefore $(fg)'(0) = 0$, but $f'(0)$ and $g'(0)$ do not exist.

3. Let $f(x) = g(x) = 1 + |x|$ and $x_0 = 0$. Then $f(x)/g(x) \equiv 1$ and therefore $(f/g)'(0) = 0$, but $f'(0)$ and $g'(0)$ do not exist.

Example 6.11 shows that Theorem 6.10 does not hold in the opposite direction.

**Definition 6.12.** *Let* $f : X \subset \mathbb{R} \to \mathbb{R}$. *Then the set*

$$\Gamma(f) := \{(x, y) \in \mathbb{R}^2 : x \in X, y = f(x)\}$$

*is said to be the* graph *of* $f$. *It is clear that* $\Gamma(f) \subset X \times f(X)$.

**Definition 6.13.** *Let* $A$ *be a point of* $\Gamma(f)$ *with coordinates* $(x_0, y_0)$, *i.e.,* $x_0 \in X$ *and* $y_0 = f(x_0)$. *Let* $P$ *be another point of* $\Gamma(f)$ *with coordinates* $(x, y)$, *i.e.,* $x \in X$ *and* $y = f(x)$. *A straight line passing through* $A$ *and* $P$ *is called a* secant *of* $\Gamma(f)$ *at the point* $A$.

**Definition 6.14.** *Let* $P$ *and* $A$ *be points of* $\Gamma(f)$, *and let* $P$ *tend to* $A$ *in the sense that* $x$ *tends to* $x_0$ *and* $y = f(x)$ *tends to* $y_0 = f(x_0)$. *If there is a limiting position of the secant* $AP$ *at* $A \in \Gamma(f)$ *then this limiting position is called the* tangent *to* $\Gamma(f)$ *at the point* $A$.

**Theorem 6.15 (Geometric meaning of derivative).** *If* $f'(x_0)$ *exists then there is a tangent to* $\Gamma(f)$ *at the point* $A = (x_0, f(x_0)) \in \Gamma(f)$ *and it satisfies the equation*

$$y = f'(x_0)(x - x_0) + f(x_0).$$

*Moreover,* $f'(x_0) = \tan \alpha$, *where* $\alpha$ *is the angle of inclination of the tangent to the* $x$-axis.

**Proof.** The statement of the theorem is equivalent to the existence of a limiting position of the angle $\varphi_h$ of the secant $AP$ if the derivative exists; see Figure 6.1. Indeed, since

$$\tan \varphi_h = \frac{f(x_0 + h) - f(x_0)}{h},$$

$\lim_{h \to 0} \tan \varphi_h = f'(x_0)$, i.e., the limiting position of the secant $AP$ exists, and this limiting position is a tangent to $\Gamma(f)$ at the point $A$. It is also true that it satisfies

$$y = f'(x_0)(x - x_0) + f(x_0).$$

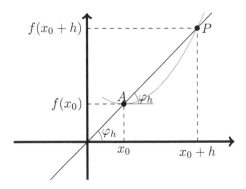

**Figure 6.1.** *Graphical illustration of limiting position of a secant.*

**Example 6.16.** Let $f(x) = \sqrt[3]{x}, x \in (-1, 1)$ and $x_0 = 0$ (see Figure 6.2). Then it is easy to see that the limiting position of the secant at $(0, 0) \in \Gamma(f)$ exists, and this position is just the $y$-axis. But $f'(0) = +\infty$. Indeed,

$$\lim_{h \to 0} \frac{f(h) - f(0)}{h} = \lim_{h \to 0} \frac{\sqrt[3]{h}}{h} = \lim_{h \to 0} h^{-2/3} = +\infty.$$

This shows that the statement in Theorem 6.15 does not hold in the opposite direction.

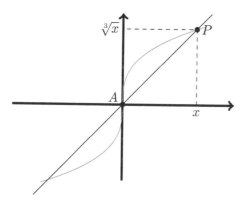

**Figure 6.2.** *Graph of $f(x) = \sqrt[3]{x}$ and its secant.*

**Theorem 6.17 (Derivative of superposition).** *Let $f : X \subset \mathbb{R} \to Y \subset \mathbb{R}$ and $\varphi : Y \subset \mathbb{R} \to \mathbb{R}$ be functions such that for $x_0 \in X \cap X'$ and for $y_0 := f(x_0) \in Y \cap Y'$ the derivatives $f'(x_0)$ and $\varphi'(y_0)$ exist. Then for the superposition $g(x) := \varphi(f(x))$ the derivative $g'(x_0)$ exists and*

$$g'(x_0) = \varphi'(y_0) f'(x_0) = \varphi'(f(x_0)) f'(x_0).$$

***Proof.*** By definition, we need to prove the existence of the limit

$$\lim_{h \to 0} \frac{g(x_0 + h) - g(x_0)}{h} = \lim_{h \to 0} \frac{\varphi(f(x_0 + h)) - \varphi(f(x_0))}{h}$$

$$= \lim_{h \to 0} \frac{\varphi(f(x_0 + h)) - \varphi(f(x_0))}{H} \frac{H}{h},$$

where $H := f(x_0 + h) - f(x_0) \neq 0$ since otherwise $f$ is a constant function in the vicinity of $x_0$. If $h \to 0$ then $H \to 0$ also due to conditions of $f$ at $x_0$. By hypothesis the latter limit becomes

$$\lim_{H \to 0} \frac{\varphi(y_0 + H) - \varphi(y_0)}{H} \lim_{h \to 0} \frac{f(x_0 + h) - f(x_0)}{h} = \varphi'(y_0) f'(x_0).$$

Thus, the theorem is proved.

**Corollary 6.18 (Derivative of inverse function).** *Let $y = f(x)$ be a function defined in $U_\delta(x_0)$ such that it has an inverse function $x = f^{-1}(y)$ in $V_\varepsilon(y_0)$ with $y_0 = f(x_0)$. Let us assume that $f'(x_0)$ exists and $f'(x_0) \neq 0$. If $f^{-1}(y)$ is continuous at $y_0$ then $(f^{-1})'(y_0)$ exists and*

$$(f^{-1})'(y_0) = \frac{1}{f'(x_0)}.$$

***Proof.*** Considering $f^{-1}(y)$ in $V_\varepsilon(y_0)$ and $H := f(x_0 + h) - f(x_0)$ such that $|H| < \varepsilon$ we have

$$\frac{f^{-1}(y_0 + H) - f^{-1}(y_0)}{H} = \frac{x_0 + h - x_0}{f(x_0 + h) - f(x_0)} = \frac{1}{\frac{f(x_0 + h) - f(x_0)}{h}},$$

because $f^{-1}(y_0 + H) = f^{-1}(y_0) + h$ with $h \to 0$ (if $H \to 0$) due to continuity of $f^{-1}(y)$ at $y_0$. Then

$$(f^{-1})'(y_0) = \lim_{H \to 0} \frac{f^{-1}(y_0 + H) - f^{-1}(y_0)}{H} = \frac{1}{\lim_{h \to 0} \frac{f(x_0 + h) - f(x_0)}{h}} = \frac{1}{f'(x_0)}.$$

This finishes the proof.

**Example 6.19.** Let $f(x) = x^3$ and $x_0 = 0$. Then this function has an inverse $f^{-1}(y) = y^{1/3}$ which is continuous at $y_0 = 0$. But $(f^{-1})'(0) = +\infty$, i.e., it does not exist. The reason is that $f'(0) = 0$.

**Exercise 6.20.**     1. Let

$$f(x) = \begin{cases} h(x), & x < x_0, \\ g(x), & x \geq x_0. \end{cases}$$

Prove that $f'(x_0)$ exists if and only if $\lim_{x \to x_0 - 0} h(x) = g(x_0)$ and $g'_+(x_0) = h'_-(x_0)$.

2. Let $f$ be defined on $\mathbb{R}$. Assume that $f'(x)$ exists at any point $x \in \mathbb{R}$. Investigate when $|f(x)|$ has a derivative.

3. Suppose that $f'(x_0)$ exists and $x_0 \neq 0$. Evaluate the limit

$$\lim_{x \to x_0} \frac{x_0^n f(x) - x^n f(x_0)}{x - x_0}, \quad n \in \mathbb{N}.$$

**Exercise 6.21.** Evaluate the derivatives of

$$y = \sqrt[n]{x}, \quad y = \log_a x, \quad y = \arcsin x,$$
$$y = \arccos x, \quad y = \arctan x, \quad y = \text{arccot}\, x$$

using Corollary 6.18.

**Exercise 6.22.** Show that the function $y = x^2 \mathcal{D}(x)$ has a derivative only at the point $x_0 = 0$.

The existence of a derivative is equivalent in the one-dimensional case to the more important concept of differentiability (used especially in the multidimensional case) which is most essential for the definitions of differentials of first or higher order.

**Definition 6.23.** *A function $f$ is said to be* differentiable *at the point $x_0$ if there is a constant $K \in \mathbb{R}$ such that*

$$f(x_0 + h) - f(x_0) = Kh + o(h)$$

*as $h \to 0$.*

**Proposition 6.24.** *A function $f$ is differentiable at the point $x_0$ if and only if the derivative $f'(x_0)$ exists (in this case $K = f'(x_0)$).*

**Exercise 6.25.** Prove Proposition 6.24.

**Definition 6.26.** *Let $f$ be differentiable at $x_0$. The principal linear part of the increment $f(x_0 + h) - f(x_0)$ of $f$ at the point $x_0$, i.e., $f'(x_0)h$, is called the* first differential *of $f$ at the point $x_0$ and is denoted by*

$$\mathrm{d}f(x_0) := f'(x_0)h.$$

*Since $h = x_0 + h - x_0$, $h = \mathrm{d}x$ and thus the first differential is equal to*

$$\mathrm{d}f(x_0) = f'(x_0)\mathrm{d}x.$$

**Proposition 6.27.** *The latter form of the first differential is invariant under the change of variable in $f$.*

**Proof.** Let $f$ have the first differential $\mathrm{d}f(x_0)$ at the point $x_0$, and let the variable $x$ be changed such that $x = \varphi(t)$. Let $\varphi$ have derivative $\varphi'(t_0)$ at $t_0$ with $x_0 = \varphi(t_0)$. By Theorem 6.17 the superposition $g(t) := f(\varphi(t))$ is differentiable at the point $t_0$ and

$$g'(t_0) = f'(x_0)\varphi'(t_0).$$

Hence the first differential of $g$ at the point $t_0$ is equal to

$$\mathrm{d}g(t_0) = g'(t_0)\mathrm{d}t = f'(x_0)\varphi'(t_0)\mathrm{d}t = f'(\varphi(t_0))\mathrm{d}\varphi(t_0) = f'(x_0)\mathrm{d}x = \mathrm{d}f(x_0).$$

This means that the form is invariant, and the proposition is proved.

**Corollary 6.28.** *Let $u$ and $v$ be two arbitrary differentiable functions. Then*

$$\mathrm{d}(u \pm v) = \mathrm{d}u \pm \mathrm{d}v, \quad \mathrm{d}(uv) = v\mathrm{d}u + u\mathrm{d}v, \quad \mathrm{d}(u/v) = \frac{v\mathrm{d}u - u\mathrm{d}v}{v^2}, \quad v \neq 0.$$

**Definition 6.29.** *Let $f : X \subset \mathbb{R} \to \mathbb{R}$ and $x_0 \in X \cap X'$. Assume that $f$ is differentiable for any $x \in X \cap U_\delta(x_0)$, and consider $g(x) := f'(x)$ for these $x$. If the limit*

$$g'(x_0) = \lim_{h \to 0} \frac{g(x_0 + h) - g(x_0)}{h} = \lim_{h \to 0} \frac{f'(x_0 + h) - f'(x_0)}{h}$$

*exists then this limit is called the* second derivative *of $f$ at the point $x_0$ and is denoted as $f''(x_0)$. In short, $f''(x_0) = (f')'(x_0)$.*

*By induction, we define the* derivative of order $n$ at the point $x_0$ *as*

$$f^{(n)}(x_0) = (f^{(n-1)})'(x_0) = \lim_{h \to 0} \frac{f^{(n-1)}(x_0 + h) - f^{(n-1)}(x_0)}{h}$$

*if this limit exists.*

**Remark 6.30.** It is clear that if $f^{(n)}(x_0)$ exists then $f^{(n-1)}(x)$ is continuous at the point $x_0$.

**Example 6.31.**     1. Let $f(x) = x|x|$ and $x_0 = 0$. Then $f'(x) = 2|x|$ for all $x \in \mathbb{R}$. But $f''(0)$ does not exist since $|x|$ is not differentiable at $x_0 = 0$.

    2. Let $x_0 = 0$ and

$$f(x) = \begin{cases} x^3 \cos(1/x), & x \neq 0, \\ 0, & x = 0. \end{cases}$$

Then for any $x \neq 0$ we have

$$f'(x) = 3x^2 \cos(1/x) + x \sin(1/x)$$

and

$$f'(0) = \lim_{h \to 0} \frac{h^3 \cos(1/h)}{h} = \lim_{h \to 0} h^2 \cos(1/h) = 0.$$

But $f''(0)$ does not exist since the limit

$$\lim_{h \to 0} \frac{3h^2 \cos(1/h) + h \sin(1/h)}{h} = \lim_{h \to 0} \sin(1/h)$$

does not exist (as we know). However, for any $x \neq 0$ we have

$$f''(x) = 6x \cos(1/x) + 4 \sin(1/x) - \frac{1}{x} \cos(1/x).$$

Moreover, this function has a derivative of any order if $x \neq 0$.

3. It is easy to show by induction that

$$(\sin x)^{(n)} = \sin(x + n\pi/2), \quad (\cos x)^{(n)} = \cos(x + n\pi/2)$$

and

$$(a^x)^{(n)} = a^x(\log a)^n, \quad (\arctan x)^{(n)} = \frac{(n-1)!}{(1+x^2)^{n/2}} \sin(n(\arctan x + \pi/2)).$$

4. The *Leibniz formula*

$$(uv)^{(n)} = \sum_{k=0}^{n} \binom{n}{k} u^{(k)} v^{(n-k)}$$

holds and its proof is precisely the same as the proof of Newton's binomial theorem.

5. Using the Leibniz formula we may calculate the derivative of order $n$ of the regular (non-degenerate) *bilinear function*

$$f(x) = \frac{ax+b}{cx+d}, \quad ad \neq bc.$$

Indeed,

$$\begin{aligned}
\left(\frac{ax+b}{cx+d}\right)^{(n)} &= \left((ax+b)\frac{1}{cx+d}\right)^{(n)} \\
&= \sum_{k=0}^{n} \binom{n}{k}(ax+b)^{(k)}((cx+d)^{-1})^{(n-k)} \\
&= (ax+b)((cx+d)^{-1})^{(n)} + na((cx+d)^{-1})^{(n-1)} \\
&= (ax+b)(-1)^n n! c^n (cx+d)^{-n-1} \\
&\quad + na(-1)^{n-1}(n-1)! c^{n-1}(cx+d)^{-n} \\
&= \frac{(-1)^n c^n n!}{(cx+d)^n}\left(\frac{ax+b}{cx+d} - \frac{a}{c}\right) = \frac{(-1)^n c^{n-1} n!}{(cx+d)^{n+1}}(bc-ad). \quad (6.1)
\end{aligned}$$

It must be mentioned that (6.1) is valid for any $n = 1, 2, \dots$ and also for $c = 0$ when $ad \neq 0$.

6. Let $f(x) = x^\alpha, x > 0$. Then

$$(x^\alpha)^{(n)} = \alpha(\alpha-1)\cdots(\alpha-n+1)x^{\alpha-n}. \quad (6.2)$$

**Exercise 6.32.**    1. Prove formula (6.2).

2. Calculate the first and second derivatives of the function $f(x) = u(x)^{v(x)}$ under the assumption that $u(x), v(x) > 0$ are both twice differentiable. Using these formulae find the derivatives of the function $f(x) = x^x, x > 0$.

3. Express the second and third order derivatives of the inverse function $x = f^{-1}(y)$ in terms of the derivatives of the direct function $y = f(x)$.

4. Show that

$$(x^n \log x)^{(n)} = n! \left( \log x + \sum_{k=1}^{n} \frac{1}{k} \right)$$

and, in particular,

$$1 + \frac{1}{2} + \cdots + \frac{1}{n} = \sum_{k=1}^{n} \binom{n}{k} \frac{(-1)^{k-1}}{k}.$$

5. Let

$$f(x) = \begin{cases} e^{-1/x^2}, & x \neq 0, \\ 0, & x = 0. \end{cases}$$

Show that $f^{(n)}(0) = 0$ for $n = 1, 2, \ldots$.

Let the first differential $\mathrm{d}f(x)$ be well-defined for all $x \in X \cap U_\delta(x_0)$, i.e., $\mathrm{d}f(x) = f'(x)\mathrm{d}x$, where $\mathrm{d}x = h$ (increment) is the same for any point $x \in X \cap U_\delta(x_0)$. In that case the first differential is a function of two variables such that

$$\mathrm{d}f(x) = f'(x)\mathrm{d}x = F(x, \mathrm{d}x)|_{\mathrm{d}x=h}.$$

Further, if $f''(x_0)$ exists then we may define the differential of order two (second differential) of $f$ at the point $x_0$.

**Definition 6.33.**

1. *The* second differential, *denoted* $\mathrm{d}^2 f(x_0)$, *of $f$ at the point $x_0$ is defined as*

$$\mathrm{d}^2 f(x_0) := \mathrm{d}(F(x, \mathrm{d}x))(x_0)|_{h=\mathrm{d}x}$$
$$= \mathrm{d}(\mathrm{d}f(x))(x_0)|_{h=\mathrm{d}x} = \mathrm{d}(f'(x)\mathrm{d}x)(x_0)|_{h=\mathrm{d}x}.$$

2. *The* differential of order $n$, *denoted* $\mathrm{d}^n f(x_0)$, *of $f$ at the point $x_0$ is defined by induction as*

$$\mathrm{d}^n f(x_0) = \mathrm{d}(\mathrm{d}^{n-1} f(x))(x_0)|_{h=\mathrm{d}x}.$$

In Definition 6.33 we need to distinguish the following two cases:

1. Let $x$ be an independent variable. In that case, by the Leibniz formula,

$$\mathrm{d}^2 f(x_0) = \mathrm{d}(\mathrm{d}f(x))(x_0)|_{h=\mathrm{d}x} = \mathrm{d}(f'(x)\mathrm{d}x)(x_0)|_{h=\mathrm{d}x}$$
$$= \mathrm{d}(f'(x))(x_0)|_{h=\mathrm{d}x} \, \mathrm{d}x + f'(x_0) \, \mathrm{d}(\mathrm{d}x)|_{h=\mathrm{d}x}$$
$$= f''(x_0)(\mathrm{d}x)^2 + f'(x_0) \, \mathrm{d}^2 x \big|_{h=\mathrm{d}x} = f''(x_0)(\mathrm{d}x)^2$$

since $\mathrm{d}^2 x = 0, \mathrm{d}^3 x = 0, \ldots$ in this case. So

$$\mathrm{d}^2 f(x_0) = f''(x_0)(\mathrm{d}x)^2$$

and, by induction,

$$\mathrm{d}^n f(x_0) = f^{(n)}(x_0)(\mathrm{d}x)^n.$$

2. Let $x$ be a dependent variable, i.e., $x = \varphi(t)$ and $t$ is independent. Then due to the Leibniz formula and invariance of the first differential we have

$$\mathrm{d}^2 f(x_0) = f''(x_0)(\mathrm{d}x)^2 + f'(x_0)\mathrm{d}^2 x = f''(x_0)(\mathrm{d}x)^2 + f'(x_0)\varphi''(t_0)(\mathrm{d}t)^2$$
$$= f''(x_0)(\varphi'(t_0)\mathrm{d}t)^2 + f'(x_0)\varphi''(t_0)(\mathrm{d}t)^2$$
$$= [f''(\varphi(t_0))(\varphi'(t_0))^2 + f'(x_0)\varphi''(t_0)](\mathrm{d}t)^2 = (f(\varphi(t)))''_t(t_0)(\mathrm{d}t)^2.$$

**Exercise 6.34.** Let $x$ be a dependent variable, i.e., $x = \varphi(t)$ with independent $t$, and let $x_0 = \varphi(t_0)$.

1. Show that

$$d^3 f(x_0)$$
$$= f'''(x_0)(dx)^3\big|_{x_0=\varphi(t_0)} + 3f''(x_0)dx d^2x\big|_{x_0=\varphi(t_0)} + f'(x_0)d^3x\big|_{x_0=\varphi(t_0)}.$$

2. Calculate $d^4 f(x_0)$.

In some cases encountered in practice, a function can be specified implicitly, that is, using an intermediate parameter (see below). However, this does not interfere with calculating derivatives of these functions with respect to the main argument, and there is a calculation procedure that does not require an explicit definition of the function.

Let $x = \varphi(t)$ and $y = \psi(t)$ for $t \in [\alpha, \beta]$. These functions of variable $t$ (parameter) may define the function $y = f(x)$ $(x = g(y))$ of variable $x$ $(y)$ parametrically. If $x = \varphi(t)$ $(y = \psi(t))$ has an inverse $t = \varphi^{-1}(x)$ $(t = \psi^{-1}(y))$ then we may write the dependence $y$ of $x$ $(x$ of $y)$ as

$$y = \psi(t) = \psi(\varphi^{-1}(x)) =: f(x),$$
$$(x = \varphi(t) = \varphi(\psi^{-1}(y)) =: g(y)),$$

and we will proceed with derivatives as above.

When we have no direct dependence $y$ of $x$ or $x$ of $y$, we proceed as follows: By definition,

$$f'(x_0) = \lim_{h\to 0} \frac{f(x_0+h)-f(x_0)}{h} = \lim_{\tau\to 0} \frac{\psi(t_0+\tau)-\psi(t_0)}{\varphi(t_0+\tau)-\varphi(t_0)} = \lim_{\tau\to 0} \frac{\frac{\psi(t_0+\tau)-\psi(t_0)}{\tau}}{\frac{\varphi(t_0+\tau)-\varphi(t_0)}{\tau}},$$

where $f(x_0) = \psi(t_0)$, $f(x_0+h) = \psi(t_0+\tau)$, and $h = x_0+h-x_0 = \varphi(t_0+\tau)-\varphi(t_0)$. If $\psi'(t_0)$ and $\varphi'(t_0)$ exist and $\varphi'(t_0) \neq 0$ then

$$f'(x_0) = \frac{\psi'(t_0)}{\varphi'(t_0)}.$$

Similarly,

$$f''(x_0) = (f')'(x_0) = \left(\frac{\psi'(t)}{\varphi'(t)}\right)'_x (x_0)$$
$$= \frac{\left(\frac{\psi'(t)}{\varphi'(t)}\right)'_t (t_0)}{\varphi'(t_0)} = \frac{\psi''(t_0)\varphi'(t_0) - \psi'(t_0)\varphi''(t_0)}{\varphi'(t_0)^3},$$

where $\varphi'(t_0) \neq 0$. In practice the derivative of a function which is defined parametrically can also exist in the more general case, i.e., not only when $\varphi'(t_0) \neq 0$.

If $\varphi'(t_0) = 0$ then the previous formulas cannot be applied, and we have the following two cases:

1. If $\psi'(t_0) \neq 0$ and $\varphi'(t_0) = 0$ then $f'(x_0)$ does not exist.

2. If $\psi'(t_0) = 0$ and $\varphi'(t_0) = 0$ then $f'(x_0)$ exists if the limit

$$\lim_{\tau\to 0} \frac{\psi(t_0+\tau)-\psi(t_0)}{\varphi(t_0+\tau)-\varphi(t_0)} =: f'(x_0)$$

exists.

**Example 6.35.** Let $x = \sin t, y = t + \cos t, t \in [0, \pi]$, and $t_0 = \pi/2$. Then $\psi'(\pi/2) = 1 - \sin(\pi/2) = 0 = \cos(\pi/2) = \varphi'(\pi/2)$. So $f'(x_0), x_0 = 1$, exists since the limit

$$\lim_{\tau \to 0} \frac{\psi(\pi/2 + \tau) - \psi(\pi/2)}{\varphi(\pi/2 + \tau) - \varphi(\pi/2)} = \lim_{\tau \to 0} \frac{\tau - \sin \tau}{\cos \tau - 1} = -\lim_{\tau \to 0} \frac{\tau(1 - \frac{\sin \tau}{\tau})}{2 \sin^2(\tau/2)} = 0$$

exists.

## 6.2 ▪ Local extrema

**Definition 6.36.** *Let* $f : X \subset \mathbb{R} \to \mathbb{R}$, *and let* $x_0 \in X$ *be an* internal point *of $X$, i.e., there exists $U_\delta(x_0)$ such that $U_\delta(x_0) \subset X$. Then*

1. *$f$ is said to be increasing (decreasing) at the point $x_0$ if for all $x \in U_\delta'(x_0)$ we have*

$$f(x) < f(x_0) \quad (f(x) > f(x_0)) \quad for \, x < x_0,$$

$$f(x) > f(x_0) \quad (f(x) < f(x_0)) \quad for \, x > x_0.$$

2. *$x_0$ is said to be a point of* local minima *(local maxima) if for all $x \in U_\delta(x_0)$ we have $f(x) \geq f(x_0) \, (f(x) \leq f(x_0))$.*

**Theorem 6.37 (Sufficient condition of monotonicity and necessary condition of local extrema).** *Let* $f : X \subset \mathbb{R} \to \mathbb{R}$ *be differentiable at $x_0 \in X$ which is internal to $X$.*

1. *If $f'(x_0) > 0 \, (f'(x_0) < 0)$ then $f$ is increasing (decreasing) at the point $x_0$.*

2. *If $x_0$ is a point of local extrema (local minima or local maxima) of $f$ then $f'(x_0) = 0$.*

*Proof.*

1. Let $f'(x_0) \neq 0$. Then, by definition, for any $\varepsilon > 0$ there exists $\delta > 0$ such that

$$\left| \frac{f(x) - f(x_0)}{x - x_0} - f'(x_0) \right| < \varepsilon$$

or

$$f'(x_0) - \varepsilon < \frac{f(x) - f(x_0)}{x - x_0} < f'(x_0) + \varepsilon$$

for any $x \in U_\delta'(x_0)$. Taking $\varepsilon = |f'(x_0)|/2 > 0$ we obtain

$$f'(x_0) - \frac{|f'(x_0)|}{2} < \frac{f(x) - f(x_0)}{x - x_0} < f'(x_0) + \frac{|f'(x_0)|}{2}.$$

This implies that for $f'(x_0) > 0$ we have

$$\frac{f'(x_0)}{2} < \frac{f(x) - f(x_0)}{x - x_0} < \frac{3f'(x_0)}{2},$$

and for $f'(x_0) < 0$ we have

$$\frac{3f'(x_0)}{2} < \frac{f(x) - f(x_0)}{x - x_0} < \frac{f'(x_0)}{2}.$$

So, for $f'(x_0) > 0$ we obtain

$$\frac{f(x) - f(x_0)}{x - x_0} > 0$$

or

$$\begin{cases} f(x) > f(x_0), & x > x_0, \\ f(x) < f(x_0), & x < x_0. \end{cases}$$

For $f'(x_0) < 0$ we may proceed similarly to get

$$\begin{cases} f(x) < f(x_0), & x > x_0, \\ f(x) > f(x_0), & x < x_0. \end{cases}$$

Thus, $f$ is increasing (decreasing) at the point $x_0$.

2. Let us assume on the contrary that $f'(x_0) \neq 0$. Then either $f'(x_0) > 0$ or $f'(x_0) < 0$. The first part of this theorem leads to the fact that $f$ is increasing or decreasing at the point $x_0$, respectively. Thus, $x_0$ cannot be a point of local extrema. This contradiction proves the second part of this theorem.

**Remark 6.38.** Let $f(x) = x^3$ and $x_0 = 0$. Then $f$ is increasing at $x_0$ and therefore does not have local extrema at $x_0$. But $f'(0) = 0$. This example shows that the first condition of Theorem 6.37 is not necessary and the second condition is not sufficient.

## 6.3 ▪ Lagrange's formula

**Theorem 6.39 (Rolle).** *Let $f \in C[a, b]$ be differentiable on open interval $(a, b)$. If $f(a) = f(b)$ then there is a point $\xi \in (a, b)$ such that $f'(\xi) = 0$.*

**Proof.** Due to Theorem 5.80

$$M = \max_{x \in [a,b]} f(x), \quad m = \min_{x \in [a,b]} f(x)$$

exist. If $M = m$ then $f$ is constant, and thus $f'(\xi) \equiv 0$. If $M > m$ then, due to $f(a) = f(b)$, at least one of the values $M$ or $m$ is attained inside of the interval $(a, b)$, i.e., there is $\xi \in (a, b)$ (possibly not unique) such that $M = f(\xi)$ or $m = f(\xi)$. This means that $\xi$ is a point of local extrema and Theorem 6.37 implies that $f'(\xi) = 0$.

**Example 6.40.**  1. Let $f(x) = |x|, x \in [-1, 1]$. Then $f \in C[-1, 1]$ and $f(-1) = f(1)$. But there is no point $\xi \in (-1, 1)$ such that $f'(\xi) = 0$. The reason is that $f$ is not differentiable at $x = 0 \in (-1, 1)$.

2. Let

$$f(x) = \begin{cases} x, & x \in (0, 1], \\ 1, & x = 0. \end{cases}$$

Then $f$ is differentiable for all $x \in (0, 1), f(0) = f(1)$ but $f'(x) \equiv 1$ for $x \in (0, 1)$. Hence there is no point $\xi \in (0, 1)$ such that $f'(\xi) = 0$. The reason is that $f$ is not continuous on $[0, 1]$.

**Remark 6.41.** Example 6.40 shows that the conditions of Rolle's theorem are sharp.

**Exercise 6.42.** Let $c_j, j = 0, 1, 2, \ldots, n$, be real constants with

$$c_0 + \frac{c_1}{2} + \cdots + \frac{c_n}{n+1} = 0.$$

Prove that the equation

$$c_0 + c_1 x + \cdots + c_n x^n = 0$$

has solutions on the interval $(0, 1)$.

**Theorem 6.43 (Lagrange).** *Let* $f \in C[a, b]$ *be differentiable on an open interval* $(a, b)$. *Then there exists* $\xi \in (a, b)$ *such that*

$$\frac{f(b) - f(a)}{b - a} = f'(\xi)$$

*or* $f(b) - f(a) = f'(\xi)(b - a)$. *This formula is called* Lagrange's formula *or the* mean value formula.

*Proof.* Let us consider the function

$$F(x) := f(x) - f(a) - \frac{f(b) - f(a)}{b - a}(x - a).$$

The function $F$ is continuous on the closed interval $[a, b]$ since $f$ is continuous there. The function $F$ is differentiable on the interval $(a, b)$, and $F(a) = F(b) = 0$. Due to Rolle's theorem there is $\xi \in (a, b)$ such that

$$F'(\xi) = f'(\xi) - \frac{f(b) - f(a)}{b - a} = 0.$$

This yields the claim.

**Corollary 6.44 (Constancy of a function having zero derivative).** *Let* $f'(x) = 0$ *for all* $x \in (a, b)$. *Then* $f(x) \equiv$ *constant on the interval* $(a, b)$.

*Proof.* Let $x_0 \in (a, b)$ be fixed and let $x \in (a, b)$ be arbitrary. Applying Lagrange's formula we obtain

$$\frac{f(x) - f(x_0)}{x - x_0} = f'(\xi), \quad x \neq x_0.$$

Since $f'(\xi) = 0$ everywhere on $(a, b)$, $f(x) = f(x_0)$ for any $x \in (a, b), x \neq x_0$.

**Theorem 6.45 (Cauchy).** *Let* $f, g \in C[a, b]$ *be differentiable on an interval* $(a, b)$. *Then there exists a point* $\xi \in (a, b)$ *such that the Cauchy formula*

$$f'(\xi)(g(b) - g(a)) = g'(\xi)(f(b) - f(a))$$

*holds.*

*Proof.* Let us consider the function

$$F(x) := f(x)(g(b) - g(a)) - g(x)(f(b) - f(a)).$$

The function $F$ is continuous on the closed interval $[a, b]$, since $f$ and $g$ are continuous there, and it is differentiable on the open interval $(a, b)$ with $F(a) = F(b) = f(a)g(b) - g(a)f(b)$. Due to Rolle's theorem there exists $\xi \in (a, b)$ such that

$$F'(\xi) = f'(\xi)(g(b) - g(a)) - g'(\xi)(f(b) - f(a)) = 0.$$

This yields the claim.

**Remark 6.46.** If we assume in Theorem 6.45 in addition that $g'(x) \neq 0$ everywhere on the open interval $(a, b)$ then the Cauchy formula can be rewritten as

$$\frac{f(b) - f(a)}{g(b) - g(a)} = \frac{f'(\xi)}{g'(\xi)}.$$

This is due to the fact that the condition $g'(x) \neq 0$ implies $g(b) \neq g(a)$.

**Exercise 6.47.**     1. Let $f(x) = x^2|x|$. Prove that $f^{(3)}(0)$ does not exist.

2. Let $f : \mathbb{R} \to \mathbb{R}$ satisfy the following condition: there exist $C > 0$ and $\alpha > 1$ such that

$$|f(x) - f(y)| \leq C|x - y|^\alpha, \quad x, y \in \mathbb{R}.$$

   Prove that $f \equiv$ constant.

3. Let $f : [a, b] \to \mathbb{R}$ be a differentiable function satisfying the condition

$$|f'(x)| \leq \gamma|f(x)|, \quad x \in [a, b], \gamma > 0.$$

   Prove that if $f(x) = 0$ at some point $x_0 \in [a, b]$ then $f \equiv 0$ on $[a, b]$. Hint: Prove first that there is $\delta > 0$ such that $f(x) \equiv 0$ for all $x \in [x_0 - \delta, x_0 + \delta]$ and then construct a chain to arbitrary $x' \in [a, b]$.

4. Let $\varphi : \mathbb{R} \to \mathbb{R}$ satisfy the condition

$$|\varphi(x_1) - \varphi(x_2)| \leq L|x_1 - x_2|, \quad x_1, x_2 \in \mathbb{R}, L > 0.$$

   Prove that if $f : [a, b] \to \mathbb{R}$ is differentiable then there is only one solution of the differential equation

$$f'(x) = \varphi(f(x)), \quad x \in [a, b],$$

   with given $f(a) = x_0$. Hint: Use the result of the previous exercise.

5. Let $f, f' \in C[a, b]$. Prove that for any $\varepsilon > 0$ there exists $\delta > 0$ such that

$$\left| \frac{f(x) - f(y)}{x - y} - f'(x) \right| < \varepsilon$$

   for all $x, y \in [a, b]$ and $0 < |x - y| < \delta$.

6. Let

$$f(x) = \begin{cases} \frac{1}{x} - \frac{1}{\sin x}, & x \in (-\pi/2, \pi/2), x \neq 0, \\ 0, & x = 0. \end{cases}$$

   Is this function differentiable at $x = 0$?

7. Let $f \in C(a, b)$. Let us assume that there is a closed interval $[c, d] \subset (a, b)$ such that

   (a) $f$ is differentiable on $(a, b) \setminus [c, d]$,
   (b) $f \equiv$ constant on $[c, d]$,
   (c) the limits

$$\lim_{x \to c-0} f'(x) = c_1, \quad \lim_{x \to d+0} f'(x) = c_2$$

   exist.

   Prove that $f$ is differentiable on the interval $(a, b)$ if and only if $c_1 = c_2$.

8. Let $f''$ exist everywhere on $[a, b]$. Prove that if $f'(a) = f'(b) = 0$ then there exists $\xi \in (a, b)$ such that

$$|f''(\xi)| \geq \frac{4|f(b) - f(a)|}{(b - a)^2}.$$

**The Weierstrass function**   In Weierstrass's original paper the following function was introduced:

$$W_\alpha(x) = \sum_{k=0}^{\infty} b^{-k\alpha} \cos(b^k \pi x), \quad x \in [-1, 1],$$

where $b$ is a positive odd integer such that $b \geq 7, 0 < \alpha < 1$, and $b^{1-\alpha} > 1 + 3\pi/2$. Since the number series $\sum_{k=0}^{\infty} b^{-k\alpha}$ converges, the Weierstrass test (see Exercise 15.48) implies that $W_\alpha \in C[-1, 1]$. But this function is nowhere differentiable. It is not so difficult to show that $W_\alpha$ satisfies the inequality

$$|W_\alpha(x) - W_\alpha(y)| \leq C_\alpha |x - y|^\alpha$$

with the same $0 < \alpha < 1$ as above. The function does not satisfy the inequality

$$|W_\alpha(x) - W_\alpha(y)| \leq C|x - y|,$$

i.e., $W_\alpha$ has no derivative at any point $x \in [-1, 1]$.

# 6.4 ▪ Consequences of Lagrange's formula

**Theorem 6.48 (Criterion of monotonicity for differentiable functions).** *Let $f : (a, b) \to \mathbb{R}$ be differentiable. Then*

1. *$f$ is nondecreasing (nonincreasing) on $(a, b)$ if and only if $f'(x) \geq 0$ ($f'(x) \leq 0$) for all $x \in (a, b)$;*

2. *if $f'(x) > 0$ ($f'(x) < 0$) for all $x \in (a, b)$ then $f$ is increasing (decreasing) in $(a, b)$.*

*Proof.*

1. Let $f'(x) \geq 0$ ($f'(x) \leq 0$) for all $x \in (a, b)$. Then for any $x_1, x_2 \in (a, b)$ such that $x_1 < x_2$ we have by Lagrange's formula that

$$f(x_2) - f(x_1) = f'(\xi)(x_2 - x_1), \quad \xi \in (x_1, x_2).$$

This formula and the above conditions for the first derivative imply that $f(x_1) \leq f(x_2)$ ($f(x_1) \geq f(x_2)$), i.e., $f$ is nondecreasing (nonincreasing) on $(a, b)$.

Conversely, assume that $f$ is nondecreasing (nonincreasing) on $(a, b)$ but there is a point $\xi \in (a, b)$ such that $f'(\xi) < 0$ ($f'(\xi) > 0$). Then by Theorem 6.37 we conclude that $f$ is decreasing (increasing) at the point $\xi$, i.e., there is $U_\delta(\xi) \subset (a, b)$ such that

$$\begin{cases} f(x) > f(\xi), & x < \xi, \quad x \in U_\delta(\xi), \\ f(x) < f(\xi), & x > \xi, \quad x \in U_\delta(\xi) \end{cases}$$

(or $f(x) < f(\xi), x < \xi$, and $f(x) > f(\xi), x > \xi$). This contradicts the fact that $f$ is nondecreasing (nonincreasing) on $(a, b)$.

2. If $f'(x) > 0$ ($f'(x) < 0$) for all $x \in (a, b)$ then the Lagrange's formula

$$f(x_1) - f(x_2) = f'(\xi)(x_2 - x_1)$$

implies that for any $x_1 < x_2$ it follows that $f(x_1) < f(x_2)$ ($f(x_1) > f(x_2)$).

**Remark 6.49.** If we consider the function $f(x) = x^3$ on the interval $(-1, 1)$ then it is increasing there but $f'(0) = 0$. Hence the conditions of part 2 of the latter theorem are only sufficient but not necessary.

**Theorem 6.50 (Passage of derivative through an intermediate value).** *Let $f$ be differentiable on an interval $(a, b)$. Assume also that $f'_+(a)$ and $f'_-(b)$ exist. If $f'_+(a) \neq f'_-(b)$ then for any $\lambda \in (f'_+(a), f'_-(b))$ ($\lambda \in (f'_-(b), f'_+(a))$) there exists $\xi \in (a, b)$ such that $\lambda = f'(\xi)$.*

*Proof.* Let $c = (a + b)/2$ and let

$$\alpha(t) = \begin{cases} a, & a \leq t \leq c, \\ 2t - b, & c \leq t \leq b, \end{cases} \qquad \beta(t) = \begin{cases} 2t - a, & a \leq t \leq c, \\ b, & c \leq t \leq b. \end{cases}$$

It is clear that $a \leq \alpha(t) < \beta(t) \leq b$ for all $t \in (a, b)$. Hence we may define the superposition

$$g(t) := \frac{f(\beta(t)) - f(\alpha(t))}{\beta(t) - \alpha(t)}, \quad t \in (a, b),$$

and obtain that

$$g(a) := \lim_{t \to a+0} g(t) = \lim_{t \to a+0} \frac{f(2t - a) - f(a)}{2t - 2a} = f'_+(a)$$

and

$$g(b) := \lim_{t \to b-0} g(t) = \lim_{t \to b-0} \frac{f(b) - f(2t - b)}{2b - 2t} = f'_-(b).$$

Therefore the function $g$ is continuous on the closed interval $[a, b]$. Using Theorem 5.54 we may conclude that for any $\lambda \in (g(a), g(b))$ ($\lambda \in (g(b), g(a))$) there exists $t_0 \in (a, b)$ such that

$$\lambda = g(t_0) = \frac{f(\beta(t_0)) - f(\alpha(t_0))}{\beta(t_0) - \alpha(t_0)}.$$

Since $\alpha(t_0) < \beta(t_0)$ and $[\alpha(t_0), \beta(t_0)] \subset (a, b)$, applying Lagrange's formula we have that there is a point $\xi \in (\alpha(t_0), \beta(t_0)) \subset (a, b)$ such that

$$\lambda = \frac{f(\beta(t_0)) - f(\alpha(t_0))}{\beta(t_0) - \alpha(t_0)} = f'(\xi).$$

This proves the theorem.

**Corollary 6.51 (Breakpoints of the derivative).** *Let $f$ be as in Theorem 6.50. Then the function $g(x) := f'(x)$ may have breakpoints only of the second kind.*

*Proof.* Let $x_0 \in (a, b)$ be a point of removable singularity for $g$, i.e.,

$$g(x_0 - 0) = g(x_0 + 0) \neq g(x_0).$$

Then there will be a gap in the set of values for $g(x) = f'(x)$ of the form $(g(x_0 - 0), g(x_0))$ or $(g(x_0), g(x_0 - 0))$. This contradicts Theorem 6.50.

If we assume now that $x_0$ is a breakpoint of the first kind then $g(x_0 \pm 0)$ exist but $g(x_0 - 0) \neq g(x_0 + 0)$. In that case there is also a gap in the set of values for $g(x) = f'(x)$ (it does not matter where $g(x_0)$ is located). Again this contradicts Theorem 6.50.

**Corollary 6.52 (Limits of the derivative from left and right).** *Let $f$ be continuous at $x_0 \in$ $(a, b)$ and let the limits*

$$\lim_{x \to x_0 - 0} f'(x) =: f'(x_0 - 0), \qquad \lim_{x \to x_0 + 0} f'(x) =: f'(x_0 + 0)$$

*exist. Then there exists $f'_\pm(x_0)$ and $f'_\pm(x_0) = f'(x_0 \pm 0)$.*

***Proof.*** Let, for example, $f'(x_0 + 0) = \lim_{x \to x_0 + 0} f'(x)$. By Lagrange's formula

$$\lim_{h \to +0} \frac{f(x_0 + h) - f(x_0)}{h} = \lim_{h \to +0} f'(\xi_h),$$

where $x_0 < \xi_h < x_0 + h$. If $h \to +0$ then $\xi_h \to x_0 + 0$, and thus $f'_+(x_0)$ exists and $f'(x_0 + 0) = \lim_{h \to +0} f'(\xi_h) = f'_+(x_0)$.

**Example 6.53.** Let

$$f(x) = \begin{cases} x^2 \cos(1/x), & x \neq 0, \\ 0, & x = 0. \end{cases}$$

Then $f'(0) = 0 = f'_\pm(0)$. For $x \neq 0$ we have

$$f'(x) = 2x \cos(1/x) + \sin(1/x).$$

Hence, it is easy to see that $\lim_{x \to \pm 0} f'(x)$ do not exist. This shows that Corollary 6.52 is not valid in the opposite direction.

There are more consequences of Lagrange's formula.

**Theorem 6.54 (Uniform continuity for functions with bounded derivative).** *Let $f : X \subset \mathbb{R} \to \mathbb{R}$ be differentiable on $X$. If $f'(x)$ is bounded on $X$ then $f$ is uniformly continuous on $X$.*

***Proof.*** Let us first note that the set $X$ must be such that for any points $x' \neq x''$ from $X$, the interval $[x', x''] \subset X$ ($[x'', x'] \subset X$).

Since $f'$ is bounded, there exists $M > 0$ such that $|f'(x)| \leq M$ for any $x \in X$. Let $\varepsilon > 0$. Applying Lagrange's formula we obtain that for any $x', x'' \in X$ with $|x' - x''| < \delta = \varepsilon/M$ we have

$$|f(x') - f(x'')| = |f'(\xi)||x' - x''| < M\delta = \varepsilon.$$

So $f$ is uniformly continuous on $X$.

**Example 6.55.**    1. Let $f(x) = x^\alpha$ and $X = [1, \infty)$. Then for $\alpha \leq 1$ the function $f$ is uniformly continuous on $X$, but for $\alpha > 1$ it is not. Indeed, if $\alpha \leq 1$ then we have that

$$|f'(x)| = |\alpha||x^{\alpha - 1}| \leq |\alpha|, \quad x \in [1, \infty).$$

By Theorem 6.54 $f$ is uniformly continuous.

If $\alpha > 1$ then we consider the sequences

$$x'_n = (n + 1)^{1/\alpha}, \quad x''_n = n^{1/\alpha}.$$

Now

$$x'_n - x''_n = n^{1/\alpha}((1 + 1/n)^{1/\alpha} - 1) = (1/n)^{1 - 1/\alpha} \frac{(1 + 1/n)^{1/\alpha} - 1}{1/n}.$$

So

$$\lim_{n\to\infty}(x_n' - x_n'') = \lim_{n\to\infty}(1/n)^{1-1/\alpha}\lim_{n\to\infty}\frac{(1+1/n)^{1/\alpha}-1}{1/n} = 0\cdot\frac{1}{\alpha} = 0$$

but $|f(x_n') - f(x_n'')| = 1$. Therefore $f$ is not uniformly continuous on $X$.

2. Let $f(x) = x^\beta\sin(x^\alpha)$, $X = [1,\infty)$, and $\alpha > 0$. It is easy to see that

$$f'(x) = \beta x^{\beta-1}\sin(x^\alpha) + \alpha x^\beta\cos(x^\alpha)x^{\alpha-1}.$$

Thus

$$|f'(x)| \le |\beta||x|^{\beta-1} + \alpha|x|^{\alpha+\beta-1} \le |\beta| + \alpha$$

for $\beta + \alpha \le 1$ and $\alpha > 0$. Hence $f$ is uniformly continuous on $X$ for $\beta + \alpha \le 1$ and $\alpha > 0$.

3. Let $f(x) = x^\beta\log x$ and $X = [1,\infty)$. Then for $\beta < 1$ the function $f$ is uniformly continuous. Indeed,

$$f'(x) = \beta x^{\beta-1}\log x + x^{\beta-1}$$

implies that

$$|f'(x)| \le C_\beta|\beta| + 1.$$

Here the constant $C_\beta$ appears due to the fact that

$$\lim_{x\to\infty}\frac{\log x}{x^{1-\beta}} = 0, \quad \beta < 1,$$

implies

$$0 \le \frac{\log x}{x^{1-\beta}} \le C_\beta, \quad x \in [1,\infty).$$

**Exercise 6.56.**    1. Investigate the function from part 2 of the latter example with respect to uniform continuity for $\alpha + \beta > 1$ and $\beta > 0$.

2. Prove that the function from part 3 of the latter example is not uniformly continuous for $\beta \ge 1$.

3. Is it true that $f$ defined on $[1,\infty)$ is uniformly continuous if and only if there exist $c_1, c_2 > 0$ such that

$$|f(x') - f(x'')| \le c_1|x' - x''| + c_2$$

for all $x', x'' \in [1,\infty)$?

**Theorem 6.57 (l'Hôpital I).** *Let $f$ and $g$ be differentiable in $U_\delta'(a)$ ($|x| > A$) and let $g'(x) \ne 0$ there. Let also*

$$\lim_{x\to a(\infty)}f(x) = \lim_{x\to a(\infty)}g(x) = 0.$$

*If the limit*

$$\lim_{x\to a(\infty)}\frac{f'(x)}{g'(x)}$$

*exists (finite or infinite) then the limit*

$$\lim_{x\to a(\infty)}\frac{f(x)}{g(x)}$$

*exists too (finite or infinite) and these two limits are equal.*

***Proof.*** First let $a \neq \infty$, and let $\{x_n\}_{n=1}^{\infty}$ be an arbitrary sequence such that

$$\lim_{n \to \infty} x_n = a, \quad x_n \neq a.$$

By the Cauchy formula (Theorem 6.45) we have, defining $f(a) := 0 =: g(a)$, that

$$\frac{f(x_n)}{g(x_n)} = \frac{f(x_n) - f(a)}{g(x_n) - g(a)} = \frac{f'(\xi_n)}{g'(\xi_n)}.$$

Since $\lim_{n \to \infty} x_n = a$, $\lim_{n \to \infty} \xi_n = a$ also. Therefore the limit

$$\lim_{n \to \infty} \frac{f(x_n)}{g(x_n)} = \lim_{n \to \infty} \frac{f'(\xi_n)}{g'(\xi_n)}$$

exists (finite or infinite) because the limit on the right-hand side exists (finite or infinite). Since $x_n$ was arbitrary, we obtain the result for $a \neq \infty$.

If $a = \infty$ then the proof can be reduced to the previous one. Indeed,

$$\lim_{x \to \infty} \frac{f(x)}{g(x)} = \lim_{t \to 0} \frac{f(1/t)}{g(1/t)} = \lim_{t \to 0} \frac{(f(1/t))_t'}{(g(1/t))_t'} = \lim_{t \to 0} \frac{-f'(1/t)/t^2}{-g'(1/t)/t^2}$$

$$= \lim_{t \to 0} \frac{f'(1/t)}{g'(1/t)} = \lim_{x \to \infty} \frac{f'(x)}{g'(x)}$$

if the latter limit exists (finite or infinite). This finishes the proof.

**Example 6.58.** Let $f(x) = x^2 \cos(1/x), x \neq 0$, and $g(x) = x$. Then

$$\lim_{x \to 0} \frac{f(x)}{g(x)} = \lim_{x \to 0} x \cos(1/x) = 0.$$

If we want to use the l'Hôpital I rule then we need to check the limit

$$\lim_{x \to 0} \frac{f'(x)}{g'(x)} = \lim_{x \to 0} (2x \cos(1/x) + \sin(1/x)).$$

But the latter limit does not exist. Thus, the l'Hôpital I rule is only a sufficient but not necessary condition for existence of the limit.

**Theorem 6.59 (l'Hôpital II).** *Let $f$ and $g$ be differentiable in $U_\delta'(a)$ ($|x| > A$) and let $g'(x) \neq 0$ there. Let also*

$$\lim_{x \to a(\infty)} f(x) = \lim_{x \to a(\infty)} g(x) = \infty.$$

*If the limit*

$$\lim_{x \to a(\infty)} \frac{f'(x)}{g'(x)}$$

*exists (finite or infinite) then the limit*

$$\lim_{x \to a(\infty)} \frac{f(x)}{g(x)}$$

*exists too (finite or infinite) and these two limits are equal.*

***Proof.*** First let $a \neq \infty$ and let $\{x_n\}_{n=1}^{\infty}$ be an arbitrary sequence such that

$$\lim_{n \to \infty} x_n = a, \quad x_n \neq a.$$

We may also assume without loss of generality that $x_n \neq x_m$. By the Cauchy formula (Theorem 6.45) we obtain for $n \neq m$ that

$$\frac{f(x_n) - f(x_m)}{g(x_n) - g(x_m)} = \frac{f'(\xi_{nm})}{g'(\xi_{nm})} = \frac{f(x_n)}{g(x_n)} \frac{1 - f(x_m)/f(x_n)}{1 - g(x_m)/g(x_n)}$$

or

$$\frac{f(x_n)}{g(x_n)} = \frac{f'(\xi_{nm})}{g'(\xi_{nm})} \frac{1 - g(x_m)/g(x_n)}{1 - f(x_m)/f(x_n)}.$$

If

$$\lim_{x \to a} \frac{f'(x)}{g'(x)} = b \neq \infty$$

then for any $\varepsilon > 0$ there exists $n_0 \in \mathbb{N}$ such that

$$\left| \frac{f'(\xi_{nm})}{g'(\xi_{nm})} - b \right| < \varepsilon/2, \quad n, m \geq n_0.$$

Now let $m \geq n_0$ and be fixed. We may choose $n > n_0$ so large that

$$\left| \frac{1 - g(x_m)/g(x_n)}{1 - f(x_m)/f(x_n)} - 1 \right| < \frac{\varepsilon/2}{|b| + \varepsilon/2}$$

since $\lim_{x \to a} f(x) = \lim_{x \to a} g(x) = \infty$. These two facts imply that

$$\left| \frac{f(x_n)}{g(x_n)} - b \right| \leq \left| \frac{f'(\xi_{nm})}{g'(\xi_{nm})} - b \right| + \left| \frac{f'(\xi_{nm})}{g'(\xi_{nm})} \right| \left| \frac{1 - g(x_m)/g(x_n)}{1 - f(x_m)/f(x_n)} - 1 \right|$$

$$< \varepsilon/2 + (|b| + \varepsilon/2) \frac{\varepsilon/2}{|b| + \varepsilon/2} = \varepsilon.$$

If

$$\lim_{x \to a} \frac{f'(x)}{g'(x)} = \infty$$

then it is equivalent to

$$\lim_{x \to a} \frac{g'(x)}{f'(x)} = 0.$$

Thus, by the proof above we have that

$$\lim_{x \to a} \frac{g(x)}{f(x)} = 0$$

or

$$\lim_{x \to a} \frac{f(x)}{g(x)} = \infty.$$

The case $a = \infty$ can be considered similarly as in the proof of l'Hôpital I (see Theorem 6.57).

**Example 6.60.**     1. We show that for any $k > 0$ and $a > 1$ it follows that

$$\lim_{x \to \infty} \frac{x^k}{a^x} = 0.$$

Indeed, applying the l'Hôpital II rule $n + 1$ times, where $n = [k]$, we obtain

$$\lim_{x \to \infty} \frac{x^k}{a^x} = \lim_{x \to \infty} \frac{kx^{k-1}}{a^x \log a} = \cdots = \lim_{x \to \infty} \frac{k(k-1)\cdots(k-n)x^{k-n-1}}{a^x (\log a)^{n+1}} = 0$$

since $k < n + 1$.

2. We show that for any fixed $\varepsilon > 0$ it follows that

$$\lim_{x \to \infty} \frac{\log x}{x^\varepsilon} = 0.$$

Indeed, by the l'Hôpital II rule we have

$$\lim_{x \to \infty} \frac{\log x}{x^\varepsilon} = \lim_{x \to \infty} \frac{1/x}{\varepsilon x^{\varepsilon-1}} = \frac{1}{\varepsilon} \lim_{x \to \infty} \frac{1}{x^\varepsilon} = 0.$$

3. Let $\varphi(x)$ and $\psi(x)$ be two functions such that

$$\lim_{x \to a(\infty)} \varphi(x) = 1, \qquad \lim_{x \to a(\infty)} \psi(x) = \infty.$$

What can we say about the limit

$$\lim_{x \to a(\infty)} \varphi(x)^{\psi(x)}?$$

Since $\log \varphi(x)^{\psi(x)} = \frac{\log \varphi(x)}{1/\psi(x)}$, we may apply the l'Hôpital I rule and obtain that if

$$\lim_{x \to a(\infty)} \frac{\log \varphi(x)}{1/\psi(x)}$$

exists then

$$\lim_{x \to a(\infty)} \varphi(x)^{\psi(x)} = \exp\left( \lim_{x \to a(\infty)} \frac{\log \varphi(x)}{1/\psi(x)} \right).$$

4. Let $\varphi(x)$ and $\psi(x)$ be two functions such that

$$\lim_{x \to a(\infty)} \varphi(x) = \infty, \qquad \lim_{x \to a(\infty)} \psi(x) = 0.$$

What can we say about the limit

$$\lim_{x \to a(\infty)} \varphi(x)^{\psi(x)}?$$

In this case we may apply the l'Hôpital II rule and obtain that

$$\lim_{x \to a(\infty)} \varphi(x)^{\psi(x)} = \exp\left( \lim_{x \to a(\infty)} \frac{\log \varphi(x)}{1/\psi(x)} \right)$$

if the limit exists.

5. Let $\varphi(x)$ and $\psi(x)$ be two functions such that

$$\lim_{x \to a(\infty)} \varphi(x) = \infty, \qquad \lim_{x \to a(\infty)} \psi(x) = \infty.$$

What can we say about the limit

$$\lim_{x \to a(\infty)} (\varphi(x) - \psi(x))?$$

We write

$$\varphi(x) - \psi(x) = \frac{1 - \psi(x)/\varphi(x)}{1/\varphi(x)}.$$

If

$$\lim_{x \to a(\infty)} \frac{\psi(x)}{\varphi(x)} = 1$$

(it can be checked by the l'Hôpital II rule) then the existence of the limit

$$\lim_{x \to a(\infty)} (\varphi(x) - \psi(x)) = \lim_{x \to a(\infty)} \frac{1 - \psi(x)/\varphi(x)}{1/\varphi(x)}$$

can be investigated by the l'Hôpital I rule.

6. It is easy to see that

$$\lim_{x \to \infty} \frac{2x^2 + x^2 \cos x}{x^3} = 0.$$

But it cannot be obtained by the l'Hôpital II rule since its application leads to the limit

$$\lim_{x \to \infty} \frac{4x + 2x \cos x - x^2 \sin x}{3x^2},$$

which does not exist.

**Exercise 6.61.**     1. Show that $\lim_{x \to \infty} x^{1/x} = 1$.

2. Show that $\lim_{x \to +0} x^x = 1$.

3. Show that

$$\lim_{x \to a(\infty)} \varphi(x)^{\psi(x)} = 0$$

if $\varphi(x) > 0, \lim_{x \to a(\infty)} \varphi(x) = 0$, and $\lim_{x \to a(\infty)} \psi(x) = \infty$.

4. Let $f$ have a second derivative. Show that

$$\lim_{h \to 0} \frac{f(a+h) - 2f(a) + f(a-h)}{h^2} = f''(a).$$

# Chapter 7

# Taylor's expansion and its applications

In this chapter, Taylor's formula is proved in the most general form, with the remainder in the Schlömilch–Roche form. The concept of convexity is introduced and with its help many classical inequalities are proved, such as the inequalities of Young, Hölder, Minkowskii, and some others. These considerations make it possible to quite effectively study graphs of real functions.

**Theorem 7.1 (Taylor's formula with remainder in the form of Schlömilch–Roche).** *Let $f$ be differentiable $n + 1$ times, $n = 0, 1, 2, \ldots$, in $U'_\delta(a)$ and continuously differentiable $n$ times in $U_\delta(a)$. Then for any $p > 0$ there is $\xi \in U'_\delta(a)$ such that*

$$f(x) = \sum_{j=0}^{n} \frac{f^{(j)}(a)}{j!}(x - a)^j + R_{n+1}(x, \xi, p), \quad x \in U_\delta(a),$$

*where*

$$R_{n+1}(x, \xi, p) = \left(\frac{x - a}{x - \xi}\right)^p \frac{(x - \xi)^{n+1}}{n!p} f^{(n+1)}(\xi)$$

*is called the remainder in the form of Schlömilch–Roche.*

***Proof.*** Let $x \in U'_\delta(a)$ (the case $x = a$ is trivial and not considered). Let

$$p_n(x, a) = \sum_{j=0}^{n} \frac{f^{(j)}(a)}{j!}(x - a)^j.$$

We may assume for definiteness and without loss of generality that $x > a$. Hence, for $t \in [a, x]$ the function

$$\varphi(t) := f(x) - p_n(x, t) - (x - t)^p \frac{R_{n+1}(x)}{(x - a)^p}$$

is well-defined, where $p > 0$ and $R_{n+1}(x) := f(x) - p_n(x, a)$.

We check that the function $\varphi$ satisfies all conditions of Rolle's theorem (Theorem 6.39). Indeed, $\varphi$ is clearly continuous on $[a, x]$, $\varphi$ is differentiable on the open interval $(a, x)$, and $\varphi(a) = \varphi(x) = 0$. Therefore, by Rolle's theorem there exists $\xi \in (a, x)$ such that $\varphi'(\xi) = 0$ or

$$-(p_n(x, t))'_t|_{t=\xi} + p(x - \xi)^{p-1} \frac{R_{n+1}(x)}{(x - a)^p} = 0$$

or

$$-f'(\xi) - \sum_{j=1}^{n} \frac{f^{(j+1)}(\xi)}{j!}(x-\xi)^j + \sum_{j=1}^{n} \frac{f^{(j)}(\xi)}{(j-1)!}(x-\xi)^{j-1} + p(x-\xi)^{p-1}\frac{R_{n+1}(x)}{(x-a)^p} = 0$$

or

$$-f'(\xi) - \sum_{j=1}^{n} \frac{f^{(j+1)}(\xi)}{j!}(x-\xi)^j + \sum_{j=0}^{n-1} \frac{f^{(j+1)}(\xi)}{j!}(x-\xi)^j + p(x-\xi)^{p-1}\frac{R_{n+1}(x)}{(x-a)^p} = 0.$$

So

$$-\frac{f^{(n+1)}(\xi)}{n!}(x-\xi)^n + p(x-\xi)^{p-1}\frac{R_{n+1}(x)}{(x-a)^p} = 0.$$

The claimed expression for $R_{n+1}$ follows by rearranging.

Choosing $p = n+1$ and $p = 1$, respectively, we obtain the following special cases.

**Corollary 7.2 (The remainder in the form of Lagrange).**

$$R_{n+1}^{L}(x,\xi) = \frac{f^{(n+1)}(\xi)}{(n+1)!}(x-a)^{n+1}.$$

**Corollary 7.3 (The remainder in the form of Cauchy).**

$$R_{n+1}^{C}(x,\xi) = \left(\frac{x-\xi}{x-a}\right)^n \frac{f^{(n+1)}(\xi)}{n!}(x-a)^{n+1}$$

$$= (1-\theta)^n \frac{f^{(n+1)}(a+\theta(x-a))}{n!}(x-a)^{n+1},$$

*where* $0 < \theta < 1$.

**Theorem 7.4 (Taylor's formula with remainder in the form of Peano).** *Let $f$ be differentiable $n-1$ times in $U_\delta(a)$, $n = 1, 2, \ldots$, and $n$ times at the point $a$. Then*

$$f(x) = \sum_{j=0}^{n} \frac{f^{(j)}(a)}{j!}(x-a)^j + o((x-a)^n), \quad x \to a.$$

***Proof.*** We proceed by induction with respect to $n$. If $n = 1$ then the conditions of this theorem say that $f$ is continuous in $U_\delta(a)$ and differentiable at $a$. Denoting

$$R_1(x,a) := f(x) - \sum_{j=0}^{1} \frac{f^{(j)}(a)}{j!}(x-a)^j = f(x) - f(a) - f'(a)(x-a)$$

we have

$$\lim_{x \to a} \frac{R_1(x,a)}{x-a} = \lim_{x \to a} \left(\frac{f(x)-f(a)}{x-a} - f'(a)\right) = 0$$

due to differentiability of $f$ at $a$. So $R_1(x,a) = o(x-a)$ as $x \to a$.

Let us assume that

$$R_n(x,a) := f(x) - \sum_{j=0}^{n} \frac{f^{(j)}(a)}{j!}(x-a)^j = o((x-a)^n), \quad x \to a.$$

Let $f$ be differentiable $n$ times in $U_\delta(a)$ and $n+1$ times differentiable at $a$. Our task is to show that

$$R_{n+1}(x,a) := f(x) - \sum_{j=0}^{n+1} \frac{f^{(j)}(a)}{j!}(x-a)^j = o((x-a)^{n+1}), \quad x \to a.$$

It is easy to see that $R_{n+1}(x,a)$ is differentiable in $U_\delta(a)$ at least once, since $n \geq 1$. Thus we have

$$R'_{n+1}(x,a) = f'(x) - \sum_{j=1}^{n+1} \frac{f^{(j)}(a)}{(j-1)!}(x-a)^{j-1} = f'(x) - \sum_{j=0}^{n} \frac{(f')^{(j)}(a)}{j!}(x-a)^j.$$

The induction hypotheses leads to the fact that $f'$ satisfies all of these conditions. Hence

$$R'_{n+1}(x,a) = o((x-a)^n), \quad x \to a.$$

Using Lagrange's formula we obtain

$$R_{n+1}(x,a) = R_{n+1}(x,a) - R_{n+1}(a,a) = R'_{n+1}(\xi,a)(x-a) = o((x-a)^{n+1})$$

as $x \to a$ since $\xi \in (a,x)$ (or $\xi \in (x,a)$). Theorem 7.4 is now completely proved by induction.

**Definition 7.5.** *If $a = 0$ then the Taylor's formula with all known remainders is called the Maclaurin formula.*

**Example 7.6.**     1. Let $f(x) = e^x$ and $a = 0$. Then $f^{(j)}(0) = 1$ for $j = 0,1,\ldots$ and we have

$$e^x = \sum_{j=0}^{n} \frac{x^j}{j!} + R_{n+1}(x),$$

where the remainder is

(a) Lagrange's form

$$R_{n+1}^L(x) = \frac{e^{\theta \cdot x}}{(n+1)!} x^{n+1}, \quad 0 < \theta < 1,$$

(b) Cauchy's form

$$R_{n+1}^C(x) = \frac{(1-\theta)^n e^{\theta \cdot x}}{n!} x^{n+1}, \quad 0 < \theta < 1,$$

(c) Peano's form

$$R_n^P(x) = o(x^n), \quad x \to 0.$$

It must be mentioned that $\theta$'s in (a) and (b) are different.

2. Let $f(x) = \sin x$ and $a = 0$. Then $f^{(j)}(x) = \sin(x + j\pi/2)$ for $j = 0,1,\ldots$ and we have

$$f^{(j)}(0) = \begin{cases} 0, & j = 2k, \\ (-1)^k, & j = 2k+1. \end{cases}$$

Thus,

$$\sin x = \sum_{k=0}^{n} (-1)^k \frac{x^{2k+1}}{(2k+1)!} + R_{2n+3}(x)$$

(since $\sin^{(2n+2)}(0) = 0$), where the remainder is

(a) Lagrange's form

$$R_{2n+3}^{L}(x) = \frac{\sin(\theta x + 3\pi/2 + n\pi)}{(2n+3)!}x^{2n+3} = \frac{(-1)^n \cos(\theta x)}{(2n+3)!}x^{2n+3},$$

where $0 < \theta < 1$,

(b) Cauchy's form

$$R_{2n+3}^{C}(x) = (1 - \theta)^{2n+2}\frac{\cos(\theta x)}{(2n+2)!}(-1)^{n+1}x^{2n+3}, \quad 0 < \theta < 1,$$

(c) Peano's form

$$R_{2n+2}^{P}(x) = o(x^{2n+2}), \quad x \to 0.$$

3. Let $f(x) = \log(1 + x)$ and $a = 0$. Then

$$f^{(j)}(x) = \frac{(-1)^{j-1}(j-1)!}{(1+x)^j}$$

so that

$$f^{(j)}(0) = (-1)^{j-1}(j-1)!, \quad j = 1, 2, \ldots, f(0) = 0.$$

Thus,

$$\log(1 + x) = \sum_{j=1}^{n}(-1)^{j-1}\frac{x^j}{j} + R_{n+1}(x),$$

where the remainder is

(a) Lagrange's form

$$R_{n+1}^{L}(x) = \frac{(-1)^n}{n+1}\frac{x^{n+1}}{(1+\theta x)^{n+1}}, \quad 0 < \theta < 1,$$

(b) Cauchy's form

$$R_{n+1}^{C}(x) = (-1)^n\frac{(1-\theta)^n}{(1+\theta x)^{n+1}}x^{n+1}, \quad 0 < \theta < 1,$$

(c) Peano's form

$$R_n^{P}(x) = o(x^n), \quad x \to 0.$$

**Exercise 7.7.** Obtain the Maclaurin's expansions with the remainders of Lagrange's, Cauchy's, and Peano's forms for the functions

1. $f(x) = \cos x$,

2. $f(x) = (1 + x)^\alpha$,

3. $f(x) = \arctan x$.

**Exercise 7.8.**    1. Show that

$$e = 2 + \frac{1}{2!} + \cdots + \frac{1}{n!} + R_{n+1}, \quad n = 2, 3, \ldots,$$

where $|R_{n+1}| < 3/(n+1)!$.

2. Using part 1 show that e is an irrational number.

3. Prove that

$$\lim_{n \to \infty} n \left[ \left( 1 + \frac{1}{n} \right)^n - e \right] = -\frac{e}{2}$$

and

$$\lim_{n \to \infty} n \left[ \left( 1 + \frac{1}{n} \right)^{n+1} - e \right] = \frac{e}{2}.$$

Hint: Use the Maclaurin formula for $e^x$ and $\log(1+x)$.

We are now in position to consider the graphs of functions and their properties. We recall that the graph of the function $f$ is defined as

$$\Gamma(f) = \{(x; y) \in \mathbb{R}^2 : x \in X \subset \mathbb{R}, y = f(x)\}.$$

**Definition 7.9.** *Let $f : X \subset \mathbb{R} \to \mathbb{R}$. The points of $X$ where $f'(x) = 0$ or $f'(x)$ does not exist (but $f$ is continuous there) are called* stationary points.

**Theorem 7.10 (Sufficient conditions of local extrema).** *Let $f$ be continuous on an open interval $(a, b)$ and differentiable there with the exception of finite number of points. Let $x_0 \in (a, b)$ be stationary. If there exists $U_\delta(x_0) \subset (a, b)$ such that*

$$\operatorname{sgn} f'(x) = \operatorname{sgn}(x - x_0)$$

*or*

$$\operatorname{sgn} f'(x) = -\operatorname{sgn}(x - x_0) = \operatorname{sgn}(x_0 - x)$$

*for all $x \in U_\delta'(x_0)$ then $x_0$ is a point of local minima or local maxima, respectively.*

**Proof.** Let $x_0$ be stationary and let $x \in U_\delta'(x_0)$. Applying Lagrange's formula we have

$$f(x) - f(x_0) = f'(\xi)(x - x_0),$$

where $\xi \in (x_0, x)$ (or $\xi \in (x, x_0)$). This implies immediately the result of the theorem.

**Remark 7.11.** If $f'$ does not change its sign across stationary point $x_0$ then $f$ increases (decreases) at this point.

**Example 7.12.**    1. Let $f$ be given by

$$f(x) = \begin{cases} (x - x_0)^2 + 1, & x \leq x_0, \\ 1, & x > x_0. \end{cases}$$

Then $f'(x) < 0$ for $x < x_0$ and $f'(x) = 0$ for $x \geq x_0$. The point $x_0$ is a point of local extrema (but not strict).

2. Let

$$f(x) = \begin{cases} e^{-1/x}, & x \neq 0, \\ 0, & x = 0. \end{cases}$$

Then $f$ has a local minima at $x = 0$. But $x = 0$ is not stationary since $f$ is not continuous at $x = 0$. The first derivative

$$f'(x) = e^{-1/x}/x^2, \quad x \neq 0,$$

is positive.

3. Let

$$f(x) = \begin{cases} \frac{x}{1+e^{1/x}}, & x \neq 0, \\ 0, & x = 0. \end{cases}$$

Since $\lim_{x \to \pm 0} f(x) = 0$, $f$ is continuous at $x = 0$. But the first derivative $f'(0)$ does not exist since $f'_+(0) = 0$ and $f'_-(0) = 1$. Thus, $x = 0$ is stationary. Moreover, for $x \neq 0$ we have

$$f'(x) = \frac{1 + e^{1/x} + e^{1/x}/x}{(1 + e^{1/x})^2} > 0,$$

and one sees easily that $x = 0$ is not a point of local extrema. Compare this with the previous example.

4. Let $f(x) = x^{2/3}, x \in (-1, 1)$. This function is continuous everywhere on $(-1, 1)$. What is more, $f'(0)$ does not exist since $f'_\pm(0) = \pm\infty$. So $x = 0$ is stationary. However, $f'(x)$ changes its sign across $x = 0$. Therefore $x = 0$ is a point of local minima.

**Theorem 7.13 (Sufficient conditions of local extrema II).** *Let $f : (a, b) \to \mathbb{R}$ be differentiable $n$ times in $U_\delta(x_0)$, $x_0 \in (a, b)$, and $n+1$ times differentiable at the point $x_0$, where $n = 1, 3, 5, \ldots$. If*

$$f'(x_0) = f''(x_0) = \cdots = f^{(n)}(x_0) = 0$$

*but $f^{(n+1)}(x_0) \neq 0$ then $x_0$ is a point of local maxima if $f^{(n+1)}(x_0) < 0$ and a point of local minima if $f^{(n+1)}(x_0) > 0$.*

**Proof.** First let $n = 1$ so that $f'(x_0) = 0$. If $f''(x_0) > 0$ ($f''(x_0) < 0$) then $f'$ increases (decreases) at the point $x_0$, i.e., $f'(x) < f'(x_0) = 0$ for $x < x_0$ and $f'(x) > f'(x_0) = 0$ for $x > x_0$ ($f'(x) > f'(x_0) = 0$ for $x < x_0$ and $f'(x) < f'(x_0) = 0$ for $x > x_0$). This is equivalent to sgn $f'(x) = \text{sgn}(x - x_0)$ (sgn $f'(x) = \text{sgn}(x_0 - x)$). The result follows from Theorem 7.10.

If $n \geq 3$ and it is odd then we have (by hypothesis) that $f^{(n)}(x) < 0$ ($f^{(n)}(x) > 0$) for $x < x_0$ and $f^{(n)}(x) > 0$ ($f^{(n)}(x) < 0$) for $x > x_0$. Applying Taylor's formula with the remainder in Lagrange's form to the function $f'$ at the point $x_0$ we obtain

$$f'(x) = f'(x_0) + \cdots + \frac{f^{(n-1)}(x_0)}{(n-2)!}(x - x_0)^{n-2} + \frac{f^{(n)}(\xi)}{(n-1)!}(x - x_0)^{n-1}$$

$$= \frac{f^{(n)}(\xi)}{(n-1)!}(x - x_0)^{n-1}, \quad \xi = x_0 + \theta(x - x_0), \quad 0 < \theta < 1,$$

where $(x - x_0)^{n-1} > 0$ for all $x \neq x_0$ since $n - 1$ is even. That's why across $x = x_0$ we have that sgn $f'(x) = \text{sgn } f^{(n)}(\xi)$. This implies the result due to Theorem 7.10.

Along with the stationary points of functions which were studied above there are so-called inflection points of functions which play an essential role in the study of functions and their graphs. These points are closely related to convexity and concavity of functions which allow one to obtain many classical inequalities (see below).

**Definition 7.14.** *A function* $f : (a, b) \to \mathbb{R}$ *is said to be* convex *on the interval* $(a, b)$ *if*

$$f(\lambda x_1 + (1 - \lambda) x_2) \leq \lambda f(x_1) + (1 - \lambda) f(x_2)$$

*for any* $x_1, x_2 \in (a, b)$ *and for any* $\lambda \in [0, 1]$. *If the latter inequality holds in the opposite direction then* $f$ *is said to be* concave.

*If the inequality is strict for any* $x_1 \neq x_2$ *and* $\lambda \in (0, 1)$ *then* $f$ *is said to be* strictly convex (strictly concave).

The inequalities in the latter definition can be rewritten equivalently in the following form. Let $x_1 < x_2$ and $x \in (x_1, x_2)$. Then with some $0 < \lambda < 1$ we have $x = \lambda x_1 + (1 - \lambda) x_2$ if and only if

$$\lambda = \frac{x - x_2}{x_1 - x_2}, \quad 1 - \lambda = \frac{x_1 - x}{x_1 - x_2}.$$

Then the condition for convexity reads

$$f(x) \leq \frac{x - x_2}{x_1 - x_2} f(x_1) + \frac{x_1 - x}{x_1 - x_2} f(x_2)$$

or

$$\frac{f(x_1) - f(x)}{x_1 - x} \leq \frac{f(x) - f(x_2)}{x - x_2}.$$

The condition for concavity is then

$$\frac{f(x_1) - f(x)}{x_1 - x} \geq \frac{f(x) - f(x_2)}{x - x_2}.$$

This equivalent formulation allows us to obtain the following important criterion.

**Theorem 7.15 (Criterion of convexity).** *Let* $f : (a, b) \to \mathbb{R}$ *be differentiable. Then* $f$ *is*

1. *convex (concave) on the interval* $(a, b)$ *if and only if its derivative* $f'$ *is nondecreasing (nonincreasing) there,*

2. *strictly convex (strictly concave) on the interval* $(a, b)$ *if and only if its derivative* $f'$ *is increasing (decreasing) there.*

***Proof.*** The proof of this criterion is literally the same for all types of convexity (concavity), strict or nonstrict. We consider for definiteness and without loss of generality the proof for convex function.

Using the equivalent definition of convex function and letting $x \to x_1 + 0$ and then $x \to x_2 - 0$ we obtain

$$f'_+(x_1) \leq \frac{f(x_1) - f(x_2)}{x_1 - x_2} \leq f'_-(x_2).$$

It follows that

$$f'(x_1) = f'_+(x_1) \leq f'_-(x_2) = f'(x_2),$$

i.e., $f'$ is nondecreasing on the interval $(a, b)$.

Conversely, if $f'$ is nondecreasing on $(a, b)$ then applying Lagrange's formula for the intervals $[x_1, x]$ and $[x, x_2]$, $x_1 < x < x_2$, we obtain

$$\frac{f(x_1) - f(x)}{x_1 - x} = f'(\xi_1) \leq f'(\xi_2) = \frac{f(x) - f(x_2)}{x - x_2},$$

where $x_1 < \xi_1 < x$ and $x < \xi_2 < x_2$. Hence $f$ is convex on the interval $(a, b)$.

**Corollary 7.16.** *Let $f : (a, b) \to \mathbb{R}$ be twice differentiable. Then*

1. *$f$ is convex (concave) if and only if $f''(x) \geq 0$ ($f''(x) \leq 0$) for all $x \in (a, b)$,*

2. *If $f''(x) > 0$ ($f''(x) < 0$) then $f$ is strictly convex (strictly concave).*

*Proof.* The proof follows immediately from the criterion of monotonicity for differentiable functions (Theorem 6.48).

**Example 7.17.** The function $f(x) = x^4, x \in (-1, 1)$ is strictly convex, but $f''(0) = 0$. This shows that part 2 of the latter corollary is only a sufficient and not necessary condition for strict convexity (strict concavity).

**Theorem 7.18 (Criterion of convexity in terms of graphs).** *Let $f : (a, b) \to \mathbb{R}$ be differentiable. Then $f$ is convex (concave) if and only if its graph $\Gamma(f)$ lies not lower (not higher) than any of its tangents.*

*Proof.* Let $f$ be convex. Then for any $x_0 \in (a, b)$ the equation for the tangent to the graph $\Gamma(f)$ at the point $(x_0, f(x_0))$ has the form

$$y = f(x_0) + f'(x_0)(x - x_0).$$

It follows that

$$f(x) - y = f(x) - f(x_0) - f'(x_0)(x - x_0) = (f'(\xi) - f'(x_0))(x - x_0),$$

where $\xi \in (x_0, x)$ (or $\xi \in (x, x_0)$). Since $f'$ is nondecreasing (see Theorem 7.15) then we obtain that $y \leq f(x)$ for all $x \in (a, b)$.

Conversely, let the graph $\Gamma(f)$ lie not lower than any of its tangents, i.e., for any $x$ and $x_0$ we have

$$f(x) - y = f(x) - f(x_0) - f'(x_0)(x - x_0) \geq 0.$$

Thus, for $x > x_0$, we have

$$\frac{f(x) - f(x_0)}{x - x_0} \geq f'(x_0)$$

and for $x < x_0$ we have

$$\frac{f(x) - f(x_0)}{x - x_0} \leq f'(x_0).$$

Now if $x_1 < x < x_2$ then these two inequalities imply

$$\frac{f(x_1) - f(x)}{x_1 - x} \leq f'(x) \leq \frac{f(x) - f(x_2)}{x - x_2}.$$

This means that $f$ is convex. The proof for concave $f$ is similar.

**Exercise 7.19.** Formulate the analogue of Theorem 7.18 for strictly convex (strictly concave) functions.

**Definition 7.20.** *Let $f : (a, b) \to \mathbb{R}$ be differentiable in $U_\delta(x_0) \subset (a, b)$. If $f$ is strictly convex (strictly concave) on the interval $(x_0 - \delta, x_0)$ and strictly concave (strictly convex) on the interval $(x_0, x_0 + \delta)$ then the point $(x_0, f(x_0)) \in \Gamma(f)$ is said to be a* graph inflection point.

**Theorem 7.21 (Necessary condition of the inflection point).** *Let $(x_0, f(x_0)) \in \Gamma(f)$ be a graph inflection point. Then $f''(x_0) = 0$ if it exists.*

**Proof.** Denoting $g(x) := f'(x)$ we may conclude from Theorem 7.15 that $g$ is increasing (decreasing) and decreasing (increasing) from the left and the right of the point $x_0$, respectively. It implies that $g$ has a local extrema at $x_0$ and thus, by the necessary condition of local extrema, $g'(x_0) = f''(x_0) = 0$ if it exists.

**Theorem 7.22 (Sufficient condition of the inflection point).** *Let $f : (a, b) \to \mathbb{R}$ be continuous everywhere and differentiable with the exception of a finite number of points. If $f''(x_0) = 0$ or $f''(x_0)$ does not exist and if*

$$\operatorname{sgn} f''(x) = \operatorname{sgn}(x - x_0), \quad x \in U_\delta'(x_0),$$

*or*

$$\operatorname{sgn} f''(x) = \operatorname{sgn}(x_0 - x), \quad x \in U_\delta'(x_0),$$

*then $(x_0, f(x_0)) \in \Gamma(f)$ is a graph inflection point.*

**Proof.** The proof follows immediately from part 2 of Corollary 7.16.

**Example 7.23.** Let $f(x) = x^{1/3}, x \in (-1, 1)$. Then $(0, 0)$ is a graph inflection point, but neither $f'(0)$ nor $f''(0)$ exists.

**Exercise 7.24.** Find the graph inflection points for the function

$$f(x) = \frac{x^2}{2} - \frac{(x+1)^3}{2}, \quad x \in \mathbb{R}.$$

**Theorem 7.25 (Sufficient condition of the inflection point II).** *Let $f : (a, b) \to \mathbb{R}$ be differentiable $n$ times, $n = 2, 4, 6, \ldots$, in $U_\delta(x_0) \subset (a, b)$ and $n + 1$ times at the point $x_0$. If*

$$f''(x_0) = f'''(x_0) = \cdots = f^{(n)}(x_0) = 0$$

*but $f^{(n+1)}(x_0) \neq 0$ then $(x_0, f(x_0)) \in \Gamma(f)$ is a graph inflection point.*

**Proof.** The conditions of the theorem imply that $f^{(n)}$ is increasing (decreasing) at the point $x_0$, i.e., $f^{(n)}(x) < 0$ for $x < x_0$ and $f^{(n)}(x) > 0$ for $x > x_0$ (or $f^{(n)}(x) > 0$ for $x < x_0$ and $f^{(n)}(x) < 0$ for $x > x_0$). Applying Taylor's formula with the remainder in Lagrange's form we obtain

$$f''(x) = f''(x_0) + \cdots + \frac{f^{(n-1)}(x_0)}{(n-3)!}(x - x_0)^{n-3} + \frac{f^{(n)}(\xi)}{(n-2)!}(x - x_0)^{n-2}$$

$$= \frac{f^{(n)}(\xi)}{(n-2)!}(x - x_0)^{n-2}, \quad \xi = x_0 + \theta(x - x_0).$$

Since $n - 2$ is even, this formula shows that $f''$ has a different sign across point $x_0$. Hence Theorem 7.22 gives the result.

**Definition 7.26.**

1. *The line* $x = a$ *on the plane is called a* vertical asymptote *for the graph* $\Gamma(f)$ *if either* $\lim_{x \to a+0} f(x) = \pm\infty$ *or* $\lim_{x \to a-0} f(x) = \pm\infty$.

2. *The line* $y = kx + b$ *on the plane is called an* oblique asymptote *for the graph* $\Gamma(f)$ *if*

$$\lim_{x \to \pm\infty} (f(x) - kx) = b,$$

*i.e.,*

(a)
$$\lim_{x \to \pm\infty} \frac{f(x)}{x} = k,$$

(b)
$$\lim_{x \to \pm\infty} (f(x) - kx) = b$$

*if the limits exist.*

**Example 7.27.**  Let

$$f(x) = \begin{cases} \frac{x}{1+e^{1/x}}, & x \neq 0, \\ 0, & x = 0. \end{cases}$$

It is easy to see that $f$ is continuous everywhere, and therefore there are no vertical asymptotes. Next,

$$\lim_{x \to \pm\infty} \frac{f(x)}{x} = \lim_{x \to \pm\infty} \frac{1}{1+e^{1/x}} = \frac{1}{2}.$$

So

$$\lim_{x \to \pm\infty} \left( f(x) - \frac{x}{2} \right) = \lim_{x \to \pm\infty} \frac{1 - e^{1/x}}{\frac{2}{x}(1 + e^{1/x})} = \frac{1}{2} \lim_{t \to 0} \frac{1 - e^t}{t(1 + e^t)}$$

$$= -\frac{1}{2} \lim_{t \to 0} \frac{e^t - 1}{t} \lim_{t \to 0} \frac{1}{1 + e^t} = -\frac{1}{4}.$$

Hence $y = \frac{x}{2} - \frac{1}{4}$ is the oblique asymptote for the graph $\Gamma(f)$ at $\pm\infty$.

**Definition 7.28.** *A polynomial of order* $n$,

$$y = a_n x^n + a_{n-1} x^{n-1} + \cdots + a_0, \quad a_n \neq 0,$$

*is said to be an* asymptote *for the graph* $\Gamma(f)$ *if*

$$\lim_{x \to \pm\infty} \frac{f(x)}{x^n} = a_n, \quad \lim_{x \to \pm\infty} \frac{f(x) - a_n x^n}{x^{n-1}} = a_{n-1},$$

$$\ldots, \lim_{x \to \pm\infty} (f(x) - a_n x^n - \cdots - a_1 x) = a_0$$

*and these limits exist.*

## Construction scheme of the graph (by example)

We consider this scheme for the function

$$f(x) = |x + 2|e^{-1/x}.$$

1. The domain and range of $f$ are

$$D(f) = \mathbb{R} \setminus \{0\}, \quad R(f) = \overline{\mathbb{R}_+}.$$

2. *Asymptotes.* Since

   (a)
   $$\lim_{x \to +0} |x + 2|e^{-1/x} = 0, \quad \lim_{x \to -0} |x + 2|e^{-1/x} = +\infty,$$

   $x = 0$ is a vertical asymptote.

   (b) Since
   $$\lim_{x \to \pm\infty} \frac{|x + 2|e^{-1/x}}{x} = \pm 1,$$

   respectively, i.e., $k = 1$ at $+\infty$ and $k = -1$ at $-\infty$ and

   $$\lim_{x \to +\infty} ((x + 2)e^{-1/x} - x) = -\lim_{x \to +\infty} \frac{e^{-1/x} - 1}{-1/x} + 2 \lim_{x \to +\infty} e^{-1/x} = 1$$

   and

   $$\lim_{x \to -\infty} ((-x - 2)e^{-1/x} + x) = \lim_{x \to -\infty} \frac{1 - e^{-1/x}}{1/x} - 2 \lim_{x \to -\infty} e^{-1/x} = -1,$$

   then $y = x + 1$ is an oblique asymptote at $+\infty$ and $y = -x - 1$ is an oblique asymptote at $-\infty$.

3. *Stationary points.* We have that

$$f'(x) = \begin{cases} -\frac{x^2 + x + 2}{x^2}e^{-1/x}, & x < -2, \\ \frac{x^2 + x + 2}{x^2}e^{-1/x}, & x > -2, x \neq 0, \end{cases}$$

   while $f'(-2)$ and $f'(0)$ do not exist. Moreover, $f'(x) \neq 0$ for $x \neq -2$ and $x \neq 0$. In addition, $f$ is continuous at $x = -2$ but is not continuous at $x = 0$ since $\lim_{x \to -0} f(x) = \infty$. It means that there is only one stationary point $x = -2$. Furthermore, $f'(x) < 0$ for $x < -2$ and $f'(x) > 0$ for $x > -2, x \neq 0$. This implies that $x = -2$ is a point of local minima. The sign of the first derivative also says that $f$ is decreasing for $x < -2$ and increasing for $-2 < x < 0$ and $x > 0$.

4. *Inflection points.* Since

$$f''(x) = \begin{cases} -\frac{2 - 3x}{4}e^{-1/x}, & x < -2, \\ \frac{2 - 3x}{4}e^{-1/x}, & x > -2, x \neq 0, \end{cases}$$

   $f''(x) = 0$ for $x = 2/3$ and $f''(x)$ does not exist for $x = -2$. That's why the points $(2/3, \frac{8}{3}e^{-3/2})$ and $(-2, 0)$ of the graph are the candidates for inflection points. Next, it is

easy to see that $f''(x)$ changes its sign across $x = -2$ and across $x = 2/3$. Thus, both
these points of the graph $\Gamma(f)$ are inflection points. More precisely, for $x < -2$ and for
$x > 2/3$ the function $f$ is strictly concave, and for $-2 < x < 0$ and $0 < x < 2/3$ it is
strictly convex

5. *Intersection points with axis.* We have $f(x) = 0$ if and only if $x = -2$ and $f(0)$ does not
exist. So the graph $\Gamma(f)$ intersects the $x$-axis at $x = -2$ and does not intersect the $y$-axis
at all.

These considerations allow us to construct the graph depicted in Figure 7.1.

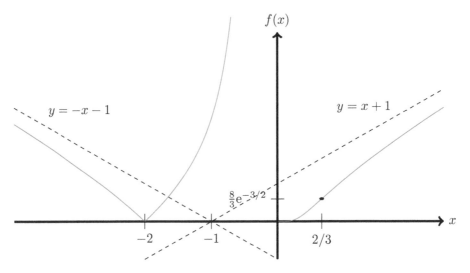

**Figure 7.1.** *Graph of $f(x) = |x + 2|e^{-1/x}$ and its asymptotes.*

Together with local extrema there is an *edge extrema*.

**Definition 7.29.** *Let $f : [a, b] \to \mathbb{R}$. The point $a$ (b) is called a* point of edge maxima (minima) *if
for some $\delta > 0$ (small enough) and for all $a \le x \le a + \delta$ ($b - \delta \le x \le b$) we have $f(x) \le f(a)$
($f(x) \le f(b)$) or $f(x) \ge f(a)$ ($f(x) \ge f(b)$), respectively.*

There is a simple sufficient condition of the edge extrema: If $f'_+(a)$ ($f'_-(b)$) exists and is not
equal to zero then for the case $f'_+(a) > 0$ ($f'_-(b) < 0$) the point $a$ (b) is a point of edge minima,
and for the case $f'_+(a) < 0$ ($f'_-(b) > 0$) the point $a$ (b) is a point of edge maxima.
     As a consequence of these conditions we obtain the necessary condition of the edge extrema.
Namely, let $f'_+(a)$ and $f'_-(b)$ exist. Then, if a point $a$ (b) is the point of edge maxima then
$f'_+(a) \le 0$ ($f'_-(b) \ge 0$), and if it is a point of edge minima then $f'_+(a) \ge 0$ ($f'_-(b) \le 0$).

**Exercise 7.30.** Prove necessary and sufficient conditions for edge extrema.

The concepts of convexity (concavity) allow us to prove well-known inequalities as follows.

1. *Young's inequality.* Let $a, b > 0$, and let $p$ and $p'$ be conjugate, i.e.,

$$\frac{1}{p} + \frac{1}{p'} = 1, \quad 1 < p < \infty, \quad p < 1, \quad p \ne 0.$$

Then

$$ab \le \frac{a^p}{p} + \frac{b^{p'}}{p'}, \quad 1 < p < \infty,$$

and

$$ab \ge \frac{a^p}{p} + \frac{b^{p'}}{p'}, \quad p < 1, p \ne 0.$$

Equalities in these two inequalities are possible if and only if $a^p = b^{p'}$.

**Proof.** Let $1 < p < \infty$ so that $1 < p' < \infty$ too. Since $e^x$ is strictly convex, for $a^p \ne b^{p'}$ we have

$$ab = e^{\log a + \log b} = e^{\frac{1}{p}\log a^p + \frac{1}{p'}\log b^{p'}} < \frac{1}{p}e^{\log a^p} + \frac{1}{p'}e^{\log b^{p'}} = \frac{a^p}{p} + \frac{b^{p'}}{p'},$$

which can be rewritten as

$$a^{1/p}b^{1/p'} < \frac{a}{p} + \frac{b}{p'}.$$

The last inequality is an equivalent form of Young's inequality. Equality in this strict inequality is possible only when $a = b$.

Let $p < 1$ and $p \ne 0$. Then $p' < 0$ for $0 < p < 1$ and $p' < 1$ for $p < 0$. Let us consider the function

$$f(x) = x^\alpha - \alpha x + \alpha - 1, \quad x > 0,$$

where $\alpha < 0$ or $\alpha > 1$. Since $f'(x) = \alpha x^{\alpha-1} - \alpha = \alpha(x^{\alpha-1} - 1)$, we have $f'(x) < 0$ for $0 < x < 1$, $f'(x) > 0$ for $x > 1$, and $f'(1) = 0$. Thus, $f$ has a local minima at $x = 1$ and this local minima equal $f(1) = 0$. Hence $f(x) > 0$ for all $x \ne 1$ and $f(x) = 0$ if and only if $x = 1$. Now, let $x = a/b$ and $\alpha = 1/p$, where $p < 1, p \ne 0$. This is equivalent to $\alpha < 0$ for $p < 0$ and $\alpha > 1$ for $0 < p < 1$. For this $x$ and $\alpha$ we have

$$x^{1/p} - \frac{x}{p} + \frac{1}{p} - 1 > 0$$

if and only if $x \ne 1$ $(a \ne b)$. This implies that

$$x^{1/p} > \frac{x}{p} + \frac{1}{p'}$$

or

$$\left(\frac{a}{b}\right)^{1/p} > \frac{a}{bp} + \frac{1}{p'}$$

or

$$a^{1/p} > \frac{ab^{1/p-1}}{p} + \frac{b^{1/p}}{p'}$$

or

$$a^{1/p}b^{1/p'} > \frac{ab^{1/p-1}b^{1/p'}}{p} + \frac{b^{1/p+1/p'}}{p'} = \frac{a}{p} + \frac{b}{p'}, \quad a \neq b.$$

Equivalently,

$$ab > \frac{a^p}{p} + \frac{b^{p'}}{p'}, \quad a^p \neq b^{p'}.$$

2. *Hölder's inequality.* Let $x_k, y_k > 0, k = 1, 2, \ldots, n, p \in \mathbb{R}, p \neq 1, p \neq 0$, and $1/p + 1/p' = 1$. Then

$$\sum_{k=1}^{n} x_k y_k \leq \left( \sum_{k=1}^{n} x_k^p \right)^{1/p} \left( \sum_{k=1}^{n} y_k^{p'} \right)^{1/p'}, \quad 1 < p < \infty,$$

and

$$\sum_{k=1}^{n} x_k y_k \geq \left( \sum_{k=1}^{n} x_k^p \right)^{1/p} \left( \sum_{k=1}^{n} y_k^{p'} \right)^{1/p'}, \quad p < 1, p \neq 0.$$

***Proof.*** Let us denote

$$X = \left( \sum_{k=1}^{n} x_k^p \right)^{1/p}, \quad Y = \left( \sum_{k=1}^{n} y_k^{p'} \right)^{1/p'}.$$

Using Young's inequality for $1 < p < \infty$ we obtain

$$\frac{x_k}{X} \frac{y_k}{Y} \leq \frac{x_k^p}{pX^p} + \frac{y_k^{p'}}{p'Y^{p'}}.$$

It follows that

$$\frac{\sum_{k=1}^{n} x_k y_k}{XY} \leq \frac{1}{p} \frac{\sum_{k=1}^{n} x_k^p}{\sum_{k=1}^{n} x_k^p} + \frac{1}{p'} \frac{\sum_{k=1}^{n} y_k^{p'}}{\sum_{k=1}^{n} y_k^{p'}} = 1.$$

The claim follows now by rearranging. For the cases $p < 0$ and $0 < p < 1$ the proof is the same if one uses the corresponding Young's inequality.

**Exercise 7.31.** Show that equality in Hölder's inequality occurs if and only if

$$x_1 = \lambda y_1^{p'-1}, \quad x_2 = \lambda y_2^{p'-1}, \quad \ldots \quad , \quad x_n = \lambda y_n^{p'-1}$$

for some $\lambda > 0$.

3. *Minkowski's inequality.* Let $x_k, y_k > 0, k = 1, 2, \ldots, n$, and $p \in \mathbb{R}, p \neq 1, p \neq 0$. Then

$$\left( \sum_{k=1}^{n} (x_k + y_k)^p \right)^{1/p} \leq \left( \sum_{k=1}^{n} x_k^p \right)^{1/p} + \left( \sum_{k=1}^{n} y_k^p \right)^{1/p}, \quad 1 < p < \infty,$$

and

$$\left(\sum_{k=1}^{n}(x_k+y_k)^p\right)^{1/p} \geq \left(\sum_{k=1}^{n}x_k^p\right)^{1/p} + \left(\sum_{k=1}^{n}y_k^p\right)^{1/p},$$

where $-\infty < p < 0$ or $0 < p < 1$.

***Proof.*** Applying Hölder's inequality for $1 < p < \infty$ we obtain

$$\sum_{k=1}^{n}(x_k+y_k)^p = \sum_{k=1}^{n}(x_k+y_k)^{p-1}x_k + \sum_{k=1}^{n}(x_k+y_k)^{p-1}y_k$$

$$\leq \left(\sum_{k=1}^{n}x_k^p\right)^{1/p}\left(\sum_{k=1}^{n}(x_k+y_k)^{(p-1)p'}\right)^{1/p'}$$

$$+ \left(\sum_{k=1}^{n}y_k^p\right)^{1/p}\left(\sum_{k=1}^{n}(x_k+y_k)^{(p-1)p'}\right)^{1/p'}$$

$$= \left(\sum_{k=1}^{n}(x_k+y_k)^p\right)^{1/p'}\left[\left(\sum_{k=1}^{n}x_k^p\right)^{1/p} + \left(\sum_{k=1}^{n}y_k^p\right)^{1/p}\right].$$

It follows that

$$\left(\sum_{k=1}^{n}(x_k+y_k)^p\right)^{1-1/p'} \leq \left(\sum_{k=1}^{n}x_k^p\right)^{1/p} + \left(\sum_{k=1}^{n}y_k^p\right)^{1/p}.$$

For the cases $-\infty < p < 0$ and $0 < p < 1$ using the corresponding Hölder's inequality we obtain Minkowski's inequality.

**Exercise 7.32.** Find necessary and sufficient conditions for $x_k$ and $y_k$ which provide equality in Minkowski's inequality.

**Exercise 7.33.** Formulate Young's inequality and Hölder's inequality for the case $p = 1$ and Minkowski's inequality for the case $p = \infty$.

**Exercise 7.34.** Let $a, b > 0$. Using convexity (or concavity) proves that

1.

$$(a+b)^p \leq 2^{p-1}(a^p+b^p), \quad 1 < p < \infty, \quad p < 0,$$
$$(a+b)^p \geq 2^{p-1}(a^p+b^p), \quad 0 < p < 1,$$

2.

$$a^p + b^p \leq (a+b)^p, \quad 1 < p < \infty,$$
$$a^p + b^p \geq (a+b)^p, \quad 0 < p < 1,$$

and show that equalities here are possible if and only if $a = b$ in part 1 and $a = 0$ or $b = 0$ in part 2.

**Exercise 7.35.** Show the following:

1. If $f : \mathbb{R} \to \mathbb{R}$ is convex and bounded then $f \equiv$ constant.

2. If $f : \mathbb{R} \to \mathbb{R}$ is convex and $\lim_{x \to \infty} f(x)/x = 0$ then $f \equiv$ constant.

3. If $f : (a, b) \to \mathbb{R}$ is convex then $f'_-(x)$ and $f'_+(x)$ exist for all $x \in (a, b)$. Show also that $f'_-(x) \leq f'_+(x)$ implies that $f$ is continuous everywhere.

4. The sum of convex functions is convex. Is this true for the product?

5. Local extrema of convex function are necessarily global extrema.

**Exercise 7.36.** Let

$$\varphi_p(x) = \begin{cases} |x|^2, & |x| \leq 1, \\ |x|^p, & |x| > 1, \end{cases}$$

for $1 < p < 2$ and $\varphi_p(x) = |x|^p$ for $p \geq 2$. Prove that there exists $c_p > 0$ such that

$$|1 + x|^p \geq 1 + px + c_p \varphi_p(x)$$

for all $x \in \mathbb{R}$.

# Chapter 8

# Indefinite Riemann integral

The indefinite Riemann integral is considered here from the most general point of view using Lagrange's formula together with a change of variables. Some wide classes of functions integrable into elementary functions are investigated. In particular, classes of rational and irrational functions of complicated arguments are investigated, including the well-known Euler's substitutions.

Throughout this chapter we assume that $X \subset \mathbb{R}$ is one of the following sets:

$$(a, b), [a, b), (a, b], [a, b], (a, \infty), [a, \infty), (-\infty, b), (-\infty, b], (-\infty, \infty)$$

or their finite unions.

**Definition 8.1.** *A function $F : X \to \mathbb{R}$ is said to be* primitive *for $f$ on $X$ if $F$ is differentiable on $X$ and $F'(x) = f(x)$ for any $x \in X$.*

**Theorem 8.2 (Main property of primitive).** *Let $F_1$ and $F_2$ be primitives for $f$ on $X \subset \mathbb{R}$. Then $F_1 - F_2$ is constant, which might be different in different parts of $X$.*

**Proof.** Since $F_1'(x) = f(x) = F_2'(x)$ on $X$ we have that $(F_1 - F_2)'(x) \equiv 0$. By Lagrange's formula on each connected part of $X$ we obtain for $F = F_1 - F_2$ that $F(x_1) - F(x_2) = F'(\xi)(x_1 - x_2)$. Hence $F$ is constant and the theorem is proved.

**Definition 8.3.** *Totality of all primitives $\{F(x)\}$ for function $f$ on a set $X \subset \mathbb{R}$ is said to be an* indefinite Riemann integral *of $f$ and is denoted as*

$$\int f(x)\mathrm{d}x, \quad x \in X.$$

Theorem 8.2 says that if $X = \bigcup_{j=1}^{n} X_j$ with $X_j$ as above then

$$\int f(x)\mathrm{d}x = F(x) + C_j, \quad x \in X_j,$$

where $F$ is an arbitrary primitive of $f$ on $X_j$ and $C_j$ is a constant.

**Example 8.4.** Let $R$ be the Riemann function. Then it is clear that an indefinite integral of $R$ is

$$\int R(t)\mathrm{dt} = 0, \quad t \in (a, x),$$

for any $a$ and $x$ such that $x > a$. This implies (see Definition 8.3) that also

$$\left( \int R(t)\mathrm{dt} \right)'_x = 0, \quad t \in (a, x).$$

But it is not equal to $R(x)$. This phenomenon will be explained in Chapter 16.

The properties of integral can be listed as follows:

1. $(\int f(x)\mathrm{d}x)' = f(x)$,

2. $\int F'(x)\mathrm{d}x = F(x) + C$,

3. $\int (f(x) \pm g(x))\mathrm{d}x = \int f(x)\mathrm{d}x \pm \int g(x)\mathrm{d}x$,

4. $\int Cf(x)\mathrm{d}x = C \int f(x)\mathrm{d}x$,

where $C$ is a constant.

**Theorem 8.5 (Change of variable).** *Let $\varphi : X \to \mathbb{R}$ be differentiable on $X$. Assume that the set $Y := \varphi(X)$ has the same structure as $X$. Let $F$ be a primitive for $f$ on $Y$. Then on the set $X$ there exists a primitive for $f(\varphi(x))\varphi'(x)$ and*

$$\int f(\varphi(x))\varphi'(x)\mathrm{d}x = F(\varphi(x)) + C, \quad x \in X.$$

**Proof.** Since $F$ and $\varphi$ are differentiable, their superposition $F(\varphi(x))$ is also differentiable and

$$(F(\varphi(x)))' = F'(\varphi(x))\varphi'(x) = f(\varphi(x))\varphi'(x).$$

Hence $F(\varphi(x))$ is a primitive for $f(\varphi(x))\varphi'(x)$, i.e.,

$$\int f(\varphi(x))\varphi'(x)\mathrm{d}x = \int f(y)\mathrm{d}y = F(\varphi(x)) + C, \quad x \in X, y \in Y.$$

**Remark 8.6.** The latter result can be reformulated as follows: let $x = \psi(y), \varphi = \psi^{-1}$, and $Y = \varphi(X)$. Then

$$\int f(x)\mathrm{d}x = \int f(\psi(y))\mathrm{d}\psi(y)$$

$$= \int f(\psi(y))\psi'(y)\mathrm{d}y = F(y) + C = F(\varphi(x)) + C, \quad x \in X, y \in Y.$$

**Theorem 8.7 (Integration by parts).** *Let $u$ and $v$ be differentiable on $X$. Assume that a primitive exists for $uv'$ $(u'v)$ on $X$. Then there is a primitive for $u'v$ $(uv')$ and*

$$\int u'(x)v(x)\mathrm{d}x = u(x)v(x) - \int v'(x)u(x)\mathrm{d}x, \quad x \in X.$$

*Proof.* Let $F$ be a primitive for $uv'$ on $X$. Then

$$(u(x)v(x) - F(x))' = u'(x)v(x) + u(x)v'(x) - F'(x) = u'(x)v(x) + u(x)v'(x) - u(x)v'(x).$$

This yields the claim by the definition of the integral.

**Example 8.8.** 1. Let $f(x) = (x^2 + a^2)^{-1/2}$ on $X = \mathbb{R}, a > 0$. A primitive for $f$ can be found as follows. Denoting $x = a \tan y, y \in (-\pi/2, \pi/2)$, we have

$$\int \frac{dx}{\sqrt{x^2 + a^2}} = \int \frac{a d \tan y}{\sqrt{a^2 \tan^2 y + a^2}} = \int \frac{\frac{1}{\cos^2 y} dy}{\sqrt{1 + \tan^2 y}}$$

$$= \int \frac{\frac{1}{\cos^2 y} dy}{\frac{1}{\cos y}} = \int \frac{\cos y dy}{1 - \sin^2 y}$$

$$= \int \frac{d \sin y}{1 - \sin^2 y} = \int \frac{dz}{1 - z^2}$$

$$= \frac{1}{2} \int \frac{dz}{1 - z} + \frac{1}{2} \int \frac{dz}{1 + z}$$

$$= -\frac{1}{2} \log |1 - z| + \frac{1}{2} \log |1 + z| = \frac{1}{2} \log \left| \frac{1 + z}{1 - z} \right|,$$

where $x \in \mathbb{R}, y \in (-\pi/2, \pi/2), z \in (-1, 1)$, and we have used the fact that $\log |x|$ is a primitive for $1/x, x \neq 0$. Thus,

$$\int \frac{dx}{\sqrt{x^2 + a^2}} = \frac{1}{2} \log \left| \frac{1 + z}{1 - z} \right| + C = \frac{1}{2} \log \frac{1 + \sin y}{1 - \sin y} + C$$

$$= \frac{1}{2} \log \frac{1 + \frac{x}{\sqrt{a^2 + x^2}}}{1 - \frac{x}{\sqrt{a^2 + x^2}}} + C = \frac{1}{2} \log \frac{x + \sqrt{a^2 + x^2}}{\sqrt{a^2 + x^2} - x} + C$$

$$= \frac{1}{2} \log \frac{(x + \sqrt{a^2 + x^2})^2}{a^2} + C = \log(x + \sqrt{a^2 + x^2}) + \tilde{C},$$

where $\tilde{C} = C - \log a$ and $x \in \mathbb{R}$.

2. Let

$$f(x) = \sqrt{\frac{a + x}{a - x}}, \quad a > 0, x \in [-a, a).$$

Denoting $x = a \cos(2t)$ we obtain

$$\int \sqrt{\frac{a + x}{a - x}} dx = \int \sqrt{\frac{1 + \cos(2t)}{1 - \cos(2t)}} (-2a \sin(2t)) dt$$

$$= -2a \int \cot t \sin(2t) dt = -4a \int \cos^2 t dt$$

$$= -2a \int (1 + \cos(2t)) dt = -2at - a \sin(2t) + C$$

$$= -a \arccos \frac{x}{a} - \sqrt{a^2 - x^2} + C, \quad t \in (0, \pi/2], x \in [-a, a).$$

3. Let $f(x) = e^{ax} \cos(bx), x \in X$, where $X$ is any set mentioned in the beginning of this chapter. Using integration by parts twice one can obtain

$$\int e^{ax} \cos(bx) dx = \int e^{ax} \left( \frac{\sin(bx)}{b} \right)' dx$$

$$= e^{ax} \frac{\sin(bx)}{b} - \frac{a}{b} \int e^{ax} \sin(bx) dx$$

$$= e^{ax} \frac{\sin(bx)}{b} - \frac{a}{b} \int e^{ax} \left( -\frac{\cos(bx)}{b} \right)' dx$$

$$= e^{ax} \frac{\sin(bx)}{b} - \frac{a}{b} \left[ -e^{ax} \frac{\cos(bx)}{b} + \frac{a}{b} \int e^{ax} \cos(bx) dx \right]$$

$$= e^{ax} \left[ \frac{\sin(bx)}{b} + \frac{a \cos(bx)}{b^2} \right] - \frac{a^2}{b^2} \int e^{ax} \cos(bx) dx.$$

By rearranging we get

$$\left( 1 + \frac{a^2}{b^2} \right) \int e^{ax} \cos(bx) dx = e^{ax} \left[ \frac{b \sin(bx) + a \cos(bx)}{b^2} \right] + C$$

or

$$\int e^{ax} \cos(bx) dx = e^{ax} \frac{b \sin(bx) + a \cos(bx)}{a^2 + b^2} + C.$$

4. Let

$$f(x) = \frac{1}{(x^2 + a^2)^\lambda}, \quad a > 0, \lambda \neq 1.$$

Denoting the primitive of this function by $K_\lambda$ and using integration by parts, we obtain the recursive relation

$$K_\lambda = \int \frac{dx}{(x^2 + a^2)^\lambda} = \frac{1}{a^2} \int \frac{x^2 + a^2 - x^2}{(x^2 + a^2)^\lambda} dx$$

$$= \frac{1}{a^2} K_{\lambda-1} - \frac{1}{a^2} \int \frac{x^2}{(x^2 + a^2)^\lambda} dx$$

$$= \frac{1}{a^2} K_{\lambda-1} - \frac{1}{2a^2} \int \frac{x d(x^2 + a^2)}{(x^2 + a^2)^\lambda}$$

$$= \frac{1}{a^2} K_{\lambda-1} - \frac{1}{2a^2} \left( x \frac{(x^2 + a^2)^{1-\lambda}}{1 - \lambda} - \frac{1}{1 - \lambda} \int \frac{dx}{(x^2 + a^2)^{\lambda-1}} \right)$$

$$= \frac{1}{a^2} K_{\lambda-1} - \frac{x}{2a^2(1 - \lambda)(x^2 + a^2)^{\lambda-1}} + \frac{1}{2a^2(1 - \lambda)} K_{\lambda-1}$$

$$= \frac{3 - 2\lambda}{2a^2(1 - \lambda)} K_{\lambda-1} - \frac{x}{2a^2(1 - \lambda)(x^2 + a^2)^{\lambda-1}}.$$

Having calculated $K_{1/2}$ in part 1, this recursive relation allows us to obtain, for example, that

$$K_{3/2} = \frac{x}{a^2 \sqrt{x^2 + a^2}} + C$$

and

$$K_{-1/2} = \frac{a^2}{2} \left[ K_{1/2} + \frac{x}{a^2} \sqrt{x^2 + a^2} \right]$$

$$= \frac{a^2}{2} \log(x + \sqrt{x^2 + a^2}) + \frac{x}{2} \sqrt{x^2 + a^2} + C.$$

We present some classes of functions that can be integrated in terms of elementary functions. Let us consider a *regular rational fraction*, i.e., a function

$$R(x) = \frac{P_l(x)}{Q_n(x)},$$

where $P_l$ and $Q_n$ are polynomials with real coefficients of order $l$ and $n$ such that $l < n$ and they have no joint roots (real or complex).

**Theorem 8.9 (Simple fraction decomposition).** *Let*

$$R(x) = \frac{P_l(x)}{Q_n(x)}$$

*be a regular rational fraction, where*

$$Q_n(x) = (x - b_1)^{\alpha_1} \cdots (x - b_m)^{\alpha_m} (x^2 + p_1 x + q_1)^{\lambda_1} \cdots (x^2 + p_r x + q_r)^{\lambda_r}$$

*and* $\alpha_1 + \cdots + \alpha_m + 2\lambda_1 + \cdots + 2\lambda_r = n$. *Then there are unique real constants* $B_j^{(k)}, M_j^{(k)}, N_j^{(k)}$ *such that*

$$\frac{P_l(x)}{Q_n(x)} = \sum_{k=1}^{m} \sum_{j=1}^{\alpha_k} \frac{B_j^{(k)}}{(x - b_k)^j} + \sum_{k=1}^{r} \sum_{j=1}^{\lambda_k} \frac{M_j^{(k)} x + N_j^{(k)}}{(x^2 + p_k x + q_k)^{\lambda_j}}.$$

**Proof.** First let $b$ be a real root of the polynomial $Q_n(x)$ of multiplicity $\alpha$. Then the following representation holds:

$$\frac{P_l(x)}{Q_n(x)} = \frac{A}{(x - b)^\alpha} + \frac{\psi(x)}{(x - b)^{\alpha - k} \varphi(x)},$$

where $k$ is integer, $\varphi(b) \neq 0 \neq \psi(b)$, and $A = P_l(b)/\varphi(b) \neq 0$, where $\psi(x)$ and $\varphi(x)$ are polynomials with real coefficients such that

$$\frac{\psi(x)}{(x - b)^{\alpha - k} \varphi(x)}$$

is a regular rational fraction. Indeed, since $b$ is real with multiplicity $\alpha$, $Q_n(x) = (x - b)^\alpha \varphi(x)$, where $\varphi(x)$ is a polynomial of order $n - \alpha$ and $\varphi(b) \neq 0$. This implies that for $A = P_l(b)/\varphi(b) \neq 0$ we have

$$\frac{P_l(x)}{Q_n(x)} - \frac{A}{(x - b)^\alpha} = \frac{P_l(x) - A\varphi(x)}{(x - b)^\alpha \varphi(x)}.$$

But the choice of $A$ says that $P_l(b) - A\varphi(b) = 0$, i.e., $b$ is the root of the polynomial $P_l(x) - A\varphi(x)$. This leads to the fact that

$$P_l(x) - A\varphi(x) = (x - b)^k \psi(x),$$

where $k$ is the multiplicity of $b$ for the polynomial $P_l(x) - A\varphi(x)$ and $\psi(b) \neq 0$. That's why we have

$$\frac{P_l(x)}{Q_n(x)} - \frac{A}{(x - b)^\alpha} = \frac{\psi(x)}{(x - b)^{\alpha - k} \varphi(x)}.$$

Since the order of the polynomial $\psi(x)$ is equal to $\max(l, n - \alpha) - k$ and the order of the polynomial $(x - b)^{\alpha - k} \varphi(x)$ is equal to $\alpha - k + n - \alpha$, we can easily see that

$$\max(l, n - \alpha) - k < \alpha - k + n - \alpha$$

or $\max(l, n - \alpha) < n$. Hence

$$\frac{\psi(x)}{(x - b)^{\alpha-k}\varphi(x)}$$

is a regular rational fraction.

Now let $Q_n(x)$ have complex root of multiplicity $\lambda$ (it also has complex conjugate root of same multiplicity since it has real coefficients), i.e.,

$$Q_n(x) = (x^2 + px + q)^\lambda\varphi(x),$$

where $x^2 + px + q = (x - z)(x - \bar{z}), p = z + \bar{z} = 2\operatorname{Re} z, q = z\bar{z} = |z|^2$, and $\varphi(z) \neq 0 \neq \varphi(\bar{z})$. We want to show that there exist unique real constants $M$ and $N$ such that

$$\frac{P_l(x)}{Q_n(x)} = \frac{Mx + N}{(x^2 + px + q)^\lambda} + \frac{\psi(x)}{(x^2 + px + q)^{\lambda-k}\varphi(x)}$$

with integer $k$ and with polynomials $\psi(x)$ and $\varphi(x)$ such that the latter term is a regular rational fraction. Indeed, let $z$ be a complex root, and let $P_l(z) = a + ib \neq 0, \varphi(z) = c + id \neq 0$ with $z = s + ir, r \neq 0$. Then we choose real constants $M$ and $N$ such that

$$P_l(z) - (Mz + N)\varphi(z) = 0$$

or

$$M(s + ir) + N = \frac{P_l(z)}{\varphi(z)} = \frac{a + ib}{c + id} = \frac{(a + ib)(c - id)}{c^2 + d^2}.$$

So

$$Ms + N = \frac{ac + bd}{c^2 + d^2}, \quad Mr = \frac{bc - ad}{c^2 + d^2}$$

or

$$M = \frac{1}{r}\frac{bc - ad}{c^2 + d^2}, \quad N = \frac{ac + bd}{c^2 + d^2} - \frac{s}{r}\frac{bc - ad}{c^2 + d^2},$$

i.e., real numbers $M$ and $N$ are uniquely determined. Hence

$$P_l(x) - (Mx + N)\varphi(x) = (x^2 + px + q)^k\psi(x),$$

where $k$ is the multiplicity of the complex root $z$ (and $\bar{z}$) for the polynomial $P_l(x) - (Mx + N)\varphi(x)$ with real coefficients and where (by our choice) $\psi(z) \neq 0 \neq \psi(\bar{z})$. These considerations imply

$$\frac{P_l(x) - (Mx + N)\varphi(x)}{(x^2 + px + q)^\lambda\varphi(x)} = \frac{\psi(x)}{(x^2 + px + q)^{\lambda-k}\varphi(x)}$$

or

$$\frac{P_l(x)}{Q_n(x)} = \frac{Mx + N}{(x^2 + px + q)^\lambda} + \frac{\psi(x)}{(x^2 + px + q)^{\lambda-k}\varphi(x)},$$

where the order of the polynomial $\psi(x)$ is equal to $\max(l, n - 2\lambda) - 2k$ and the order of the polynomial $(x^2 + px + q)^{\lambda-k}\varphi(x)$ is equal to $2\lambda - 2k + n - 2\lambda$. So

$$\max(l, n - 2\lambda) < n.$$

To end the proof we consistently apply these two representations with respect to all roots of the polynomial $Q_n(x)$. This finishes the proof.

We are in position now to consider some classes of functions which can be integrated.

1. Let $R(x)$ be an arbitrary rational fraction (not necessarily regular). But clearly it suffices to consider only regular rational fractions. Theorem 8.9 reduces the integration of regular rational fractions to the integration of the terms

$$\frac{1}{(x-b)^\alpha} \quad \text{and} \quad \frac{Mx+N}{(x^2+px+q)^\lambda}$$

with real numbers $b, p, q, M$, and $N$ and integers $\alpha$ and $\lambda$. Next,

$$\int \frac{1}{(x-b)^\alpha}\mathrm{d}x = \begin{cases} \log|x-b| + C, & \alpha = 1, \\ \frac{(x-b)^{1-\alpha}}{1-\alpha} + C, & \alpha > 1, \end{cases}$$

and, denoting $a^2 = q - p^2/4 > 0$, we have

$$\begin{aligned}
\int \frac{Mx+N}{(x^2+px+q)^\lambda}\mathrm{d}x &= \int \frac{(Mx+N)\mathrm{d}x}{((x+p/2)^2+q-p^2/4)^\lambda} \\
&= \int \frac{(M(x+p/2)+N-Mp/2)\mathrm{d}x}{((x+p/2)^2+a^2)^\lambda} \\
&= \frac{M}{2}\int \frac{2t\mathrm{d}t}{(t^2+a^2)^\lambda} + (N-Mp/2)\int \frac{\mathrm{d}t}{(t^2+a^2)^\lambda} \\
&= (N-Mp/2)K_\lambda + \frac{M}{2}\begin{cases} \log(t^2+a^2), & \lambda=1, \\ \frac{(t^2+a^2)^{1-\lambda}}{1-\lambda}, & \lambda>1. \end{cases}
\end{aligned}$$

Since $K_1 = \frac{1}{a}\arctan\frac{t}{a} + C$, all other $K_\lambda$ can be calculated recursively using $K_1$ since $\lambda$ is an integer. So any rational function $R(x)$ can be integrated (has a primitive) in terms of elementary functions.

2. Let $R(x, y)$ be a rational function of two variables, i.e.,

$$R(x, y) = \frac{P_l(x, y)}{Q_n(x, y)},$$

where $P_l(x, y)$ and $Q_n(x, y)$ are polynomials of two variables $x$ and $y$ with real coefficients. We want to integrate

$$\int_{(-\pi,\pi)} R(\sin x, \cos x)\mathrm{d}x.$$

Introducing $t = \tan(x/2)$ (this might be considered as a universal substitution of variables for such integrals) we obtain

$$\int R(\sin x, \cos x)\mathrm{d}x$$

$$= \int R\left(\frac{2t}{1+t^2}, \frac{1-t^2}{1+t^2}\right)\frac{2\mathrm{d}t}{1+t^2} = \int \widetilde{R}(t)\mathrm{d}t, \quad x \in (-\pi, \pi), t \in \mathbb{R},$$

where $\widetilde{R}(t)$ is a rational function of one variable. Thus, this integration reduces to the class considered in part 1.

3. We want to integrate the function

$$R\left(x, \sqrt[n]{\frac{ax+b}{cx+d}}\right), \quad n \in \mathbb{N}, \quad n \geq 2, \quad bc \neq ad,$$

where $R(x, y)$ is a rational function of two variables $x$ and $y$ with real coefficients. Introducing

$$t = \sqrt[n]{\frac{ax+b}{cx+d}}$$

we obtain that

$$x = \frac{b - t^n d}{ct^n - a}$$

and

$$\int R\left(x, \sqrt[n]{\frac{ax+b}{cx+d}}\right) dx = \int R\left(\frac{b - t^n d}{ct^n - a}, t\right) \frac{(ad - bc)nt^{n-1}}{(a - ct^n)^2} dt = \int \widetilde{R}(t)dt.$$

So again the problem is reduced to the class considered in part 1.

4. We want to integrate the function

$$R(x, \sqrt{ax^2 + bx + c}),$$

where $a, b, c$ are real, $a \neq 0$, and $R(x, y)$ is a rational function of two variables $x$ and $y$ with real coefficients. There are two possibilities for the quadratic polynomial $ax^2 + bx + c$.

(a) Let $ax^2 + bx + c$ have no real roots, i.e., $a > 0$ and $b^2 - 4ac < 0$. Introducing the *first Euler's substitution*

$$t = \sqrt{ax^2 + bx + c} + x\sqrt{a}$$

we obtain

$$x = \frac{t^2 - c}{2t\sqrt{a} + b}.$$

Then

$$\int R(x, \sqrt{ax^2 + bx + c})dx$$
$$= \int R\left(\frac{t^2 - c}{2t\sqrt{a} + b}, t - \frac{(t^2 - c)\sqrt{a}}{2t\sqrt{a} + b}\right) 2\frac{t^2\sqrt{a} + bt + c\sqrt{a}}{(2t\sqrt{a} + b)^2} dt$$
$$= \int \widetilde{R}(t)dt,$$

where $\widetilde{R}(t)$ is a rational function of one variable with real coefficients.

(b) Let $ax^2 + bx + c$ have real roots, i.e., $ax^2 + bx + c = a(x - x_1)(x - x_2), x_1 \neq x_2$. Introducing the *second Euler's substitution*

$$t = \frac{\sqrt{ax^2 + bx + c}}{x - x_1}$$

we have

$$x = \frac{t^2 x_1 - ax_2}{t^2 - a}.$$

So

$$\int R(x, \sqrt{ax^2 + bx + c})\mathrm{d}x$$

$$= \int R\left(\frac{t^2 x_1 - ax_2}{t^2 - a}, t\left(\frac{t^2 x_1 - ax_2}{t^2 - a} - x_1\right)\right)\frac{2a(x_2 - x_1)}{(t^2 - a)^2}\mathrm{d}t$$

$$= \int \widetilde{R}(t)\mathrm{d}t,$$

where $\widetilde{R}(t)$ is again a rational function of one variable with real coefficients.

**Example 8.10.**    1. Let us calculate

$$\int \frac{1}{\sin^4 x + \cos^4 x}\mathrm{d}x.$$

Since

$$\sin^4 x + \cos^4 x = (\sin^2 x + \cos^2 x)^2 - 2\sin^2 x \cos^2 x = 1 - \frac{1}{2}\sin^2(2x)$$

$$= 1 - \frac{1}{4}(1 - \cos(4x)) = \frac{1}{4}\cos(4x) + \frac{3}{4},$$

we denote $t = \tan(z/2)$, and get

$$\int \frac{1}{\sin^4 x + \cos^4 x}\mathrm{d}x = \int \frac{4\mathrm{d}x}{\cos(4x) + 3} = \int \frac{\mathrm{d}z}{\cos z + 3}$$

$$= \int \frac{\frac{2}{1+t^2}\mathrm{d}t}{\frac{1-t^2}{1+t^2} + 3} = \int \frac{\mathrm{d}t}{t^2 + 2}$$

$$= \frac{1}{\sqrt{2}}\arctan\frac{t}{\sqrt{2}} + C = \frac{1}{\sqrt{2}}\arctan\frac{\tan 2x}{\sqrt{2}} + C.$$

2. Let us calculate

$$\int \frac{1}{x^4 + 1}\mathrm{d}x.$$

Since

$$\frac{1}{x^4 + 1} = \frac{1}{x^4 + 2x^2 + 1 - 2x^2} = \frac{1}{(x^2 + 1 - x\sqrt{2})(x^2 + 1 + x\sqrt{2})}$$

$$= \frac{\frac{1}{2\sqrt{2}}x + \frac{1}{2}}{x^2 + x\sqrt{2} + 1} - \frac{\frac{1}{2\sqrt{2}}x - \frac{1}{2}}{x^2 - x\sqrt{2} + 1},$$

part 1 above allows us to obtain

$$\int \frac{1}{x^4 + 1}\mathrm{d}x = \int \frac{\frac{1}{2\sqrt{2}}x + \frac{1}{2}}{x^2 + x\sqrt{2} + 1}\mathrm{d}x - \int \frac{\frac{1}{2\sqrt{2}}x - \frac{1}{2}}{x^2 - x\sqrt{2} + 1}\mathrm{d}x$$

$$= \frac{1}{4\sqrt{2}}\log(x^2 + x\sqrt{2} + 1) + \sqrt{2}\arctan\frac{x + 1/\sqrt{2}}{1/\sqrt{2}}$$

$$- \frac{1}{4\sqrt{2}}\log(x^2 - x\sqrt{2} + 1) + \sqrt{2}\arctan\frac{x - 1/\sqrt{2}}{1/\sqrt{2}}$$

$$= \frac{1}{4\sqrt{2}}\log\frac{x^2 + x\sqrt{2} + 1}{x^2 - x\sqrt{2} + 1}$$

$$+ \sqrt{2}\arctan(x\sqrt{2} + 1) + \sqrt{2}\arctan(x\sqrt{2} - 1).$$

3. We calculate

$$\int \frac{\mathrm{d}x}{(\sin^2 x + 2\cos^2 x)^2} = \int \frac{\frac{1}{\cos^4 x}\mathrm{d}x}{(\tan^2 x + 2)^2} = \int \frac{(\tan^2 x + 1)\mathrm{d}(\tan x)}{(\tan^2 x + 2)^2}$$

$$= \int \frac{(t^2 + 1)\mathrm{d}t}{(t^2 + 2)^2} = \int \frac{(t^2 + 2)\mathrm{d}t}{(t^2 + 2)^2} - \int \frac{\mathrm{d}t}{(t^2 + 2)^2}$$

$$= K_1 - K_2$$

$$= \frac{1}{\sqrt{2}} \arctan \frac{t}{\sqrt{2}}$$

$$- \left( \frac{3 - 4}{4(1 - 2)}K_1 - \frac{t}{4(1 - 2)(t^2 + 2)} \right)$$

$$= \frac{3}{4\sqrt{2}} \arctan \frac{t}{\sqrt{2}} - \frac{t}{4(t^2 + 2)} + C$$

$$= \frac{3}{4\sqrt{2}} \arctan \frac{\tan x}{\sqrt{2}} - \frac{\tan x}{4(\tan^2 x + 2)} + C.$$

**Exercise 8.11.** Calculate the integrals

1.
$$\int e^{ax} \sin(bx)\mathrm{d}x,$$

2.
$$\int |x|\mathrm{d}x,$$

3.
$$\int (|1 + x| - |1 - x|)\mathrm{d}x,$$

4.
$$\int \frac{\mathrm{d}x}{3\sin x + 4\cos x + 5},$$

5.
$$\int \frac{2\sin x + 3\cos x}{\sin^2 x \cos x + 9\cos^3 x}\mathrm{d}x,$$

6.
$$\int \frac{\sin^2 x \cos^2 x}{\sin^8 x + \cos^8 x}\mathrm{d}x,$$

7.
$$\int \sqrt{1 - \sin(2x)}\mathrm{d}x,$$

8.
$$\int \frac{\mathrm{d}x}{\sin^6 x + \cos^6 x},$$

9.
$$\int \frac{\mathrm{d}x}{x^6 + 1},$$

10.

$$\int \frac{\sin^2 x \, dx}{\sin x + \cos x},$$

11.

$$\int \frac{dx}{\sin x}, \quad x \in [\pi/4, 3\pi/4],$$

12.

$$\int_{|x|<a} \frac{1}{\sqrt{a^2 - x^2}} \, dx.$$

**Exercise 8.12.**    1. Prove that on the set $X = (0, 1)$ we have

$$\int \frac{dx}{1-x} = \log(1-x) + C, \quad x \in X.$$

Use this fact to show that

$$\log(1-x) = \sum_{k=0}^{\infty} \frac{x^{k+1}}{k+1}, \quad x \in X.$$

2. Use integration by parts to calculate the integral

$$\int \frac{x^2 \, dx}{(x \sin x + \cos x)^2}.$$

# Chapter 9

# Riemann–Stieltjes integral

This chapter discusses the definite Riemann–Stieltjes integral and its properties. The approach here is closely related to the functions of bounded variation. The classical mean value formulas for the Riemann–Stieltjes integral are proved, and the properties of the integral as a function of a variable upper or lower limit are investigated. It is shown that in reality the change of variables and integration by parts in the usual Riemann integral lead to the Riemann–Stieltjes integral. The Hölder and Minkowskii inequalities are also proved for the Riemann–Stieltjes integral.

**Definition 9.1.** *A partition $P$ of a closed interval $[a, b]$ is a collection of points $P := \{x_0, x_1, \ldots, x_n\}$ such that*

$$a = x_0 < x_1 < \cdots < x_n = b.$$

*Denoting $\Delta x_j = x_j - x_{j-1}, j = 1, 2, \ldots, n$, we set $\mu(P) := \max_{1 \leq j \leq n} \Delta x_j$ and call $\mu(P)$ the* diameter of partition $P$.

Let $f : [a, b] \to \mathbb{R}$ be bounded. For any partition $P$ of the interval $[a, b]$ we introduce the finite numbers

$$M_j = \sup_{[x_{j-i}, x_j]} f(x), \quad m_j = \inf_{[x_{j-i}, x_j]} f(x).$$

Also let $\alpha : [a, b] \to \mathbb{R}$ be increasing.

**Definition 9.2.** *The values*

$$U(P, f, \alpha) = \sum_{j=1}^{n} M_j \Delta \alpha_j, \quad L(P, f, \alpha) = \sum_{j=1}^{n} m_j \Delta \alpha_j,$$

*where $\Delta \alpha_j = \alpha(x_j) - \alpha(x_{j-1}) > 0$, are said to be* upper and lower sums of Darboux–Stieltjes.

It is easy to see that for each partition $P$ and for functions $f$ and $\alpha$ as above we have

1. $U(P, f, \alpha) \geq L(P, f, \alpha)$,

2. $m(\alpha(b) - \alpha(a)) \leq L(P, f, \alpha) \leq U(P, f, \alpha) \leq M(\alpha(b) - \alpha(a))$, where $m = \inf_{[a,b]} f(x)$ and $M = \sup_{[a,b]} f(x)$.

These properties of the sums of Darboux–Stieltjes justify the following definition.

**Definition 9.3.** *The values*

$$\overline{\int}_{[a,b]} f(x)\mathrm{d}\alpha(x) := \inf_P U(P,f,\alpha), \quad \underline{\int}_{[a,b]} f(x)\mathrm{d}\alpha(x) := \sup_P L(P,f,\alpha)$$

*are called the* upper and lower integrals of Darboux–Stieltjes.

**Remark 9.4.** It is quite clear that the values

$$\overline{\int}_{[a,b]} f(x)\mathrm{d}\alpha(x), \quad \underline{\int}_{[a,b]} f(x)\mathrm{d}\alpha(x)$$

exist for any bounded function $f$. Moreover,

$$\underline{\int}_{[a,b]} f(x)\mathrm{d}\alpha(x) \le \overline{\int}_{[a,b]} f(x)\mathrm{d}\alpha(x)$$

as we shall soon see.

**Definition 9.5.** *A partition $P'$ of the interval $[a,b]$ is called a* refinement of partition $P$ of the
*same interval if $P \subset P'$. If $P_1$ and $P_2$ are two arbitrary partitions then $P' := P_1 \cup P_2$ is called
their* common refinement.

**Theorem 9.6 (Darboux's lemma).** *If $P \subset P'$ then*

$$L(P,f,\alpha) \le L(P',f,\alpha), \quad U(P,f,\alpha) \ge U(P',f,\alpha).$$

***Proof.*** It is enough to consider only the case when $P' = P \cup \{x'\}$ and $x' \notin P$, i.e., $x_{j-1} < x' <
x_j$ for some $j = 1,2,\ldots,n$. For this $j$ we denote

$$m'_{j-1} = \inf_{[x_{j-1},x']} f, \quad m'_j = \inf_{[x',x_j]} f, \quad M'_{j-1} = \sup_{[x_{j-1},x']} f, \quad M'_j = \sup_{[x',x_j]} f$$

and obtain

$$m'_{j-1}, m'_j \ge m_j, \quad M'_{j-1}, M'_j \le M_j.$$

Therefore

$$
\begin{aligned}
L(P',f,\alpha) &- L(P,f,\alpha) \\
&= m'_{j-1}(\alpha(x') - \alpha(x_{j-1})) + m'_j(\alpha(x_j) - \alpha(x')) - m_j(\alpha(x_j) - \alpha(x_{j-1})) \\
&\ge m_j[\alpha(x') - \alpha(x_{j-1}) + \alpha(x_j) - \alpha(x') - \alpha(x_j) - \alpha(x_{j-1})] = 0.
\end{aligned}
$$

The proof for upper sums is similar. This finishes the proof.

**Corollary 9.7.** *Let $P_1$ and $P_2$ be two arbitrary partitions of the interval $[a,b]$. Then*

$$L(P_1,f,\alpha) \le U(P_2,f,\alpha)$$

*and consequently*

$$\underline{\int}_{[a,b]} f(x)\mathrm{d}\alpha(x) \le \overline{\int}_{[a,b]} f(x)\mathrm{d}\alpha(x).$$

**Proof.** Denoting $P' = P_1 \cup P_2$ we have (see Theorem 9.6) that

$$L(P_1, f, \alpha) \le L(P', f, \alpha) \le U(P', f, \alpha) \le U(P_2, f, \alpha).$$

It follows that

$$\underline{\int_{[a,b]}} f(x) d\alpha(x) = \sup_{P_1} L(P_1, f, \alpha) \le U(P_2, f, \alpha)$$

and, further,

$$\underline{\int_{[a,b]}} f(x) d\alpha(x) \le \inf_{P_2} U(P_2, f, \alpha) = \overline{\int_{[a,b]}} f(x) d\alpha(x).$$

**Definition 9.8.** *A bounded function $f : [a, b] \to \mathbb{R}$ is said to be integrable on an interval $[a, b]$ with respect to increasing function $\alpha$, denoted by $f \in \mathcal{R}(\alpha)[a, b]$, if*

$$\underline{\int_{[a,b]}} f(x) d\alpha(x) = \overline{\int_{[a,b]}} f(x) d\alpha(x).$$

*This value is called the* Riemann–Stieltjes integral *of $f$ with respect to $\alpha$ and is denoted as*

$$\int_a^b f(x) d\alpha(x).$$

*If $\alpha(x) = x$ then this integral is called the* definite Riemann integral *and we write $f \in \mathcal{R}[a, b]$.*

**Theorem 9.9 (Integrability condition).** *A bounded function $f \in \mathcal{R}(\alpha)[a, b]$ if and only if for any $\varepsilon > 0$ there exists a partition $P$ such that*

$$U(P, f, \alpha) - L(P, f, \alpha) < \varepsilon.$$

**Proof.** Suppose that for any $\varepsilon > 0$ there is partition $P$ such that

$$U(P, f, \alpha) - L(P, f, \alpha) < \varepsilon.$$

Using a corollary of Darboux's lemma we obtain

$$U(P, f, \alpha) \ge \overline{\int_{[a,b]}} f(x) d\alpha(x) \ge \underline{\int_{[a,b]}} f(x) d\alpha(x) \ge L(P, f, \alpha).$$

It follows that

$$0 \le \overline{\int_{[a,b]}} f(x) d\alpha(x) - \underline{\int_{[a,b]}} f(x) d\alpha(x) < \varepsilon.$$

Since $\varepsilon > 0$ is arbitrary we get

$$\overline{\int_{[a,b]}} f(x) d\alpha(x) = \underline{\int_{[a,b]}} f(x) d\alpha(x) = \int_a^b f(x) d\alpha(x).$$

Conversely, let $f \in \mathcal{R}(\alpha)[a, b]$, i.e.,

$$\overline{\int_{[a,b]}} f(x) d\alpha(x) = \underline{\int_{[a,b]}} f(x) d\alpha(x).$$

By the definition of upper and lower integrals we may conclude that for any $\varepsilon > 0$ there exists $P_1, P_2$ such that

$$\underline{\int_{[a,b]}} f(x)\mathrm{d}\alpha(x) - L(P_1, f, \alpha) < \varepsilon/2$$

and

$$U(P_2, f, \alpha) - \overline{\int_{[a,b]}} f(x)\mathrm{d}\alpha(x) < \varepsilon/2.$$

Setting $P = P_1 \cup P_2$ we obtain from Darboux's lemma that

$$0 \le U(P, f, \alpha) - L(P, f, \alpha) \le U(P_1, f, \alpha) - L(P_2, f, \alpha)$$
$$< \overline{\int_{[a,b]}} f(x)\mathrm{d}\alpha(x) + \varepsilon/2 - \underline{\int_{[a,b]}} f(x)\mathrm{d}\alpha(x) + \varepsilon/2 = \varepsilon.$$

Since $\varepsilon > 0$ was arbitrary, the theorem is proved.

**Theorem 9.10 (Integrability of continuous functions).** *Let $f : [a, b] \to \mathbb{R}$ be continuous. Then $f \in \mathcal{R}(\alpha)[a, b]$, and moreover for any $\varepsilon > 0$ there exists $\delta > 0$ such that*

$$\left| \sum_{j=1}^{n} f(\xi_j)\Delta\alpha_j - \int_a^b f(x)\mathrm{d}\alpha(x) \right| < \varepsilon$$

*for any $P$ with $\mu(P) < \delta$ and for any $\xi_j \in [x_{j-1}, x_j]$. Here $\sum_{j=1}^{n} f(\xi_j)\Delta\alpha_j =: \sigma(P, f, \alpha)$ is called the integral sum corresponding to $P$.*

**Proof.** Let $\varepsilon > 0$ be arbitrary and let $\eta$ be chosen such that $(\alpha(b) - \alpha(a))\eta < \varepsilon$. Next, since $f \in C[a, b]$, by virtue of the Cantor theorem it is uniformly continuous on $[a, b]$, and therefore for any $\eta > 0$ there exists $\delta > 0$ such that

$$|f(x') - f(x'')| < \eta$$

for all $x', x'' \in [a, b]$ with $|x' - x''| < \delta$. Hence, choosing $\mu(P) < \delta$ we obtain

$$M_j - m_j = \sup_{[x_{j-1}, x_j]} f - \inf_{[x_{j-1}, x_j]} f \le \eta, \quad j = 1, 2, \dots, n.$$

It follows that

$$U(P, f, \alpha) - L(P, f, \alpha) = \sum_{j=1}^{n} (M_j - m_j)\Delta\alpha_j \le \eta \sum_{j=1}^{n} (\alpha(x_j) - \alpha(x_{j-1}))$$
$$= \eta(\alpha(b) - \alpha(a)) < \varepsilon.$$

Moreover, for any partition $P$ with $\mu(P) < \delta$ we have

$$U(P, f, \alpha) \ge \sigma(P, f, \alpha) \ge L(P, f, \alpha)$$

and

$$U(P, f, \alpha) \ge \int_a^b f(x)\mathrm{d}\alpha(x) \ge L(P, f, \alpha).$$

This implies that

$$\left| \sigma(P, f, \alpha) - \int_a^b f(x) \mathrm{d}\alpha(x) \right| < \varepsilon.$$

Theorem 9.10 is proved.

**Definition 9.11.** *Let $f : [a, b] \to \mathbb{R}$ and let $P$ be a partition of $[a, b]$ such that*

$$\sigma(P, f, \alpha) = \sum_{j=1}^n f(\xi_j) \Delta \alpha_j.$$

*A number $I$ is a limit of $\sigma(P, f, \alpha)$ as $\mu(P) \to 0$ if for any $\varepsilon > 0$ there exists $\delta > 0$ such that for any $P$ with $\mu(P) < \delta$ and for any $\xi_j \in [x_{j-1}, x_j]$ we have*

$$|I - \sigma(P, f, \alpha)| < \varepsilon.$$

*This fact is denoted as*

$$\lim_{\mu(P) \to 0} \sigma(P, f, \alpha) = I.$$

**Theorem 9.12 (Equivalence of two definitions).** *Let $f : [a, b] \to \mathbb{R}$. Then $f$ is integrable with respect to $\alpha$, i.e., $f \in \mathcal{R}(\alpha)[a, b]$ if and only if $f$ is bounded and there exists*

$$\lim_{\mu(P) \to 0} \sigma(P, f, \alpha) = I,$$

*and, in this case,*

$$I = \int_a^b f(x) \mathrm{d}\alpha(x).$$

**Proof.** First let $f \in \mathcal{R}(\alpha)[a, b]$ in the sense of Definition 9.8. Then $f$ is bounded (by definition) and for any $\varepsilon > 0$ there exists $P$ such that

$$U(P, f, \alpha) - L(P, f, \alpha) < \varepsilon.$$

But then

$$L(P, f, \alpha) \leq \sigma(P, f, \alpha) \leq U(P, f, \alpha)$$

and

$$L(P, f, \alpha) \leq \int_a^b f(x) \mathrm{d}\alpha(x) \leq U(P, f, \alpha).$$

It follows that

$$\left| \sigma(P, f, \alpha) - \int_a^b f(x) \mathrm{d}\alpha(x) \right| < \varepsilon.$$

If we consider now any refinement $P'$ of $P$ with $\mu(P') < \mu(P) = \delta$ then Darboux's lemma gives us that

$$\left| \sigma(P', f, \alpha) - \int_a^b f(x) \mathrm{d}\alpha(x) \right| < \varepsilon.$$

This means that by Definition 9.11 there is

$$\lim_{\mu(P) \to 0} \sigma(P, f, \alpha) = \int_a^b f(x) \mathrm{d}\alpha(x).$$

Conversely, if we assume that

$$\lim_{\mu(P)\to 0} \sigma(P,f,\alpha) = I$$

then for any $\varepsilon > 0$ there exists $\delta > 0$ such that

$$I - \varepsilon < \sum_{j=1}^{n} f(\xi_j)\Delta\alpha_j < I + \varepsilon$$

for any $P$ with $\mu(P) < \delta$ and for any $\xi_j \in [x_{j-1}, x_j]$. This inequality implies first that $f$ is bounded on $[a, b]$ and second that

$$I - \varepsilon \le \sum_{j=1}^{n} \inf_{[x_{j-1},x_j]} f(x)\Delta\alpha_j \le \sum_{j=1}^{n} \sup_{[x_{j-1},x_j]} f(x)\Delta\alpha_j \le I + \varepsilon$$

or

$$I - \varepsilon \le L(P,f,\alpha) \le U(P,f,\alpha) \le I + \varepsilon.$$

Therefore

$$U(P,f,\alpha) - L(P,f,\alpha) < 2\varepsilon.$$

This means that $f \in \mathcal{R}(\alpha)[a, b]$ in the sense of Definition 9.8 and

$$I = \int_a^b f(x)\mathrm{d}\alpha(x).$$

Hence, the theorem is proved.

**Remark 9.13.** The limit in Theorem 9.10, if it exists, can be considered as an alternative definition of integrability of $f$ with respect to $\alpha$ and as the definition of the Riemann–Stieltjes integral, too.

**Theorem 9.14 (Integrability of monotone function).** *Let $f : [a, b] \to \mathbb{R}$ be monotone and let $\alpha : [a, b] \to \mathbb{R}$ be increasing and continuous. Then $f \in \mathcal{R}(\alpha)[a, b]$.*

*Proof.* We assume for definiteness and without loss of generality that $f$ is nondecreasing. Then

$$U(P,f,\alpha) - L(P,f,\alpha) = \sum_{j=1}^{n}(M_j - m_j)\Delta\alpha_j = \sum_{j=1}^{n}(f(x_j) - f(x_{j-1}))\Delta\alpha_j.$$

Since $\alpha$ is increasing and continuous we can find a partition $P$ such that

$$\Delta\alpha_j = \frac{\alpha(b) - \alpha(a)}{n}.$$

Thus, for this $P$ we have

$$U(P,f,\alpha) - L(P,f,\alpha) = \frac{\alpha(b) - \alpha(a)}{n}\sum_{j=1}^{n}(f(x_j) - f(x_{j-1}))$$

$$= \frac{(\alpha(b) - \alpha(a))(f(b) - f(a))}{n} < \varepsilon$$

if we choose, for given $\varepsilon > 0$, $n$ large enough. Thus, the theorem is proved.

Continuous and monotone functions do not exhaust the class of functions integrable in the Riemann–Stieltjes sense. Even if a bounded function is not continuous or monotone but its discontinuity points satisfy a certain property (there should not be too many of them and they should be distributed in the right way) then such functions will also be Riemann–Stieltjes integrable.

**Definition 9.15.** *Let $f : [a, b] \to \mathbb{R}$ be bounded. The function $f$ is said to have an "I-property" if for any $\varepsilon > 0$ there exists a finite number of intervals $I_1, I_2, \ldots, I_{k(\varepsilon)}$ such that all breakpoints of $f$ belong to $\bigcup_{j=1}^{k(\varepsilon)} I_j$ and $\sum_{j=1}^{k(\varepsilon)} |I_j| < \varepsilon$.*

**Exercise 9.16.** Show that

1. function $f$ has an "I-property" if the number of breakpoints of $f$ is finite,

2. function $f$ has an "I-property" if the set of all breakpoints of $f$ is a convergent sequence,

3. Dirichlet's function is not integrable.

**Theorem 9.17 ("I-property").** *Let $f : [a, b] \to \mathbb{R}$ satisfy the "I-property" and let $\alpha$ be continuous and increasing on $[a, b]$. Then $f \in \mathcal{R}(\alpha)[a, b]$.*

**Proof.** Since $f$ satisfies the "I-property," for any $\delta > 0$ there is a finite number of intervals $\{I_j\}_{j=1}^{k(\delta)}$ covering all breakpoints of $f$ such that

$$\sum_{j=1}^{k(\delta)} |I_j| < \delta.$$

Next, let us consider the set $[a, b] \setminus \bigcup_{j=1}^{k(\delta)} I_j$. This set is equal to the union

$$\bigcup_{l=1}^{N} [a_l, b_l], \quad [a_l, b_l] \cap [a_j, b_j] = \emptyset, \quad j \neq l.$$

Since $N$ is finite, by applying Cantor's theorem for each closed interval $[a_l, b_l]$ and for continuous function $f$ we obtain that for any $\varepsilon > 0$ there exists $\mu_l > 0$ such that

$$|f(x') - f(x'')| < \frac{\varepsilon}{2(\alpha(b) - \alpha(a))}$$

whenever $x', x'' \in [a_l, b_l]$ with $|x' - x''| < \mu_l$. Denoting $\mu = \min_{1 \le l \le n} \mu_l > 0$ we obtain that

$$|f(x') - f(x'')| < \frac{\varepsilon}{2(\alpha(b) - \alpha(a))}$$

whenever $x', x'' \in \bigcup_{l=1}^{N} [a_l, b_l]$ with $|x' - x''| < \mu$.

Due to uniform continuity of $\alpha$ for any $\varepsilon > 0$ we can find $\delta > 0$ such that for each interval $(p, q) \in \{I_j\}_{j=1}^{k(\delta)}$ we have

$$\alpha(q) - \alpha(p) < \frac{\varepsilon}{2(M - m)k(\delta)},$$

where $\delta > 0$, which we have used above in connection to arbitrary $\varepsilon > 0$. We consider a partition

$P$ of the union of closed intervals $[a_l, b_l]$ and of the union $\bigcup_{j=1}^{k(\delta)} I_j$ such that $\mu(P) < \mu$. Then

$$U(P, f, \alpha) - L(P, f, \alpha) = \sum_{j \in \cup_{l=1}^N [a_l, b_l]} (M_j - m_j)\Delta\alpha_j + \sum_{j \notin \cup_{l=1}^N [a_l, b_l]} (M_j - m_j)\Delta\alpha_j$$

$$< \frac{\varepsilon}{2(\alpha(b) - \alpha(a))} \sum{}' \Delta\alpha_j + (M - m)\sum{}'' \Delta\alpha_j$$

$$< \frac{\varepsilon}{2(\alpha(b) - \alpha(a))}(\alpha(b) - \alpha(a)) + (M - m)k(\delta)\frac{\varepsilon}{2(M - m)k(\delta)} = \varepsilon.$$

This proves the theorem.

**Example 9.18.**    1. Let $f(x) = \text{sgn}(\sin(\pi/x))$, $f(0) = 1$ and $x \in [0, 2]$. This function is bounded and its breakpoints are $\{1/n\}_{n=1}^\infty \cup \{0\}$. Because $\lim_{n \to \infty} \frac{1}{n} = 0$ (see Exercise 9.16), $f$ possesses an "I-property" and therefore $f \in \mathcal{R}(\alpha)[0, 2]$ with continuous $\alpha$.

2. Let $R(x)$ be the Riemann function. As we know, $R$ is not continuous at any rational number. $R(x)$ does not possess an "I-property" on any closed interval $[a, b]$ because its breakpoints are dense everywhere. But nevertheless $R \in \mathcal{R}[a, b]$ for any interval $[a, b]$. Indeed, since for any partition of $[a, b]$ it follows that $L(P, f) = 0$, for the integrability it suffices to show that for any $\varepsilon > 0$ there exists $P$ such that $U(P, f) < \varepsilon$.

For given $\varepsilon > 0$ we have

$$U(P, f) = \sum_{M_j < \varepsilon/(2(b-a))}{}' M_j \Delta x_j + \sum_{\varepsilon/(2(b-a)) < M_j \leq 1}{}'' M_j \Delta x_j$$

$$< \frac{\varepsilon}{2(b-a)}(b - a) + \sum_{\varepsilon/(2(b-a)) < M_j \leq 1}{}'' \Delta x_j < \varepsilon$$

since the number of points in the second sum is finite and we can cover them by $\sum{}'' \Delta x_j < \varepsilon/2$.

**Theorem 9.19 (Properties of Riemann–Stieltjes integral).**

1. *If $f_1, f_2 \in \mathcal{R}(\alpha)[a, b]$ then $c_1 f_1 + c_2 f_2 \in \mathcal{R}(\alpha)[a, b]$ for any constants $c_1, c_2$ and*

$$\int_a^b (c_1 f_1(x) + c_2 f_2(x))d\alpha(x) = c_1 \int_a^b f_1(x)d\alpha(x) + c_2 \int_a^b f_2(x)d\alpha(x).$$

2. *If $f \in \mathcal{R}(\alpha)[a, b]$ then for any $\xi \in [a, b]$ we have $f \in \mathcal{R}(\alpha)[a, \xi]$ and $f \in \mathcal{R}(\alpha)[\xi, b]$ and*

$$\int_a^b f(x)d\alpha(x) = \int_a^\xi f(x)d\alpha(x) + \int_\xi^b f(x)d\alpha(x).$$

3. *If $f_1, f_2 \in \mathcal{R}(\alpha)[a, b]$ and $f_1(x) \leq f_2(x)$ everywhere on $[a, b]$ then*

$$\int_a^b f_1(x)d\alpha(x) \leq \int_a^b f_2(x)d\alpha(x).$$

4. *If $f \in \mathcal{R}(\alpha)[a, b]$ and $M = \sup_{[a,b]} f(x)$ and $m = \inf_{[a,b]} f(x)$ then*

$$m(\alpha(b) - \alpha(a)) \leq \int_a^b f(x)d\alpha(x) \leq M(\alpha(b) - \alpha(a))$$

*so that*

$$\left| \int_a^b f(x) d\alpha(x) \right| \le A(\alpha(b) - \alpha(a)), \quad A = \max(|m|, |M|).$$

5. *If $f \in \mathcal{R}(\alpha_1)[a,b]$ and $f \in \mathcal{R}(\alpha_2)[a,b]$ then $f \in \mathcal{R}(\alpha_1 + \alpha_2)[a,b]$ and $f \in \mathcal{R}(c\alpha_1)[a,b]$ with $c > 0$ and*

$$\int_a^b f(x) d(\alpha_1(x) + \alpha_2(x)) = \int_a^b f(x) d\alpha_1(x) + \int_a^b f(x) d\alpha_2(x)$$

*and*

$$\int_a^b f(x) d(c\alpha_1(x)) = c \int_a^b f(x) d\alpha_1(x).$$

***Proof.*** We give the proofs of parts 1 and 2. Parts 3–5 can be proved in a similar manner. First, we obtain that $cf \in \mathcal{R}(\alpha)[a,b]$ since

$$U(P, cf, \alpha) - L(P, cf, \alpha) = |c|(U(P, f, \alpha) - L(P, f, \alpha)) < \varepsilon,$$

which can be provided since $f \in \mathcal{R}(\alpha)[a,b]$. The equality

$$\int_a^b cf(x) d\alpha(x) = c \int_a^b f(x) d\alpha(x)$$

then follows straightforwardly.

For the sum $f = f_1 + f_2$ we have

$$U(P, f, \alpha) \le U(P, f_1, \alpha) + U(P, f_2, \alpha)$$

and

$$L(P, f, \alpha) \ge L(P, f_1, \alpha) + L(P, f_2, \alpha).$$

Also, for any $\varepsilon > 0$ there exist $P_1$ and $P_2$ such that

$$U(P_1, f_1, \alpha) - L(P_1, f_1, \alpha) < \varepsilon/2$$

and

$$U(P_2, f_2, \alpha) - L(P_2, f_2, \alpha) < \varepsilon/2.$$

Considering now $P = P_1 \cup P_2$ and all the above inequalities we obtain

$$\begin{aligned}
U(P, f, \alpha) - L(P, f, \alpha) &\le U(P, f_1, \alpha) + U(P, f_2, \alpha) - L(P, f_1, \alpha) - L(P, f_2, \alpha) \\
&\le U(P_1, f_1, \alpha) + U(P_2, f_2, \alpha) - L(P_1, f_1, \alpha) - L(P_2, f_2, \alpha) \\
&< \varepsilon/2 + \varepsilon/2 = \varepsilon.
\end{aligned}$$

Hence $f = f_1 + f_2 \in \mathcal{R}(\alpha)[a,b]$ and

$$\int_a^b (f_1(x) + f_2(x)) d\alpha(x) \le U(P, f_1 + f_2, \alpha) \le U(P, f_1, \alpha) + U(P, f_2, \alpha)$$

$$< \int_a^b f_1(x) d\alpha(x) + \varepsilon/2 + \int_a^b f_2(x) d\alpha(x) + \varepsilon/2.$$

Since $\varepsilon > 0$ is arbitrary we obtain

$$\int_a^b (f_1(x) + f_2(x))\mathrm{d}\alpha(x) \leq \int_a^b f_1(x)\mathrm{d}\alpha(x) + \int_a^b f_2(x)\mathrm{d}\alpha(x).$$

This inequality holds also in the opposite direction since

$$\int_a^b ((-f_1(x)) + (-f_2(x)))\mathrm{d}\alpha(x) \leq \int_a^b (-f_1(x))\mathrm{d}\alpha(x) + \int_a^b (-f_2(x))\mathrm{d}\alpha(x)$$

or

$$-\int_a^b (f_1(x) + f_2(x))\mathrm{d}\alpha(x) \leq -\int_a^b f_1(x)\mathrm{d}\alpha(x) - \int_a^b f_2(x)\mathrm{d}\alpha(x).$$

So part 1 is proved.

In order to prove part 2 let us consider the partition $P = P_1 \cup P_2$ with $P_1 \cap P_2 = \xi$, where $P_1$ is a partition of $[a, \xi]$ and $P_2$ is a partition of $[\xi, b]$ for fixed arbitrary $\xi \in (a, b)$ (the cases $\xi = a$ and $\xi = b$ are trivial). Then

$$L(P, f, \alpha) = L(P_1, f, \alpha) + L(P_2, f, \alpha), \quad U(P, f, \alpha) = U(P_1, f, \alpha) + U(P_2, f, \alpha).$$

Therefore we obtain

$$\underline{\int}_{[a,b]} f(x)\mathrm{d}\alpha(x) \leq \underline{\int}_{[a,\xi]} f(x)\mathrm{d}\alpha(x) + \underline{\int}_{[\xi,b]} f(x)\mathrm{d}\alpha(x)$$

and

$$\overline{\int}_{[a,b]} f(x)\mathrm{d}\alpha(x) \geq \overline{\int}_{[a,\xi]} f(x)\mathrm{d}\alpha(x) + \overline{\int}_{[\xi,b]} f(x)\mathrm{d}\alpha(x).$$

Since $f \in \mathcal{R}(\alpha)[a, b]$, we have

$$\underline{\int}_{[a,b]} f(x)\mathrm{d}\alpha(x) = \overline{\int}_{[a,b]} f(x)\mathrm{d}\alpha(x).$$

Hence

$$\underline{\int}_{[a,\xi]} f(x)\mathrm{d}\alpha(x) + \underline{\int}_{[\xi,b]} f(x)\mathrm{d}\alpha(x) \geq \overline{\int}_{[a,\xi]} f(x)\mathrm{d}\alpha(x) + \overline{\int}_{[\xi,b]} f(x)\mathrm{d}\alpha(x).$$

But the opposite inequality is always true and we get

$$\int_a^b f(x)\mathrm{d}\alpha(x) = \int_a^\xi f(x)\mathrm{d}\alpha(x) + \int_\xi^b f(x)\mathrm{d}\alpha(x).$$

**Definition 9.20.** *Let* $\varphi : [c, d] \to \mathbb{R}$ *be bounded. We say that it satisfies the* Lipschitz *condition with index* $s \in (0, 1]$ *if there is a constant* $c_s > 0$ *such that*

$$|\varphi(x_1) - \varphi(x_2)| \leq c_s |x_1 - x_2|^s$$

*for any* $x_1, x_2 \in [c, d]$.

**Remark 9.21.** If the Lipschitz condition holds with index $s > 1$ then $f \equiv$ constant (see Exercise 6.47).

**Theorem 9.22 (Integrability of superposition).** *Let $f \in \mathcal{R}(\alpha)[a, b]$ with $m = \inf_{[a,b]} f(x)$ and $M = \sup_{[a,b]} f(x)$. Let $\varphi$ be defined on the interval $[m, M]$ and satisfy the Lipschitz condition with index $s \in (0, 1]$. Then the superposition $h(x) = \varphi(f(x))$ belongs to $\mathcal{R}(\alpha)[a, b]$.*

*Proof.* By hypothesis

$$U(P, h, \alpha) - L(P, h, \alpha) = \sum_{j=1}^{n} (M_j^h - m_j^h)\Delta\alpha_j \leq c_s \sum_{j=1}^{n} (M_j^f - m_j^f)^s \Delta\alpha_j$$

$$= c_s \sum_{j=1}^{n} ((M_j^f - m_j^f)\Delta\alpha_j)^s (\Delta\alpha_j)^{1-s},$$

where $M_j^h, m_j^h, M_j^f, m_j^f$ denote the supremum and infimum of the functions $h$ and $f$ on the interval $[x_{j-1}, x_j]$, respectively. Applying Hölder's inequality we obtain

$$U(P, h, \alpha) - L(P, h, \alpha) \leq c_s \left( \sum_{j=1}^{n} (M_j^f - m_j^f)\Delta\alpha_j \right)^s \left( \sum_{j=1}^{n} \Delta\alpha_j \right)^{1-s}$$

$$= c_s (U(P, f, \alpha) - L(P, f, \alpha))^s (\alpha(b) - \alpha(a))^{1-s} < \varepsilon$$

if $P$ is chosen (due to integrability of $f$) such that

$$U(P, f, \alpha) - L(P, f, \alpha) < \left( \frac{\varepsilon}{c_s(\alpha(b) - \alpha(a))^{1-s}} \right)^{1/s}.$$

This proves the theorem.

**Exercise 9.23.** Prove that if $f \in \mathcal{R}(\alpha)[a, b]$ and $\varphi$ is continuous then the superposition $h(x) = \varphi(f(x))$ belongs to $\mathcal{R}(\alpha)[a, b]$.

**Example 9.24.** Let $f(x) = R(x)$ be the Riemann function on the interval $[1, 2]$ and $\varphi(y) = \operatorname{sgn} y$. Then the superposition $h(x) = \operatorname{sgn}(R(x)) = D(x)$ is the Dirichlet function. But it is known that $D(x) \notin \mathcal{R}[1, 2]$. This shows that the continuity condition for superposition (see Exercise 9.23) is essential.

**Theorem 9.25 (Integrability of modulus).** *Let $f$ and $g$ be integrable in the sense of the Riemann–Stieltjes integral on the interval $[a, b]$. Then*

1. *function $f(x)g(x) \in \mathcal{R}(\alpha)[a, b]$,*

2. *functions $|f(x)|, |g(x)| \in \mathcal{R}(\alpha)[a, b]$ too, and*

$$\left| \int_a^b f(x)\,d\alpha(x) \right| \leq \int_a^b |f(x)|\,d\alpha(x).$$

*Proof.*

1. Due to

$$fg = \frac{1}{4}((f + g)^2 - (f - g)^2)$$

it suffices to prove that $f^2(x) \in \mathcal{R}(\alpha)[a, b]$ if $f(x) \in \mathcal{R}(\alpha)[a, b]$. This fact can be provided using the superposition

$$f^2(x) = \varphi(f(x)), \quad \varphi(y) = y^2.$$

It remains to show that $\varphi(y) = y^2$ satisfies the Lipschitz condition. Indeed,

$$|y_1^2 - y_2^2| \le (|y_1| + |y_2|)|y_1 - y_2| \le 2\max(|m|, |M|)|y_1 - y_2|,$$

where $y_1, y_2 \in [m, M]$. The integrability of $f^2(x)$ follows now from Theorem 9.22.

2. In order to prove the claim for modulus we consider the superposition

$$|f(x)| = \varphi(f(x)), \quad \varphi(y) = |y|.$$

Clearly, $\varphi$ satisfies the Lipschitz condition since

$$\big||y_1| - |y_2|\big| \le |y_1 - y_2|.$$

Furthermore,

$$\left| \int_a^b f(x)\mathrm{d}\alpha(x) \right| = c \int_a^b f(x)\mathrm{d}\alpha(x) = \int_a^b cf(x)\mathrm{d}\alpha(x) \le \int_a^b |f(x)|\mathrm{d}\alpha(x),$$

where $c = \pm 1$ and $cf(x) \le |f(x)|$ everywhere on the interval $[a, b]$.

The theorem is completely proved. $\qquad\blacksquare$

**Exercise 9.26.** Prove that if $f \in \mathcal{R}(\alpha)[a, b]$ then $|f|^s \in \mathcal{R}(\alpha)[a, b]$ for any $s > 0$.

**Theorem 9.27 (First mean value theorem).** *Let $f$ and $g$ be integrable on an interval $[a, b]$. Assume in addition that $g(x) \ge 0$ ($g(x) \le 0$) everywhere on the interval $[a, b]$. Then there is $\mu \in [m, M]$, where $m = \inf_{[a,b]} f(x)$ and $M = \sup_{[a,b]} f(x)$ such that*

$$\int_a^b f(x)g(x)\mathrm{d}\alpha(x) = \mu \int_a^b g(x)\mathrm{d}\alpha(x).$$

*If additionally $f$ is continuous on the interval $[a, b]$ then there is $\xi \in [a, b]$ such that*

$$\int_a^b f(x)g(x)\mathrm{d}\alpha(x) = f(\xi) \int_a^b g(x)\mathrm{d}\alpha(x).$$

***Proof.*** Let $g(x) \ge 0$ for definiteness. In that case

$$m \int_a^b g(x)\mathrm{d}\alpha(x) \le \int_a^b f(x)g(x)\mathrm{d}\alpha(x) \le M \int_a^b g(x)\mathrm{d}\alpha(x).$$

If it turns out that $\int_a^b g(x)\mathrm{d}\alpha(x) = 0$ then $\int_a^b f(x)g(x)\mathrm{d}\alpha(x) = 0$ also and thus

$$\int_a^b f(x)g(x)\mathrm{d}\alpha(x) = \mu \int_a^b g(x)\mathrm{d}\alpha(x)$$

holds for any $\mu$. If $\int_a^b g(x)\mathrm{d}\alpha(x) > 0$ then

$$m \le \frac{\int_a^b f(x)g(x)\mathrm{d}\alpha(x)}{\int_a^b g(x)\mathrm{d}\alpha(x)} \le M$$

and so

$$\mu = \frac{\int_a^b f(x)g(x)\mathrm{d}\alpha(x)}{\int_a^b g(x)\mathrm{d}\alpha(x)}$$

will do. If $f$ is continuous on $[a, b]$ then $f$ takes any value from the interval $[m, M]$. Hence there is $\xi \in [a, b]$ such that $\mu = f(\xi)$.

**Corollary 9.28.** *Let $f \in C[a, b]$ and $g \equiv 1$ on the interval $[a, b]$. Then there is $\xi \in [a, b]$ such that*

$$\int_a^b f(x)\mathrm{d}\alpha(x) = f(\xi)(\alpha(b) - \alpha(a)).$$

Let $f$ be integrable on the interval $[a, b]$. Then for any $x \in [a, b]$ the function

$$F(x) := \int_a^x f(x)\mathrm{d}\alpha(x), \quad x \in [a, b],$$

is well-defined. It is called an *integral with variable upper bound*.

**Theorem 9.29 (Properties of the integral with variable upper bound).**

1. *Let $f \in \mathcal{R}(\alpha)[a, b]$ and let $\alpha(x)$ be continuous at some point $x_0 \in [a, b]$. Then $F(x)$ is continuous at $x_0$ too.*

2. *Let $f \in \mathcal{R}(\alpha)[a, b]$ and be continuous at some point $x_0 \in [a, b]$. If $\alpha(x)$ is differentiable at $x_0$ then $F(x)$ is also differentiable at $x_0$ and*

$$F'(x_0) = f(x_0)\alpha'(x_0).$$

*Proof.*

1. Let $x_0 \in [a, b]$ and let $h \neq 0$ such that $x_0 + h \in [a, b]$. Then

$$F(x_0 + h) - F(x_0) = \int_a^{x_0+h} f(x)\mathrm{d}\alpha(x) - \int_a^{x_0} f(x)\mathrm{d}\alpha(x)$$

$$= \begin{cases} \int_{x_0}^{x_0+h} f(x)\mathrm{d}\alpha(x), & h > 0, \\ -\int_{x_0+h}^{x_0} f(x)\mathrm{d}\alpha(x), & h < 0. \end{cases}$$

Since $f$ is bounded, we have

$$|F(x_0 + h) - F(x_0)| \leq A|\alpha(x_0 + h) - \alpha(x_0)| \to 0$$

as $h \to 0$ due to continuity of $\alpha$ at the point $x_0$.

2. Let $x_0$ and $h$ be as above. Then we have

$$\frac{F(x_0 + h) - F(x_0)}{h} = \begin{cases} \frac{1}{h}\int_{x_0}^{x_0+h} f(x)\mathrm{d}\alpha(x), & h > 0, \\ -\frac{1}{h}\int_{x_0+h}^{x_0} f(x)\mathrm{d}\alpha(x), & h < 0, \end{cases}$$

$$= f(x_0)\frac{\alpha(x_0 + h) - \alpha(x_0)}{h} + \begin{cases} \frac{1}{h}\int_{x_0}^{x_0+h}(f(x) - f(x_0))\mathrm{d}\alpha(x), & h > 0, \\ -\frac{1}{h}\int_{x_0+h}^{x_0}(f(x) - f(x_0))\mathrm{d}\alpha(x), & h < 0, \end{cases}$$

$$=: I_1 + I_2.$$

Conditions of the theorem imply that

$$\lim_{h \to 0} I_1 = f(x_0)\alpha'(x_0).$$

It remains to prove that $\lim_{h \to 0} I_2 = 0$. To this end, since $f$ is continuous at $x_0$, for any $\varepsilon > 0$ there exists $\delta > 0$ such that

$$|f(x) - f(x_0)| < \varepsilon$$

whenever $x \in [a, b]$ and $|x - x_0| < \delta$. Taking $0 < |h| < \delta$ we obtain

$$|I_2| < \varepsilon \frac{\alpha(x_0 + h) - \alpha(x_0)}{h} \to 0$$

as $\varepsilon \to 0$.

Theorem 9.29 is completely proved.

**Exercise 9.30.**      1.  Assume that $f \in \mathcal{R}[a, b]$ has a breakpoint of the first kind at $x_0 \in (a, b)$. Prove that

$$F'_{\pm}(x_0) = f(x_0 \pm 0),$$

i.e., $F$ is not differentiable at $x_0$.

2.  Let $f \in \mathcal{R}[a, b]$ be continuous on the interval $[a, b]$. Let $a(x)$ and $b(x)$ be differentiable and let $a \leq a(x), b(x) \leq b$ for all $x \in [a, b]$. Prove that

$$F(x) := \int_{a(x)}^{b(x)} f(t)\mathrm{d}t$$

is differentiable on the interval $[a, b]$ and

$$F'(x) = f(b(x))b'(x) - f(a(x))a'(x).$$

**Exercise 9.31.**      1.  Let $f$ be differentiable on the interval $[a, b]$ with $f' \in C[a, b]$. Prove that $f \in BV[a, b]$ and

$$V_a^b(f) = \int_a^b |f'(x)|\mathrm{d}x.$$

2.  Let $f$ be differentiable on the interval $[a, b]$ with $f' \in C[a, b]$. Prove that $V_a^x(f)$ is also differentiable in $x$ and

$$(V_a^x(f))' = |f'(x)|.$$

3.  Let $f$ be differentiable on the interval $[a, b]$ such that $|f'(x)|$ is integrable on $[a, b]$ (this might be in the sense of improper integral; see Chapter 10). Prove that $f \in BV[a, b]$ and

$$V_a^b(f) \leq \int_a^b |f'(x)|\mathrm{d}x.$$

4. Using part 3, show that

(a) function

$$f(x) = \begin{cases} x^\alpha \sin(x^\beta), & x \in (0,1], \\ 0, & x = 0, \end{cases}$$

is of bounded variation if $\alpha + \beta > 0$ and

$$V_0^1(f) \le \begin{cases} \frac{|\alpha| + \beta}{\alpha + \beta}, & \beta > 0, \\ \frac{\alpha}{\alpha + \beta}, & \beta < 0, \end{cases}$$

(b) function

$$f(x) = \begin{cases} x^\alpha \cos(x^\beta), & x \in (0,1], \\ 0, & x = 0, \end{cases}$$

is of bounded variation if $\alpha > 0$ and $\alpha + \beta > 0$ with

$$V_0^1(f) \le \begin{cases} \frac{\alpha + 3\beta}{\alpha + 2\beta}, & \beta > 0, \\ \frac{\alpha - \beta}{\alpha + \beta}, & \beta < 0. \end{cases}$$

**Theorem 9.32 (Second mean value formula I).** *Let $f, g \in \mathcal{R}(\alpha)[a,b]$ with $g \ge 0$ and be nonincreasing. If $\alpha \in C[a,b]$ then there is $\xi \in [a,b]$ such that*

$$\int_a^b f(x)g(x)\mathrm{d}\alpha(x) = g(a) \int_a^\xi f(x)\mathrm{d}\alpha(x).$$

*Proof.* Let $P$ be a partition of $[a,b]$. Then

$$\int_a^b f(x)g(x)\mathrm{d}\alpha(x) = \sum_{j=1}^n \int_{x_{j-1}}^{x_j} f(x)g(x)\mathrm{d}\alpha(x)$$

$$= \sum_{j=1}^n g(x_{j-1}) \int_{x_{j-1}}^{x_j} f(x)\mathrm{d}\alpha(x) + \sum_{j=1}^n \int_{x_{j-1}}^{x_j} f(x)(g(x) - g(x_{j-1}))\mathrm{d}\alpha(x) =: I_1 + I_2.$$

We can make $I_2$ as small as we want due to the choice of partition $P$. Indeed,

$$|I_2| \le \sum_{j=1}^n \int_{x_{j-1}}^{x_j} |f(x)||g(x) - g(x_{j-1})|\mathrm{d}\alpha(x) \le A \sum_{j=1}^n (M_j^g - m_j^g)\Delta\alpha_j$$

$$= A(U(P,g,\alpha) - L(P,g,\alpha)) < \varepsilon$$

due to integrability of $g$. It means that for any integrable $f$ and $g$ we have

$$\int_a^b f(x)g(x)\mathrm{d}\alpha(x) = \lim_{\mu(P) \to 0} \sum_{j=1}^n g(x_{j-1}) \int_{x_{j-1}}^{x_j} f(x)\mathrm{d}\alpha(x).$$

Furthermore, we have

$$I_1 = \sum_{j=1}^n g(x_{j-1}) \int_{x_{j-1}}^{x_j} f(x)\mathrm{d}\alpha(x) = \sum_{j=1}^n g(x_{j-1})(F(x_j) - F(x_{j-1})),$$

where

$$F(x) = \int_a^x f(t)\mathrm{d}\alpha(t).$$

This allows us to write $I_1$ as

$$I_1 = \sum_{j=1}^n g(x_{j-1})F(x_j) - \sum_{j=1}^n g(x_{j-1})F(x_{j-1})$$

$$= \sum_{j=1}^n g(x_{j-1})F(x_j) - \sum_{j=0}^{n-1} g(x_j)F(x_j)$$

$$= \sum_{j=1}^{n-1}(g(x_{j-1}) - g(x_j))F(x_j) + g(x_{n-1})F(x_n) - g(x_0)F(x_0)$$

$$= \sum_{j=1}^{n-1}(g(x_{j-1}) - g(x_j))F(x_j) + g(x_{n-1})F(b)$$

since $F(x_0) = F(a) = 0$ and $F(x_n) = F(b)$. Function $g$ is nonincreasing, and therefore we have

$$m^F(g(a) - g(x_{n-1})) \le \sum_{j=1}^{n-1}(g(x_{j-1}) - g(x_j))F(x_j) \le M^F(g(a) - g(x_{n-1})).$$

It follows that

$$m^F(g(a) - g(x_{n-1})) + g(x_{n-1})F(b) \le I_1 \le M^F(g(a) - g(x_{n-1})) + g(x_{n-1})F(b).$$

Since $g \ge 0$, we obtain

$$m^F g(a) \le I_1 = \sum_{j=1}^n g(x_{j-1}) \int_{x_{j-1}}^{x_j} f(x)\mathrm{d}\alpha(x) \le M^F g(a)$$

so that

$$m^F g(a) \le \lim_{\mu(P) \to 0} \sum_{j=1}^n g(x_{j-1}) \int_{x_{j-1}}^{x_j} f(x)\mathrm{d}\alpha(x) \le M^F g(a).$$

Thus

$$m^F g(a) \le \int_a^b f(x)g(x)\mathrm{d}\alpha(x) \le M^F g(a).$$

Finally, we may use the fact that $\alpha$ is continuous to conclude that $F$ is also continuous, and therefore there exists $\xi \in [a, b]$ such that

$$\int_a^b f(x)g(x)\mathrm{d}\alpha(x) = F(\xi)g(a) = g(a) \int_a^\xi f(x)\mathrm{d}\alpha(x).$$

This finishes the proof.

**Theorem 9.33 (Second mean value formula II).** *Let $f, g \in \mathcal{R}(\alpha)[a, b]$. If $g$ is monotone and $\alpha$ is continuous then there exists $\xi \in [a, b]$ such that*

$$\int_a^b f(x)g(x)\mathrm{d}\alpha(x) = g(a) \int_a^\xi f(x)\mathrm{d}\alpha(x) + g(b) \int_\xi^b f(x)\mathrm{d}\alpha(x).$$

*Proof.* Let us assume first that $g$ is nondecreasing. Then $G(x) := g(b) - g(x)$ is nonincreasing and $G(x) \geq 0$. Applying Theorem 9.32 to $f$ and $G$ we obtain

$$\int_a^b f(x)G(x)\mathrm{d}\alpha(x) = G(a) \int_a^\xi f(x)\mathrm{d}\alpha(x)$$

or

$$\int_a^b f(x)g(b)\mathrm{d}\alpha(x) - \int_a^b f(x)g(x)\mathrm{d}\alpha(x) = (g(b) - g(a)) \int_a^\xi f(x)\mathrm{d}\alpha(x).$$

This yields

$$\int_a^b f(x)g(x)\mathrm{d}\alpha(x)$$
$$= g(a) \int_a^\xi f(x)\mathrm{d}\alpha(x) + g(b)\left( \int_a^b f(x)\mathrm{d}\alpha(x) - \int_a^\xi f(x)\mathrm{d}\alpha(x)\right)$$
$$= g(a) \int_a^\xi f(x)\mathrm{d}\alpha(x) + g(b) \int_\xi^b f(x)\mathrm{d}\alpha(x).$$

If $g$ is nonincreasing then we denote $G(x) := g(x) - g(b)$ and apply the same technique as above to obtain the same result. Thus, the theorem is completely proved.

**Exercise 9.34.**     1. Let function $f$ be Riemann integrable on the interval $[a, b]$, and let $\alpha$ be increasing and differentiable with $\alpha' \in \mathcal{R}[a, b]$. Prove that $f \in \mathcal{R}(\alpha)[a, b]$ and

$$\int_a^b f(x)\mathrm{d}\alpha(x) = \int_a^b f(x)\alpha'(x)\mathrm{d}x.$$

2. Let function $f$ be Riemann–Stieltjes integrable on the interval $[a, b]$, and let $\alpha$ be differentiable with $\alpha' \in \mathcal{R}[a, b]$. Prove that $f\alpha' \in \mathcal{R}[a, b]$ and

$$\int_a^b f(x)\alpha'(x)\mathrm{d}x = \int_a^b f(x)\mathrm{d}\alpha(x).$$

**Theorem 9.35 (Newton–Leibniz formula).** *Let $f$ be continuous on an interval $[a, b]$. Then it has a primitive $F$ on this interval of the form*

$$F(x) = \int_a^x f(t)\mathrm{d}t + \text{constant}.$$

*Moreover,*

$$\int_a^b f(t)\mathrm{d}t = F(b) - F(a),$$

*where $F$ is any primitive for $f$ on the interval $[a, b]$.*

*Proof.* Denoting

$$\widetilde{F}(x) := \int_a^x f(t)\mathrm{d}t$$

(the Riemann integral with variable upper bound) we obtain for continuous $f$ (see Theorem 9.29) that

$$\widetilde{F}'(x) = f(x), \quad x \in [a, b].$$

Hence, $\widetilde{F}$ is a primitive for $f$ on the interval $[a,b]$. Since all primitives for $f$ differ by a constant (see Theorem 8.2), we obtain that any primitive $F$ for $f$ can be written in the form

$$F(x) = \int_a^x f(t)\mathrm{d}t + C, \quad C = F(a).$$

This implies the Newton–Leibniz formula, and theorem is proved.

**Corollary 9.36.** *Let* $f : [a,b] \to \mathbb{R}$ *be bounded. If* $f$ *has a finite number* $\{x_j\}_{j=1}^m$ *of breakpoints of the first kind,*

$$x_0 = a < x_1 < x_2 < \cdots < x_m < b = x_{m+1},$$

*then*

$$\int_a^b f(x)\mathrm{d}x = \sum_{j=0}^m (F_j(x_{j+1}) - F_j(x_j)),$$

*where*

$$F_j(x) = \int_{x_j}^x f(t)\mathrm{d}t, \quad j = 0, 1, \ldots, m, \quad x \in [x_j, x_{j+1}].$$

**Exercise 9.37.** Prove the latter corollary.

**Theorem 9.38 (Change of variable).** *Let* $f : [a,b] \to \mathbb{R}$ *be a Riemann integrable function. Assume that* $\varphi$ *is continuous and increasing on the interval* $[a,b]$. *Then the function* $h(y) := f(\psi(y)), \psi = \varphi^{-1}$ *is Riemann–Stieltjes integrable, i.e.,* $h \in \mathcal{R}(\psi)[\varphi(a), \varphi(b)]$, *and*

$$\int_a^b f(x)\mathrm{d}x = \int_{\varphi(a)}^{\varphi(b)} f(\psi(y))\mathrm{d}\psi(y) = \int_{\varphi(a)}^{\varphi(b)} h(y)\mathrm{d}\psi(y).$$

*This formula is called the* change of variable *formula.*

*Proof.* Let $P$ and $Q$ be partitions of $[a,b]$ and $[\varphi(a), \varphi(b)]$, respectively. Since $\varphi$ is increasing, there is one-to-one correspondence between $P$ and $Q$, i.e.,

$$y_j = \varphi(x_j), \quad x_j = \psi(y_j), \quad \psi = \varphi^{-1}, \quad j = 1, 2, \ldots, n.$$

Then we have

$$L(P,f) = \sum_{j=1}^n m_j^f \Delta x_j = \sum_{j=1}^n m_j^f \Delta \psi_j = \sum_{j=1}^n m_j^h \Delta \psi_j$$
$$= L(Q, h, \psi) \le U(Q, h, \psi) = U(P, f).$$

This implies that

$$L(P,f) \le \sup_Q L(Q, h, \psi) = \inf_Q U(Q, h, \psi) \le U(P, f)$$

and further

$$\sup_P L(P,f) = \inf_P U(P,f) = \sup_Q L(Q, h, \psi) = \inf_Q U(Q, h, \psi).$$

So

$$\int_a^b f(x)\mathrm{d}x = \int_{\varphi(a)}^{\varphi(b)} h(y)\mathrm{d}\psi(y) = \int_{\varphi(a)}^{\varphi(b)} f(\psi(y))\mathrm{d}\psi(y).$$

Here we have used the fact that $\mu(P) \to 0$ if and only if $\mu(Q) \to 0$.

**Corollary 9.39.** *Let* $f \in \mathcal{R}(\alpha)[a,b]$ *and let* $\alpha$ *be continuous on the interval* $[a,b]$. *Then the superposition* $h(t) = f(\beta(t))$ *with* $\beta = \alpha^{-1}$ *belongs to* $\mathcal{R}[\alpha(a), \alpha(b)]$ *and*

$$\int_a^b f(x)\mathrm{d}\alpha(x) = \int_{\alpha(a)}^{\alpha(b)} h(t)\mathrm{d}t = \int_{\alpha(a)}^{\alpha(b)} f(\beta(t))\mathrm{d}t.$$

*If, in addition,* $\alpha$ *is differentiable then*

$$\int_a^b f(x)\mathrm{d}\alpha(x) = \int_a^b f(x)\alpha'(x)\mathrm{d}x = \int_{\alpha(a)}^{\alpha(b)} f(\beta(t))\mathrm{d}t.$$

**Theorem 9.40 (Integration by parts).** *Let* $u$ *and* $v$ *be continuously differentiable on the interval* $[a,b]$. *Then*

$$\int_a^b u(x)v'(x)\mathrm{d}x = u(b)v(b) - u(a)v(a) - \int_a^b u'(x)v(x)\mathrm{d}x.$$

***Proof.*** By hypothesis $(uv)'$ is continuous on the interval $[a,b]$. Hence, the Newton–Leibniz formula gives that

$$\int_a^b u'(x)v(x)\mathrm{d}x + \int_a^b u(x)v'(x)\mathrm{d}x = \int_a^b (u(x)v(x))'\mathrm{d}x = u(b)v(b) - u(a)v(a).$$

The claim follows now by rearranging.

**Corollary 9.41.** *Let* $u$ *and* $v$ *be continuous and increasing on the interval* $[a,b]$. *Then*

$$\int_a^b u(x)\mathrm{d}v(x) = u(b)v(b) - u(a)v(a) - \int_a^b v(x)\mathrm{d}u(x),$$

*where both Riemann–Stieltjes integrals exist.*

**Corollary 9.42 (Taylor's formula with remainder in integral form).** *Let* $f$ *be* $n+1$ *times continuously differentiable in* $U_\delta(a)$. *Then*

$$f(x) = \sum_{j=0}^n \frac{f^{(j)}(a)}{j!}(x-a)^j + \frac{1}{n!}\int_a^x f^{(n+1)}(t)(x-t)^n\mathrm{d}t$$

*for any* $x \in U_\delta'(a)$.

**Corollary 9.43.** *Let* $f, g \in \mathcal{R}(\alpha)[a,b]$. *Then for any* $1 < p < \infty$ *we have the* Hölder's inequality *for integrals*

$$\int_a^b |f(x)||g(x)|\mathrm{d}\alpha(x) \leq \left(\int_a^b |f(x)|^p \mathrm{d}\alpha(x)\right)^{1/p} \left(\int_a^b |g(x)|^{p'} \mathrm{d}\alpha(x)\right)^{1/p'}$$

*and* Minkowski's inequality *for integrals*

$$\left(\int_a^b |f(x) \pm g(x)|^p \mathrm{d}\alpha(x)\right)^{1/p} \leq \left(\int_a^b |f(x)|^p \mathrm{d}\alpha(x)\right)^{1/p} + \left(\int_a^b |g(x)|^p \mathrm{d}\alpha(x)\right)^{1/p}.$$

**Exercise 9.44.**     1. Prove Corollaries 9.41, 9.42, and 9.43.

2. Generalize the Hölder's and Minkowski's inequalities for $p = 1$ and $p = \infty$.

**Exercise 9.45.**     1. Using the change of variable formula prove that

$$\int_0^\pi \frac{x \sin x}{1 + \cos^2 x}\mathrm{d}x = \frac{\pi^2}{4}$$

and

$$\int_0^{\pi/2} \log(\sin x)\mathrm{d}x = \int_0^{\pi/2} \log(\cos x)\mathrm{d}x = -\frac{\pi}{2}\log 2.$$

2. Using the change of variable formula and recursive connections prove that

$$I_n = \int_0^{\pi/2} \sin^n x\mathrm{d}x = \int_0^{\pi/2} \cos^n x\mathrm{d}x$$

$$= \frac{(n-1)!!}{n!!}\begin{cases} \frac{\pi}{2}, & n = 2k, k = 1, 2, \ldots, \\ 1, & n = 2k+1, k = 0, 1, \ldots, \end{cases}$$

where $(2k)!! = 2 \cdot 4 \cdot 6 \cdots 2k$ and $(2k+1)!! = 1 \cdot 3 \cdot 5 \cdots (2k+1)$. Using this prove the famous *Wallis formula*

$$\lim_{n\to\infty} \left[\frac{(2n)!!}{(2n-1)!!}\right]^2 \frac{1}{2n} = \frac{\pi}{2}.$$

3. Compute

$$\lim_{n\to\infty} \int_{-2}^2 \frac{\mathrm{d}x}{1 + x^{2n}}.$$

**Exercise 9.46.**     1. Using the change of variable formula prove that

$$\int_0^1 \frac{\log(1+x)}{1+x^2}\mathrm{d}x = \frac{\pi}{8}\log 2.$$

2. Using the limit of integral sums prove that

$$\int_0^\pi \log(1 - 2a\cos x + a^2)\mathrm{d}x = \begin{cases} 0, & |a| < 1, \\ \pi \log a^2, & |a| \geq 1. \end{cases}$$

Hint: Write $1 - 2a\cos x + a^2 = (a - e^{\mathrm{i}x})(a - e^{-\mathrm{i}x})$ and consider

$$\int_0^\pi \log(1 - 2a\cos x + a^2)\mathrm{d}x = \lim_{n\to\infty} \frac{\pi}{n}\log\left[\prod_{k=0}^{n-1}(a - e^{\mathrm{i}\pi k/n})(a - e^{-\mathrm{i}\pi k/n})\right]$$

$$= \lim_{n\to\infty} \frac{\pi}{n}\log\frac{(a-1)(a^{2n}-1)}{a+1}.$$

3. Let a real-valued function $f$ satisfy the following conditions:

(a)

$$\int_{-\pi/2}^{\pi/2} \frac{\cos x}{f(x)}\mathrm{d}x$$

is well-defined.

(b) $f(x) + f(-x) = f(x)f(-x)$ for $x \in [-\pi/2, \pi/2]$.

Prove that

$$\int_{-\pi/2}^{\pi/2} \frac{\cos x}{f(x)} \mathrm{d}x = 1.$$

4. Prove that

$$\int_0^{\pi/2} \frac{\sqrt{\sin x}}{\sqrt{\sin x} + \sqrt{\cos x}} \mathrm{d}x = \frac{\pi}{4}.$$

**Exercise 9.47.** Obtain a recursion formula for

$$I_n(a, b) = \int_a^b x^n \mathrm{e}^x \mathrm{d}x, \quad n \in \mathbb{N},$$

and compute $I_1(a, b)$ and $I_2(a, b)$.

**Exercise 9.48.** Show that for any $\lambda < 1$ it holds that

$$\int_{-1}^1 \frac{\mathrm{d}y}{|x - y|^\lambda} = \frac{1}{1-\lambda} \begin{cases} (1-x)^{1-\lambda} - (-1-x)^{1-\lambda}, & x < -1, \\ (1+x)^{1-\lambda} + (1-x)^{1-\lambda}, & -1 \le x \le 1, \\ (1+x)^{1-\lambda} - (-1+x)^{1-\lambda}, & x > 1. \end{cases}$$

Using this fact prove that if $f \in \mathcal{R}[-1, 1]$ and bounded then the function

$$F(x) := \int_{-1}^1 \frac{f(y)\mathrm{d}y}{|x - y|^\lambda}, \quad \lambda < 1,$$

is continuous in $x \in \mathbb{R}$.

**Exercise 9.49.** Let $\gamma$ be the Euler's constant. Prove that

1.

$$\int_0^1 \left\{ \frac{1}{x} \right\} \mathrm{d}x = 1 - \gamma,$$

2.

$$\int_0^1 \left\{ \frac{1}{x} \right\}^2 \mathrm{d}x = \log(2\pi) - 1 - \gamma,$$

3.

$$\int_0^1 \left\{ \frac{k}{x} \right\} \mathrm{d}x = k \left( 1 + \frac{1}{2} + \cdots + \frac{1}{k} - \log k - \gamma \right),$$

where $k \in \mathbb{N}$,

4.

$$\int_0^1 \left\{ \frac{s}{x} \right\} \mathrm{d}x$$

$$= \begin{cases} s(1 - \gamma - \log s), & 0 < s \le 1, \\ s \left( 1 + \frac{1}{2} + \cdots + \frac{1}{1+[s]} - \log s - \gamma \right) + \frac{[s](\{s\}-1)}{s([s]+1)}, & s > 1, \end{cases}$$

where $s$ is an arbitrary real number.

**Exercise 9.50.** Let $f : [0, 1] \to \mathbb{R}$ be bounded and monotone. Prove that

$$\int_0^1 f(x)\mathrm{d}x = \frac{1}{n} \sum_{k=1}^n f(k/n) + O(1/n), \quad n \to \infty.$$

**Exercise 9.51.** Using the previous exercise calculate the limits

1.

$$\lim_{n\to\infty} \sum_{k=1}^n \frac{n}{n^2 + k^2},$$

2.

$$\lim_{n\to\infty} \frac{1}{n^2} \sum_{k=1}^n \sqrt{n^2 - k^2},$$

3.

$$\lim_{n\to\infty} \sum_{k=1}^{n-1} \frac{k}{n^2},$$

4.

$$\lim_{n\to\infty} \frac{1}{n} \sum_{k=1}^{n-1} \sin(\pi k/n),$$

5.

$$\lim_{n\to\infty} \frac{1}{n} \sum_{k=1}^n \frac{2^{k/n}}{1 + 1/(kn)},$$

6.

$$\lim_{n\to\infty} \sqrt[n]{\frac{n!}{n^n}}.$$

Hint: Take the logarithm of this sequence.

**Exercise 9.52.**     1. Prove that

$$\lim_{n\to\infty} \sum_{k=1}^n \left(\frac{k}{n}\right)^n = \frac{\mathrm{e}}{\mathrm{e} - 1}.$$

Hint: Divide the sum into terms corresponding to $k \leq \sigma n$ and $k > \sigma n$ with $0 < \sigma < 1$ chosen appropriately, and for the second term use part 1 of Exercise 8.12.

2. Using the result of the previous exercise calculate the limit

$$\lim_{n\to\infty} \frac{\sum_{k=1}^n n^k}{\sum_{k=1}^n k^n}.$$

**Weierstrass approximation theorem**    Summing up the global properties of continuous functions we prove perhaps the most important theorem of classical mathematical analysis of continuous functions and show its application to summation of trigonometric Fourier series.

**Theorem 9.53 (Weierstrass approximation theorem).**  *Let $f \in C[a,b]$. Then for any $\varepsilon > 0$ there exists an algebraic polynomial $P_n(x)$ of order $n$ depending on $\varepsilon$ such that*

$$\sup_{x \in [a,b]} |f(x) - P_n(x)| < \varepsilon.$$

*Proof.* We may consider without loss of generality the interval $[0,1]$ because otherwise we can use the transformation $x = (b-a)t + a, t \in [0,1]$. Moreover, we may assume that $f(0) = f(1) = 0$ because otherwise we can consider the function

$$g(x) = f(x) - f(0) - x(f(1) - f(0)),$$

which differs from $f$ by a first order polynomial. These assumptions allow us to extend the function $f$ to the whole line as equaling zero outside the interval $[0,1]$. Moreover, this extended function will be uniformly continuous on the whole line (see Exercise 5.91).

Let us consider the sequence of nonnegative polynomials of order $2n$ given by

$$Q_{2n}(x) = c_n(1 - x^2)^n, \quad x \in [-1,1], n = 1, 2, \ldots,$$

with constants $c_n > 0$ chosen such that

$$\int_{-1}^{1} Q_{2n}(x)\mathrm{d}x = 1.$$

These constants can be calculated precisely (see Exercise 10.31, part 5) but for our purposes it is enough to estimate them as

$$1 = c_n \int_{-1}^{1} (1 - x^2)^n \mathrm{d}x = 2c_n \int_{0}^{1} (1 - x^2)^n \mathrm{d}x > 2c_n \int_{0}^{1/\sqrt{n}} (1 - x^2)^n \mathrm{d}x$$

$$\geq 2c_n \int_{0}^{1/\sqrt{n}} (1 - nx^2)\mathrm{d}x = \frac{4}{3}\frac{c_n}{\sqrt{n}},$$

where we have used Bernoulli's inequality. This implies that $c_n < \sqrt{n}$ and that for all $x \in [\delta, 1], 0 < \delta < 1$, we have

$$0 \leq Q_{2n}(x) \leq \sqrt{n}(1 - \delta^2)^n$$

with

$$\lim_{n \to \infty} \sqrt{n}(1 - \delta^2)^n = 0 \qquad (9.1)$$

(see Exercise 3.16).

Next, we introduce for $0 \leq x \leq 1$ the functions

$$P_{2n}(x) = \int_{-1}^{1} f(x + t)Q_{2n}(t)\mathrm{d}t.$$

Since $f(x) = 0$ for $x \notin [0,1]$,

$$P_{2n}(x) = \int_{-x}^{1-x} f(x + t)Q_{2n}(t)\mathrm{d}t = \int_{0}^{1} f(t)Q_{2n}(t - x)\mathrm{d}t.$$

This equality yields that $P_{2n}(x)$ is a polynomial of order $2n$. We show now that $\{P_{2n}\}$ is the desired sequence of polynomials to prove the theorem. Indeed, since $f$ is uniformly continuous on the whole line,

- there is $M > 0$ such that $|f(x)| \leq M$ for all $x \in \mathbb{R}$,

- for any $\varepsilon > 0$ there is $\delta > 0$ such that $|f(x) - f(y)| < \varepsilon/2$ for all $x, y \in \mathbb{R}$ with $|x - y| < \delta$.

This implies, for all $x \in [0, 1]$, that

$$
\begin{aligned}
|P_{2n}(x) - f(x)| &= \left| \int_{-1}^{1} (f(x+t) - f(x)) Q_{2n}(t) \mathrm{d}t \right| \\
&\leq \int_{-1}^{-\delta} |f(x+t) - f(x)| Q_{2n}(t) \mathrm{d}t \\
&\quad + \int_{-\delta}^{\delta} |f(x+t) - f(x)| Q_{2n}(t) \mathrm{d}t \\
&\quad + \int_{\delta}^{1} |f(x+t) - f(x)| Q_{2n}(t) \mathrm{d}t \\
&\leq 4M \int_{\delta}^{1} Q_{2n}(t) \mathrm{d}t + \frac{\varepsilon}{2} \int_{-\delta}^{\delta} Q_{2n}(t) \mathrm{d}t \leq 4M \sqrt{n}(1 - \delta^2)^n + \frac{\varepsilon}{2}.
\end{aligned}
$$

By (9.1) there exists $n_0(\varepsilon) > 0$ (for given $\varepsilon > 0$) such that

$$
\sup_{x \in [0,1]} |P_{2n}(x) - f(x)| < \varepsilon
$$

for all $n \geq n_0$. This proves the theorem.

As a direct consequence of this theorem one can obtain the Weierstrass approximation theorem in terms of trigonometric polynomials, i.e.,

$$
T_n(x) = \frac{a_0}{2} + \sum_{k=1}^{n} (a_k \cos(kx) + b_k \sin(kx)), \quad x \in [-\pi, \pi], \tag{9.2}
$$

where $a_k, b_k$ are arbitrary real numbers. It is clear that if $P_n(x)$ is some algebraic polynomial then $P_n(\cos x)$ and $P_n(\sin x)$ are trigonometric polynomials. In that case Theorem 9.53 can be formulated as follows.

**Theorem 9.54 (Weierstrass approximation theorem).** *Let $f \in C[-\pi, \pi]$ and $f(-\pi) = f(\pi)$. Then for any $\varepsilon > 0$ there exists a trigonometric polynomial $T_n(x)$ with number $n$ depending on $\varepsilon$ such that*

$$
\sup_{x \in [-\pi, \pi]} |f(x) - T_n(x)| < \varepsilon.
$$

This theorem has many applications. One of them concerns the approximation of a continuous function by the polynomials (9.2), where the coefficients $a_k$ and $b_k$ are the Fourier coefficients, i.e.,

$$
a_k = \frac{1}{\pi} \int_{-\pi}^{\pi} f(x) \cos(kx) \mathrm{d}x, \quad k = 0, 1, 2 \ldots,
$$

and

$$
b_k = \frac{1}{\pi} \int_{-\pi}^{\pi} f(x) \sin(kx) \mathrm{d}x, \quad k = 1, 2 \ldots.
$$

Moreover, in practice these coefficients are not given precisely but approximately, i.e., we have $\widetilde{a_k}$ and $\widetilde{b_k}$ instead of $a_k$ and $b_k$ as above.

In this case we consider the regularization method due to Tychonoff. The idea is to find a "good" approximation for $f(x)$ using $\widetilde{a_k}$ and $\widetilde{b_k}$.

**Theorem 9.55 (Tychonoff).** *Let $f \in C[-\pi, \pi]$ and $f(-\pi) = f(\pi)$. Assume that the coefficients $a_k, b_k, \widetilde{a_k}$, and $\widetilde{b_k}$ satisfy the condition*

$$\frac{(a_0 - \widetilde{a_0})^2}{2} + \sum_{k=1}^{\infty}[(a_k - \widetilde{a_k})^2 + (b_k - \widetilde{b_k})^2] \leq \delta^2.$$

*Then for any $\delta > 0$ (as small as needed) it is true that*

$$\sup_{x \in [-\pi, \pi]} \left| \frac{\widetilde{a_0}}{2} + \sum_{k=1}^{\infty}(\widetilde{a_k}\cos(kx) + \widetilde{b_k}\sin(kx))\frac{1}{1+k^2\delta} - f(x) \right| \leq \varepsilon(\delta),$$

*where $\varepsilon(\delta) \to 0$ as $\delta \to 0$.*

*Proof.* Applying the Cauchy–Schwarz–Bunjakovskii inequality (see (1.4)) for infinite sums we get

$$\left| \frac{\widetilde{a_0} - a_0}{2} + \sum_{k=1}^{\infty}((\widetilde{a_k} - a_k)\cos(kx) + (\widetilde{b_k} - b_k)\sin(kx))\frac{1}{1+k^2\delta} \right|$$

$$\leq \left( \frac{(\widetilde{a_0} - a_0)^2}{4} + \sum_{k=1}^{\infty}((\widetilde{a_k} - a_k)^2 + (\widetilde{b_k} - b_k)^2) \right)^{1/2} \left( \sum_{k=0}^{\infty}\frac{1}{1+k^4\delta^2} \right)^{1/2}$$

$$\leq \left( \frac{(\widetilde{a_0} - a_0)^2}{4} + \sum_{k<1/\delta}((\widetilde{a_k} - a_k)^2 + (\widetilde{b_k} - b_k)^2) \right)^{1/2} \left( \sum_{k<1/\delta}\frac{1}{1+k^4\delta^2} \right)^{1/2}$$

$$+ \left( \sum_{k\geq1/\delta}((\widetilde{a_k} - a_k)^2 + (\widetilde{b_k} - b_k)^2) \right)^{1/2} \left( \sum_{k\geq1/\delta}\frac{1}{k^4\delta^2} \right)^{1/2}$$

$$\leq \left( \delta^2 \sum_{k<1/\delta}\frac{1}{1+k^4\delta^2} \right)^{1/2} + \left( \delta^2 \sum_{k\geq1/\delta}\frac{1}{k^4\delta^2} \right)^{1/2}$$

$$= O(\delta^{3/4}) + O(\delta^{3/2}) = O(\delta^{3/4}) < \varepsilon/4$$

with given $\varepsilon > 0$ if $\delta > 0$ is chosen small enough.

Next, since $f \in C[-\pi, \pi]$, it is uniformly continuous (see Theorem 5.88). Thus for $\varepsilon > 0$ from above there exists $\eta > 0$ such that $|f(x) - f(y)| < \varepsilon/4$ for any $x, y \in [-\pi, \pi]$ with $|x - y| < \eta$. Consider now the function

$$v_x(y) = \begin{cases} \frac{\pi}{2\sqrt{\delta}}e^{-|x-y|/\sqrt{\delta}}, & -\eta < y - x < \eta, \\ 0, & \eta \leq y - x \leq 2\pi - \eta, \end{cases}$$

where $0 < \eta < \pi$ and $v_x(y)$ as a function of $y$ is extended periodically with period $2\pi$ to the whole line. This definition implies that the Fourier coefficients of $v_y$ become

$$A_k = \frac{\cos(kx)}{1+k^2\delta} + \frac{\sigma_k}{\sqrt{\delta}}e^{-\eta/\sqrt{\delta}}\cos(kx), \quad k = 0, 1, 2, \ldots,$$

and

$$B_k = \frac{\sin(kx)}{1 + k^2\delta} + \frac{\sigma_k}{\sqrt{\delta}} e^{-\eta/\sqrt{\delta}} \sin(kx), \quad k = 1, 2, \ldots,$$

where

$$\sigma_k = \frac{k\sin(k\eta) - \frac{\cos(k\eta)}{\sqrt{\delta}}}{k^2 + 1/\delta}.$$

**Exercise 9.56.** Prove these formulas for $A_k$, $B_k$, and $\sigma_k$. Hint: Use part 3 of Example 8.8.

The *generalized Parseval equality* (valid for the trigonometric Fourier series) leads to

$$\frac{1}{\pi} \int_{-\pi}^{\pi} v_x(y)f(y)\mathrm{d}y := \frac{A_0 a_0}{2} + \sum_{k=1}^{\infty}(A_k a_k + B_k b_k)$$

$$= \frac{a_0}{2}(1 - e^{-\eta/\sqrt{\delta}}) + \sum_{k=1}^{\infty}\left(\frac{a_k\cos(kx) + b_k\sin(kx)}{1 + k^2\delta}\right)$$

$$+ \frac{e^{-\eta/\sqrt{\delta}}}{\sqrt{\delta}}\sum_{k=1}^{\infty}\sigma_k\left(a_k\cos(kx) + b_k\sin(kx)\right).$$

This shows that in order to prove the statement of the theorem it is enough to justify the inequalities

$$\left|\frac{1}{\pi}\int_{-\pi}^{\pi} v_x(y)f(y)\mathrm{d}y - f(x)\right| < \varepsilon/2$$

and

$$\left|-\frac{a_0}{2}e^{-\eta/\sqrt{\delta}} + \frac{e^{-\eta/\sqrt{\delta}}}{\sqrt{\delta}}\sum_{k=1}^{\infty}\sigma_k\left(a_k\cos(kx) + b_k\sin(kx)\right)\right| < \varepsilon/4.$$

**Exercise 9.57.** Prove that if $f$ is periodic (and integrable) with period $T > 0$ then

$$\int_0^T f(x)\mathrm{d}x = \int_a^{a+T} f(x)\mathrm{d}x$$

for any $a \in \mathbb{R}$.

Based on the latter exercise we have

$$\frac{1}{\pi}\int_{-\pi}^{\pi} v_x(y)f(y)\mathrm{d}y = \frac{1}{\pi}\int_{x-\eta}^{x-\eta+2\pi} v_x(y)f(y)\mathrm{d}y$$

$$= \frac{1}{2\sqrt{\delta}}f(x)\int_{x-\eta}^{x+\eta} e^{-|x-y|/\sqrt{\delta}}\mathrm{d}y$$

$$+ \frac{1}{2\sqrt{\delta}}\int_{x-\eta}^{x+\eta}(f(y) - f(x))e^{-|x-y|/\sqrt{\delta}}\mathrm{d}y$$

$$= \frac{f(x)}{2\sqrt{\delta}}\int_{-\eta}^{\eta} e^{-|t|/\sqrt{\delta}}\mathrm{d}t$$

$$+ \frac{1}{2\sqrt{\delta}}\int_{x-\eta}^{x+\eta}(f(y) - f(x))e^{-|x-y|/\sqrt{\delta}}\mathrm{d}y$$

$$= f(x)(1 - e^{-\eta/\sqrt{\delta}}) + \frac{1}{2\sqrt{\delta}}\int_{x-\eta}^{x+\eta}(f(y) - f(x))e^{-|x-y|/\sqrt{\delta}}\mathrm{d}y.$$

Hence the first term above can be estimated as

$$\left| \frac{1}{\pi} \int_{-\pi}^{\pi} v_x(y) f(y) \mathrm{d}y - f(x) \right|$$

$$\leq |f(x)| \mathrm{e}^{-\eta/\sqrt{\delta}} + \frac{1}{2\sqrt{\delta}} \int_{x-\eta}^{x+\eta} |f(y) - f(x)| \mathrm{e}^{-|x-y|/\sqrt{\delta}} \mathrm{d}y$$

$$\leq |f(x)| \mathrm{e}^{-\eta/\sqrt{\delta}} + \frac{\varepsilon}{4} (1 - \mathrm{e}^{-\eta/\sqrt{\delta}}) \leq \frac{\varepsilon}{4} + M \mathrm{e}^{-\eta/\sqrt{\delta}} < \varepsilon/2$$

since $|f(x)| \leq M$ for all $x \in [-\pi, \pi]$ and $\lim_{\delta \to 0+} \mathrm{e}^{-\eta/\sqrt{\delta}} = 0$.

To estimate the second term above we first obtain easily that $|\sigma_k| \leq 2/k$ for $k = 1, 2, \ldots$ and then get

$$\left| -\frac{a_0}{2} \mathrm{e}^{-\eta/\sqrt{\delta}} + \frac{\mathrm{e}^{-\eta/\sqrt{\delta}}}{\sqrt{\delta}} \sum_{k=1}^{\infty} \sigma_k \left( a_k \cos(kx) + b_k \sin(kx) \right) \right|$$

$$\leq \frac{\mathrm{e}^{-\eta/\sqrt{\delta}}}{\sqrt{\delta}} \left( \frac{|a_0|}{2} \sqrt{\delta} + 2 \sum_{k=1}^{\infty} \frac{|a_k| + |b_k|}{k} \right)$$

$$\leq \frac{\mathrm{e}^{-\eta/\sqrt{\delta}}}{\sqrt{\delta}} \left( \frac{a_0^2 \delta}{4} + 2 \sum_{k=1}^{\infty} (a_k^2 + b_k^2) \right)^{1/2} \left( 1 + 4 \sum_{k=1}^{\infty} \frac{1}{k^2} \right)^{1/2}.$$

Here we have used the Cauchy–Schwarz–Bunjakovskii inequality again. Finally, since

$$\lim_{\delta \to 0+} \frac{\mathrm{e}^{-\eta/\sqrt{\delta}}}{\sqrt{\delta}} = 0$$

by Exercise 3.16 we may conclude that the theorem is proved.

# Chapter 10

# Improper integrals

In this chapter we introduce improper integrals along with the usual comparison criteria of the Cauchy criterion, the Dirichlet–Abel test, and others, and a very important concept of improper integrals in the sense of principal value. In addition, Euler's Gamma and Beta functions are considered here in an equivalent way (compared with infinite products) using improper integrals, and an auxiliary connection between them is also established.

Let function $f : [a, \infty) \to \mathbb{R}$ be integrable with respect to the Riemann integral on each interval $[a, A]$, $A > a$. Then it defines a continuous function

$$F(A) := \int_a^A f(t) \mathrm{d}t$$

of the variable upper bound.

**Definition 10.1.** *If the limit*

$$\lim_{A \to +\infty} F(A) := \int_a^\infty f(x) \mathrm{d}x$$

*exists then it is called a* converging improper integral of the first kind. *If this limit does not exist then this integral is called a* diverging improper integral of the first kind, *and the same notation is retained.*

**Remark 10.2.** The improper integrals

$$\int_{-\infty}^b f(x) \mathrm{d}x, \quad \int_{-\infty}^\infty f(x) \mathrm{d}x$$

are defined similarly, i.e., in terms of convergence and divergence of the integrals

$$\int_{-\infty}^b f(x) \mathrm{d}x := \lim_{A \to +\infty} \int_{-A}^b f(x) \mathrm{d}x$$

and

$$\int_{-\infty}^\infty f(x) \mathrm{d}x := \int_0^\infty f(x) \mathrm{d}x + \int_{-\infty}^0 f(x) \mathrm{d}x.$$

**Example 10.3.**     1. Let us consider

$$\int_a^\infty \frac{1}{x^\lambda}\mathrm{d}x, \quad a > 0, \lambda \in \mathbb{R}.$$

Since for $A > a$ we have

$$F(A) = \int_a^A \frac{1}{x^\lambda}\mathrm{d}x = \begin{cases} \frac{A^{1-\lambda}-a^{1-\lambda}}{1-\lambda}, & \lambda \neq 1, \\ \log A - \log a, & \lambda = 1, \end{cases}$$

then

$$\lim_{A \to +\infty} F(A) = \begin{cases} \frac{a^{1-\lambda}}{\lambda-1}, & \lambda > 1, \\ +\infty, & \lambda \leq 1, \end{cases}$$

i.e., the given integral converges if and only if $\lambda > 1$.

2. Let us consider

$$\int_a^\infty \frac{1}{x(\log x)^\mu}\mathrm{d}x, \quad a > 1, \mu \in \mathbb{R}.$$

Using the change of variable formula with $t = \log x$ we get

$$F(A) = \int_a^A \frac{1}{x(\log x)^\mu}\mathrm{d}x = \int_{\log a}^{\log A} \frac{1}{t^\mu}\mathrm{d}t = \begin{cases} \frac{(\log A)^{1-\mu}-(\log a)^{1-\mu}}{1-\mu}, & \mu \neq 1, \\ \log\log A - \log\log a, & \mu = 1. \end{cases}$$

Hence

$$\lim_{A \to +\infty} F(A) = \begin{cases} \frac{(\log a)^{1-\mu}}{\mu-1}, & \mu > 1, \\ +\infty, & \mu \leq 1, \end{cases}$$

i.e., the given integral converges if and only if $\mu > 1$.

Definition 10.1 allows us to apply and formulate immediately the Cauchy criterion for convergence of improper integrals of the first kind.

**Theorem 10.4 (Cauchy criterion).** *The improper integral*

$$\int_a^\infty f(x)\mathrm{d}x$$

*converges if and only if for any $\varepsilon > 0$ there exists $A_0 > a$ such that*

$$\left|\int_{A'}^{A''} f(x)\mathrm{d}x\right| < \varepsilon$$

*for any $A'' > A' \geq A_0$.*

**Proof.** The proof follows from the proof of the Cauchy criterion for functions.

**Remark 10.5.** The improper integral

$$\int_a^\infty f(x)\mathrm{d}x$$

diverges if and only if there exists $\varepsilon_0 > 0$ such that for any $A > 0$ there exist $A'' > A' > A$ and

$$\left|\int_{A'}^{A''} f(x)\mathrm{d}x\right| \geq \varepsilon_0.$$

**Exercise 10.6.**    1.  Prove that the improper integral

$$\int_a^\infty \frac{\mathrm{d}x}{x^\lambda (\log x)^\mu}, \quad a > 1, \lambda, \mu \in \mathbb{R},$$

converges for $\lambda > 1$ and any $\mu \in \mathbb{R}$ and diverges for $\lambda < 1$ and any $\mu \in \mathbb{R}$.

2.  Investigate the convergence of the integral

$$\int_a^\infty \frac{\mathrm{d}x}{x(\log x)^\lambda (\log\log x)^\mu}, \quad a > e.$$

**Theorem 10.7 (Signs of comparison).**

1.  *Suppose that $|f(x)| \leq g(x)$ for all $x \geq x_0 \geq a$. Then the convergence of the integral*

$$\int_a^\infty g(x)\mathrm{d}x$$

*implies the convergence of the integrals*

$$\int_a^\infty f(x)\mathrm{d}x, \quad \int_a^\infty |f(x)|\mathrm{d}x.$$

2.  *Suppose that $f(x) \geq g(x) \geq 0$ for all $x \geq x_0 \geq a$. Then the divergence of the integral*

$$\int_a^\infty g(x)\mathrm{d}x$$

*implies the divergence of the integral*

$$\int_a^\infty f(x)\mathrm{d}x.$$

*Proof.*

1.  The Cauchy criterion (see Theorem 10.4) gives that for any $\varepsilon > 0$ there exists $A_0 > x_0$ such that

$$\left| \int_{A'}^{A''} f(x)\mathrm{d}x \right| \leq \int_{A'}^{A''} |f(x)|\mathrm{d}x \leq \int_{A'}^{A''} g(x)\mathrm{d}x < \varepsilon$$

for any $A'' > A' \geq A_0$ by virtue of the convergence of the integral $\int_a^\infty g(x)\mathrm{d}x$.

2.  By virtue of the divergence of the integral $\int_a^\infty g(x)\mathrm{d}x$ we have that there exists $\varepsilon_0 > 0$ such that for all $A > x_0$ there exist $A'' > A' \geq A$ and

$$\int_{A'}^{A''} f(x)\mathrm{d}x \geq \int_{A'}^{A''} g(x)\mathrm{d}x \geq \varepsilon_0.$$

Thus, the theorem is completely proved.

**Corollary 10.8.** *Suppose that the limit*

$$\lim_{x \to +\infty} x^\lambda f(x) = K \neq 0$$

*exists, i.e., $f(x) = O^*(1/x^\lambda)$. Then the integral $\int_a^\infty f(x)\mathrm{d}x$ converges for $\lambda > 1$ and diverges for $\lambda \leq 1$.*

**Exercise 10.9.**     1. Prove the latter corollary.

2. Investigate the convergence of the integral

$$\int_1^\infty \frac{\arctan x}{x^\lambda} \mathrm{d}x.$$

**Exercise 10.10.** Let positive function $f$ be integrable on any finite interval in $\mathbb{R}_+$ and monotone decreasing. Prove that

$$\int_1^\infty f(x)\mathrm{d}x \le \sum_{k=1}^\infty f(k) \le \int_1^\infty f(x)\mathrm{d}x + f(1).$$

Conclude that the latter series and integral converge and diverge simultaneously.

**Definition 10.11.** *The improper integral $\int_a^\infty f(x)\mathrm{d}x$ is said to be* absolutely convergent *if the integral $\int_a^\infty |f(x)|\mathrm{d}x$ converges. The improper integral $\int_a^\infty f(x)\mathrm{d}x$ is said to be* conditionally convergent *if the integral $\int_a^\infty f(x)\mathrm{d}x$ converges but the integral $\int_a^\infty |f(x)|\mathrm{d}x$ diverges.*

**Remark 10.12.** The Cauchy criterion gives that absolute convergence implies convergence but not vice versa.

**Theorem 10.13 (Dirichlet–Abel test).** *Suppose that $f$ is integrable on each interval $[a, A]$, $A > a$, the function $F(A) := \int_a^A f(x)\mathrm{d}x$ is bounded, and a function $g$ is monotone and integrable with $\lim_{x\to+\infty} g(x) = 0$. Then the integral $\int_a^\infty f(x)g(x)\mathrm{d}x$ converges (possibly not absolutely).*

***Proof.*** Let $\varepsilon > 0$ be arbitrary. The conditions for $f$ and $g$ allow us to apply the second mean value formula (see Theorem 9.33) and we obtain

$$\int_{A'}^{A''} f(x)g(x)\mathrm{d}x = g(A') \int_{A'}^\xi f(x)\mathrm{d}x + g(A'') \int_\xi^{A''} f(x)\mathrm{d}x, \quad A'' \ge \xi \ge A'.$$

Hence we have

$$\left| \int_{A'}^{A''} f(x)g(x)\mathrm{d}x \right| \le 2C_0(|g(A')| + |g(A'')|),$$

where the constant $C_0$ is due to

$$\left| \int_a^A f(x)\mathrm{d}x \right| \le C_0.$$

Since $\lim_{x\to+\infty} g(x) = 0$ we can choose $A'' > A'$ so large that

$$|g(A')|, |g(A'')| < \frac{\varepsilon}{4C_0}.$$

Thus

$$\left| \int_{A'}^{A''} f(x)g(x)\mathrm{d}x \right| < \varepsilon$$

and the Cauchy criterion yields the result of the theorem.

**Example 10.14.**    1. Let us consider the integral

$$\int_1^\infty \frac{\sin x}{x^\lambda} dx, \quad \lambda \in \mathbb{R}.$$

If $\lambda > 0$ then the Dirichlet–Abel test implies the convergence of the integral since

$$\left| \int_1^A \sin x dx \right| = |\cos A - \cos 1| \le 2.$$

Furthermore, since

$$\left| \frac{\sin x}{x^\lambda} \right| \le \frac{1}{x^\lambda},$$

this integral converges absolutely for $\lambda > 1$. Let us show that for $0 < \lambda \le 1$ this integral converges conditionally. In other words, we will show that the integral

$$\int_1^\infty \frac{|\sin x|}{x^\lambda} dx$$

diverges for $0 < \lambda \le 1$. Indeed,

$$\int_1^A \frac{|\sin x|}{x^\lambda} dx \ge \int_1^A \frac{\sin^2 x}{x^\lambda} dx = \frac{1}{2} \int_1^A \frac{1}{x^\lambda} dx - \frac{1}{2} \int_1^A \frac{\cos(2x)}{x^\lambda} dx.$$

But the first integral in the right-hand side of the latter equality diverges for $0 < \lambda \le 1$ (see Example 10.3) while the second integral converges due to the Dirichlet–Abel test.

2. Let us consider the *Fresnel integrals*

$$\int_0^\infty \sin(x^2) dx, \quad \int_0^\infty \cos(x^2) dx.$$

Let us show that they converge but not absolutely. Since

$$\int_0^\infty \sin(x^2) dx = \int_0^1 \sin(x^2) dx + \int_1^\infty \sin(x^2) dx$$

(and similarly for cos), we investigate the convergence of improper integrals

$$\int_1^\infty \sin(x^2) dx, \quad \int_1^\infty \cos(x^2) dx.$$

Using the change of variable formula we obtain

$$\int_1^A \sin(x^2) dx = \frac{1}{2} \int_1^{A^2} \frac{\sin t}{\sqrt{t}} dt.$$

By the Dirichlet–Abel test the limit,

$$\lim_{A \to +\infty} \int_1^{A^2} \frac{\sin t}{\sqrt{t}} dt$$

exists. Hence

$$\int_1^\infty \sin(x^2) dx = \lim_{A \to +\infty} \int_1^A \sin(x^2) dx$$

exists. The same considerations hold for cos also.

**Exercise 10.15.**     1.  Prove that the integral

$$\int_a^\infty \frac{e^{\sin x} \sin 2x}{x^p} \, dx$$

converges for any $a > 0$ and $p > 0$.

2.  Prove that the integral

$$\int_1^\infty \sin(x^\alpha) \, dx$$

converges for any $|\alpha| > 1$ and diverges for any $|\alpha| \le 1$.

3.  Prove that the integral

$$\int_1^\infty \frac{\sin x}{x^\lambda + \sin x} \, dx$$

converges if and only if $\lambda > 1/2$.

4.  Define the positive parameters $\mu, \nu, p$ such that the integral

$$\int_0^\infty \frac{x^\mu}{1 + x^\nu |\sin x|^p} \, dx$$

converges.

5.  Show that the integral

$$\int_\pi^\infty \frac{1}{x^2 (\sin x)^{2/3}} \, dx$$

exists.

6.  Let $f$ be continuous on the interval $[0, +\infty)$. Calculate the *Frullani integrals*

$$\int_0^\infty \frac{f(ax) - f(bx)}{x} \, dx, \quad a, b > 0,$$

if

    (a)  $f$ is periodic with period $T > 0$, or

    (b)  $f$ is such that the limit $\lim_{x \to +\infty} f(x) = L$ exists.

7.  Calculate the integral

$$\int_0^\infty \frac{\arctan(ax^n) - \arctan(bx^n)}{x} \, dx.$$

8.  Investigate the convergence of the integral

$$\int_0^\infty \frac{\sin^3 x}{x^\lambda} \, dx.$$

9.  Show that the integral

$$\int_0^\infty x e^{-x^6 \sin^2 x} \, dx$$

converges.

In addition to the improper integrals of the first kind considered above there are improper integrals of the second kind which correspond to functions having singular points on a finite interval.

Let $f : [a,b] \to \mathbb{R}$ be Riemann integrable on each interval $[a, b - \delta]$, where $\delta > 0$ (and small enough). Then the function

$$F(\delta) := \int_a^{b-\delta} f(x)\mathrm{d}x$$

is well-defined and continuous in $\delta$.

**Definition 10.16.** *If the limit*

$$\lim_{\delta \to +0} F(\delta) := \int_a^b f(x)\mathrm{d}x$$

*exists then it is called the* converging improper integral of the second kind. *If this limit does not exist then this integral is called the* diverging improper integral of the second kind.

**Remark 10.17.** We may define similarly an improper integral with singularity (unboundedness) at the point $a$, i.e.,

$$\int_a^b f(x)\mathrm{d}x = \lim_{\delta \to +0} \int_{a+\delta}^b f(x)\mathrm{d}x$$

if this limit exists (or does not exist). If the singularity occurs at some point $c \in (a,b)$ then an improper integral is defined by

$$\int_a^b f(x)\mathrm{d}x = \lim_{\delta,\mu \to +0} \left( \int_a^{c-\delta} f(x)\mathrm{d}x + \int_{c+\mu}^b f(x)\mathrm{d}x \right)$$

if these limits exist (or do not exist).

**Theorem 10.18 (Cauchy criterion).** *The improper integral of the second kind (at the point b)*

$$\int_a^b f(x)\mathrm{d}x$$

*converges if and only if for any $\varepsilon > 0$ there exists $\delta_0 > 0$ such that*

$$\left| \int_{b-\delta'}^{b-\delta''} f(x)\mathrm{d}x \right| < \varepsilon$$

*for any $\delta', \delta'' > 0$ with $0 < \delta', \delta'' < \delta_0$.*

**Exercise 10.19.**    1. Prove that the integral

$$\int_0^1 \frac{1}{x^\lambda}\mathrm{d}x$$

converges if and only if $\lambda < 1$.

2. Prove that the integral

$$\int_0^{1/2} \frac{1}{x^\lambda (\log(1/x))^\mu}\mathrm{d}x$$

converges for $\lambda < 1$ and for any $\mu$, diverges for $\lambda > 1$ and for any $\mu$, and converges for $\lambda = 1$ if and only if $\mu > 1$.

3. Investigate the convergence of the integral

$$\int_{1/2}^{1} \frac{1}{(\log(1/x))^{\mu}} \mathrm{d}x.$$

4. Let $f : [a, b) \to \mathbb{R}$ be continuous. Show that the integrals

$$\int_{a}^{b} f(x)\mathrm{d}x, \qquad \int_{1/(b-a)}^{\infty} \frac{f(b - 1/t)}{t^2} \mathrm{d}t$$

   converge or diverge simultaneously.

5. Show that the integral

$$\int_{0}^{\infty} \frac{\log \frac{1+x^{\alpha}}{1+x^{\beta}}}{(1 + x^2) \log x} \mathrm{d}x$$

   converges for all $\alpha, \beta \in \mathbb{R}$ and is equal to $\frac{\pi}{4}(\alpha - \beta)$.

6. Show that the integral

$$\int_{0}^{1} \log x \log(1 - x)\mathrm{d}x$$

   converges and is equal to $2 - \pi^2/6$. Hint: Use Exercise 8.12 and the fact that

$$\sum_{k=1}^{\infty} \frac{1}{k^2} = \frac{\pi^2}{6}.$$

7. Show that the integral

$$\int_{0}^{1} \frac{\sin(\log x)}{\log x} \mathrm{d}x$$

   converges and is equal to $\pi/4$. Hint: Use the substitution $t = \log x$ and apply the technique from Example 10.20 below.

8. Show that the integral

$$\int_{0}^{1} \frac{\log x}{x - 1} \mathrm{d}x$$

   converges and is equal to $\pi^2/6$. Hint: Use the same technique as in part 6.

**Example 10.20 (Integral of Dirichlet).** Let us show that

$$J(\alpha) := \int_{0}^{\infty} \frac{\sin(\alpha x)}{x} \mathrm{d}x = \frac{\pi}{2} \operatorname{sgn} \alpha.$$

It is clear that $J(0) = 0$ and $J(-\alpha) = -J(\alpha)$. That's why it is enough to consider only $\alpha > 0$. Moreover, this integral is constant with respect to $\alpha > 0$ or $\alpha < 0$. Indeed, using the change of variable formula we obtain

$$\int_{0}^{\infty} \frac{\sin(\alpha x)}{x} \mathrm{d}x = \int_{0}^{\infty} \frac{\sin t}{t} \mathrm{d}t.$$

We regularize this integral as

$$\tilde{J}(\varepsilon) = \int_{0}^{\infty} \mathrm{e}^{-\varepsilon x} \frac{\sin x}{x} \mathrm{d}x, \quad \varepsilon > 0,$$

such that

$$\int_0^\infty \frac{\sin x}{x} \mathrm{d}x = J(0) := \lim_{\varepsilon \to +0} \widetilde{J}(\varepsilon).$$

This allows us to differentiate $J(\varepsilon)$ with respect to $\varepsilon$ and obtain

$$\widetilde{J}'(\varepsilon) = -\int_0^\infty e^{-\varepsilon x} \sin x \mathrm{d}x.$$

By Example 8.8 we have

$$\int e^{-\varepsilon x} \sin x \mathrm{d}x = \frac{e^{-\varepsilon x}}{1+\varepsilon^2}(-\varepsilon \sin x - \cos x).$$

Hence

$$\int_0^\infty e^{-\varepsilon x} \sin x \mathrm{d}x = -\frac{1}{1+\varepsilon^2}(-\varepsilon \sin 0 - \cos 0) = \frac{1}{1+\varepsilon^2}.$$

Thus

$$\widetilde{J}'(\varepsilon) = -\frac{1}{1+\varepsilon^2}$$

so that

$$\widetilde{J}(\varepsilon) = -\arctan \varepsilon + C.$$

But it is easy to see that $\widetilde{J}(+\infty) = 0$. Hence $C = \pi/2$ and

$$\int_0^\infty \frac{\sin x}{x} \mathrm{d}x = J(0) := \lim_{\varepsilon \to +0} \widetilde{J}(\varepsilon) = \frac{\pi}{2}.$$

So finally we obtain

$$\int_0^\infty \frac{\sin(\alpha x)}{x} \mathrm{d}x = \frac{\pi}{2} \operatorname{sgn} \alpha.$$

**Definition 10.21.**

1. *Let $f \in \mathcal{R}[-A, A]$ for any $A > 0$. If the limit*

$$\lim_{A \to +\infty} \int_{-A}^A f(x) \mathrm{d}x$$

   *exists then it is called the* principal value (p.v.) integral *and denoted by*

$$\mathrm{p.\,v.} \int_{-\infty}^\infty f(x) \mathrm{d}x.$$

2. *Let $f \in \mathcal{R}[a, c - \delta]$ and $f \in \mathcal{R}[c + \delta, b]$ for any $\delta > 0$ (small enough). If the limit*

$$\lim_{\delta \to +0} \left( \int_a^{c-\delta} f(x) \mathrm{d}x + \int_{c+\delta}^b f(x) \mathrm{d}x \right)$$

   *exists then it is called the* principal value integral *and denoted by*

$$\mathrm{p.\,v.} \int_a^b f(x) \mathrm{d}x.$$

**Exercise 10.22.** Show that items 1, 2, 4, and 5 exist as improper pv integrals and that item 3 does not exist as one.

1.
$$\mathrm{p.\,v.} \int_{-\infty}^{\infty} f(x)\mathrm{d}x = \begin{cases} 0, & f \text{ is odd,} \\ 2\int_{0}^{\infty} f(x)\mathrm{d}x, & f \text{ is even.} \end{cases}$$

2.
$$\mathrm{p.\,v.} \int_{a}^{b} \frac{\mathrm{d}x}{x-c} = \log \frac{b-c}{c-a}, \quad a < c < b.$$

3.
$$\mathrm{p.\,v.} \int_{-\infty}^{\infty} \cos x\mathrm{d}x, \quad \mathrm{p.\,v.} \int_{-\infty}^{\infty} x \sin x\mathrm{d}x.$$

4.
$$\mathrm{p.\,v.} \int_{-\infty}^{\infty} \frac{\mathrm{d}x}{x(x^2+1)} = 0.$$

5.
$$\mathrm{p.\,v.} \int_{-\infty}^{\infty} \frac{x \sin x\mathrm{d}x}{x^2 - \pi^2} = -\pi.$$

Hint: Use the integral of Dirichlet.

The Gamma function of Euler was introduced earlier by (4.4). One can define it equivalently as follows.

**Definition 10.23.** *Let $p > 0$. The integral*

$$\Gamma(p) := \int_{0}^{\infty} t^{p-1}\mathrm{e}^{-t}\mathrm{d}t \tag{10.1}$$

*defines the* Gamma function of Euler.

**Theorem 10.24 (Properties of Gamma function).** *For $p > 0$ the integral* (10.1) *converges absolutely, and the following properties are satisfied:*

1. $\Gamma(p + n) = (p + n - 1) \cdots p\Gamma(p)$ *for $n \in \mathbb{N}$.*

2. $\Gamma(n + 1/2) = \frac{(2n-1)!!}{2^n}\Gamma(1/2)$ *for $n \in \mathbb{N}$.*

3. $\Gamma(1/2) = \sqrt{\pi}$.

4. $\lim_{p \to -n}(p + n)\Gamma(p) = \frac{(-1)^n}{n!}$ *for $n \in \mathbb{N}_0$.*

***Proof.*** Let $p > 0$. Then we write

$$\Gamma(p) = \int_{0}^{1} t^{p-1}\mathrm{e}^{-t}\mathrm{d}t + \int_{1}^{\infty} t^{p-1}\mathrm{e}^{-t}\mathrm{d}t =: I_1 + I_2.$$

For the first term $I_1$ we have

$$0 \le I_1 \le \int_{0}^{1} t^{p-1}\mathrm{d}t = \frac{1}{p} < \infty$$

since $p > 0$. For the second term $I_2$ we use the estimate (see Example 6.60)

$$0 < t^N \le C_N e^t, \quad 1 \le t < \infty,$$

where $N$ can be chosen arbitrarily large. This implies

$$0 \le I_2 \le C_N \int_1^\infty t^{p-N-1} dt < \infty$$

if $N$ is chosen bigger than $p$. Hence the integral in (10.1) for $p > 0$ converges absolutely and correctly defines Gamma function of Euler.

Next we integrate by parts to obtain

$$\Gamma(p+1) = \int_0^\infty t^p e^{-t} dt = - \lim_{t \to \infty} t^p e^{-t} + \int_0^\infty p t^{p-1} e^{-t} dt = p\Gamma(p)$$

since substitutions at 0 and at $+\infty$ vanish due to conditions. Now the equality in part 1 for any $n \in \mathbb{N}$ follows by induction with respect to $n$. Taking $p = 1/2$ yields part 2. For part 3 we change the variables as

$$\Gamma(1/2) = \int_0^\infty t^{-1/2} e^{-t} dt = 2 \int_0^\infty e^{-y^2} dy.$$

By two-dimensional polar coordinates $(r \cos \omega, r \sin \omega)$ we obtain

$$\Gamma(1/2)^2 = 4 \int_0^\infty \int_0^\infty e^{-y^2 - z^2} dy dz = 4 \int_0^\infty r e^{-r^2} dr \int_0^{\pi/2} d\omega$$

$$= 2\pi \int_0^\infty r e^{-r^2} dr = \pi \int_0^\infty e^{-\rho} d\rho = \pi,$$

and part 3 follows. The limit in part 4 is proved in Chapter 4 (see (4.7)) with $\Gamma(-n) := \infty, n \in \mathbb{N}_0$. Therefore this theorem is completely proved.

**Corollary 10.25.** *The Gamma function $\Gamma(p)$ is well-defined for any $p \in \mathbb{R}$.*

*Proof.* If $p \in \mathbb{R}_+$ then $\Gamma(p)$ is well-defined by (10.1). If $p \in \mathbb{R}_-$ then for any $p > -n, p \ne 0, -1, -2, \ldots$ we have the equality

$$\Gamma(p) = \frac{\Gamma(p+n)}{p(p+1) \cdots (p+n-1)}, \quad p + n > 0,$$

which can be considered as the definition of $\Gamma(p)$ for these values of $p$. Since $\Gamma(-n) = \infty$ for $n = 0, 1, 2, \ldots$, this corollary is completely proved.

**Corollary 10.26.** *The Gamma function $\Gamma(p)$ is infinitely many times differentiable for $p > 0$ with*

$$\Gamma^{(k)}(p) = \int_0^\infty t^{p-1} (\log t)^k e^{-t} dt$$

*for $k = 0, 1, 2, \ldots$.*

*Proof.* Taking the first derivative with respect to $p$ in (10.1) one obtains formally

$$\Gamma'(p) = \int_0^\infty t^{p-1} (\log t) e^{-t} dt.$$

This integral converges (even uniformly in $p \in [p_0, p_1], p_0 > 0, p_1 < \infty$) since Example 6.60 gives us the estimates

$$|\log t| \leq C_\varepsilon t^{-\varepsilon}, \quad 0 < t < 1,$$

for any $\varepsilon > 0$ arbitrarily small and

$$t^N \leq C_N e^t, \quad 1 \leq t < \infty,$$

for any $N > 0$ arbitrarily large. By induction on $k$ and similar considerations as above we obtain the needed formula for $\Gamma^{(k)}(p)$.

**Exercise 10.27.**     1.  Prove that for any $p \in \mathbb{R} \setminus \mathbb{Z}$ it holds that

$$\Gamma(p)\Gamma(1-p) = \frac{\pi}{\sin(p\pi)}.$$

2.  Prove that for any $k \in \mathbb{N}_0$ it holds that

$$\Gamma(-k - 1/2) = \frac{(-2)^{k+1}\sqrt{\pi}}{(2k+1)!!}.$$

3.  Prove that for any $m \in \mathbb{N}_0$ and $\lambda > 0$ it holds that

$$\int_0^\infty t^{2m} e^{-\lambda t^2} \, dt = \frac{(2m-1)!!\sqrt{\pi}}{2^{m+1}\lambda^{m+1/2}}.$$

4.  Prove that for any $\alpha > -1$ and $\beta > \alpha + 1$ it holds that

$$\int_0^\infty \frac{x^\alpha}{(1+x)^\beta} \, dx = \frac{\Gamma(\beta - \alpha - 1)\Gamma(\alpha + 1)}{\Gamma(\beta)}.$$

In particular for any $-1 < \alpha < 0$ we have

$$\int_0^\infty \frac{x^\alpha}{1+x} \, dx = -\frac{\pi}{\sin(\alpha\pi)}.$$

**Definition 10.28.** Beta function of Euler *is defined as*

$$B(p, q) := \int_0^1 t^{p-1}(1-t)^{q-1} \, dt, \quad p, q > 0. \tag{10.2}$$

Due to conditions $p > 0$ and $q > 0$ the improper integral of the second kind (10.2) converges absolutely. Moreover $B(p, q) = B(q, p)$.

**Theorem 10.29 (Properties of Beta function).** *Let $p, q > 0$. Then*

1.

$$B(p, q) = \int_0^\infty \frac{t^{q-1}}{(1+t)^{p+q}} \, dt.$$

2.

$$B(p, q) = \frac{\Gamma(p)\Gamma(q)}{\Gamma(p+q)}.$$

3.  $pB(p, q+1) = qB(p+1, q)$.

*Proof.* Changing the variables in (10.2) as $t = 1/(1+x)$ we obtain

$$B(p,q) = \int_\infty^0 (1+x)^{1-p} \left(1 - \frac{1}{1+x}\right)^{q-1} \left(-\frac{dx}{(1+x)^2}\right) = \int_0^\infty \frac{x^{q-1}}{(1+x)^{p+q}} dx.$$

This proves part 1. For part 2 we first write

$$\Gamma(p+q) = (1+t)^{p+q} \int_0^\infty y^{p+q-1} e^{-(1+t)y} dy.$$

Using part 1 one can obtain

$$\Gamma(p+q)B(p,q) = \Gamma(p+q) \int_0^\infty \frac{t^{q-1}}{(1+t)^{p+q}} dt$$
$$= \int_0^\infty t^{q-1} \left(\int_0^\infty y^{p+q-1} e^{-(1+t)y} dy\right) dt.$$

Hence we get

$$\Gamma(p+q)B(p,q) = \int_0^\infty y^{p+q-1} e^{-y} \left(\int_0^\infty t^{q-1} e^{-ty} dt\right) dy$$
$$= \int_0^\infty y^{p+q-1} e^{-y} \left(\int_0^\infty (z/y)^{q-1} e^{-z} \frac{dz}{y}\right) dy$$
$$= \int_0^\infty y^{p-1} e^{-y} \left(\int_0^\infty z^{q-1} e^{-z} dz\right) dy = \Gamma(p)\Gamma(q).$$

This proves part 2. To prove part 3 we integrate by parts in (10.2) to obtain

$$B(p, q+1) = \int_0^1 t^{p-1}(1-t)^q dt = \frac{q}{p} \int_0^1 t^p (1-t)^{q-1} dt = \frac{q}{p} B(p+1, q)$$

since $p, q > 0$.

**Corollary 10.30.** *Beta function $B(p,q)$ can be extended by part 2 of Theorem 10.29 for all $p, q \in \mathbb{R}$.*

**Exercise 10.31.** Prove parts 1–8:

1.
$$B(p, q+1) = \frac{q}{p+q} B(p, q), \quad p, q > 0.$$

2. $B(p,q) = B(p+1, q) + B(p, q+1), p, q > 0.$

3.
$$B(p,q) = 2 \int_0^{\pi/2} (\cos\theta)^{2p-1} (\sin\theta)^{2q-1} d\theta, \quad p, q > 0.$$

In particular, verify

$$\int_0^{\pi/2} (\sin\theta)^{\alpha-1} d\theta = \frac{\sqrt{\pi}\,\Gamma(\alpha/2)}{2\Gamma((\alpha+1)/2)}, \quad \alpha > 0.$$

4. $B(p,q) = (b-a)^{1-p-q} \int_a^b (t-a)^{p-1}(b-t)^{q-1} dt, p, q > 0.$

5.
$$\int_{-1}^{1} (1 - x^2)^n \mathrm{d}x = \frac{2^{n+1} n!}{(2n+1)!!}, \quad n \in \mathbb{N}_0.$$

6. $\lim_{q \to 0} q B(p+1, q) = 1 = \lim_{p \to 0} p B(p, 1-p)$.

7. $B(p, q) = 0, p, q \notin \mathbb{N}_0, p + q = -n, n \in \mathbb{N}_0$.

8.
$$\psi(p+1) - \psi(p) = \frac{1}{p}, \quad \psi(p) - \psi(1-p) = -\frac{\pi}{\tan(p\pi)},$$

where $\psi(p) := \frac{\Gamma'(p)}{\Gamma(p)}, -p \notin \mathbb{N}_0$.

9. Show that the integral
$$\int_0^1 x^{-x} \mathrm{d}x$$

converges and is equal to
$$\sum_{k=1}^{\infty} \frac{1}{k^k}.$$

Hint: Use the fact that
$$x^{-x} = \sum_{j=0}^{\infty} \frac{(-x \log x)^j}{j!}, \quad 0 < x < 1.$$

10. Show that for any $s > 1$ we have
$$\Gamma(s)\zeta(s) = \int_0^{\infty} \frac{x^{s-1}}{e^x - 1} \mathrm{d}x,$$

where $\zeta$ is the $\zeta$-function of Riemann. In particular,
$$\int_0^{\infty} \frac{x}{e^x - 1} \mathrm{d}x = \frac{\pi^2}{6}.$$

# Chapter 11

# Approximate methods

The approximate methods discussed in this chapter are mainly based on the concept of fixed point of mapping and iterative sequences. Sufficient conditions for the convergence of iterative sequences to fixed point are obtained. Special methods of chords and tangents are considered which lead to finding fixed points despite the fact that the sufficient conditions are not satisfied. The results can be obtained due to the correct choice of the initial approximation. In addition, approximate methods for calculating definite Riemann integrals are considered, namely the methods of rectangles, trapezoids, and parabolas (Simpson), and accurate estimates of the errors are obtained.

**Definition 11.1.** *Let function $F$ map a set $X$ into itself and let $x_0 \in X$. A sequence $\{x_n\}_{n=1}^\infty$ of the form*

$$x_n := F(x_{n-1}), \quad n = 1, 2, \ldots,$$

*is said to be* iterative *with respect to $F$, and $x_0$ is called an* initial approximation.

**Example 11.2.**    1. Let initial approximation $x_0 \in (0, 1)$. Then

$$x_n := x_{n-1}(1 - x_{n-1})$$

is obviously iterative with $F(x) = x(1 - x)$.

2. Let initial approximation $x_0 \in \mathbb{R}$. Then

$$x_n := \sin(\sin x_{n-1})$$

is iterative with $F(x) = \sin(\sin x)$.

**Exercise 11.3.** Prove that iterative sequences from Example 11.2 converge. Prove also that $x_n = x_{n-1}(1 - x_{n-1})$ behaves like $x_n = O^*(1/n)$ as $n \to \infty$.

**Theorem 11.4 (The properties of iterative sequences).** *Let a function $F : [a, b] \to [a, b]$ be continuous. Then*

1. *there is a point $\eta \in [a, b]$ (maybe not unique) such that $F(\eta) = \eta$; this point $\eta$ is called a* fixed point *of $F$;*

2.  *if $\{x_n\}_{n=1}^{\infty}$ is iterative with respect to $F$ with arbitrary initial approximation $x_0 \in [a, b]$
    then assuming the existence of a limit $\lim_{n \to \infty} x_n = \xi$ we obtain that $F(\xi) = \xi$, i.e., the
    iterative convergent sequence converges to a fixed point of $F$;*

3.  *if, in addition, $F$ is differentiable on $[a, b]$ and $|F'(x)| \leq \alpha < 1$ for all $x \in [a, b]$ then for
    any initial approximation $x_0 \in [a, b]$ it follows that the iterative sequence $x_n = F(x_{n-1})$
    converges and its limit is a fixed point of $F$ which is unique in this case.*

**Proof.**

1.  Denoting $G(x) := F(x) - x$ we have $G(a) \geq 0$ and $G(b) \leq 0$ since $F : [a, b] \to [a, b]$.
    Thus, by continuity of $G$ we may conclude that there is $\eta \in [a, b]$ such that $G(\eta) = 0$ or
    $F(\eta) = \eta$.

2.  If $\{x_n\}_{n=1}^{\infty}$ is iterative with respect to $F$ and it has a limit $\lim_{n \to \infty} x_n = \xi$ then due to
    continuity of $F$ we obtain

$$F(\xi) = \lim_{n \to \infty} F(x_n) = \lim_{n \to \infty} x_{n+1} = \xi.$$

3.  Let $x_0 \in [a, b]$ be an arbitrary initial approximation for iterative sequence $\{x_n\}_{n=1}^{\infty}$. Then,
    for $m > n$,

$$\begin{aligned}
|x_m - x_n| &\leq |x_m - x_{m-1}| + |x_{m-1} - x_{m-2}| + \cdots + |x_{n+1} - x_n| \\
&= |F(x_{m-1}) - F(x_{m-2})| + \cdots + |F(x_n) - F(x_{n-1})| \\
&\leq \alpha|x_{m-1} - x_{m-2}| + \alpha|x_{m-2} - x_{m-3}| + \cdots + \alpha|x_n - x_{n-1}| \\
&\leq \alpha^{m-1}|x_1 - x_0| + \alpha^{m-2}|x_1 - x_0| + \cdots + \alpha^n|x_1 - x_0| \\
&= \alpha^n|x_1 - x_0|(\alpha^{m-n-1} + \alpha^{m-n-2} + \cdots + 1) \\
&< \alpha^n|x_1 - x_0|(1 + \alpha + \alpha^2 + \cdots) = \alpha^n|x_1 - x_0|\frac{1}{1-\alpha} \to 0
\end{aligned}$$

as $n \to \infty$ since $0 \leq \alpha < 1$. This means that $\{x_n\}_{n=1}^{\infty}$ is a Cauchy sequence and therefore
converges to some point $\xi$. Part 2 of this theorem gives that $F(\xi) = \xi$, i.e., $\xi$ is a fixed
point of $F$. If we assume that there are (at least) two different fixed points $\xi_1$ and $\xi_2$ then

$$\xi_1 - \xi_2 = F(\xi_1) - F(\xi_2) = F'(\eta)(\xi_1 - \xi_2).$$

It follows that

$$|\xi_1 - \xi_2| \leq \alpha|\xi_1 - \xi_2|$$

and so $1 \leq \alpha$. This contradiction proves the uniqueness of the fixed point.

The main result of the previous theorem can be generalized to obtain the Banach fixed point
theorem.

**Theorem 11.5 (Banach fixed point theorem).** *Let $I \subset \mathbb{R}$ be a closed, not necessarily bounded,
interval and let $F : I \to \mathbb{R}$ be a function with $F(I) \subset I$ and which satisfies for fixed $\alpha$,
$0 \leq \alpha < 1$ the inequality*

$$|F(x) - F(y)| \leq \alpha|x - y|, \quad x, y \in I.$$

*Then there exists exactly one fixed point $\xi$ of $F$, i.e., $F(\xi) = \xi$.*

*Proof.* The proof is exactly the same as that of Theorem 11.4.

Now we consider the solution of equation $f(x) = 0$. For function $f$ having the first derivative we consider four possibilities:

1. $f'(x) > 0$ and $f'$ is nondecreasing,

2. $f'(x) < 0$ and $f'$ is nondecreasing,

3. $f'(x) > 0$ and $f'$ is nonincreasing,

4. $f'(x) < 0$ and $f'$ is nonincreasing.

We will consider carefully only the first case since all the other cases can be considered quite similarly.

**Method of chords** Let function $f$ have continuous derivative on the interval $[a, b]$ and satisfy the first assumption. Introducing function $F$ by

$$F(x) := x - \frac{(b-x)f(x)}{f(b) - f(x)}$$

we can see that $f(x) = 0$ if and only if $F(x) = x$. The function $F$ is continuous on the interval $[a, b]$ since it can be defined at the point $b$ (the only possible singular point) as

$$F(b) := \lim_{x \to b-0} \left( x - \frac{(b-x)f(x)}{f(b) - f(x)} \right) = b - \frac{f(b)}{f'(b)}.$$

We consider in this case an initial approximation $x_0 = a$ and iterative sequence

$$x_n = F(x_{n-1}) = x_{n-1} - \frac{(b - x_{n-1})f(x_{n-1})}{f(b) - f(x_{n-1})}.$$

Assuming now that there is a point $c \in (a, b)$ such that $f(c) = 0$ our task is to prove that this iterative sequence converges to $c$. To this end we show that $x_n \in [a, c]$ for all $n = 1, 2, \ldots$ and $\{x_n\}$ is increasing. We proceed by induction on $n$. Clearly $x_0 = a \in [a, c]$. Let us assume that $x_n \in [a, c]$. Then

$$
\begin{aligned}
x_{n+1} - x_n &= \frac{(b - x_n)(f(c) - f(x_n))}{f(b) - f(c) + f(c) - f(x_n)} \\
&= \frac{(b - x_n)f'(\xi_n)(c - x_n)}{f'(\xi)(b - c) + f'(\xi_n)(c - x_n)} \\
&\leq \frac{(b - x_n)f'(\xi_n)(c - x_n)}{f'(\xi_n)(b - c + c - x_n)} = c - x_n.
\end{aligned}
$$

So $x_{n+1} \leq c$. Here we have used the fact that $f'(\xi) \geq f'(\xi_n) > 0$. By induction we obtain that $x_n \in [a, c]$ for all $n = 1, 2, \ldots$. Moreover, $\{x_n\}$ is increasing since $f'(x) > 0$ on the interval $[a, b]$. Therefore the iterative sequence $\{x_n\}$ converges as a monotone increasing sequence bounded from above, i.e., $\lim_{n \to \infty} x_n = \xi$. But due to Theorem 11.4 we have $F(\xi) = \xi$ or $f(\xi) = 0$. Due to monotonicity of $f$ we may conclude that $c = \xi$ since $f(c) = 0$ too.

**Newton's method (method of tangents)**  Under the same conditions for function $f$ from above we introduce the function $F$ by

$$F(x) = x - \frac{f(x)}{f'(x)}$$

such that $F(x) = x$ if and only if $f(x) = 0$. The initial approximation in this case will be $x_0 = b$, and the iterative sequence is

$$x_n := F(x_{n-1}), \quad n = 1, 2, \ldots.$$

We prove by induction that $x_n \in [c, b]$ for all $n = 1, 2, \ldots$ and $x_n$ is decreasing, where $f(c) = 0, a < c < b$. Indeed,

$$x_n - x_{n+1} = \frac{f(x_n) - f(c)}{f'(x_n)} = \frac{f'(\xi_n)(x_n - c)}{f'(x_n)} \le x_n - c$$

since $0 < f'(\xi_n) \le f'(x_n)$ for $\xi_n \in [c, x_n]$. Hence $x_{n+1} \ge c$. By induction we may conclude that $x_n \in [c, b]$ for all $n = 1, 2, \ldots$. The monotonicity of $\{x_n\}$ follows from the fact that $f'(x) > 0$ for all $x \in [a, b]$.

**Remark 11.6.** It should be recognized that the convergence of the iterative sequences in both methods above take place contrary to the conditions of Theorem 11.4 (it is easy to check that the conditions are not met) and it occurs only due to the right choice of the initial approximations. It should also be noted that the names of these methods follow from the fact that the equation of the chord connecting two points $(x_0, f(x_0))$ and $(b, f(b))$ on the plane is equal to

$$y = (x - x_0)\frac{f(b)}{b - x_0} + \frac{b - x}{b - x_0}f(x_0).$$

Similarly the equation of the tangent at $(x_0, f(x_0))$ is equal to

$$y = f'(x_0)(x - x_0) + f(x_0).$$

We consider now approximate methods for computing a definite Riemann integral. For these purposes we first consider a so-called symmetric template, i.e., the integrals over the interval $[-c, c]$ for $c > 0$ small enough, and we assume that $f \in \mathcal{R}[-c, c]$. Then

1.
$$\int_{-c}^{c} f(x)\mathrm{d}x = 2cf(0) + R_1,$$

where $R_1$ is the remainder term in the *method of rectangles* such that

$$\int_{-c}^{c} f(x)\mathrm{d}x \approx 2cf(0);$$

2.
$$\int_{-c}^{c} f(x)\mathrm{d}x = \frac{f(c) + f(-c)}{2}2c + R_2,$$

where $R_2$ is the remainder term in the *method of trapezoids* such that

$$\int_{-c}^{c} f(x)\mathrm{d}x \approx \frac{f(c) + f(-c)}{2}2c;$$

3.
$$\int_{-c}^{c} f(x)\mathrm{d}x = \int_{-c}^{c} (Ax^2 + Bx + D)\mathrm{d}x + R_3,$$

where $R_3$ is the remainder term in the *Simpson's method* (*method of parabolas*) such that

$$\int_{-c}^{c} f(x)\mathrm{d}x \approx \frac{f(c) + 4f(0) + f(-c)}{6}2c.$$

Indeed, this parabola goes through the points $(-c, f(-c)), (0, f(0))$ and $(c, f(c))$ on the plane. Hence

$$A = \frac{f(c) - 2f(0) + f(-c)}{2c^2}, \quad B = \frac{f(c) - f(-c)}{2c}, \quad D = f(0).$$

This implies that

$$\int_{-c}^{c} (Ax^2 + Bx + D)\mathrm{d}x = \frac{2}{3}Ac^3 + 2Dc$$

$$= \frac{2}{3}c^3\frac{f(c) - 2f(0) + f(-c)}{2c^2} + 2f(0)c$$

$$= \frac{f(c) + 4f(0) + f(-c)}{6}2c.$$

There is a modification of Simpson's method in the form

$$\int_{-c}^{c} f(x)\mathrm{d}x \approx \frac{f(c) + \gamma f(0) + f(-c)}{2 + \gamma}2c,$$

where $\gamma$ is a positive parameter. It should be mentioned that if $\gamma \to +0$ then we obtain the method of trapezoids and if $\gamma \to +\infty$ then we obtain the method of rectangles.

### Evaluation of the remainders $R_1$, $R_2$, and $R_3$

1. To estimate the remainder term $R_1$ we assume that the primitive $F$ of $f$ has the third derivative which is continuous on the interval $[-c, c]$. Then using Taylor's expansion we have

$$\int_{-c}^{c} f(x)\mathrm{d}x = F(c) - F(-c) = F(0) + F'(0)c + \frac{F''(0)}{2}c^2 + \frac{F'''(\xi_1)}{6}c^3$$

$$- \left( F(0) - F'(0)c + \frac{F''(0)}{2}c^2 - \frac{F'''(\xi_2)}{6}c^3 \right)$$

$$= 2cf(0) + \frac{c^3}{3}\frac{f''(\xi_1) + f''(\xi_2)}{2} = 2cf(0) + \frac{c^3}{3}\frac{f''(\xi)}{2}.$$

The last step follows from the continuity of $f''$. Thus,

$$R_1 = \frac{c^3}{3}f''(\xi).$$

2. To estimate the remainder term $R_2$ we use the same conditions for $F$. Denoting $\varphi(x) := F(x) - F(-x)$ and using Taylor's expansion with remainder in the integral form we obtain

$$\varphi(c) = \varphi(0) + \varphi'(0)c + \frac{\varphi''(0)}{2}c^2 + \frac{1}{2}\int_0^c \varphi'''(t)(c - t)^2\mathrm{d}t$$

$$= 2cf(0) + \frac{1}{2}\int_0^c \varphi'''(t)(c - t)^2\mathrm{d}t$$

since $\varphi(0) = F(0) - F(0) = 0, \varphi''(0) = F''(0) - F''(0) = 0$ and $\varphi'(0) = 2f(0)$. Differentiating with respect to $c$ we obtain

$$\varphi'(c) = 2f(0) + \int_0^c \varphi'''(t)(c-t)\mathrm{d}t.$$

It follows that

$$2f(0) = \varphi'(c) - \int_0^c \varphi'''(t)(c-t)\mathrm{d}t = f(c) + f(-c) - \int_0^c \varphi'''(t)(c-t)\mathrm{d}t.$$

Combining these considerations we obtain

$$\int_{-c}^c f(x)\mathrm{d}x = F(c) - F(-c) = \varphi(c)$$

$$= 2c\frac{f(c) + f(-c)}{2} - c\int_0^c \varphi'''(t)(c-t)\mathrm{d}t + \frac{1}{2}\int_0^c \varphi'''(t)(c-t)^2\mathrm{d}t$$

$$= 2c\frac{f(c) + f(-c)}{2} + \frac{1}{2}\int_0^c \varphi'''(t)(t^2 - c^2)\mathrm{d}t.$$

Hence

$$R_2 = -\frac{1}{2}\int_0^c \varphi'''(t)(c^2 - t^2)\mathrm{d}t.$$

Applying the first mean value formula for the latter integral we get

$$R_2 = -\frac{1}{2}\varphi'''(\xi)\int_0^c (c^2 - t^2)\mathrm{d}t = -\frac{f''(\xi) + f''(-\xi)}{2}\frac{2}{3}c^3 = -f''(\eta)\frac{2}{3}c^3$$

due to continuity of $f''$.

3. To estimate the remainder term $R_3$ in Simpson's method we note that

$$\int_{-c}^c f(x)\mathrm{d}x = \frac{1}{3}\frac{f(c) + f(-c)}{2}2c + \frac{2}{3}f(0)2c + R_3$$

$$= \frac{1}{3}\left[\int_{-c}^c f(x)\mathrm{d}x - R_2\right] + \frac{2}{3}\left[\int_{-c}^c f(x)\mathrm{d}x - R_1\right] + R_3$$

$$= \int_{-c}^c f(x)\mathrm{d}x - \frac{1}{3}R_2 - \frac{2}{3}R_1 + R_3.$$

Hence the evaluation of $R_3$ follows straightforwardly from the estimates of $R_1$ and $R_2$ as

$$R_3 = \frac{2}{3}R_1 + \frac{1}{3}R_2 = \frac{2}{9}(f''(\xi) - f''(\eta))c^3.$$

Now we are in position to consider three methods for an arbitrary interval $[a, b]$, i.e., we want to calculate approximately the integral $\int_a^b f(x)\mathrm{d}x$. For these purposes we divide this interval into $n$ equal parts of length $(b-a)/n$ and denote the points of the partition as

$$a = x_0 < x_2 < x_4 < \cdots < x_{2n} = b,$$

while the middle points of these small intervals are denoted by

$$x_0 < x_1 < x_3 < \cdots < x_{2n-1}.$$

It means that we have the intervals $[x_{2j}, x_{2j+2}]$ for $j = 0, 1, \ldots, n-1$ and

$$x_{2j+1} = \frac{x_{2j} + x_{2j+2}}{2}, \quad j = 0, 1, \ldots, n-1,$$

i.e.,

$$x_{2j} = a + j(b-a)/n, \quad x_{2j+1} = a + (j+1/2)(b-a)/n,$$

where the intervals $[x_{2j}, x_{2j+2}]$ are symmetric with respect to $x_{2j+1}$. Applying methods from the symmetric template to the general case we obtain

$$\int_a^b f(x)\mathrm{d}x = \sum_{j=0}^{n-1} \int_{x_{2j}}^{x_{2j+2}} f(x)\mathrm{d}x$$

$$= \frac{b-a}{n} \begin{cases} \displaystyle\sum_{j=0}^{n-1} f(x_{2j+1}) + \sum_{j=0}^{n-1} R_1^{(j)} \\[2ex] \displaystyle\sum_{j=0}^{n-1} \frac{1}{2}(f(x_{2j}) + f(x_{2j+2})) + \sum_{j=0}^{n-1} R_2^{(j)} \\[2ex] \displaystyle\sum_{j=0}^{n-1} \frac{1}{6}(f(x_{2j}) + 4f(x_{2j+1}) + f(x_{2j+2})) + \sum_{j=0}^{n-1} R_3^{(j)}, \end{cases}$$

where $R_1^{(j)}$, $R_2^{(j)}$, and $R_3^{(j)}$ are the remainder terms on the partial intervals $[x_{2j}, x_{2j+2}]$ for the method of rectangles, trapezoids, and parabolas (Simpson's method), respectively.

In this case the formulas are said to be the method of rectangles, trapezoids, and parabolas, and the values

$$R_1 = \sum_{j=0}^{n-1} R_1^{(j)}, \quad R_2 = \sum_{j=0}^{n-1} R_2^{(j)}, \quad R_3 = \sum_{j=0}^{n-1} R_3^{(j)}$$

are said to be the remainder terms in these three methods, respectively. Due to continuity of $f''$ and the evaluation of $R_1^{(j)}$, $R_2^{(j)}$, and $R_3^{(j)}$ on the partial intervals we have

$$R_1 = \frac{(b-a)^3}{24n^3} \sum_{j=0}^{n-1} f''(\xi_j) = \frac{(b-a)^3}{24n^2} f''(\xi),$$

$$R_2 = -\frac{(b-a)^3}{24n^3} 2 \sum_{j=0}^{n-1} f''(\xi_j) = -\frac{(b-a)^3}{12n^2} f''(\xi),$$

$$R_3 = \frac{2}{9} \frac{(b-a)^3}{8n^3} \left( \sum_{j=0}^{n-1} f''(\xi_j) - \sum_{j=0}^{n-1} f''(\eta_j) \right) = \frac{(b-a)^3}{36n^2} (f''(\xi) - f''(\eta)).$$

**Exercise 11.7.** Prove that if a function $g$ is continuous on the interval $[a, b]$ and $\xi_1, \xi_2, \ldots, \xi_n \in [a, b]$ then there is $\xi \in [a, b]$ such that

$$g(\xi) = \frac{1}{n} \sum_{j=1}^{n} g(\xi_j).$$

**Exercise 11.8.** Prove formulas for $A$, $B$, and $D$ for the Simpson's method on the symmetric template.

# Part II

# Analysis of multivariable functions and Lebesgue integration

# Chapter 12

# Geometric applications of integrals. Elementary measure theory

The geometric applications appearing in this chapter are primarily related to the application of the definite Riemann integral and to the theory of Jordan measure. The length of a parametrized smooth rectifiable curve in $\mathbb{R}^n$ is calculated as an integral of the modulus of its derivative. Jordan measurable sets in $\mathbb{R}^n$ are considered, and measurability criteria are obtained in terms of elementary figures which are unions of rectangular parallelepipeds. In particular, it is proved that a curvilinear trapezium in the plane and a rotation body in three-dimensional space are measurable in the sense of Jordan, and their Jordan measures are calculated using the definite Riemann integral.

In this chapter we consider also real vector-valued functions of one real variable as the following mapping:

$$\overrightarrow{f} : [\alpha, \beta] \to \mathbb{R}^n, \quad \overrightarrow{f} = (f_1, f_2, \ldots, f_n),$$

where

1. $\overrightarrow{f}(t) \in C[\alpha, \beta]$, i.e., $f_j(t) \in C[\alpha, \beta]$ for each $j = 1, 2, \ldots, n$;

2. $\overrightarrow{f}(t)$ is differentiable, i.e., $f_j(t)$ is differentiable for each $j = 1, 2, \ldots, n$ and $\overrightarrow{f'}(t) = (f'_1(t), f'_2(t), \ldots, f'_n(t))$;

3. $|\overrightarrow{f}(t)| = \sqrt{f_1^2(t) + f_2^2(t) + \cdots + f_n^2(t)}$;

4. $\overrightarrow{f}(t) = \overrightarrow{g}(t)$ if and only if $f_j(t) = g_j(t)$ for each $j = 1, 2, \ldots, n$.

If we interpret $t \in [\alpha, \beta]$ as time then the equations $x_j = f_j(t), j = 1, 2, \ldots, n$, define a law of motion of a point $M = M(x_1, x_2, \ldots, x_n)$ with coordinates $(x_1, x_2, \ldots, x_n)$ on $\mathbb{R}^n$ and the set

$$\{x \in \mathbb{R}^n : x = \overrightarrow{f}(t), t \in [\alpha, \beta]\}$$

is said to be a *trace point* moving according to this law. It can be denoted also as a *curve* in $\mathbb{R}^n$, i.e.,

$$\gamma : x = \overrightarrow{f}(t), \quad t \in [\alpha, \beta].$$

**Definition 12.1.** *A curve* $\gamma : x = \overrightarrow{f}(t), t \in [\alpha, \beta]$, *is called a* simple curve *if the vector-valued function* $\overrightarrow{f}(t)$ *is continuous and* $\overrightarrow{f}(t_1) \neq \overrightarrow{f}(t_2)$ *for any* $t_1, t_2 \in [\alpha, \beta]$ *with* $t_1 \neq t_2$. *In this case the curve* $\gamma$ *is called a* closed simple curve *if* $\overrightarrow{f}(\alpha) = \overrightarrow{f}(\beta)$.

**Remark 12.2.** The equation $x = \overrightarrow{f}(t), t \in [\alpha, \beta]$, is also called a *parametrization of the curve* $\gamma$. We consider this parametrization up to the following transformation:

$$x = \overrightarrow{f}(t) = \overrightarrow{f}(s^{-1}(s(t))) = \overrightarrow{f}(s^{-1})(s) = \overrightarrow{f_1}(s),$$

where $s : [\alpha, \beta] \to [\alpha_1, \beta_1]$ is increasing and continuous, and $\alpha_1 = s(\alpha)$ and $\beta_1 = s(\beta)$.

**Definition 12.3.** *Let* $P$ *be a partition of the interval* $[\alpha, \beta]$ *such that*

$$\alpha = t_0 < t_1 < \cdots < t_m = \beta$$

*and* $\overrightarrow{f}(t_k) =: M_k \in \gamma$. *By* $\overline{M_{k-1}M_k}$ *we denote the* straight line segment *connecting* $M_{k-1}$ *and* $M_k$, *and by* $l(P) := \bigcup_{k=1}^{m} \overline{M_{k-1}M_k}$ *we denote the* inscribed broken line *corresponding to* $P$ *with the length*

$$|l(P)| = \sum_{k=1}^{m} |\overline{M_{k-1}M_k}| = \sum_{k=1}^{m} |\overrightarrow{f}(t_{k-1}) - \overrightarrow{f}(t_k)| = \sum_{k=1}^{m} \sqrt{\sum_{j=1}^{n} (f_j(t_{k-1}) - f_j(t_k))^2}.$$

**Definition 12.4.** *A simple curve* $\gamma : x = \overrightarrow{f}(t)$ *is said to be* rectifiable *if*

$$\sup_{P} |l(P)| < \infty,$$

*and in this case*

$$\sup_{P} |l(P)| =: |\gamma|$$

*is called the* length of the curve $\gamma$.

**Remark 12.5.** The latter definition is justified by the obvious property

$$|l(P)| \leq |l(P')|$$

whenever $P \subset P'$.

**Theorem 12.6 (Properties of rectifiable curves).**

1. *Suppose a curve* $\gamma$ *is rectifiable. Then its length is independent on the parametrization.*

2. *Let rectifiable curve* $\gamma$ *be divided by the points* $M_0, M_1, \ldots, M_m \in \gamma$ *into a finite number of curves* $\gamma_1, \gamma_2, \ldots, \gamma_m$ *such that*

$$\gamma = \bigcup_{k=1}^{m} \gamma_k.$$

   *Then* $\gamma_k, k = 1, 2, \ldots, m$, *are rectifiable and*

$$|\gamma| = \sum_{k=1}^{m} |\gamma_k|.$$

*Proof.*

1. This part is obvious due to the conditions for parametrizations that we consider.

2. It suffices to consider the case of only two curves $\gamma_1$ and $\gamma_2$ such that $\gamma = \gamma_1 \cup \gamma_2$. Indeed, let $M_0 = \overrightarrow{f}(\alpha)$, $M_1 = \overrightarrow{f}(t')$, and $M_2 = \overrightarrow{f}(\beta)$, where $\alpha < t' < \beta$ and $\gamma_1 : x = \overrightarrow{f}(t), t \in [\alpha, t'], \gamma_2 : x = \overrightarrow{f}(t), t \in [t', \beta]$ with $\gamma_1 \cap \gamma_2 = M_1$.

If $P_1$ and $P_2$ are partitions of $[\alpha, t']$ and $[t', \beta]$ then $P := P_1 \cup P_2$ is a partition of $[\alpha, \beta]$ such that $P_1 \cap P_2 = \{t'\}$. In this case

$$|l(P)| = |l(P_1)| + |l(P_2)|$$

so that $|l(P_1)|, |l(P_2)| \leq |l(P)|$. Therefore $\gamma_1$ and $\gamma_2$ are rectifiable since $\gamma$ is rectifiable. Moreover,

$$\sup_{P := P_1 \cup P_2} |l(P)| = \sup_{P_1} |l(P_1)| + \sup_{P_2} |l(P_2)|.$$

This implies

$$|\gamma| = \sup_P |l(P)| \geq \sup_{P := P_1 \cup P_2} |l(P)| = \sup_{P_1} |l(P_1)| + \sup_{P_2} |l(P_2)| = |\gamma_1| + |\gamma_2|.$$

In order to prove the opposite inequality we proceed as follows. By the definition of the length of $\gamma$ we have that for any $\varepsilon > 0$ there is a partition $P$ of the interval $[\alpha, \beta]$ such that

$$|\gamma| < |l(P)| + \varepsilon.$$

Now let $P' := P \cup \{t'\}$. Then

$$|\gamma| < |l(P)| + \varepsilon \leq |l(P')| + \varepsilon$$

and $P' = P_1 \cup P_2$ for some $P_1$ and $P_2$, which are partitions of $[\alpha, t']$ and $[t', \beta]$, respectively. So

$$|\gamma| < |l(P')| + \varepsilon = |l(P_1)| + |l(P_2)| + \varepsilon \leq |\gamma_1| + |\gamma_2| + \varepsilon.$$

Since $\varepsilon$ was arbitrary and since $|\gamma|, |\gamma_1|$, and $|\gamma_2|$ do not depend on $\varepsilon$ we may let $\varepsilon \to +0$ and obtain $|\gamma| \leq |\gamma_1| + |\gamma_2|$.

The theorem is completely proved.

**Theorem 12.7 (Length of the curve).** *Let* $\gamma : x = \overrightarrow{f}(t), t \in [\alpha, \beta]$, *be a simple curve. If* $\overrightarrow{f}$ *is continuously differentiable on the interval* $[\alpha, \beta]$ *then* $\gamma$ *is rectifiable and*

$$|\gamma| = \int_\alpha^\beta |\overrightarrow{f}'(t)| \mathrm{d}t = \int_\alpha^\beta \sqrt{(f_1'(t))^2 + \cdots + (f_n'(t))^2} \mathrm{d}t.$$

*Proof.* Let $P$ be a partition of the interval $[\alpha, \beta]$. Then

$$|l(P)| = \sum_{k=1}^m |\overrightarrow{f}(t_{k-1}) - \overrightarrow{f}(t_k)| = \sum_{k=1}^m \sqrt{\sum_{j=1}^n (f_j(t_{k-1}) - f_j(t_k))^2}$$

$$= \sum_{k=1}^m \sqrt{\sum_{j=1}^n \left( \int_{t_{k-1}}^{t_k} f_j'(t) \mathrm{d}t \right)^2} = \sum_{k=1}^m \left| \int_{t_{k-1}}^{t_k} \overrightarrow{f}'(t) \mathrm{d}t \right|$$

$$\leq \sum_{k=1}^m \int_{t_{k-1}}^{t_k} \left| \overrightarrow{f}'(t) \right| \mathrm{d}t = \int_\alpha^\beta \left| \overrightarrow{f}'(t) \right| \mathrm{d}t,$$

where the integral of the vector-valued function is understood as a vector of integrals of corresponding coordinates. Hence

$$|\gamma| \leq \int_\alpha^\beta \left|\vec{f}'(t)\right| \mathrm{d}t.$$

We have used here the following lemma.

**Lemma 12.8.** *Let vector-valued function $\vec{g}$ be integrable on the interval $[\alpha, \beta]$. Then*

$$\left|\int_\alpha^\beta \vec{g}(t)\mathrm{d}t\right| \leq \int_\alpha^\beta |\vec{g}(t)| \, \mathrm{d}t.$$

*Proof.* Denoting by

$$\vec{y} = \int_\alpha^\beta \vec{g}(t)\mathrm{d}t$$

the constant vector we obtain

$$|\vec{y}|^2 = \sum_{j=1}^n y_j y_j = \sum_{j=1}^n y_j \int_\alpha^\beta g_j(t)\mathrm{d}t = \sum_{j=1}^n \int_\alpha^\beta y_j g_j(t)\mathrm{d}t$$

$$= \int_\alpha^\beta \left(\sum_{j=1}^n y_j g_j(t)\right) \mathrm{d}t \leq \int_\alpha^\beta \left(\sum_{j=1}^n y_j^2\right)^{1/2} \left(\sum_{j=1}^n g_j(t)^2\right)^{1/2} \mathrm{d}t$$

$$= |\vec{y}| \int_\alpha^\beta |\vec{g}(t)|\mathrm{d}t$$

by the Cauchy–Schwarz–Bunjakovskii inequality. The lemma follows now by rearranging.

To finish the proof of the theorem let us prove the converse inequality. Since $\vec{f}' \in C[\alpha, \beta]$, it is uniformly continuous due to Cantor's theorem. Hence for any $\varepsilon > 0$ there exists $\delta > 0$ such that

$$|\vec{f}'(t') - \vec{f}'(t'')| < \varepsilon$$

for any $t', t'' \in [\alpha, \beta]$ and $|t' - t''| < \delta$. Let $P$ be a partition of the interval $[\alpha, \beta]$ such that $\mu(P) < \delta$. Then for all $t \in [t_{k-1}, t_k], k = 1, 2, \ldots, m$, we have

$$|\vec{f}'(t) - \vec{f}'(t_k)| < \varepsilon.$$

It follows that

$$|\vec{f}'(t)| < |\vec{f}'(t_k)| + \varepsilon.$$

Therefore

$$\int_{t_{k-1}}^{t_k} |\vec{f}'(t)|\mathrm{d}t < \int_{t_{k-1}}^{t_k} |\vec{f}'(t_k)|\mathrm{d}t + \varepsilon\Delta t_k = \left|\int_{t_{k-1}}^{t_k} \vec{f}'(t_k)\mathrm{d}t\right| + \varepsilon\Delta t_k$$

since $\overrightarrow{f}'(t_k)$ is a constant vector on the interval $[t_{k-1}, t_k]$. Next,

$$\int_{t_{k-1}}^{t_k} |\overrightarrow{f}'(t)| \mathrm{d}t < \left| \int_{t_{k-1}}^{t_k} (\overrightarrow{f}'(t_k) - \overrightarrow{f}'(t) + \overrightarrow{f}'(t)) \mathrm{d}t \right| + \varepsilon \Delta t_k$$

$$\leq \int_{t_{k-1}}^{t_k} \left| \overrightarrow{f}'(t_k) - \overrightarrow{f}'(t) \right| \mathrm{d}t + \left| \int_{t_{k-1}}^{t_k} \overrightarrow{f}'(t) \mathrm{d}t \right| + \varepsilon \Delta t_k$$

$$= \int_{t_{k-1}}^{t_k} \left| \overrightarrow{f}'(t_k) - \overrightarrow{f}'(t) \right| \mathrm{d}t + \left| \overrightarrow{f}(t_k) - \overrightarrow{f}(t_{k-1}) \right| + \varepsilon \Delta t_k$$

$$< 2\varepsilon \Delta t_k + \left| \overrightarrow{f}(t_k) - \overrightarrow{f}(t_{k-1}) \right|.$$

Taking the sums we get

$$\sum_{k=1}^{m} \int_{t_{k-1}}^{t_k} |\overrightarrow{f}'(t)| \mathrm{d}t < 2\varepsilon \sum_{k=1}^{m} \Delta t_k + \sum_{k=1}^{m} \left| \overrightarrow{f}(t_k) - \overrightarrow{f}(t_{k-1}) \right|$$

or

$$\int_{\alpha}^{\beta} |\overrightarrow{f}'(t)| \mathrm{d}t < 2\varepsilon(\beta - \alpha) + |l(P)| \leq 2\varepsilon(\beta - \alpha) + |\gamma|.$$

Letting $\varepsilon \to +0$ we obtain

$$\int_{\alpha}^{\beta} |\overrightarrow{f}'(t)| \mathrm{d}t \leq |\gamma|.$$

This opposite inequality proves the theorem.

**Remark 12.9.** If we assume only that $\overrightarrow{f}'$ is bounded (not continuous as in the theorem), i.e., $|\overrightarrow{f}'(t)| \leq M$ with some positive constant $M$, then the previous proof gives us in this case that $\gamma$ is rectifiable and $|\gamma| \leq M(\beta - \alpha)$ but not more.

**Remark 12.10.** Under the conditions of the latter theorem we interpret the formula for the length of the curve $\gamma$ as

$$|\gamma| = \int_{\alpha}^{\beta} |\overrightarrow{f}'(t)| \mathrm{d}t$$

as the Riemann–Stieltjes integral. Indeed, let us denote by $\mathrm{d}l(t) := |\overrightarrow{f}'(t)| \mathrm{d}t$ an element of the curve length. Then

$$|\gamma| = \int_{\alpha}^{\beta} \mathrm{d}l(t)$$

is a Riemann–Stieltjes integral of the unit with respect to monotone increasing function $l(t)$ which equals the length of the part of $\gamma$ from $\alpha$ to $t$.

For function $f(x)$ and vector-valued function $\overrightarrow{f}(x)$ both defined on the rectifiable curve $\gamma$ : $x = \overrightarrow{\varphi}(t), t \in [\alpha, \beta]$, we may introduce the following curvilinear integrals. If the function $\overrightarrow{\varphi}(t)$ is continuously differentiable on the interval $[\alpha, \beta]$ and the functions $f$ and $\overrightarrow{f}$ are continuous with respect to their variables then we define

$$\int_{\gamma} f(x) \mathrm{d}l(x) := \int_{\alpha}^{\beta} f(\overrightarrow{\varphi}(t)) |\overrightarrow{\varphi}'(t)| \mathrm{d}t,$$

$$\int_{\gamma} \sum_{j=1}^{n} f_j(x) \mathrm{d}x_j := \int_{\alpha}^{\beta} \sum_{j=1}^{n} f_j(\overrightarrow{\varphi}(t)) \varphi_j'(t) \mathrm{d}t,$$

which are called the *curvilinear integrals of the first and second kinds*, respectively. Due to the Cauchy–Schwarz–Bunjakovskii inequality we obtain

$$\left| \int_\gamma \sum_{j=1}^n f_j(x)\mathrm{d}x_j \right| \le \int_\alpha^\beta \left| \sum_{j=1}^n f_j(\overrightarrow{\varphi}(t))\varphi_j'(t) \right| \mathrm{d}t \le \int_\alpha^\beta \left| \overrightarrow{f}(\overrightarrow{\varphi}(t)) \right| \left| \overrightarrow{\varphi}'(t) \right| \mathrm{d}t$$

$$= \int_\alpha^\beta |\overrightarrow{f}(x)|\mathrm{d}l(x),$$

i.e., the curvilinear integral of the second kind can be estimated from above by the corresponding curvilinear integral of the first kind.

**Applications to the theory of curves. Frenet formulas**  Let $\gamma : x = \overrightarrow{f}(t), t \in [\alpha, \beta]$, be a simple curve in $\mathbb{R}^n, n = 2, 3$. If $\overrightarrow{f}$ is twice differentiable on the interval $[\alpha, \beta]$ then the curve $\gamma$ has at any point *curvature*, denoted by $k_1(t)$, which is defined as the limit

$$k_1(t) = \lim_{l \to 0} \frac{\varphi}{l},$$

where $l$ is the arc length between $\overrightarrow{f}(t)$ and $\overrightarrow{f}(t+\Delta t)$ along the curve and $\varphi$ is the angle between tangent vectors to the curve at the points $\overrightarrow{f}(t)$ and $\overrightarrow{f}(t+\Delta t)$, i.e., between the vectors $\overrightarrow{f}'(t)$ and $\overrightarrow{f}'(t+\Delta t)$. We show that this limit exists at any point $t$. Indeed, since $l \to 0$ implies that $\Delta t \to 0$, $\sin \varphi$ can be calculated as

$$\sin \varphi = \frac{|\overrightarrow{f}'(t) \times \overrightarrow{f}'(t+\Delta t)|}{|\overrightarrow{f}'(t)||\overrightarrow{f}'(t+\Delta t)|},$$

where $\times$ indicates the vector product in $\mathbb{R}^n, n = 2, 3$ (we may assume without loss of generality that $\Delta t > 0$). The arc length (see Theorem 12.7) can be obtained as

$$l = \int_t^{t+\Delta t} |\overrightarrow{f}'(t)|\mathrm{d}t = |\overrightarrow{f}'(\xi)|\Delta t = |\overrightarrow{f}'(t)|\Delta t + o(\Delta t).$$

We have used here the continuity of $|\overrightarrow{f}'(t)|$. Next, by Taylor's expansion ($\overrightarrow{f}$ is twice differentiable) we have

$$\overrightarrow{f}'(t + \Delta t) = \overrightarrow{f}'(t) + \overrightarrow{f}''(t)\Delta t + o(\Delta t);$$

see Theorem 7.4. Using this expansion we obtain

$$\sin \varphi = \frac{|\overrightarrow{f}'(t) \times \overrightarrow{f}''(t)| + o(1)}{|\overrightarrow{f}'(t)|^2 + o(1)}\Delta t,$$

where we have used the fact that the vector product satisfies $\overrightarrow{a} \times \overrightarrow{a} = 0$ for any vector $\overrightarrow{a}$. The formulas for $l$ and $\sin \varphi$ lead to

$$\frac{\varphi}{l} = \frac{\varphi}{\sin \varphi} \frac{|\overrightarrow{f}'(t) \times \overrightarrow{f}''(t)| + o(1)}{(|\overrightarrow{f}'(t)|^2 + o(1))(|\overrightarrow{f}'(t)| + o(1))}$$

as $\Delta t \to 0$. Since

$$\lim_{l \to 0 (\Delta t \to 0)} \frac{\varphi}{\sin \varphi} = 1$$

then $\lim_{l \to 0} \varphi/l$ exists also and the curvature is equal to

$$k_1(t) = \frac{|\overrightarrow{f}'(t) \times \overrightarrow{f}''(t)|}{|\overrightarrow{f}'(t)|^3}.$$

**Exercise 12.11.** Prove that

1.

$$k_1(t) = \frac{|f_1' f_2'' - f_2' f_1''|}{((f_1')^2 + (f_2')^2)^{3/2}}, \quad n = 2,$$

2.

$$k_1(t) = \frac{\sqrt{(f_3'' f_2' - f_2'' f_3')^2 + (f_1'' f_3' - f_3'' f_1')^2 + (f_2'' f_1' - f_1'' f_2')^2}}{((f_1')^2 + (f_2')^2 + (f_3')^2)^{3/2}}, \quad n = 3.$$

**Exercise 12.12.** Assume that $F(x, y)$ is twice differentiable and a curve is defined implicitly by the equation $F(x, y) = 0$. Prove that

$$k_1 = \frac{|F_y^2 F_{xx} - 2F_x F_y F_{xy} + F_x^2 F_{yy}|}{(F_x^2 + F_y^2)^{3/2}},$$

where $F_x$ and $F_{xy}$ are derivatives with respect to $x$ and with respect to $x$ and $y$, and so on. In particular, if the curve is defined explicitly as $y = f(x)$ then

$$k_1 = \frac{|f''(x)|}{(1 + (f'(x))^2)^{3/2}}.$$

**Example 12.13.** Consider the parabola $y = ax^2 + bx + c$. Let us parametrize it as $x = f_1(t) = t, y = f_2(t) = at^2 + bt + c$. Then the curvature of the parabola is equal to

$$k_1(x) = k_1(t) = \frac{2|a|}{(1 + (2ax + b)^2)^{3/2}}$$

by the formula above. This formula shows that the curvature is maximal for $x = -b/(2a)$, i.e., at the stationary point at the vertex of the parabola.

**Example 12.14.** Consider the curve defined in polar coordinates by $r = r(\theta), \theta \in [\alpha, \beta]$. We can parametrize it as $f_1(\theta) = r(\theta) \cos \theta, f_2(\theta) = r(\theta) \sin \theta$. Then the curvature is

$$k_1(\theta) = \frac{|r^2(\theta) + 2(r'(\theta))^2 - r(\theta) r''(\theta)|}{(r^2(\theta) + (r'(\theta))^2)^{3/2}}$$

by Exercise 12.11. In particular, for the circle $r(\theta) = r > 0$ we obtain

$$k_1(\theta) = \frac{1}{r}.$$

Let now $\gamma : x = \overrightarrow{f}(t), t \in [\alpha, \beta]$, be a simple curve in $\mathbb{R}^n, n = 2, 3$, such that $\overrightarrow{f}$ is three times differentiable. Then the *absolute torsion*, denoted by $|k_2(t)|$, is defined as the limit (if it exists)

$$|k_2(t)| = \lim_{l \to 0} \frac{\psi}{l},$$

where $l$ is the arc length between $\overrightarrow{f}(t)$ and $\overrightarrow{f}(t + \Delta t)$ along the curve and $\psi$ is the angle between contiguous planes to the curve at the points $\overrightarrow{f}(t)$ and $\overrightarrow{f}(t + \Delta t)$. It is clear that the absolute torsion in the two-dimensional case is zero. In the three-dimensional case we have that the normal vector to the contiguous plane at the point $\overrightarrow{f}(t)$ is equal to $\overrightarrow{f}'(t) \times \overrightarrow{f}''(t)$. Thus, sine of the angle $\psi$ can be calculated as

$$\sin \psi = \frac{|(\overrightarrow{f}'(t) \times \overrightarrow{f}''(t)) \times (\overrightarrow{f}'(t + \Delta t) \times \overrightarrow{f}''(t + \Delta t))|}{|\overrightarrow{f}'(t) \times \overrightarrow{f}''(t)||\overrightarrow{f}'(t + \Delta t) \times \overrightarrow{f}''(t + \Delta t)|}.$$

Using Taylor's expansion we get

$$\sin \psi = \frac{|(\overrightarrow{f}'(t) \times \overrightarrow{f}''(t)) \times [(\overrightarrow{f}'(t) \times \overrightarrow{f}''(t))\Delta t + o(\Delta t)]|}{|\overrightarrow{f}'(t) \times \overrightarrow{f}''(t)|^2 + o(\Delta t)}$$

$$= \frac{|\overrightarrow{f}'(t)(\overrightarrow{f}'(t) \times \overrightarrow{f}''(t), \overrightarrow{f}'''(t))_{\mathbb{R}^3}\Delta t + \overrightarrow{f}'''(t)(\overrightarrow{f}''(t) \times \overrightarrow{f}'(t), \overrightarrow{f}'(t))_{\mathbb{R}^3}\Delta t + o(\Delta t)|}{|\overrightarrow{f}'(t) \times \overrightarrow{f}''(t)|^2 + o(\Delta t)}.$$

Here we have used the fact that

$$\overrightarrow{a} \times (\overrightarrow{b} \times \overrightarrow{c}) = \overrightarrow{b}(\overrightarrow{a}, \overrightarrow{c})_{\mathbb{R}^3} - \overrightarrow{c}(\overrightarrow{a}, \overrightarrow{b})_{\mathbb{R}^3}, \quad \overrightarrow{a} \times \overrightarrow{a} = 0,$$

where $(\cdot, \cdot)_{\mathbb{R}^3}$ denotes the usual inner product in $\mathbb{R}^3$ (see Chapter 13). Since also $(\overrightarrow{f}''(t) \times \overrightarrow{f}'(t), \overrightarrow{f}'(t))_{\mathbb{R}^3} = 0$ we have

$$\sin \psi = \frac{|\overrightarrow{f}'(t)(\overrightarrow{f}'(t) \times \overrightarrow{f}''(t), \overrightarrow{f}'''(t))_{\mathbb{R}^3}\Delta t + o(\Delta t)|}{|\overrightarrow{f}'(t) \times \overrightarrow{f}''(t)|^2 + o(\Delta t)}.$$

Taking into account that $l = \overrightarrow{f}'(t)\Delta t + o(\Delta t)$ we obtain that the limit $\lim_{l \to 0} \psi/l$ exists ($l \to 0$ implies $\Delta t \to 0$) and is equal to

$$|k_2(t)| = \lim_{l \to 0} \frac{\psi}{l} = \frac{|(\overrightarrow{f}'(t) \times \overrightarrow{f}''(t), \overrightarrow{f}'''(t))_{\mathbb{R}^3}|}{|\overrightarrow{f}'(t) \times \overrightarrow{f}''(t)|^2}.$$

This shows that the absolute torsion exists and we define the *torsion* by

$$k_2(t) = \frac{(\overrightarrow{f}'(t) \times \overrightarrow{f}''(t), \overrightarrow{f}'''(t))_{\mathbb{R}^3}}{|\overrightarrow{f}'(t) \times \overrightarrow{f}''(t)|^2}.$$

Let $\gamma : x = \overrightarrow{f}(t)$ be a simple smooth (as above) curve in $\mathbb{R}^3$. Let $T(t)$ be the unit tangent vector and $N(t)$ the unit normal vector to the curve at the point $\overrightarrow{f}(t)$. Let us define a unit vector $B(t)$ as

$$B = T \times N.$$

These three mutually orthogonal vectors $T$, $N$, and $B$ form at any point $t$ an orthonormal basis in $\mathbb{R}^3$. Moreover, this basis satisfies the following system of first order differential equations:

$$\begin{cases} T'(t) = k_1(t)N(t), \\ N'(t) = -k_1(t)T(t) + k_2(t)B(t), \\ B'(t) = -k_2(t)N(t), \end{cases}$$

where $k_1(t)$ is the curvature and $k_2(t)$ is the torsion of the curve $\gamma$. These formulas are called the *Frenet formulas* for the three-dimensional smooth simple curve.

**Exercise 12.15.** Prove Frenet formulas.

**Remark 12.16.** In the two-dimensional case $k_2(t) = 0$ and $B = 0$. So the Frenet formulas become

$$\begin{cases} T'(t) = k_1(t)N(t), \\ N'(t) = -k_1(t)T(t). \end{cases}$$

In particular, we obtain that

$$k_1(t) = (T'(t), N(t))_{\mathbb{R}^2} = -(N'(t), T(t))_{\mathbb{R}^2}.$$

The analogues of these formulas in the three-dimensional case are

$$k_1(t) = (T'(t), N(t))_{\mathbb{R}^3} = -(N'(t), T(t))_{\mathbb{R}^3},$$
$$k_2(t) = (N'(t), B(t))_{\mathbb{R}^3} = -(B'(t), N(t))_{\mathbb{R}^3}.$$

These formulas yield that the curvature $k_1(t)$ and torsion $k_2(t)$ (in two dimensions only $k_1(t)$) define the curve completely (up to orientation in the corresponding space).

Next we consider sets $X \subset \mathbb{R}^n$, i.e., the sets of elements $x \in X$ with $x = (x_1, x_2, \ldots, x_n) \in \mathbb{R}^n$.

**Definition 12.17.** *The set*

$$B_R(x^0) = \{x \in \mathbb{R}^n : |x - x^0| < R\}$$

*is called the* open ball *of radius $R > 0$ centered at $x^0$. The set*

$$S_R(x^0) = \{x \in \mathbb{R}^n : |x - x^0| = R\}$$

*is said to be a* sphere *of radius $R > 0$ centered at $x^0$. The set*

$$\overline{B_R(x^0)} = B_R(x^0) \cup S_R(x^0)$$

*is said to be a* closed ball *of radius $R > 0$ centered at $x^0$.*

**Definition 12.18.** *A set $X \subset \mathbb{R}^n$ is said to be* bounded *if there exists $A > 0$ such that $|x| \leq A$ for all $x \in X$. It is equivalent that $X$ is a subset of a closed ball of radius $A$ centered at $\{0\}$, i.e.,*

$$X \subset \overline{B_A(0)} = \{x \in \mathbb{R}^n : |x| \leq A\}.$$

**Exercise 12.19.** Define the unbounded sets.

**Definition 12.20.** *A point $x^0 \in X$ is said to be an* internal point *of the set $X$ if there is an open ball $B_\delta(x^0)$ such that $B_\delta(x^0) \subset X$. A set $X \subset \mathbb{R}^n$ is said to be* open *if any point $x \in X$ is internal. The set of all internal points of $X$ is denoted as* int $X$.

**Definition 12.21.** *A point $x^0 \in X$ is said to be a* limiting point *of the set $X$ if for any $\delta > 0$ (small enough)*

$$B'_\delta(x^0) \cap X \neq \emptyset.$$

*The set of all limiting points of $X$ is denoted by $X'$. A set $X \subset \mathbb{R}^n$ is said to be* closed *if $X' \subset X$. The union $X' \cup X$ is called the* closure *of $X$ and is denoted $\overline{X} = X' \cup X$.*

**Exercise 12.22.** Prove that the set $X$

1. is closed if and only if $X = \overline{X}$,

2. is open if and only if $\mathbb{R}^n \setminus X$ is closed.

**Definition 12.23.** *A point $x^0$ is called*

1. *an* isolated point *of a set $X$ if there exists $\delta > 0$ such that $B_\delta(x^0) \cap X = \{x^0\}$,*

2. *a* boundary point *of a set $X$ if for any $\delta > 0$ (small enough) there are two points $x'$ and $x''$ such that $x', x'' \in B_\delta(x^0)$ and $x' \in X$ but $x'' \notin X$.*

**Definition 12.24.** *Let $X \subset \mathbb{R}^n$ be an arbitrary set. Then the set*

$$\partial X := \overline{X} \cap \left( \overline{\mathbb{R}^n \setminus X} \right)$$

*is called the* boundary *of $X$.*

**Exercise 12.25.** Prove that the boundary $\partial X$ of a set $X$ is equal to

1. the set of all boundary points of $X$,

2. the set $\overline{X} \setminus \operatorname{int} X$.

**Definition 12.26.** *Let $X \subset \mathbb{R}^n$ be an arbitrary set. Then the number*

$$\operatorname{diam} X := \sup_{x', x'' \in X} |x' - x''|$$

*is called the* diameter *of $X$.*

**Exercise 12.27.** Prove that a set $X$ is bounded if and only if $\operatorname{diam} X < \infty$.

A *rectangular parallelepiped* $\Pi$ in $\mathbb{R}^n$ is defined as the closed set

$$\Pi := \{x \in \mathbb{R}^n : x_j \in [a_j, b_j], j = 1, 2, \ldots, n\} = [a_1, b_1] \times [a_2, b_2] \times \cdots \times [a_n, b_n].$$

Its volume or Jordan's measure is defined to be the number

$$\mu(\Pi) = \prod_{j=1}^{n} (b_j - a_j).$$

**Definition 12.28.** *A set $F \subset \mathbb{R}^n$ is said to be an* elementary figure *if*

$$F = \bigcup_{k=1}^{m} \Pi_k,$$

*where $\Pi_k$ for each $k$ is a rectangular parallelepiped such that $\Pi_k \cap \Pi_j = \emptyset, k \neq j$, accepting some common parts of the boundaries, i.e.,*

$$\operatorname{int} \Pi_k \cap \operatorname{int} \Pi_j = \emptyset, \quad k \neq j.$$

*In that case Jordan's measure of $F$ is defined by*

$$\mu(F) := \sum_{k=1}^{m} \mu(\Pi_k).$$

Jordan's measure of elementary figures satisfies the following properties:

1. If $F$ is elementary figure then $\mu(F) > 0$.

2. If $F_1$ and $F_2$ are two elementary figures such that int $F_1 \cap$ int $F_2 = \emptyset$ then

$$\mu(F_1 \cup F_2) = \mu(F_1) + \mu(F_2).$$

3. If $F_1$ and $F_2$ are two elementary figures such that $F_1 \subset F_2$ then

$$\mu(F_1) \leq \mu(F_2).$$

Let a set $X \subset \mathbb{R}^n$ be bounded. Then there is an elementary figure $G$ such that $X \subset G$. Assume also that there is an elementary figure $F$ such that $F \subset X$. Then $\mu(F) \leq \mu(G)$, and the set of numbers $\{\mu(F)\}_{F \subset X}$ is bounded from above by, for example, $\mu(G)$. The set of numbers $\{\mu(G)\}_{X \subset G}$ is obviously bounded from below. Thus, the finite numbers

$$\sup_{F \subset X} \mu(F), \quad \inf_{X \subset G} \mu(G)$$

exist. The first number is said to be *lower measure of Jordan* of $X$ and the second number is called the *upper measure of Jordan* of $X$. They are denoted as $\mu_*(X)$ and $\mu^*(X)$, respectively. If it turns out that there is no elementary figure $F \subset X$ then we put $\mu_*(X) = 0$ by definition.

**Remark 12.29.** It is clear that the numbers $\mu_*(X)$ and $\mu^*(X)$ both exist for any bounded set $X \subset \mathbb{R}^n$ and $\mu_*(X) \leq \mu^*(X)$.

**Definition 12.30.** *Let a set $X \subset \mathbb{R}^n$ be bounded. Then $X$ is said to be* Jordan measurable *if $\mu_*(X) = \mu^*(X)$. In that case the latter number is called* Jordan's measure *of $X$ and denoted by $\mu(X)$.*

**Theorem 12.31 (Jordan measurability test).** *Let a set $X \subset \mathbb{R}^n$ be bounded. Then $X$ is Jordan measurable if and only if for any $\varepsilon > 0$ there exist elementary figures $F$ and $G$ (or only $G$) such that*

$$F \subset X \subset G$$

*and*

$$\mu(G) - \mu(F) < \varepsilon$$

*(or $X \subset G$ only and $\mu(G) < \varepsilon$). In the case when $\mu(G) < \varepsilon$ it follows that $\mu(X) = 0$.*

**Proof.** Let a set $X \subset \mathbb{R}^n$ be Jordan measurable, i.e., $\mu(X) = \mu_*(X) = \mu^*(X)$. Due to the definitions of $\mu_*(X)$ and $\mu^*(X)$ we have that for any $\varepsilon > 0$ there exist elementary figures $F$ and $G$ (or only $G$ in the case when $\mu_*(X) = \mu^*(X) = 0$) such that

$$F \subset X \subset G$$

and

$$\mu_*(X) - \mu(F), \mu(G) - \mu^*(X) < \varepsilon/2$$

(or $X \subset G$ only and $\mu(G) < \varepsilon/2$). It follows that

$$\mu(G) - \mu(F) < \varepsilon$$

(or $\mu(G) < \varepsilon/2$).

Conversely, let us assume that for any $\varepsilon > 0$ there exist elementary figures $F$ and $G$ (or only $G$) such that

$$F \subset X \subset G$$

and

$$\mu(G) - \mu(F) < \varepsilon$$

(or $X \subset G$ only and $\mu(G) < \varepsilon$). It follows that

$$\mu^*(X) - \mu_*(X) = \inf_{X \subset G} \mu(G) - \sup_{F \subset X} \mu(F) \leq \mu(G) - \mu(X) < \varepsilon$$

(or $\mu^*(X) < \varepsilon$). Letting $\varepsilon \to +0$ we obtain $\mu^*(X) = \mu_*(X)$ (or $\mu^*(X) = 0$). It means that $X$ is Jordan measurable. Hence the theorem is proved.

**Theorem 12.32 (Jordan measurability test with respect to boundary).** *Let a set $X \subset \mathbb{R}^n$ be bounded. Then $X$ is Jordan measurable if and only if $\mu(\partial X) = 0$.*

**Proof.** We prove first that if $F \subset X \subset G$ (or only $X \subset G$) with elementary figures $F$ and $G$ then

$$\partial X \subset G \setminus \operatorname{int} F$$

(or $\partial X \subset G$). Since elementary figures are closed, $F \subset \overline{X} \subset G$ (or $\overline{X} \subset G$). In addition, $\operatorname{int} F \subset \operatorname{int} G$. By Exercise 12.25 we have $\partial X = \overline{X} \setminus \operatorname{int} X \subset G \setminus \operatorname{int} F$ (or $\partial X \subset G$).

Suppose now that a set $X$ is Jordan measurable. Then for any $\varepsilon > 0$ there are elementary figures $F$ and $G$ (or only $G$) such that

$$\mu(G) - \mu(F) < \varepsilon$$

(or $\mu(G) < \varepsilon$). By the above argument we have

$$\mu^*(\partial X) \leq \mu(G \setminus \operatorname{int} F) = \mu(G) - \mu(F) < \varepsilon$$

(or $\mu^*(\partial X) \leq \mu(G) < \varepsilon$). Letting $\varepsilon \to +0$ yields in both cases that $\mu^*(\partial X) = 0$ or $\mu(\partial X) = 0$.

Conversely, let $\mu(\partial X) = 0$. It means that for any $\varepsilon > 0$ there is an elementary figure $G_1$ such that $\partial X \subset G_1$ with $\mu(G_1) < \varepsilon$. Next we represent $G_1$ as the difference

$$G_1 = \overline{G \setminus F}, \quad \partial X \subset \overline{G \setminus F} = G \setminus \operatorname{int} F.$$

This leads to

$$\mu(G_1) = \mu(G) - \mu(F) < \varepsilon$$

(or $\mu(G) < \varepsilon$). Due to Exercise 12.25 we obtain

$$F \subset \overline{X} \subset G$$

(or $\overline{X} \subset G$). Hence, Theorem 12.31 yields the Jordan measurability of $X$. The theorem is proved.

**Theorem 12.33 (Sufficient condition of measurability in $\mathbb{R}^2$).** *Let a set $X \subset \mathbb{R}^2$ be bounded and let its boundary $\partial X$ be equal to*

$$\partial X = \bigcup_{k=1}^{m} \gamma_k,$$

*where $\gamma_k$ is simple rectifiable curve for each $k = 1, 2, \ldots, m$. Then $X$ is Jordan measurable.*

***Proof.*** By virtue of Theorem 12.32 it suffices to show that $\mu(\partial X) = 0$, i.e., $\mu(\gamma) = 0$ whenever $\gamma$ is rectifiable. Let $\gamma$ be a simple rectifiable curve with length $|\gamma|$. We may divide this curve into $N$ parts such that the length of each part is equal to $|\gamma|/N$. Indeed, since

$$|\gamma| = \int_{\alpha}^{\beta} \mathrm{d}l(t),$$

where $l(t)$ is the length of the curve $\gamma(t) : x = \overrightarrow{f}(s), s \in [\alpha, t]$, with continuous function $\overrightarrow{f}$. Due to continuity and the fact that $l(\gamma)$ is nondecreasing we may find $t_1 > \alpha$ such that

$$\int_{\alpha}^{t_1} \mathrm{d}l(t) = |\gamma|/N.$$

Next we may find $t_2 > t_1$ such that

$$\int_{\alpha}^{t_2} \mathrm{d}l(t) = 2|\gamma|/N.$$

Continuing this process we may find $t_j > t_{j-1}, j = 2, 3, \ldots, N$, such that

$$\int_{\alpha}^{t_j} \mathrm{d}l(t) = j|\gamma|/N.$$

Considering now our curve for $t \in [t_{j-1}, t_j], j = 2, \ldots, N$, we obtain that

$$\int_{t_{j-1}}^{t_j} \mathrm{d}l(t) = |\gamma|/N, \quad j = 2, 3, \ldots, N.$$

Furthermore, at each point $\alpha, t_1, t_2, \ldots, t_N$ we consider the square centered at $\alpha$ and $t_j, j = 1, 2, \ldots, N$, with the length of the side $2|\gamma|/N$. Denoting these squares by $G_j, j = 0, 1, \ldots, N$, we obtain

$$\gamma \subset \bigcup_{j=0}^{N} G_j$$

and

$$\mu\left(\bigcup_{j=0}^{N} G_j\right) \leq \sum_{j=0}^{N} \mu(G_j) = \sum_{j=0}^{N} 4|\gamma|^2/N^2 = \frac{4(N+1)|\gamma|^2}{N^2}.$$

The latter terms tends to zero as $N \to +\infty$. Since

$$G := \bigcup_{j=0}^{N} G_j$$

is an elementary figure, for any $\varepsilon > 0$ we may find $N$ so big that $\gamma \subset G$ and $\mu(G) < \varepsilon$. Hence $\mu(\gamma) = 0$ and the theorem is proved.

**Exercise 12.34.** Prove that if a curve $\gamma$ is rectifiable in $\mathbb{R}^n$ then $\mu(\gamma) = 0$.

**Theorem 12.35 (Properties of measurable sets).** *Let sets $X_1, X_2 \subset \mathbb{R}^n$ be Jordan measurable. Then the sets $X_1 \cup X_2, X_1 \cap X_2$ and $X_1 \setminus X_2$ are also Jordan measurable. Moreover,*

1. *if $X_1 \subset X_2$ then $\mu(X_1) \leq \mu(X_2)$;*

2. $\mu(X_1 \cup X_2) = \mu(X_1) + \mu(X_2) - \mu(X_1 \cap X_2)$ so that $\mu(X_1 \cup X_2) \leq \mu(X_1) + \mu(X_2)$, in particular, $\mu(X_1 \cup X_2) = \mu(X_1) + \mu(X_2)$ if $X_1 \cap X_2 = \emptyset$;

3. $\mu(X_1 \cap X_2) = \mu(X_1) - \mu(X_1 \setminus X_2)$ and $\mu(X_1 \cap X_2) = \mu(X_2) - \mu(X_2 \setminus X_1)$ so that $2\mu(X_1 \cap X_2) = \mu(X_1) + \mu(X_2) - \mu(\Delta(X_1, X_2))$.

**Proof.** The measurability of the sets $X_1 \cup X_2$, $X_1 \cap X_2$, and $X_1 \setminus X_2$ follows from the fact that

$$\partial(X_1 \cup X_2), \partial(X_1 \cap X_2), \partial(X_1 \setminus X_2) \subset \partial X_1 \cup \partial X_2$$

and Theorem 12.32.

Let us prove that if $X_1 \cap X_2 = \emptyset$ then

$$\mu(X_1 \cup X_2) = \mu(X_1) + \mu(X_2).$$

Indeed, by Theorem 12.31 we have that for any $\varepsilon > 0$ there exist elementary figures $F_1, F_2, G_1, G_2$ such that

$$F_1 \subset X_1 \subset G_1, \quad F_2 \subset X_2 \subset G_2,$$

and

$$\mu(G_1) - \mu(F_1), \mu(G_2) - \mu(F_2) < \varepsilon.$$

But $F_1 \cap F_2 = \emptyset$ since $X_1 \cap X_2 = \emptyset$. Hence

$$\mu(F_1 \cup F_2) = \mu(F_1) + \mu(F_2) \leq \mu(X_1) + \mu(X_2) \leq \mu(G_1) + \mu(G_2)$$

and

$$\mu(F_1 \cup F_2) \leq \mu(X_1 \cup X_2) \leq \mu(G_1) + \mu(G_2).$$

It follows that

$$|\mu(X_1) + \mu(X_2) - \mu(X_1 \cup X_2)| < 2\varepsilon.$$

Letting $\varepsilon \to +0$ we obtain that

$$\mu(X_1) + \mu(X_2) = \mu(X_1 \cup X_2).$$

Now we are in position to prove parts 1–3.

1. If $X_1 \subset X_2$ then $X_2 = X_1 \cup (X_2 \setminus X_1)$ and $X_1 \cap (X_2 \setminus X_1) = \emptyset$. Hence, as proved above,

$$\mu(X_2) = \mu(X_1) + \mu(X_2 \setminus X_1),$$

implying that $\mu(X_1) \leq \mu(X_2)$.

2. We write

$$X_1 \cup X_2 = X_1 \cup (X_2 \setminus X_1), \quad X_1 \cap (X_2 \setminus X_1) = \emptyset$$

and

$$X_1 \cup X_2 = X_2 \cup (X_1 \setminus X_2), \quad X_2 \cap (X_1 \setminus X_2) = \emptyset.$$

This implies that

$$\mu(X_1 \cup X_2) = \mu(X_1) + \mu(X_2 \setminus X_1)$$

and

$$\mu(X_1 \cup X_2) = \mu(X_2) + \mu(X_1 \setminus X_2).$$

Therefore

$$2\mu(X_1 \cup X_2) = \mu(X_1) + \mu(X_2) + \mu(X_2 \setminus X_1) + \mu(X_1 \setminus X_2).$$

Next,

$$(X_2 \setminus X_1) \cup (X_1 \setminus X_2) = (X_1 \cup X_2) \setminus (X_1 \cap X_2)$$

and

$$(X_2 \setminus X_1) \cap (X_1 \setminus X_2) = \emptyset.$$

Thus,

$$\mu(X_2 \setminus X_1) + \mu(X_1 \setminus X_2) = \mu((X_2 \setminus X_1) \cup (X_1 \setminus X_2)) = \mu(X_1 \cup X_2) - \mu(X_1 \cap X_2).$$

So finally we have

$$2\mu(X_1 \cup X_2) = \mu(X_1) + \mu(X_2) + \mu(X_1 \cup X_2) - \mu(X_1 \cap X_2)$$

or

$$\mu(X_1 \cup X_2) = \mu(X_1) + \mu(X_2) - \mu(X_1 \cap X_2).$$

3. Since

$$X_1 = (X_1 \setminus X_2) \cup (X_1 \cap X_2), \quad (X_1 \setminus X_2) \cap (X_1 \cap X_2) = \emptyset,$$

we have

$$\mu(X_1) = \mu(X_1 \setminus X_2) + \mu(X_1 \cap X_2),$$

which yields the claim after rearranging.

Theorem 12.35 is completely proved.

**Definition 12.36.** *Let a function* $f : [a, b] \to \mathbb{R}$ *be continuous on the interval* $[a, b]$ *and let* $f(x) \geq 0$ *for all* $x \in [a, b]$. *By the symbol* $T_f$ *we denote the set*

$$T_f = \{(x, y) \in \mathbb{R}^2 : x \in [a, b], 0 \leq y \leq f(x)\}$$

*and call it the* curvilinear trapezium.

**Theorem 12.37 (Geometric meaning of Riemann integral).** *The curvilinear trapezium is Jordan measurable, and*

$$\mu(T_f) = \int_a^b f(x)\mathrm{d}x.$$

*Proof.* Since the function $f$ is integrable on the interval $[a, b]$, for any $\varepsilon > 0$ there is a partition $P$ of $[a, b]$ such that

$$U(P, f) - L(P, f) = \sum_{j=1}^{m}(M_j - m_j)\Delta x_j < \varepsilon.$$

But the values $U(P, f)$ and $L(P, f)$ are equal to the measures of elementary figures $G$ and $F$ such that

$$F = \bigcup_{j=1}^{m} F_j, \quad G = \bigcup_{j=1}^{m} G_j,$$

where

$$F_j = \{(x,y) : x \in [x_{j-1}, x_j], y \in [0, m_j]\}$$

and

$$G_j = \{(x,y) : x \in [x_{j-1}, x_j], y \in [0, M_j]\}.$$

The set $F$ is illustrated in Figure 12.1.

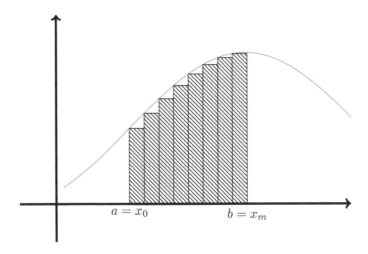

**Figure 12.1.** *Illustration of the set $F$.*

Hence

$$\mu(F) = \sum_{j=1}^{m} \mu(F_j) = \sum_{j=1}^{m} m_j \Delta x_j,$$

$$\mu(G) = \sum_{j=1}^{m} \mu(G_j) = \sum_{j=1}^{m} M_j \Delta x_j,$$

and

$$\mu(G) - \mu(F) = U(P, f) - L(P, f) < \varepsilon.$$

It means (see Theorem 12.31) that the curvilinear trapezium $T_f$ is Jordan measurable since

$$F \subset T_f \subset G, \quad \mu(G) - \mu(F) < \varepsilon.$$

In order to calculate $\mu(T_f)$ we proceed as follows:

$$\mu(T_f) = \inf_{T_f \subset \widetilde{G}} \mu(\widetilde{G}) \le \inf_{T_f \subset G} \mu(G),$$

$$\mu(T_f) = \sup_{\widetilde{F} \subset T_f} \mu(\widetilde{F}) \ge \sup_{F \subset T_f} \mu(F),$$

where $\widetilde{F}$ and $\widetilde{G}$ are arbitrary elementary figures such that $\widetilde{F} \subset T_f \subset \widetilde{G}$ and $F$ and $G$ are as above. But due to integrability of $f$ we have

$$\inf_{T_f \subset G} \mu(G) = \sup_{F \subset T_f} \mu(F) = \int_a^b f(x)\mathrm{d}x.$$

It follows that

$$\inf_{T_f \subset G} \mu(G) \geq \mu(T_f) \geq \sup_{F \subset T_f} \mu(F)$$

and so

$$\mu(T_f) = \int_a^b f(x)\mathrm{d}x.$$

This proves the theorem.

**Exercise 12.38.** Prove that the Jordan measure of the curvilinear trapezium $T_p$ defined by

$$T_p = \{(r, \theta) : \theta \in [\alpha, \beta], 0 \leq r \leq r(\theta)\},$$

where $(r, \theta)$ are polar coordinates on the plane (see Figure 12.2), can be calculated as

$$\mu(T_p) = \frac{1}{2} \int_\alpha^\beta r^2(\theta)\mathrm{d}\theta.$$

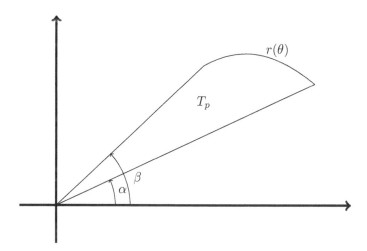

**Figure 12.2.** *Sketch of trapezium $T_p$.*

**Definition 12.39.** *A set $C \subset \mathbb{R}^{n+1}$ defined as*

$$C = X \times [a, b] = \{(x', x_{n+1}) : x' \in X \subset \mathbb{R}^n, x_{n+1} \in [a, b]\}$$

*is called a* rectangular cylinder.

**Exercise 12.40.** Prove that if $X \subset \mathbb{R}^n$ is Jordan measurable in $\mathbb{R}^n$ with measure $\mu_n(X)$ then a rectangular cylinder $C = X \times [a, b]$ is Jordan measurable in $\mathbb{R}^{n+1}$ and $\mu(C) = \mu_n(X)(b - a)$.

**Definition 12.41.** *Let a function $f$ be continuous on the interval $[a, b]$. Then the set $V \subset \mathbb{R}^3$ formed by rotation of the curvilinear trapezium $T_{|f|}$ around the $x$-axis is called a* rotation body.

**Theorem 12.42 (The volume of rotation body).** *Let a function $f : [a, b] \to \mathbb{R}$ be continuous. Then the rotation body $V$ is Jordan measurable in $\mathbb{R}^3$ and*

$$\mu_3(V) = \pi \int_a^b f^2(x)\mathrm{d}x.$$

**Proof.** Let $P$ be a partition of the interval $[a, b]$ (see Figure 12.3) for the curvilinear trapezium. Denoting by $C_j'$ and $C_j''$ the rectangular cylinders which are obtained by the rotation of the rectangles around the $x$-axis we obtain

$$\mu_3(C_j') = \pi m_j^2 \Delta x_j, \quad \mu_3(C_j'') = \pi M_j^2 \Delta x_j.$$

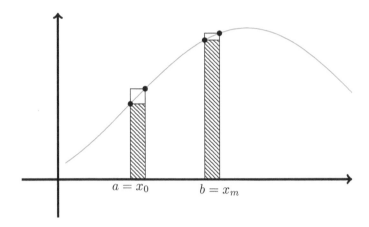

**Figure 12.3.** *Illustration of the rectangular cylinders around the x-axis.*

Now, if we denote the unions of these cylinders by

$$X_1 = \bigcup_{j=1}^{m} C_j', \quad X_2 = \bigcup_{j=1}^{m} C_j'',$$

respectively, then we obtain that

$$\mu(X_1) = \pi \sum_{j=1}^{m} m_j^2 \Delta x_j, \quad \mu(X_2) = \pi \sum_{j=1}^{m} M_j^2 \Delta x_j.$$

But these values can be interpreted as

$$\mu(X_1) = U(P, \pi f^2), \quad \mu(X_2) = L(P, \pi f^2).$$

This implies that
$$\mu(X_2) - \mu(X_1) = U(P, \pi f^2) - L(P, \pi f^2) < \varepsilon$$

if a partition is chosen with respect to $\varepsilon > 0$. It is obvious that $X_1 \subset V \subset X_2$. Hence $V$ is measurable and

$$\mu_3(V) = \inf_{V \subset X_2} \mu(X_2) = \sup_{X_1 \subset V} \mu(X_1) = \pi \int_a^b f^2(x)\,\mathrm{d}x.$$

This finishes the proof.

**Corollary 12.43.** *For $V_R = B_R(0) \subset \mathbb{R}^3$, the ball of radius $R > 0$ centered at origin, we have*

$$\mu_3(V) = \frac{4}{3}\pi R^3.$$

***Proof.*** It is easy to check that $V_R$ is a rotation body of the curvilinear trapezium $T_{|f|}$, where $|f| = \sqrt{R^2 - x^2}, x \in [-R, R]$. By Theorem 12.42 we obtain

$$\mu_3(V_R) = \pi \int_{-R}^{R} (R^2 - x^2)\mathrm{d}x = \pi \left( 2R^3 - \frac{2}{3}R^3 \right) = \frac{4}{3}\pi R^3.$$

**Exercise 12.44.** Let a set $V \subset \mathbb{R}^3$ be bounded such that for any $x \in [a, b]$, a cross section by the plane perpendicular to the $x$-axis is a Jordan measurable set in $\mathbb{R}^2$ with measure $S(x)$. Prove that $V$ is Jordan measurable in $\mathbb{R}^3$ and

$$\mu(V) = \int_{a}^{b} S(x)\mathrm{d}x.$$

# Chapter 13

# Continuity and differentiability of functions of several variables

In this chapter we extend the concepts of continuity and differentiability from the one-dimensional case of scalar functions to the case of vector-valued functions of several variables. Moreover, most of the main results (local and global) carry over to this general case also without any significant changes. However, for functions of several variables (two or more) some special results appear, such as equality of mixed derivatives or orthogonality of the gradient to level surfaces. It should also be noted that the presence of partial and directional derivatives does not guarantee continuity of a function (in comparison to the one-dimensional case) and even less its differentiability.

We return again to the Euclidean space $\mathbb{R}^n$ with $x \in \mathbb{R}^n$ such that $x = (x_1, x_2, \ldots, x_n)$. The *Euclidean length* of $x$ is defined by

$$|x| = \sqrt{x_1^2 + \cdots + x_n^2}$$

and the standard *inner product* by

$$(x, y) = x_1 y_1 + \cdots + x_n y_n.$$

We use the Cauchy–Schwarz–Bunjakovskii inequality in $\mathbb{R}^n$ as

$$|(x, y)| \leq |x| \cdot |y|.$$

A sequence $\{x^{(k)}\}_{k=1}^{\infty} \subset \mathbb{R}^n$ is defined as $x^{(k)} = (x_1^{(k)}, \ldots, x_n^{(k)})$, where $x_j^{(k)}, j = 1, 2, \ldots, n$, is a sequence of real numbers.

**Definition 13.1.** *A sequence $\{x^{(k)}\}_{k=1}^{\infty} \subset \mathbb{R}^n$ is said to be*

1. bounded *if there exists $M > 0$ such that $|x^{(k)}| = \sqrt{(x_1^{(k)})^2 + \cdots + (x_n^{(k)})^2} \leq M$ for all $k \in \mathbb{N}$,*

2. not bounded *if for any $M > 0$ there exists $k_0 \in \mathbb{N}$ such that $|x^{(k_0)}| > M$,*

3. infinitely large *if for any $M > 0$ there exists $k_0 \in \mathbb{N}$ such that $|x^{(k)}| > M$ for all $k \geq k_0$. In this case we write*

$$\lim_{k \to \infty} x^{(k)} = \infty$$

*or*

$$\lim_{k \to \infty} |x^{(k)}| = +\infty.$$

225

**Exercise 13.2.** Prove that

1. $\{x^{(k)}\}_{k=1}^{\infty} \subset \mathbb{R}^n$ is bounded if and only if $\{x_j^{(k)}\}_{k=1}^{\infty}$ is bounded for each $j = 1, 2, \ldots, n$,

2. $\{x^{(k)}\}_{k=1}^{\infty}$ is not bounded if and only if there is $j_0 \in \{1, 2, \ldots, n\}$ such that $\{x_{j_0}^{(k)}\}_{k=1}^{\infty}$ is not bounded,

3. if a sequence $\{x_j^{(k)}\}_{k=1}^{\infty}$ is infinitely large for at least one $j = 1, 2, \ldots, n$ then $\{x^{(k)}\}_{k=1}^{\infty} \subset \mathbb{R}^n$ is infinitely large in $\mathbb{R}^n$. Show that the converse is not true.

**Definition 13.3.** *A sequence $\{x^{(k)}\}_{k=1}^{\infty} \subset \mathbb{R}^n$ is said to be* convergent *to a point $x^0 \in \mathbb{R}^n$ if for any $\varepsilon > 0$ there exists $k_0 \in \mathbb{N}$ such that $|x^{(k)} - x^0| < \varepsilon$ for all $k \geq k_0$. We denote this fact as*

$$\lim_{k \to \infty} x^{(k)} = x^0$$

*or*

$$\lim_{k \to \infty} |x^{(k)} - x^0| = 0.$$

**Exercise 13.4.** Prove that

$$\lim_{k \to \infty} x^{(k)} = x^0$$

if and only if

$$\lim_{k \to \infty} x_j^{(k)} = x_j^0, \quad j = 1, 2, \ldots, n.$$

**Definition 13.5.** *A sequence $\{x^{(k)}\}_{k=1}^{\infty} \subset \mathbb{R}^n$ is called a* Cauchy sequence *if for any $\varepsilon > 0$ there exists $k_0 \in \mathbb{N}$ such that $|x^{(k)} - x^{(m)}| < \varepsilon$ for all $k, m \geq k_0$.*

**Exercise 13.6.** Prove that $\{x^{(k)}\}_{k=1}^{\infty}$ is a Cauchy sequence if and only if $\{x_j^{(k)}\}_{k=1}^{\infty}$ is a Cauchy sequence for each $j = 1, 2, \ldots, n$.

**Theorem 13.7 (Cauchy criterion).** *A sequence $\{x^{(k)}\}_{k=1}^{\infty} \subset \mathbb{R}^n$ is convergent (to some point $x^0 \in \mathbb{R}^n$) if and only if $\{x^{(k)}\}_{k=1}^{\infty}$ is a Cauchy sequence.*

**Theorem 13.8 (Bolzano–Weierstrass principle).** *Let a sequence $\{x^{(k)}\}_{k=1}^{\infty} \subset \mathbb{R}^n$ be bounded. Then there exists a convergent subsequence $\{x^{(l_k)}\}_{k=1}^{\infty}$ of the sequence $\{x^{(k)}\}_{k=1}^{\infty}$.*

**Exercise 13.9.** Prove the Cauchy criterion and Bolzano–Weierstrass principles. Hint: Use the one-dimensional proofs of these statements coordinatewise.

The Heine–Borel lemma (and also the finite covering lemma) is the following fact, which plays a fundamental role in classical analysis.

**Theorem 13.10 (Heine–Borel).** *For a set $K \subset \mathbb{R}^n$ the following statements are equivalent:*

1. *$K$ is closed and bounded.*

2. *$K$ is compact, that is, every open cover of $K$ of the form*

$$K \subset \bigcup_{\alpha \in I} G_\alpha, \quad G_\alpha \text{ is open,}$$

*has a finite subcover.*

***Proof.*** Let us assume that $K$ is compact but not closed. Then there is $x^0 \in K'$ and $x^0 \notin K$, that is,

$$B_\delta'(x^0) \cap K \neq \emptyset, \quad x^0 \notin K.$$

Consider the open cover

$$K \subset \bigcup_{x \in K} B_\delta(x)$$

for $\delta > 0$ small enough. Since $x^0 \notin K$, we may find $\delta_0 > 0$ so small that for each $x \in K$ it holds that

$$B_\delta(x) \cap B_{\delta_0}(x^0) = \emptyset.$$

Due to compactness of $K$ there is a finite subcover

$$K \subset \bigcup_{j=1}^{l} B_\delta(x^{(j)}).$$

By hypothesis and by the choice of open cover it means that

$$K \cap B_{\delta_0}'(x^0) = \emptyset, \quad x^0 \notin K.$$

This contradiction shows that $K$ is closed.

Let us now prove that any compact set in $\mathbb{R}^n$ is also bounded. Indeed, let $\cup_{x \in K} B_1(x)$ be an open cover of $K$. Then there is a finite subcover

$$\bigcup_{j=1}^{l} B_1(x^{(j)})$$

of $K$. But all balls $B_1(x^{(j)}), j = 1, 2, \dots, l$, are bounded open sets, so the same is true about their union.

Conversely, let us assume that $K$ is closed and bounded. We aim to show that any open cover has a finite subcover. Since $K$ is bounded, it can be enclosed within a cube $C_0 = [-R, R]^n$. We prove first that $C_0$ is compact. Assume on the contrary that $C_0$ is not compact. Then there exists an infinite open cover of $C_0$ that does not admit any finite subcover. Through bisection of each of the sides of $C_0$ the cube $C_0$ can be broken up into $2^n$ subcubes. Then at least one of the $2^n$ subcubes of $C_0$ must require an infinite subcover, for otherwise this open cover itself would have a finite subcover. Call this subcube $C_1$. Likewise, the sides of $C_1$ can be bisected, yielding $2^n$ sections of $C_1$, at least one of which must require an infinite subcover. Continuing in this manner yields a decreasing sequence of nested cubes

$$C_0 \supset C_1 \supset C_2 \supset \cdots \supset C_k \supset \cdots,$$

where the length of the sides of $C_k$ is $R/2^{k-1}, k = 0, 1, 2, \dots$, which tends to 0 as $k \to \infty$. Let $x^{(k)} \in C_k$. Then the sequence $\{x^{(k)}\}_{k=1}^{\infty}$ is obviously a Cauchy sequence, converging to a limit $\xi$. Since all $C_k$ are closed, and for each $k$ the sequence is inside $C_k$, we see that $\xi \in C_k$ for each $k$. Since the original open cover contains $C_0$, it has a member $G$ such that $G$ is open and $\xi \in G$. There is a ball $B_\delta(\xi) \subset G$ and, for $k$ large enough, $C_k \subset B_\delta(\xi)$ also. But this means that the infinite open cover needed to cover $C_k$ can be replaced by just one, $B_\delta(\xi)$. This contradiction proves that a cube $[-R, R]^n$ is compact.

Next, since $K$ is closed and $K \subset [-R, R]^n$, $\mathbb{R}^n \backslash K$ is open, and for any open cover $\{G_\alpha\}_{\alpha \in I}$ of $K$ the set

$$\left( \bigcup_{\alpha \in I} G_\alpha \right) \bigcup (\mathbb{R}^n \backslash K)$$

is an open cover of $[-R, R]^n$. It has a finite subcover that also covers $K$. Since $\mathbb{R}^n \setminus K$ does not contain any point of $K$, the set $K$ is already covered by a finite subcollection of $\{G_\alpha\}_{\alpha \in I}$. Thus, the theorem is completely proved.

A mapping of some set $X \subset \mathbb{R}^n$ to some set $Y \subset \mathbb{R}^m$ is said to be a *vector-valued real function* $\overrightarrow{f}$ such that

$$\overrightarrow{f} : X \subset \mathbb{R}^n \to Y \subset \mathbb{R}^m,$$

where

$$y_l = f_l(x_1, x_2, \ldots, x_n), \quad l = 1, 2, \ldots, m,$$

i.e., $\overrightarrow{f} = (f_1, f_2, \ldots, f_m)$.

**Definition 13.11.** *Let $\overrightarrow{f} : X \subset \mathbb{R}^n \to Y \subset \mathbb{R}^m$, and let $x^0$ be a limiting point of $X$, denoted $x^0 \in X'$, i.e., there is a sequence $\{x^{(k)}\}_{k=1}^\infty \subset X, x^{(k)} \neq x^0$, such that $\lim_{k \to \infty} x^{(k)} = x^0$. Then a vector $\overrightarrow{b} \in \mathbb{R}^m$ is said to be a* limit *of $\overrightarrow{f}(x)$ as $x$ tends to $x^0$ if for any $\varepsilon > 0$ there exists $\delta > 0$ such that $|\overrightarrow{f}(x) - \overrightarrow{b}| < \varepsilon$ for all $x \in X \cap B'_\delta(x^0)$. We denote this as*

$$\lim_{x \to x^0} \overrightarrow{f}(x) = \overrightarrow{b}.$$

**Exercise 13.12.** 1. Prove that

$$\lim_{x \to x^0} \overrightarrow{f}(x) = \overrightarrow{b}$$

if and only if

$$\lim_{x \to x^0} f_l(x) = b_l, \quad l = 1, 2, \ldots, m,$$

i.e., for any $\varepsilon > 0$ there exists $\delta > 0$ such that $|f_l(x) - b_l| < \varepsilon$ for all $x \in X \cap B'_\delta(x^0)$ and $l = 1, 2, \ldots, m$.

2. Prove that

$$\lim_{x \to x^0} \overrightarrow{f}(x) = \overrightarrow{b}$$

if and only if

$$\lim_{k \to \infty} \overrightarrow{f}(x^{(k)}) = \overrightarrow{b}$$

for any $\{x^{(k)}\}_{k=1}^\infty \subset X$ with

$$\lim_{k \to \infty} x^{(k)} = x^0, \quad x^{(k)} \neq x^0.$$

**Definition 13.13.**

1. *Let a function $\overrightarrow{f} : X \subset \mathbb{R}^n \to \mathbb{R}^m$ be defined on an unbounded set $X$. Then $\overrightarrow{b}$ is said to be a limit of $\overrightarrow{f}(x)$ as $x \to \infty$ if for any $\varepsilon > 0$ there exists $A_0 > 0$ such that $|\overrightarrow{f}(x) - \overrightarrow{b}| < \varepsilon$ for all $x \in X$ and $|x| > A_0$. This fact is denoted as*

$$\lim_{x \to \infty, x \in X} \overrightarrow{f}(x) = \overrightarrow{b}.$$

2. *The limit (special case)*

$$\lim_{x_1 \to \infty, \ldots, x_n \to \infty} \overrightarrow{f}(x) = \overrightarrow{b}$$

*is defined as follows: for any $\varepsilon > 0$ there exists $A_0 > 0$ such that $|\overrightarrow{f}(x) - \overrightarrow{b}| < \varepsilon$ for all $x \in X$ and $|x_j| > A_0$ for each $j = 1, 2, \ldots, n$.*

**Exercise 13.14.** Let

$$f(x_1, x_2) = \sin\frac{1}{x_1} + \sin\frac{1}{x_2}.$$

Prove that

$$\lim_{x_1 \to \infty, x_2 \to \infty} f(x_1, x_2) = 0$$

exists but $\lim_{x \to \infty} f(x)$ does not exist.

**Definition 13.15.** *Let $\overrightarrow{f} : X \subset \mathbb{R}^n \to \mathbb{R}^m$. Then*

1. *$\overrightarrow{f}$ is called* bounded *on a set $X$ if there exists $M > 0$ such that $|\overrightarrow{f}(x)| \le M$ for all $x \in X$,*

2. *$\overrightarrow{f}$ is called* unbounded *on a set $X$ if for any $M > 0$ there exists $x_M \in X$ such that $|\overrightarrow{f}(x_M)| > M$,*

3. *$\overrightarrow{f}$ is called* infinitely large *at the point $x^0$ (or at infinity) if for any $M > 0$ there exists $\delta > 0$ (or $A > 0$) such that $|\overrightarrow{f}(x)| > M$ for all $x \in X \cap B'_\delta(x^0)$ (or $x \in X \cap \{|x| > A\}$). We denote this fact as*

$$\lim_{x \to x^0 (x \to \infty)} \overrightarrow{f}(x) = \infty.$$

**Exercise 13.16.** Prove that $\overrightarrow{f}$ is

1. unbounded on a set $X$ if and only if there exists a sequence $\{x^{(k)}\}_{k=1}^\infty \subset X$ such that $\lim_{k \to \infty} |\overrightarrow{f}(x^{(k)})| = +\infty$,

2. infinitely large at the point $x^0$ (or at infinity) if $\lim_{k \to \infty} \overrightarrow{f}(x^{(k)}) = \infty$ for any sequence $\{x^{(k)}\}_{k=1}^\infty \subset X$ with $\lim_{k \to \infty} x^{(k)} = x^0, x^{(k)} \ne x^0$ (or $\lim_{k \to \infty} x^{(k)} = \infty$).

**Example 13.17.**    1. Let

$$f(x_1, x_2) = \frac{|x_1|^\alpha |x_2|^\beta}{|x_1|^\gamma + |x_2|^\delta},$$

where $\alpha, \beta \ge 0, \gamma, \delta > 0$, and $\alpha + \beta > 0$. Then $f$ is unbounded at $(0,0)$ if $\alpha/\gamma + \beta/\delta < 1$, $f$ is bounded if $\alpha/\gamma + \beta/\delta = 1$, and $f$ tends to zero as $(x_1, x_2) \to 0$ if $\alpha/\gamma + \beta/\delta > 1$. Indeed, using the quasi-polar coordinates

$$|x_1| = r^{2/\gamma}(\sin\theta)^{2/\gamma}, \quad |x_2| = r^{2/\delta}(\cos\theta)^{2/\delta}, \quad 0 < \theta < \pi/2,$$

we obtain that

$$f(x_1, x_2) = r^{2\alpha/\gamma + 2\beta/\delta}(\sin\theta)^{2\alpha/\gamma}(\cos\theta)^{2\beta/\gamma}/r^2$$
$$= r^{2(\alpha/\gamma + \beta/\delta - 1)}(\sin\theta)^{2\alpha/\gamma}(\cos\theta)^{2\beta/\gamma}.$$

This representation shows that if $\alpha/\gamma + \beta/\delta < 1$ then the function $f(x_1, x_2)$ is not bounded at the point $(0,0)$. If $\alpha/\gamma + \beta/\delta = 1$ then this function is bounded everywhere but has no limit as $(x_1, x_2) \to 0$ since the result depends on the choice of angle $\theta \in (0, \pi/2)$. Finally, if $\alpha/\gamma + \beta/\delta > 1$ then

$$\lim_{(x_1, x_2) \to 0} f(x_1, x_2) = \lim_{r \to 0} r^{2(\alpha/\gamma + \beta/\delta - 1)}(\sin\theta)^{2\alpha/\gamma}(\cos\theta)^{2\beta/\gamma} = 0$$

for any choice of the angle $\theta \in (0, \pi/2)$.

2. Let

$$f(x_1, x_2) = \frac{|x_1|^\alpha |x_2|^\beta}{|x_1|^\gamma + |x_2|^\delta},$$

where $\alpha, \beta \geq 0, \delta \geq 0, \alpha + \beta > 0$ but $\gamma \leq 0$. Then we have

$$f(x_1, x_2) = \frac{|x_1|^{\alpha - \gamma} |x_2|^\beta}{1 + |x_1|^{-\gamma} |x_2|^\delta}.$$

This implies that if $\alpha - \gamma \geq 0, \beta \geq 0, \alpha + \beta > \gamma$, and $\delta \geq 0$ then

$$\lim_{(x_1, x_2) \to 0} f(x_1, x_2) = \lim_{(x_1, x_2) \to 0} |x_1|^{\alpha - \gamma} |x_2|^\beta = 0.$$

**Exercise 13.18.**     1. Prove that the function

$$f(x_1, x_2) = \frac{|x_2|^\beta}{|x_1|^\alpha (|x_1|^\gamma + |x_2|^\delta)}$$

is unbounded at $(0, 0)$ if $\alpha, \beta > 0, \gamma, \delta \geq 0$ but not infinitely large as $(x_1, x_2) \to 0$.

2. Prove that

$$\lim_{(x_1, x_2) \to 0} |x_1|^\alpha |x_2|^\beta \log(x_1^2 + x_1 x_2 + x_2^2) = 0$$

if and only if $\alpha, \beta \geq 0$ and $\alpha + \beta > 0$.

**Theorem 13.19 (Cauchy criterion for functions).** *Let* $\overrightarrow{f} : X \subset \mathbb{R}^n \to \mathbb{R}^m$. *Then the limit* $\lim_{x \to x^0(\infty)} \overrightarrow{f}(x)$ *exists if and only if for any* $\varepsilon > 0$ *there exists* $\delta > 0$ *(or* $A > 0$*) such that* $|\overrightarrow{f}(x') - \overrightarrow{f}(x'')| < \varepsilon$ *for all* $x', x'' \in X \cap B'_\delta(x^0)$ *(or* $x', x'' \in X, |x'|, |x''| > A$*).*

**Proof.** The proof literally repeats the case of one function of one real variable (see Theorem 5.27). ∎

The following local properties of functions which have limits at some point $x^0$ or at infinity can be proved similar to the case of one function of one variable:

1. If the limit $\lim_{x \to x^0(\infty)} \overrightarrow{f}(x)$ exists then $\overrightarrow{f}$ is bounded at $x^0$ (at infinity).

2. If the limits $\lim_{x \to x^0(\infty)} \overrightarrow{f}_1(x)$ and $\lim_{x \to x^0(\infty)} \overrightarrow{f}_2(x)$ exist then the limits

$$\lim_{x \to x^0(\infty)} \left( \overrightarrow{f}_1(x) \pm \overrightarrow{f}_2(x) \right) = \lim_{x \to x^0(\infty)} \overrightarrow{f}_1(x) \pm \lim_{x \to x^0(\infty)} \overrightarrow{f}_2(x)$$

and

$$\lim_{x \to x^0(\infty)} \left( \overrightarrow{f}_1(x), \overrightarrow{f}_2(x) \right) = \left( \lim_{x \to x^0(\infty)} \overrightarrow{f}_1(x), \lim_{x \to x^0(\infty)} \overrightarrow{f}_2(x) \right)$$

exist, where $(\overrightarrow{f}_1, \overrightarrow{f}_2)$ denotes the inner product in $\mathbb{R}^n$.

There is another definition of the limit for functions of several variables which has important applications. This definition concerns the so-called repeated limits. Namely,

$$\lim_{x_n \to x_n^0(\infty)} \left( \lim_{x_{n-1} \to x_{n-1}^0(\infty)} \left( \cdots \left( \lim_{x_1 \to x_1^0(\infty)} \overrightarrow{f}(x_1, x_2, \ldots, x_n) \right) \right) \right)$$

if it exists. For existence of the above limit we need to have the limit

$$\lim_{x_1 \to x_1^0 (\infty)} \overrightarrow{f}(x_1, x_2, \ldots, x_n)$$

for each $(x_1^0, x_2, \ldots, x_n) \in B_\delta'(x^0)$ and then the existence of the limit

$$\lim_{x_2 \to x_2^0 (\infty)} \left( \lim_{x_1 \to x_1^0 (\infty)} \overrightarrow{f}(x_1, x_2, \ldots, x_n) \right)$$

for each $(x_1^0, x_2^0, x_3, \ldots, x_n) \in B_\delta'(x^0)$ and so on. It is clear that such a limit depends on the order of the repeated limits. Indeed, let us consider, for example, the function

$$f(x_1, x_2) = \frac{x_1^2 - x_2^2}{x_1^2 + x_2^2}.$$

Then we have the limits

$$\lim_{x_1 \to 0} \left( \lim_{x_2 \to 0} \frac{x_1^2 - x_2^2}{x_1^2 + x_2^2} \right) = 1, \quad \lim_{x_2 \to 0} \left( \lim_{x_1 \to 0} \frac{x_1^2 - x_2^2}{x_1^2 + x_2^2} \right) = -1$$

which are not equal to each other. It must be mentioned that

$$\lim_{(x_1, x_2) \to 0} \frac{x_1^2 - x_2^2}{x_1^2 + x_2^2}$$

does not exist. Another example is

$$\lim_{(x_1, x_2) \to 0} x_1 \sin \frac{1}{x_2} = 0, \quad \lim_{x_2 \to 0} \left( \lim_{x_1 \to 0} x_1 \sin \frac{1}{x_2} \right) = 0,$$

but

$$\lim_{x_1 \to 0} \left( \lim_{x_2 \to 0} x_1 \sin \frac{1}{x_2} \right)$$

does not exist.

**Exercise 13.20.** Prove that

$$\lim_{(x_1, x_2) \to 0} \left( x_1 \sin \frac{1}{x_2} + x_2 \sin \frac{1}{x_1} \right) = 0$$

but neither of the repeated limits exists.

These examples and the latter exercise show that the new definition of the (repeated) limits is different compared with the old one. But nevertheless the following statement holds.

**Proposition 13.21.** *Let a scalar function $f(x_1, x_2)$ of two variables satisfy the following conditions:*

1. *the limit $\lim_{x \to x^0} f(x_1, x_2)$ exists,*

2. *the limit $\lim_{x_2 \to x_2^0} f(x_1, x_2)$ exists for any $0 < |x_1 - x_1^0| < \delta_1$ for some $\delta_1 > 0$,*

3. *the limit $\lim_{x_1 \to x_1^0} f(x_1, x_2)$ exists for any $0 < |x_2 - x_2^0| < \delta_2$ for some $\delta_2 > 0$.*

*Then these three limits are equal to one another.*

**Proof.** Let $f : X \subset \mathbb{R}^2 \to \mathbb{R}$ and let $x^0 \in X'$. Let $b = \lim_{x \to x^0} f(x_1, x_2)$. Then for any $\varepsilon > 0$ there exists $\delta > 0$ such that $|f(x_1, x_2) - b| < \varepsilon$ or

$$b - \varepsilon < f(x_1, x_2) < b + \varepsilon$$

for all $x \in X \cap B'_\delta(x^0)$, where $\delta \leq \min\{\delta_1, \delta_2\}$. Due to conditions 2 and 3 of this proposition we may consider the limit passage in these inequalities (see Theorem 5.24) and obtain

$$b - \varepsilon \leq \lim_{x_1 \to x_1^0} f(x_1, x_2) \leq b + \varepsilon$$

and

$$b - \varepsilon \leq \lim_{x_2 \to x_2^0} f(x_1, x_2) \leq b + \varepsilon$$

for all $(x_1^0, x_2) \in B'_\delta(x^0)$ and $(x_1, x_2^0) \in B'_\delta(x^0)$, respectively. This implies

$$\lim_{x_2 \to x_2^0} \lim_{x_1 \to x_1^0} f(x_1, x_2) = \lim_{x_1 \to x_1^0} \lim_{x_2 \to x_2^0} f(x_1, x_2) = b.$$

This proves the proposition.

**Remark 13.22.** The latter proposition can be generalized for the case of function $\overrightarrow{f} : X \subset \mathbb{R}^n \to \mathbb{R}^m$.

**Definition 13.23.** *Let* $\overrightarrow{f} : X \subset \mathbb{R}^n \to \mathbb{R}^m$ *and let* $x^0 \in X$. *Then* $\overrightarrow{f}$ *is said to be* continuous *at the point* $x^0$ *if for any* $\varepsilon > 0$ *there exists* $\delta > 0$ *such that* $|\overrightarrow{f}(x) - \overrightarrow{f}(x^0)| < \varepsilon$ *for all* $x \in X \cap B_\delta(x^0)$.

**Remark 13.24.**     1. If $x^0 \in X \cap X'$ then the definition is equivalent to

$$\lim_{x \to x^0} \overrightarrow{f}(x) = \overrightarrow{f}(x^0).$$

2. This definition is also equivalent to the fact that the scalar function $f_j(x)$ is continuous at the point $x^0$ for each $j = 1, 2, \ldots, m$.

**Definition 13.25.** *A function* $\overrightarrow{f} : X \subset \mathbb{R}^n \to \mathbb{R}^m$ *is said to be* continuous for each of the arguments separately *at the point* $x^0 \in X$ *if a function of one variable*

$$\overrightarrow{g}(x_j) = \overrightarrow{f}(x_1^0, x_2^0, \ldots, x_j, \ldots, x_n^0), \quad j = 1, 2, \ldots, n,$$

*is continuous at the point* $x_j^0$.

Continuity at the point $x^0$ implies the continuity for each of the arguments separately, but the converse is not always true.

**Example 13.26.**     1. Let $\alpha, \beta \geq 0$, $\alpha + \beta > 0$, and $\delta, \gamma > 0$. Let

$$f(x_1, x_2) = \frac{|x_1|^\alpha |x_2|^\beta}{|x_1|^\gamma + |x_2|^\delta}, \quad f(0, 0) = 0.$$

By Example 13.17 we know that

$$\lim_{(x_1, x_2) \to 0} \frac{|x_1|^\alpha |x_2|^\beta}{|x_1|^\gamma + |x_2|^\delta} = 0$$

if and only if $\alpha/\gamma + \beta/\delta > 1$. Hence $f$ is continuous at $(0,0)$ if and only if $\alpha/\gamma + \beta/\delta > 1$. It is also easy to see that the function $f$ is continuous for each of the arguments ($x_1$ or $x_2$) separately if and only if $\alpha, \beta, \gamma, \delta > 0$.

2. Let $\alpha, \beta \geq 0$, $\alpha + \beta > 0$, and $\delta \geq 0$. Let

$$f(x_1, x_2) = \frac{|x_1|^\alpha |x_2|^\beta}{1 + |x_2|^\delta}, \quad f(0,0) = 0.$$

Again by Example 13.17 we have

$$\lim_{(x_1, x_2) \to 0} \frac{|x_1|^\alpha |x_2|^\beta}{1 + |x_2|^\delta} = 0$$

if and only if $\alpha + \beta > 0$. Hence $f$ is continuous at $(0,0)$. And the function $f$ is continuous for each of the arguments separately if and only if $\alpha + \beta > 0$.

3. Let $\alpha, \beta \geq 0$, $\alpha + \beta > 0$. Let

$$f(x_1, x_2) = |x_1|^\alpha |x_2|^\beta \frac{x_1^2 - x_2^2}{x_1^2 + x_2^2}, \quad f(0,0) = 0.$$

Since $(x_1^2 - x_2^2)/(x_1^2 + x_2^2)$ is bounded, the function $f$ is continuous at $(0,0)$ if and only if $\alpha + \beta > 0$. But the function $f$ is continuous for each of the arguments separately if and only if $\alpha, \beta > 0$.

**Definition 13.27.** *A function $\overrightarrow{f} : X \subset \mathbb{R}^n \to \mathbb{R}^m$ is said to be* continuous *on a set $X$ if $\overrightarrow{f}$ is continuous at each point $x \in X$. This is denoted as $\overrightarrow{f} \in C(X)$.*

**Theorem 13.28 (Local properties of continuous functions).**

1. *Let functions $\overrightarrow{f}$ and $\overrightarrow{g}$ be continuous at the point $x^0$. Then $\overrightarrow{f} \pm \overrightarrow{g}$ and $(\overrightarrow{f}, \overrightarrow{g})_{\mathbb{R}^m}$ are continuous at $x^0$.*

2. *Let function $\overrightarrow{f}$ be continuous at the point $x^0$. Then $\overrightarrow{f}$ is bounded in $B_\delta(x^0)$ for some $\delta > 0$.*

3. *Let function $\overrightarrow{f}$ be continuous at the point $x^0$ and $\overrightarrow{f}(x^0) \neq 0$. Then there is $j_0 \in \{1, 2, \ldots, m\}$ such that $f_{j_0}(x^0) \neq 0$ and*

$$\operatorname{sgn} f_{j_0}(x) = \operatorname{sgn} f_{j_0}(x^0)$$

*for all $x \in B_\delta(x^0)$ for some $\delta > 0$. Moreover,*

$$|\overrightarrow{f}(x)| > |\overrightarrow{f}(x^0)|/2$$

*for all $x \in B_\delta(x^0)$.*

4. *Let function $\overrightarrow{g}$ be a superposition of the functions $\overrightarrow{f} : X \subset \mathbb{R}^n \to Y \subset \mathbb{R}^m$ and $\overrightarrow{\varphi} : Y \subset \mathbb{R}^m \to \mathbb{R}^l$ such that*

$$\overrightarrow{g} : X \subset \mathbb{R}^n \to \mathbb{R}^l, \quad \overrightarrow{g}(x) = \overrightarrow{\varphi}(\overrightarrow{f}(x)).$$

*Then $\overrightarrow{g}$ is continuous at the point $x^0$ if $\overrightarrow{f}$ is continuous at the point $x^0$ and $\overrightarrow{\varphi}$ is continuous at the point $\overrightarrow{f}(x^0) \in Y$.*

*Proof.* The proof literally repeats the corresponding proof in the one-dimensional case and for one scalar function.

**Theorem 13.29 (Weierstrass I).** *Let $\overrightarrow{f} \in C(X)$ and let $X$ be a closed and bounded set. Then $\overrightarrow{f}$ is bounded on $X$.*

*Proof.* Let us assume on the contrary that $\overrightarrow{f}$ is not bounded on $X$. Then there is a sequence $\{x^{(k)}\}_{k=1}^{\infty} \subset X$ such that

$$\lim_{k \to \infty} \overrightarrow{f}(x^{(k)}) = \infty,$$

i.e., $\overrightarrow{f}(x^{(k)})$ is infinitely large. Since $X$ is bounded, the Bolzano–Weierstrass principle leads to the existence of the subsequence $\{x^{(l_k)}\}_{k=1}^{\infty}$ which is convergent, say to the point $x^0$. Since $X$ is closed, $x^0 \in X$ and therefore $\overrightarrow{f}$ is continuous at this point, i.e.,

$$\lim_{k \to \infty} \overrightarrow{f}(x^{(l_k)}) = \overrightarrow{f}(x^0).$$

This contradicts the fact that $\overrightarrow{f}$ is infinitely large. Thus the theorem is proved.

**Theorem 13.30 (Weierstrass II).** *Let a scalar function $f : X \subset \mathbb{R}^n \to \mathbb{R}$ be continuous on closed and bounded set $X$. Then there exist $x', x'' \in X$ such that*

$$\inf_{X} f(x) = f(x'), \quad \sup_{X} f(x) = f(x'').$$

*Proof.* The proof literally repeats the proof in the one-dimensional case.

**Corollary 13.31.** *Let function $\overrightarrow{f} : X \subset \mathbb{R}^n \to \mathbb{R}^m$ be continuous on closed and bounded set $X$. Then the function $g(x) := |\overrightarrow{f}(x)|$ is continuous on $X$ and therefore satisfies all conditions of Theorems 13.29 and 13.30.*

In the framework of Theorem 13.30 and Corollary 13.31 we substitute inf and sup by min and max, respectively.

**Definition 13.32.** *A function $\overrightarrow{f} : X \subset \mathbb{R}^n \to \mathbb{R}^m$ is said to be* uniformly continuous *on $X$ if for any $\varepsilon > 0$ there exists $\delta > 0$ such that*

$$|\overrightarrow{f}(x') - \overrightarrow{f}(x'')| < \varepsilon$$

*for all $x', x'' \in X$ with $|x' - x''| < \delta$.*

**Theorem 13.33 (Cantor).** *Let function $\overrightarrow{f} : X \subset \mathbb{R}^n \to \mathbb{R}^m$ be continuous on closed and bounded set $X$. Then $\overrightarrow{f}$ is uniformly continuous on $X$.*

*Proof.* The proof literally repeats the proof in the one-dimensional case.

**Example 13.34.**      1. Let us consider the function

$$f(x_1, x_2) = \sin \frac{1}{1 - |x|^2}$$

on the set $X = \{x \in \mathbb{R}^2 : |x| < 1\}$. It is clear that $f$ is continuous on $X$ as the superposition of continuous functions. But it is not uniformly continuous on this set. Indeed, let

$$\{x^{(k),1}\}_{k=1}^\infty = \{(\sqrt{1 - 1/(2\pi k)}, 0)\}_{k=1}^\infty$$

and

$$\{x^{(k),2}\}_{k=1}^\infty = \{(\sqrt{1 - 1/(\pi/2 + 2\pi k)}, 0)\}_{k=1}^\infty$$

be two sequences from $X$. Then

$$|x^{(k),1} - x^{(k),2}|^2$$
$$= 2 - \frac{1}{2\pi k} - \frac{1}{\pi/2 + 2\pi k} - 2\sqrt{(1 - 1/(2\pi k))(1 - 1/(\pi/2 + 2\pi k))} \to 0$$

as $k \to \infty$ but

$$|f(x^{(k),1}) - f(x^{(k),2})| = |\sin(2\pi k) - \sin(\pi/2 + 2\pi k)| = 1$$

does not tend to zero as $k \to \infty$.

2. Let us consider the function

$$f(x_1, x_2) = \log \frac{1}{1 - |x|^2}$$

on the set $X = \{x \in \mathbb{R}^2 : |x| < 1\}$. This function is continuous on $X$ as the superposition of continuous functions. Let us investigate its uniform continuity. Let

$$\{x^{(k),1}\}_{k=2}^\infty = \{(\sqrt{1 - 1/k}, 0)\}_{k=2}^\infty$$

and

$$\{x^{(k),2}\}_{k=2}^\infty = \{(\sqrt{1 - 2/k}, 0)\}_{k=2}^\infty$$

be two sequences from $X$. Then

$$|x^{(k),1} - x^{(k),2}|^2 = 2 - \frac{3}{k} - 2\sqrt{(1 - 1/k)(1 - 2/k)} \to 0$$

as $k \to \infty$ and

$$|f(x^{(k),1}) - f(x^{(k),2})| = |\log k - \log(k/2)| = \log 2 > 0$$

does not tend to zero as $k \to \infty$. So $f$ is not uniformly continuous.

**Exercise 13.35.**     1. Prove that if function $\vec{f} : X \subset \mathbb{R}^n \to \mathbb{R}^m$ is uniformly continuous on open and bounded set $X$ then it can be extended to $\overline{X}$ as a continuous function.

2. Prove that if a scalar function $f : X \subset \mathbb{R}^n \to \mathbb{R}$ is continuous on unbounded and closed set $X$ and the limit $\lim_{x \to \infty, x \in X} f(x)$ exists then $f$ is uniformly continuous.

3. Define the values for parameter $\beta > 0$ for which the function $f(x) = \sin |x|^\beta, x \in \mathbb{R}^n, |x| \geq 1$, is uniformly continuous.

Analogously to the one-dimensional case we can now introduce a very efficient notion of differentiability of functions of several variables and subsequently the concept of differentials of first and higher order.

Let function $\overrightarrow{f} : X \subset \mathbb{R}^n \to \mathbb{R}^m$ be defined on an open set $X$. Let $x^0 \in X$. Then there is a ball $B_\delta(x^0)$ with some $\delta > 0$ such that $B_\delta(x^0) \subset X$. Considering $h \in \mathbb{R}^n$ with $0 < |h| < \delta$ we may define the *increment* of $\overrightarrow{f}$ at the point $x^0$ as

$$\Delta_h \overrightarrow{f}(x^0) := \overrightarrow{f}(x^0 + h) - \overrightarrow{f}(x^0).$$

**Definition 13.36.** *Function $\overrightarrow{f} : X \subset \mathbb{R}^n \to \mathbb{R}^m$ is said to be* differentiable *at the point $x^0 \in X$ if*

$$\Delta_h \overrightarrow{f}(x^0) = A(x^0)h + o(|h|),$$

*where $A(x^0)$ is a bounded linear operator form $\mathbb{R}^n$ to $\mathbb{R}^m$, i.e., $A(x^0)$ is a matrix $\{a_{kj}(x^0)\}_{m \times n}$ such that $A(x^0)h$ is a vector of dimension $m$ and $o(|h|)$ is also a vector of dimension $m$.*

**Definition 13.37.** *Let*

$$\Delta_t^{(j)} \overrightarrow{f}(x^0) := \overrightarrow{f}(x^0 + te_j) - \overrightarrow{f}(x^0)$$

*be an increment of $\overrightarrow{f}$ at the point $x^0$ along the $j$th coordinate, where $t \in \mathbb{R}, 0 < |t| < \delta$, and $e_j = (0, \dots, 0, 1, 0, \dots, 0)$ is a vector of the normal basis in $\mathbb{R}^n$. The limit*

$$\lim_{t \to 0} \frac{\Delta_t^{(j)} \overrightarrow{f}(x^0)}{t}$$

*is called, if it exists, a* partial derivative *of $\overrightarrow{f}$ at the point $x^0$ with respect to $x_j$ and is denoted as*

$$\frac{\partial \overrightarrow{f}}{\partial x_j}(x^0) = \left( \frac{\partial f_1}{\partial x_j}(x^0), \dots, \frac{\partial f_m}{\partial x_j}(x^0) \right)^T.$$

**Proposition 13.38.** *Let function $\overrightarrow{f}$ be differentiable at the point $x^0$. Then the partial derivative $\frac{\partial \overrightarrow{f}}{\partial x_j}(x^0)$ exists for $j = 1, 2, \dots, n$ and*

$$a_{kj} = \frac{\partial f_k}{\partial x_j}(x^0),$$

*where $a_{kj}$ are the elements of the matrix $A(x^0)$.*

**Proof.** Since $\overrightarrow{f}$ is differentiable at the point $x^0$, for any $h \in \mathbb{R}^n, 0 < |h| < \delta$, we have

$$\Delta_h \overrightarrow{f}(x^0) = A(x^0)h + o(|h|).$$

Considering now $h = te_j$ we obtain

$$\Delta_{te_j} \overrightarrow{f}(x^0) = \Delta_t^{(j)} \overrightarrow{f}(x^0) = tA(x^0)e_j + o(|t|).$$

It follows that

$$\frac{\Delta_t^{(j)} \overrightarrow{f}(x^0)}{t} = A(x^0)e_j + o(1).$$

Hence the limit

$$\lim_{t \to 0} \frac{\Delta_t^{(j)} \overrightarrow{f}(x^0)}{t} = A(x^0)e_j = (a_{1j}, \dots, a_{mj})^T,$$

i.e., the partial derivative $\frac{\partial \overrightarrow{f}}{\partial x_j}(x^0)$, exists and

$$a_{kj} = \frac{\partial f_k}{\partial x_j}(x^0).$$

This finishes the proof.

**Remark 13.39.** The latter proposition can be interpreted as follows. Whenever $\overrightarrow{f}$ is differentiable at the point $x^0$ then

$$\Delta_h \overrightarrow{f}(x^0) = \frac{\partial \overrightarrow{f}}{\partial x}(x^0)h + o(|h|),$$

where

$$\frac{\partial \overrightarrow{f}}{\partial x}(x^0) = \left\{ \frac{\partial f_k}{\partial x_j}(x^0) \right\}_{m \times n}$$

is called the *full derivative* of $\overrightarrow{f}$.

**Example 13.40.** Let

$$f(x) = \sqrt[3]{x_1 x_2 x_3}, \quad x^0 = (0,0,0).$$

Then

$$\frac{\partial f}{\partial x_j}(0) = \lim_{t \to 0} \frac{f(0 + te_j) - f(0)}{t} = \lim_{t \to 0} 0 = 0, \quad j = 1,2,3.$$

Assuming that $f$ is differentiable at the point 0, we must have

$$f(h) - f(0) = \frac{\partial f}{\partial x_1}(0)h_1 + \frac{\partial f}{\partial x_2}(0)h_2 + \frac{\partial f}{\partial x_3}(0)h_3 + o(|h|)$$

or

$$\sqrt[3]{h_1 h_2 h_3} = o(|h|) = o\left( \sqrt{h_1^2 + h_2^2 + h_3^2} \right).$$

But this is impossible because for $h_1 = h_2 = h_3 = t$ we must have $t = o(|t|)$, which is not true. Hence our assumption about the differentiability of $f$ is wrong. This example shows that the differentiability is not equivalent to the existence of partial derivatives.

**Proposition 13.41.**

1. *Let function $\overrightarrow{f}$ be differentiable at the point $x^0$. Then $\overrightarrow{f}$ is continuous at $x^0$.*

2. *Let function $\overrightarrow{f}$ have partial derivative $\frac{\partial \overrightarrow{f}}{\partial x_j}$ at the point $x^0$ for each $j = 1,2,\dots,n$. Then $\overrightarrow{f}$ is continuous for each of the arguments separately at $x^0$.*

*Proof.* Both statements follow immediately from the definitions of the differentiability of $\overrightarrow{f}$ at the point $x^0$ and of the partial derivative of $\overrightarrow{f}$ with respect to $x_j$ at the point $x^0$.

**Exercise 13.42.**     1. Prove Proposition 13.41. Prove also that the converse assertions are not
true.

2. Let

$$f(x) = \sqrt[3]{x_1^3 + x_2^3 + x_3^3}, \quad x^0 = (0,0,0).$$

Show that $\frac{\partial f}{\partial x_j}(0) = 1, j = 1,2,3$, but $f$ is not differentiable at $x^0$. Prove that $f$ is
continuous at $x^0$.

3. Let

$$f(x) = \frac{x_1 x_2}{x_1^2 + x_2^2}, \quad x^0 = (0,0), \quad f(0) := 0.$$

Prove that $\frac{\partial f}{\partial x_j}(0), j = 1,2$, exists but $f$ is not continuous at $x^0$.

4. Let

$$f(x) = \frac{x_1 x_2}{\sqrt{x_1^2 + x_2^2}} \sin \frac{1}{\sqrt{x_1^2 + x_2^2}}, \quad f(0) := 0.$$

Investigate the differentiability of $f$ at the point $x^0 = (0,0)$.

**Theorem 13.43 (Sufficient condition of differentiability).** *Let a scalar function $f : X \subset \mathbb{R}^n \to \mathbb{R}$ be defined on open set $X$. Let $x^0 \in X$ and let $\frac{\partial f}{\partial x_j}(x), j = 1,2,\ldots,n-1$, exist in $B_\delta(x^0) \subset X$ for some $\delta > 0$ and be continuous at $x^0$. Let also $\frac{\partial f}{\partial x_n}(x^0)$ exist. Then $f$ is differentiable at $x^0$.*

**Proof.** The increment $\Delta_h f(x^0)$ at the point $x^0$ can be represented as

$$\begin{aligned}
\Delta_h f(x^0) = {}& f(x_1^0 + h_1, \ldots, x_n^0 + h_n) - f(x_1^0, x_2^0 + h_2, \ldots, x_n^0 + h_n) \\
& + f(x_1^0, x_2^0 + h_2, \ldots, x_n^0 + h_n) - f(x_1^0, x_2^0, x_3^0 + h_3, \ldots, x_n^0 + h_n) \\
& + \cdots + f(x_1^0, x_2^0, \ldots, x_{n-1}^0, x_n^0 + h_n) - f(x_1^0, x_2^0, \ldots, x_n^0).
\end{aligned}$$

Applying the one-dimensional Lagrange formula (see Theorem 6.43) to each difference with
respect to variables $x_1, \ldots, x_{n-1}$, respectively, and using the definition of $\frac{\partial f}{\partial x_n}(x^0)$ we obtain
that

$$\begin{aligned}
\Delta_h f(x^0) = {}& \frac{\partial f}{\partial x_1}(x_1^0 + \theta_1 h_1, x_2^0 + h_2, \ldots, x_n^0 + h_n) h_1 \\
& + \frac{\partial f}{\partial x_2}(x_1^0, x_2^0 + \theta_2 h_2, x_3^0 + h_3, \ldots, x_n^0 + h_n) h_2 \\
& + \cdots + \frac{\partial f}{\partial x_{n-1}}(x_1^0, x_2^0, \ldots, x_{n-2}^0, x_{n-1}^0 + \theta_{n-1} h_{n-1}, x_n^0 + h_n) h_{n-1} \\
& + \frac{\partial f}{\partial x_n}(x^0) h_n + o(h_n),
\end{aligned}$$

where $0 < \theta_j < 1, j = 1,2,\ldots,n-1$. Since the derivatives $\frac{\partial f}{\partial x_j}(x), j = 1,2,\ldots,n-1$, are continuous at $x^0$, we conclude that

$$\Delta_h f(x^0) = \left( \frac{\partial f}{\partial x_1}(x^0) + \alpha_1(h) \right) h_1 + \left( \frac{\partial f}{\partial x_2}(x^0) + \alpha_2(h) \right) h_2$$

$$+ \cdots + \left( \frac{\partial f}{\partial x_{n-1}}(x^0) + \alpha_{n-1}(h) \right) h_{n-1} + \frac{\partial f}{\partial x_n}(x^0) h_n + o(h_n)$$

$$= \left( \frac{\partial f}{\partial x}(x^0), h \right)_{\mathbb{R}^n} + \sum_{j=1}^{n-1} \alpha_j(h) h_j + o(h_n),$$

where $\lim_{h \to 0} \alpha_j(h) = 0, j = 1, 2, \ldots, n-1$. This representation implies immediately that

$$\Delta_h f(x^0) = \left( \frac{\partial f}{\partial x}(x^0), h \right)_{\mathbb{R}^n} + o(|h|),$$

i.e., $f$ is differentiable at $x^0$.

**Example 13.44.** Let

$$f(x) = \frac{x_1 x_2}{\sqrt{x_1^2 + x_2^2}}, \quad x^0 = (0,0), \quad f(0) := 0.$$

Obviously

$$\frac{\partial f}{\partial x_1}(0) = \frac{\partial f}{\partial x_2}(0) = 0.$$

Moreover,

$$\frac{\partial f}{\partial x_1}(x_1, x_2) = \frac{x_2}{\sqrt{x_1^2 + x_2^2}} - \frac{x_1 x_2 x_1}{(x_1^2 + x_2^2)^{3/2}} = \frac{x_2^3}{(x_1^2 + x_2^2)^{3/2}} = \operatorname{sgn}(x_2) \left( \frac{x_2^2}{x_1^2 + x_2^2} \right)^{3/2}$$

and similarly

$$\frac{\partial f}{\partial x_2}(x_1, x_2) = \operatorname{sgn}(x_1) \left( \frac{x_1^2}{x_1^2 + x_2^2} \right)^{3/2}.$$

These formulas and Example 13.26 show that both derivatives $\frac{\partial f}{\partial x_1}$ and $\frac{\partial f}{\partial x_2}$ are not continuous at $x^0 = (0,0)$ since $\alpha/\gamma + \beta/\delta = 1$. But both derivatives are bounded at $x^0$. Function $f$ is not differentiable at $x^0$ since

$$\frac{h_1 h_2}{\sqrt{h_1^2 + h_2^2}} \neq o \left( \sqrt{h_1^2 + h_2^2} \right)$$

(set, for example, $h_1 = h_2$). This example also shows that the conditions of Theorem 13.43 are quite precise.

**Definition 13.45.** *Let a scalar function $f : X \subset \mathbb{R}^n \to \mathbb{R}$ be differentiable at the point $x^0 \in X$. The row vector*

$$\frac{\partial f}{\partial x}(x^0) = \left( \frac{\partial f}{\partial x_1}(x^0), \ldots, \frac{\partial f}{\partial x_n}(x^0) \right) =: \operatorname{grad} f(x^0) = \nabla f(x^0)$$

*is called the* gradient *of $f$ at $x^0$.*

Let a scalar function $f : X \subset \mathbb{R}^n \to \mathbb{R}$ be defined on a set $X$. Then the set

$$\Gamma(f) := \{ (x, y) \in \mathbb{R}^{n+1} : x \in X, y = f(x) \}$$

is called the *graph* of $f$. The set $P \subset \mathbb{R}^{n+1}$ defined as

$$P := \{(x, y) \in \mathbb{R}^{n+1} : x \in \mathbb{R}^n, y \in \mathbb{R}, ((x - x^0, y - y_0), \overrightarrow{\nu})_{R^{n+1}} = 0\}$$

is called the *hyperplane* passing through the point $(x^0, y_0) \in \mathbb{R}^{n+1}$. Here $\overrightarrow{\nu}$ is a fixed unit vector in $\mathbb{R}^{n+1}$ which is orthogonal to the hyperplane $P$.

**Definition 13.46.** *A hyperplane $P$ passing through the point $(x^0, y_0) \in \mathbb{R}^{n+1}$ of the graph $\Gamma(f)$ is said to be the* tangent *if the angle $\varphi$ between the vector $(x - x^0, y - y_0)$, where $(x, y) \in \Gamma(f)$, and $P$ tends to zero as $(x, y) \in \Gamma(f)$ tends to $(x^0, y_0) \in \Gamma(f)$.*

**Theorem 13.47 (Geometric meaning of differentiability).** *Let a scalar function $f : X \subset \mathbb{R}^n \to \mathbb{R}$ be differentiable at the point $x^0$. Then the graph $\Gamma(f)$ has at the point $(x^0, y_0) \in \Gamma(f)$ a tangent hyperplane $P$. Moreover, the vector*

$$\overrightarrow{\nu} := \frac{(\nabla f(x^0), -1)}{\sqrt{|\nabla f(x^0)|^2 + 1}}$$

*is orthogonal to this hyperplane $P$ at the point $(x^0, y_0)$. In other words this vector defines the hyperplane $P$.*

**Proof.** Since $f$ is differentiable at the point $x^0$, $\nabla f(x^0)$ exists. Defining a hyperplane $P$ as

$$P := \{(x, y) \in \mathbb{R}^{n+1} : ((x - x^0, y - y_0), \overrightarrow{\nu})_{\mathbb{R}^{n+1}} = 0\},$$

where vector $\overrightarrow{\nu}$ is as above, we obtain that

$$y - y_0 = (\nabla f(x^0), x - x^0)_{\mathbb{R}^n}$$

for $(x, y) \in P$. Let us prove that $P$ is a tangent hyperplane at $(x^0, y_0) \in \Gamma(f)$. If $(x, y) \in \Gamma(f)$ is an arbitrary point such that $(x, y) \neq (x^0, y_0)$ then denoting by $\psi$ the angle between the vector $(x - x^0, y - y_0)$ and $\overrightarrow{\nu}$ we have, due to differentiability, that

$$\cos \psi = \frac{((\nabla f(x^0), -1), (x - x^0, y - y_0))_{\mathbb{R}^{n+1}}}{\sqrt{|\nabla f(x^0)|^2 + 1}|(x - x^0, y - y_0)|}$$

$$= \frac{(\nabla f(x^0), x - x^0)_{\mathbb{R}^n} - (y - y_0)}{\sqrt{|\nabla f(x^0)|^2 + 1}|(f(x) - f(x^0), x - x^0)|}$$

$$= \frac{(\nabla f(x^0), h)_{\mathbb{R}^n} - \Delta_h f(x^0)}{\sqrt{|\nabla f(x^0)|^2 + 1}|(\Delta_h f(x^0), h)|}$$

$$= \frac{o(|h|)}{\sqrt{|\nabla f(x^0)|^2 + 1}\sqrt{(\Delta_h f(x^0))^2 + h^2}}.$$

Hence

$$|\cos \psi| \leq \frac{|o(|h|)|}{|h|} \to 0$$

as $h \to 0$. By continuity of cos (and its inverse) this means that $\psi \to \pi/2$. But this is equivalent to (see Figure 13.1) the fact that $\varphi \to 0$, i.e., the hyperplane $P$ is tangent. The theorem is proved.

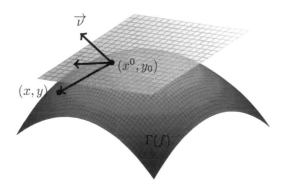

**Figure 13.1.** *Tangent hyperplane.*

**Theorem 13.48 (Differentiability of superposition).** *Let function $\vec{g}$ be a superposition of the functions $\vec{f} : X \subset \mathbb{R}^n \to Y \subset \mathbb{R}^m$ and $\vec{\varphi} : Y \subset \mathbb{R}^m \to Z \subset \mathbb{R}^l$ such that*

$$\vec{g} : X \subset \mathbb{R}^n \to Z \subset \mathbb{R}^l, \quad \vec{g}(x) = \vec{\varphi}(\vec{f}(x)).$$

*If $\vec{f}$ is differentiable at the point $x^0 \in X$ and $\vec{\varphi}$ is differentiable at the point $y^0 = \vec{f}(x^0) \in Y$ then $\vec{g}$ is differentiable at $x^0$, and the full derivative of $\vec{g}$ at $x^0$ can be calculated as*

$$\underbrace{\frac{\partial \vec{g}}{\partial x}(x^0)}_{l \times n} = \underbrace{\frac{\partial \vec{\varphi}}{\partial y}(\vec{f}(x^0))}_{l \times m} \underbrace{\frac{\partial \vec{f}}{\partial x}(x^0)}_{m \times n},$$

*where the right-hand side involves matrix multiplication.*

***Proof.*** The increment of $\vec{g}$ at the point $x^0$ can be written as

$$\Delta_h \vec{g}(x^0) = \vec{\varphi}(\vec{f}(x^0 + h)) - \vec{\varphi}(\vec{f}(x^0)) = \vec{\varphi}(y^0 + H) - \vec{\varphi}(y^0),$$

where $y^0 = \vec{f}(x^0)$ and $H = \vec{f}(x^0 + h) - \vec{f}(x^0)$. Since $\vec{f}$ is differentiable at $x^0$, $H \to 0$ as $h \to 0$. Due to differentiability of $\vec{\varphi}$ at $y^0$ we have that

$$\vec{\varphi}(y^0 + H) - \vec{\varphi}(y^0) = \frac{\partial \vec{\varphi}}{\partial y}(y^0)H + o(|H|)$$

$$= \frac{\partial \vec{\varphi}}{\partial y}(y^0)\left(\frac{\partial \vec{f}}{\partial x}(x^0)h + o(|h|)\right) + o(|H|)$$

$$= \frac{\partial \vec{\varphi}}{\partial y}(y^0)\frac{\partial \vec{f}}{\partial x}(x^0)h + o(|h|) + o(|H|).$$

But since

$$H = \vec{f}(x^0 + h) - \vec{f}(x^0) = \frac{\partial \vec{f}}{\partial x}(x^0)h + o(|h|),$$

we have

$$|H| \le C|h|.$$

Hence we obtain finally

$$\Delta_h \vec{g}(x^0) = \frac{\partial \vec{\phi}}{\partial y}(y^0)\frac{\partial \vec{f}}{\partial x}(x^0)h + o(|h|).$$

This means that $\vec{g}$ is differentiable at $x^0$ and that

$$\frac{\partial \vec{g}}{\partial x}(x^0) = \frac{\partial \vec{\phi}}{\partial y}(y^0)\frac{\partial \vec{f}}{\partial x}(x^0), \quad y^0 = \vec{f}(x^0).$$

Thus, the theorem is proved.

**Exercise 13.49.**     1. Let a scalar function $f : X \subset \mathbb{R}^n \to \mathbb{R}$ be differentiable at any point $x \in X$ and homogeneous of degree $p$, i.e., $f(tx) = t^p f(x), t > 0$. Prove that

$$(\nabla f(x), x)_{\mathbb{R}^n} = pf(x).$$

   2. Using part 1 prove that for the function

$$f(x_1, x_2) = \frac{x_1 x_2}{(x_1^2 + x_2^2)^\alpha}$$

   the equality

$$\frac{\partial f}{\partial x_1}(x)x_1 + \frac{\partial f}{\partial x_2}(x)x_2 = (2 - \alpha/2)f(x)$$

   holds. In particular, if $\alpha = 4$ then

$$\frac{\partial f}{\partial x_1}(x)x_1 + \frac{\partial f}{\partial x_2}(x)x_2 = 0, \quad x \neq 0.$$

   3. Compute

$$\nabla \log \log \sqrt{x_1^2 + x_2^2 + \cdots + x_n^2}$$

   and

$$\nabla \left( \nabla \log \log \sqrt{x_1^2 + x_2^2 + \cdots + x_n^2} \right).$$

**Definition 13.50.** *Let function $f : X \subset \mathbb{R}^n \to \mathbb{R}^m$ be differentiable at the point $x^0 \in X$. The value $\frac{\partial \vec{f}}{\partial x}(x^0)h$ is said to be the* first differential *of $\vec{f}$ at $x^0$ and is denoted by*

$$\mathrm{d}\vec{f}(x^0) := \frac{\partial \vec{f}}{\partial x}(x^0)h = \frac{\partial \vec{f}}{\partial x}(x^0)\mathrm{d}x,$$

*where $\mathrm{d}x = h$ is the differential of the independent $n$-dimensional variable $x$.*

**Corollary 13.51 (From Theorem 13.48).** *The form of the first differential is invariant under the superposition (change of variables).*

***Proof.*** Let $\vec{g}(x) = \vec{\phi}(\vec{f}(x))$ be a superposition of two differentiable functions $\vec{\phi}$ and $\vec{f}$. Then Theorem 13.48 and Definition 13.50 imply that

$$\mathrm{d}\vec{g}(x^0) = \frac{\partial \vec{g}}{\partial x}(x^0)h = \frac{\partial \vec{\phi}}{\partial y}(y^0)\frac{\partial \vec{f}}{\partial x}(x^0)h = \frac{\partial \vec{\phi}}{\partial y}(y^0)\mathrm{d}\vec{f}(x^0) = \frac{\partial \vec{\phi}}{\partial y}(y^0)\mathrm{d}y.$$

**Definition 13.52.** *Let $\overrightarrow{l} \in \mathbb{R}^n$ be a nonzero fixed vector and let $t \in \mathbb{R}, t \neq 0$. Then*

$$\Delta_{t\overrightarrow{l}} \overrightarrow{f}(x^0) = \overrightarrow{f}(x^0 + t\overrightarrow{l}) - \overrightarrow{f}(x^0)$$

*is called an* increment *of $\overrightarrow{f}$ in $x^0$ along $\overrightarrow{l}$. In addition, if the limit*

$$\lim_{t \to 0} \frac{\Delta_{t\overrightarrow{l}} \overrightarrow{f}(x^0)}{t}$$

*exists then this limit is called a* derivative *of $\overrightarrow{f}$ at $x^0$ along $\overrightarrow{l}$ and is denoted as*

$$\frac{\partial \overrightarrow{f}}{\partial \overrightarrow{l}}(x^0).$$

**Proposition 13.53.** *Let function $\overrightarrow{f} : X \subset \mathbb{R}^n \to \mathbb{R}^m$ be differentiable at the point $x^0 \in X$ and let $\overrightarrow{l}$ be an arbitrary nonzero vector. Then the derivative*

$$\frac{\partial \overrightarrow{f}}{\partial \overrightarrow{l}}(x^0)$$

*exists and*

$$\frac{\partial \overrightarrow{f}}{\partial \overrightarrow{l}}(x^0) = \frac{\partial \overrightarrow{f}}{\partial x}(x^0)\,\overrightarrow{l}.$$

**Proof.** Since $\overrightarrow{f}$ is differentiable at $x^0$, for $h = t\overrightarrow{l}$ we have

$$\Delta_{t\overrightarrow{l}} \overrightarrow{f}(x^0) = \frac{\partial \overrightarrow{f}}{\partial x}(x^0)t\overrightarrow{l} + o(|t\overrightarrow{l}|)$$

or

$$\frac{\Delta_{t\overrightarrow{l}} \overrightarrow{f}(x^0)}{t} = \frac{\partial \overrightarrow{f}}{\partial x}(x^0)\,\overrightarrow{l} + o(1).$$

Thus

$$\lim_{t \to 0} \frac{\Delta_{t\overrightarrow{l}} \overrightarrow{f}(x^0)}{t} = \frac{\partial \overrightarrow{f}}{\partial \overrightarrow{l}}(x^0) = \frac{\partial \overrightarrow{f}}{\partial x}(x^0)\,\overrightarrow{l}.$$

**Exercise 13.54.** 1. Let

$$f(x) = \frac{|x_1|x_2}{\sqrt{x_1^2 + x_2^2}}, \quad x^0 = (0,0), \quad f(x^0) = 0.$$

Prove that

$$\frac{\partial \overrightarrow{f}}{\partial \overrightarrow{l}}(0) = \frac{|l_1|l_2}{|\overrightarrow{l}|}, \quad \overrightarrow{l} = (l_1, l_2) \neq 0.$$

2. Let

$$f(x) = \frac{x_1|x_2|^{1/2}}{\sqrt{x_1^2 + |x_2|}}, \quad x^0 = (0,0), \quad f(x^0) = 0.$$

Prove that

$$\frac{\partial \overrightarrow{f}}{\partial \overrightarrow{l}}(0) = l_1$$

for any vector $\overrightarrow{l} = (l_1, l_2), l_2 \neq 0$ and that

$$\frac{\partial \overrightarrow{f}}{\partial \overrightarrow{l}}(0)$$

does not exist if $l_2 = 0$.

3. Let

$$f(x) = \frac{|x_1|^\alpha |x_2|^\beta}{|x_1|^\gamma + |x_2|^\delta}, \quad x^0 = (0,0), \quad f(x^0) = 0, \quad \alpha, \beta, \gamma, \delta \geq 0.$$

Find conditions for $\alpha, \beta, \gamma$, and $\delta$ which guarantee the differentiability of $f$ at $x^0$. Find also conditions for $\alpha, \beta, \gamma$, and $\delta$ which guarantee the existence of the derivative of $f$ along any vector $\overrightarrow{l} = (l_1, l_2)$ such that $l_1 \neq 0 \neq l_2$.

**Remark 13.55.** Let a scalar function $f : X \subset \mathbb{R}^n \to \mathbb{R}$ be differentiable at the point $x^0 \in X$. Then

$$\frac{\partial f}{\partial \overrightarrow{l}}(x^0) = (\nabla f(x^0), \overrightarrow{l})_{\mathbb{R}^n} = |\nabla f(x^0)|| \overrightarrow{l} | \cos \angle (\nabla f, \overrightarrow{l})$$

for any vector $\overrightarrow{l} \neq 0$. Here $\angle (\nabla f, \overrightarrow{l})$ denotes the angle between vectors $\nabla f$ and $\overrightarrow{l}$. If, for example, $\overrightarrow{l} = \lambda \nabla f(x^0)$ then

$$\frac{\partial f}{\partial \overrightarrow{l}}(x^0) = |\lambda||\nabla f(x^0)|^2 \cos \angle (\nabla f(x^0), \lambda \nabla f(x^0)) = \lambda |\nabla f(x^0)|^2.$$

So

$$\frac{\partial f}{\partial \overrightarrow{l}}(x^0) > 0$$

for $\lambda > 0$ and

$$\frac{\partial f}{\partial \overrightarrow{l}}(x^0) < 0$$

for $\lambda < 0$. In other words, the gradient, as a vector, indicates the direction of fastest change of the function at the point $x^0$.

**Definition 13.56.** *Let a scalar function $f : X \subset \mathbb{R}^n \to \mathbb{R}$ be continuous on an open set $X$. Then the set*

$$S_c(f) := \{x \in X : f(x) = c\}$$

*is called the* level surface *of $f$.*

**Proposition 13.57.** *Let a scalar function $f : X \subset \mathbb{R}^n \to \mathbb{R}$ be differentiable at the point $x^0 \in X$. If $x^0 \in S_c(f)$ then the gradient $\nabla f(x^0) \neq 0$ is orthogonal to $S_c(f)$ at $x^0$.*

**Proof.** It suffices to show that a hyperplane

$$P = \{x \in X : (x - x^0, \nabla f(x^0))_{\mathbb{R}^n} = 0\}$$

is tangent to $S_c(f)$ at $x^0$. Indeed, let $x, x^0 \in S_c(f), x \neq x^0$. Then

$$\begin{aligned}
\cos \angle (x - x^0, \nabla f(x^0)) &= \frac{(x - x^0, \nabla f(x^0))_{\mathbb{R}^n}}{|x - x^0||\nabla f(x^0)|} \\
&= \frac{f(x) - f(x^0) + o(|x - x^0|)}{|x - x^0||\nabla f(x^0)|} = \frac{c - c + o(|x - x^0|)}{|x - x^0||\nabla f(x^0)|} = o(1).
\end{aligned}$$

Hence $P$ is tangent to $S_c(f)$ at $x^0$, and the proposition is proved.

Let function $\overrightarrow{f} : X \subset \mathbb{R}^n \to \mathbb{R}^m$ be defined on an open set $X$, and let the derivative

$$\frac{\partial \overrightarrow{f}}{\partial x_j}(x)$$

exist for all $x \in B_\delta(x^0) \subset X$. If the derivative

$$\frac{\partial}{\partial x_k} \left( \frac{\partial \overrightarrow{f}}{\partial x_j}(x) \right) (x^0)$$

exists, i.e., the limit

$$\lim_{t \to 0} \frac{\frac{\partial \overrightarrow{f}}{\partial x_j}(x^0 + t\overrightarrow{e}_k) - \frac{\partial \overrightarrow{f}}{\partial x_j}(x^0)}{t}$$

exists, then this limit is said to be the *second partial derivative* of $f$ at $x^0$ and is denoted by

$$\frac{\partial^2 \overrightarrow{f}}{\partial x_k \partial x_j}(x^0).$$

It must be mentioned here that the result depends on the order of differentiation.

**Example 13.58.** Let

$$f(x) = x_1 x_2 \frac{x_1^2 - x_2^2}{x_1^2 + x_2^2}, \quad x^0 = (0,0), \quad f(0) = 0.$$

Then, first,

$$\frac{\partial f}{\partial x_j}(0) = \lim_{t \to 0} \frac{f(x^0 + te_j) - f(x^0)}{t} = \lim_{t \to 0} 0 = 0, \quad j = 1, 2.$$

Second,

$$\frac{\partial f}{\partial x_1}(x) = x_2 \frac{x_1^2 - x_2^2}{x_1^2 + x_2^2} + x_1 x_2 \frac{2x_1(x_1^2 + x_2^2) - 2x_1(x_1^2 - x_2^2)}{(x_1^2 + x_2^2)^2} = \frac{x_2 x_1^4 - x_2^5 + 4x_1^2 x_2^3}{(x_1^2 + x_2^2)^2}$$

so that

$$\frac{\partial^2 f}{\partial x_2 \partial x_1}(x^0) = \lim_{t \to 0} \frac{\frac{\partial f}{\partial x_1}(0,t) - \frac{\partial f}{\partial x_1}(0,0)}{t} = \lim_{t \to 0} \frac{-t^5}{5^5} = -1.$$

Similarly, using antisymmetry of $f$ with respect to $x_1$ and $x_2$ we have that

$$\frac{\partial^2 f}{\partial x_1 \partial x_2}(x^0) = 1.$$

This shows the dependence on the order of differentiation.

**Exercise 13.59.** Let

$$f(x) = \frac{x_1 x_2}{x_1^2 + x_2^2}, \quad x^0 = (0,0), \quad f(x^0) = 0.$$

Prove that

1.

$$\frac{\partial^2 f}{\partial x_1^2}(x^0) = \frac{\partial^2 f}{\partial x_2^2}(x^0) = 0,$$

2.

$$\frac{\partial^2 f}{\partial x_2 \partial x_1}(x^0), \quad \frac{\partial^2 f}{\partial x_1 \partial x_2}(x^0)$$

do not exist,

3. $f$ is not continuous at $x^0$.

By induction we define the derivatives

$$\frac{\partial^l \overrightarrow{f}}{\partial x_{j_1} \partial x_{j_2} \cdots \partial x_{j_l}}(x^0)$$

$$:= \lim_{t \to 0} \frac{1}{t} \left( \frac{\partial^{l-1} \overrightarrow{f}}{\partial x_{j_2} \partial x_{j_3} \cdots \partial x_{j_l}}(x^0 + t\overrightarrow{e_{j_1}}) - \frac{\partial^{l-1} \overrightarrow{f}}{\partial x_{j_2} \partial x_{j_3} \cdots \partial x_{j_l}}(x^0) \right)$$

if they exist. It must again be mentioned that the result depends on the order of differentiation. Moreover (see Exercise 13.59), the presence of mixed derivatives does not guarantee the continuity in the totality of variables.

**Definition 13.60.** *Let function* $\overrightarrow{f} : X \subset \mathbb{R}^n \to \mathbb{R}^m$ *be defined on an open set $X$ and let $x^0 \in X$. Let also $\frac{\partial \overrightarrow{f}}{\partial x_j}(x), j = 1, 2, \ldots, n$, exist for all $x \in B_\delta(x^0) \subset X$. If $\frac{\partial \overrightarrow{f}}{\partial x_j}(x)$ is differentiable at $x^0$ for all $j = 1, 2, \ldots, n$ then $\overrightarrow{f}$ is said to be* twice differentiable *at $x^0$. Furthermore, $\overrightarrow{f}$ is said to be differentiable $l$ times at the point $x^0$ if any of its derivatives of order $l - 1$, i.e.,*

$$\frac{\partial^{l-1} \overrightarrow{f}}{\partial x_{j_1} \partial x_{j_2} \cdots \partial x_{j_{l-1}}}(x)$$

*is differentiable at $x^0$.*

The next important result due to Young clarifies the situation with mixed derivatives.

**Theorem 13.61 (Young).** *Let a scalar function $f : X \subset \mathbb{R}^2 \to \mathbb{R}$ be twice differentiable at the point $x^0 \in X$, where $X$ is an open set. Then*

$$\frac{\partial^2 f}{\partial x_2 \partial x_1}(x^0) = \frac{\partial^2 f}{\partial x_1 \partial x_2}(x^0).$$

***Proof.*** Let us denote by $\varphi$ and $\psi$ the functions of one variable

$$\varphi(x_1) := f(x_1, x_2^0 + t) - f(x_1, x_2^0), \quad \psi(x_2) := f(x_1^0 + t, x_2) - f(x_1^0, x_2),$$

where $t \neq 0$ is a parameter. Then it is easy to see that

$$\Delta_t \varphi(x_1^0) = f(x_1^0 + t, x_2^0 + t) - f(x_1^0 + t, x_2^0) - f(x_1^0, x_2^0 + t) + f(x_1^0, x_2^0) = \Delta_t \psi(x_2^0).$$

Using the one-dimensional Lagrange formula we obtain that

$$\Delta_t \varphi(x_1^0) = \varphi'(x_1^0 + \theta_1 t)t = \left( \frac{\partial f}{\partial x_1}(x_1^0 + \theta_1 t, x_2^0 + t) - \frac{\partial f}{\partial x_1}(x_1^0 + \theta_1 t, x_2^0) \right) t$$

and

$$\Delta_t \psi(x_2^0) = \psi'(x_2^0 + \theta_2 t)t = \left( \frac{\partial f}{\partial x_2}(x_1^0 + t, x_2^0 + \theta_2 t) - \frac{\partial f}{\partial x_2}(x_1^0, x_2^0 + \theta_2 t) \right) t.$$

The differentiability of the functions $\frac{\partial f}{\partial x_1}(x_1, x_2)$ and $\frac{\partial f}{\partial x_2}(x_1, x_2)$ at $x^0$ implies that

$$\Delta_t \varphi(x_1^0) = \left( \frac{\partial^2 f}{\partial x_1^2}(x_1^0, x_2^0)\theta_1 t + \frac{\partial^2 f}{\partial x_2 \partial x_1}(x_1^0, x_2^0)t \right) t - \frac{\partial^2 f}{\partial x_1^2}(x_1^0, x_2^0)\theta_1 t^2 + o(t^2)$$

and

$$\Delta_t \psi(x_2^0) = \left( \frac{\partial^2 f}{\partial x_2^2}(x_1^0, x_2^0)\theta_2 t + \frac{\partial^2 f}{\partial x_1 \partial x_2}(x_1^0, x_2^0)t \right) t - \frac{\partial^2 f}{\partial x_2^2}(x_1^0, x_2^0)\theta_2 t^2 + o(t^2).$$

Due to equality $\Delta_t \varphi(x_1^0) = \Delta_t \psi(x_2^0)$ we may now obtain that

$$\frac{\partial^2 f}{\partial x_1 \partial x_2}(x_1^0, x_2^0)t^2 + o(t^2) = \frac{\partial^2 f}{\partial x_2 \partial x_1}(x_1^0, x_2^0)t^2 + o(t^2)$$

as $t \to 0$. Hence

$$\frac{\partial^2 f}{\partial x_1 \partial x_2}(x_1^0, x_2^0) = \frac{\partial^2 f}{\partial x_2 \partial x_1}(x_1^0, x_2^0).$$

Thus, the theorem is proved.

**Corollary 13.62.** *Let the mixed derivatives*

$$\frac{\partial^2 f}{\partial x_1 \partial x_2}(x), \qquad \frac{\partial^2 f}{\partial x_2 \partial x_1}(x)$$

*exist for all $x \in B_\delta(x^0) \subset X$ and be continuous at the point $x^0$. Then*

$$\frac{\partial^2 f}{\partial x_1 \partial x_2}(x_1^0, x_2^0) = \frac{\partial^2 f}{\partial x_2 \partial x_1}(x_1^0, x_2^0).$$

*Proof.* Proceeding as in the proof of Young's theorem one can obtain (using the Lagrange formula twice) that

$$\Delta_t \varphi(x_1^0) = \frac{\partial^2 f}{\partial x_2 \partial x_1}(x_1^0 + \theta_1 t, x_2^0 + \widetilde{\theta_2} t)t^2$$

and

$$\Delta_t \psi(x_2^0) = \frac{\partial^2 f}{\partial x_1 \partial x_2}(x_1^0 + \widetilde{\theta_1} t, x_2^0 + \theta_2 t)t^2.$$

Thus, continuity of $\frac{\partial^2 f}{\partial x_1 \partial x_2}(x)$ and $\frac{\partial^2 f}{\partial x_2 \partial x_1}(x)$ at $x^0$ implies immediately that

$$\frac{\partial^2 f}{\partial x_1 \partial x_2}(x_1^0, x_2^0) = \frac{\partial^2 f}{\partial x_2 \partial x_1}(x_1^0, x_2^0).$$

**Corollary 13.63.** *Let a scalar function $f : X \subset \mathbb{R}^n \to \mathbb{R}$ be defined on an open set $X$ and let $x^0 \in X$. If $f$ is $l$ times differentiable at $x^0 \in X, l \geq 2$, then any derivative of order $l$,*

$$\frac{\partial^l f(x^0)}{\partial x_{j_1} \partial x_{j_2} \cdots \partial x_{j_l}},$$

*is independent on the order in which the derivatives are taken.*

*Proof.* The result is obtained by applying Young's theorem for any two different variables and the corresponding mixed derivatives.

**Example 13.64.** Let

$$f(x) = x_1^2 \sin \frac{1}{x_1} + x_2^2 \sin \frac{1}{x_2}, \quad x^0 = (0,0), \quad f(x^0) = 0.$$

Then it is quite evident that

$$\frac{\partial^2 f(x)}{\partial x_1 \partial x_2} = \frac{\partial^2 f(x)}{\partial x_2 \partial x_1} = 0$$

for all $x \in \mathbb{R}^2$. But the derivatives

$$\frac{\partial^2 f(x^0)}{\partial x_1^2}, \quad \frac{\partial^2 f(x^0)}{\partial x_2^2}$$

do not exist. It means that $f$ is not twice differentiable at $x^0$ and therefore Young's theorem cannot be applied, i.e., it gives only sufficient but not necessary conditions for the equality of mixed derivatives.

**Exercise 13.65.**    1. Let

$$f(x) = \frac{|ax_1 + bx_2|^3}{\sqrt{x_1^2 + x_2^2}}, \quad x^0 = (0,0), \quad f(x^0) = 0.$$

Prove that

$$\frac{\partial^2 f}{\partial x_2 \partial x_1}(x^0) = 3ab|b|, \quad \frac{\partial^2 f}{\partial x_1 \partial x_2}(x^0) = 3ab|a|.$$

Investigate the result for all possibilities of $a$ and $b$ and establish a connection with Young's theorem.

2. Let
$$f(x) = x_1 x_2 + x_2^2 \mathcal{D}(x_2),$$

where $\mathcal{D}$ is the Dirichlet function. Investigate where in the $(x_1, x_2)$-plane the conditions of Young's theorem (or its corollary) are satisfied.

Taking into account Young's theorem (or its corollaries) one may write any derivative of order $l$ in the form
$$\frac{\partial^l f(x)}{\partial x_{j_1} \partial x_{j_2} \cdots \partial x_{j_l}} = \frac{\partial^l f(x)}{\partial x_1^{\alpha_1} \partial x_2^{\alpha_2} \cdots \partial x_n^{\alpha_n}}$$

(since the result is independent on the order) where $\alpha_j \in \mathbb{N}_0 = \mathbb{N} \cup \{0\}$ and $\alpha_1 + \alpha_2 + \cdots + \alpha_n = l$ and $\alpha_j$ shows how many times the derivative with respect to $x_j$ occurs. Furthermore, this derivative of order $l$ can be written in shorter form,

$$\partial_1^{\alpha_1} \partial_2^{\alpha_2} \cdots \partial_n^{\alpha_n} f(x) = \partial^\alpha f(x),$$

where $\partial_j := \frac{\partial}{\partial x_j}$ and the vector $\alpha := (\alpha_1, \alpha_2, \ldots, \alpha_n)$ is called a *multi-index* with the length $|\alpha| := \alpha_1 + \alpha_2 + \cdots + \alpha_n = l$.

The following properties of a multi-index are used:

1. $\alpha! = \alpha_1!\alpha_2!\cdots\alpha_n!$ and $0! = 1$,

2. $x^\alpha = x_1^{\alpha_1}x_2^{\alpha_2}\cdots x_n^{\alpha_n}$ and $0^0 = 1$,

3. $\alpha + \beta = (\alpha_1 + \beta_1, \alpha_2 + \beta_2, \ldots, \alpha_n + \beta_n)$ and $|\alpha + \beta| = |\alpha| + |\beta|$,

4. $\alpha \geq \beta$ if and only if $\alpha_j \geq \beta_j$ for each $j = 1, 2, \ldots, n$.

The next lemma can also turn out to be useful.

**Lemma 13.66 (Newton's binomial formula in the multidimensional case).** *If $l \in \mathbb{N}$ then*

$$(a_1 + a_2 + \cdots + a_n)^l = \sum_{|\alpha|=l} \frac{l!}{\alpha!}a^\alpha,$$

*where $a = (a_1, a_2, \ldots, a_n) \in \mathbb{R}^n$ and $\alpha$ is a multi-index.*

**Exercise 13.67.** Prove Newton's binomial formula using induction.

**Definition 13.68.** *Let a scalar function $f : X \subset \mathbb{R}^n \to \mathbb{R}$ be defined on an open set $X$ and be twice differentiable at the point $x^0 \in X$. Then*

$$d^2 f(x^0) := d(df(x))(x^0)$$

*is called the* second differential *of $f$ at $x^0$.*

Using this definition and the invariance of the form of first differential we obtain that

$$d^2 f(x^0) = d\left(\frac{\partial f}{\partial x_1}(x)dx_1 + \cdots + \frac{\partial f}{\partial x_n}(x)dx_n\right)(x^0)$$

$$= d\left(\frac{\partial f}{\partial x_1}(x)\right)(x^0)dx_1 + \cdots + d\left(\frac{\partial f}{\partial x_n}(x)\right)(x^0)dx_n$$

$$+ \frac{\partial f}{\partial x_1}(x^0)d^2 x_1 + \cdots + \frac{\partial f}{\partial x_n}(x^0)d^2 x_n.$$

Assuming the independence of the variables $x_1, x_2, \ldots, x_n$ (it means that they are not functions of some other variables) we obtain that $d^2 x_j = 0$ for each $j = 1, 2, \ldots, n$. Hence,

$$d^2 f(x^0) = \frac{\partial^2 f}{\partial x_1^2}(x^0)(dx_1)^2 + \frac{\partial^2 f}{\partial x_1 \partial x_2}(x^0)dx_1 dx_2 + \cdots + \frac{\partial^2 f}{\partial x_1 \partial x_n}(x^0)dx_1 dx_n$$

$$+ \frac{\partial^2 f}{\partial x_2 \partial x_1}(x^0)dx_2 dx_1 + \frac{\partial^2 f}{\partial x_2^2}(x^0)(dx_2)^2 + \cdots + \frac{\partial^2 f}{\partial x_2 \partial x_n}(x^0)dx_2 dx_n$$

$$+ \cdots$$

$$+ \frac{\partial^2 f}{\partial x_n \partial x_1}(x^0)dx_n dx_1 + \frac{\partial^2 f}{\partial x_n \partial x_2}(x^0)dx_n dx_2 + \cdots + \frac{\partial^2 f}{\partial x_n^2}(x^0)(dx_n)^2$$

$$= \sum_{k,j=1}^{n} \frac{\partial^2 f}{\partial x_j \partial x_k}(x^0)dx_j dx_k = \left(\frac{\partial}{\partial x_1}dx_1 + \cdots + \frac{\partial}{\partial x_n}dx_n\right)^2 f(x^0)$$

$$= (\partial_1 dx_1 + \cdots + \partial_n dx_n)^2 f(x^0) = \sum_{|\alpha|=2} \frac{2!}{\alpha!}\partial^\alpha f(x^0)(dx)^\alpha$$

by Newton's binomial formula. One can define by induction (in the case of independent variables $x_1, x_2, \ldots, x_n$) that

$$d^l f(x^0) := d(d^{l-1} f(x))(x^0) = \sum_{|\alpha|=l} \frac{l!}{\alpha!} \partial^\alpha f(x^0)(dx)^\alpha.$$

**Theorem 13.69 (Taylor's formula).** *Let a scalar function* $f : X \subset \mathbb{R}^n \to \mathbb{R}$ *be defined on an open set* $X$ *and be differentiable* $l+1$ *times,* $l = 0, 1, \ldots,$ *in some neighborhood* $B_\delta(x^0) \subset X$ *of the point* $x^0$*. Then for any* $x \in B'_\delta(x^0)$ *we have the Taylor expansion*

$$f(x) = \sum_{k=0}^{l} \frac{d^k f(x^0)}{k!} + \frac{d^{l+1} f(\xi)}{(l+1)!},$$

*where* $\xi = x^0 + \theta(x - x^0), 0 < \theta < 1.$

**Proof.** Let $h = x - x^0$ such that $0 < |h| < \delta$. For $t \in [0, 1]$ we define the function $F(t) := f(x^0 + th)$. Using Taylor's formula for $F(t)$ as a function of one variable we obtain

$$F(1) = F(0) + F'(0) + \frac{F''(0)}{2!} + \cdots + \frac{F^{(l)}(0)}{l!} + \frac{F^{(l+1)}(\theta)}{(l+1)!}, \quad 0 < \theta < 1.$$

Next we note that the following formulas hold:

$$F'(0) = \sum_{j=1}^{n} \frac{\partial f}{\partial x_j}(x^0 + th)h_j \Big|_{t=0} = df(x^0 + th)\big|_{t=0},$$

$$F''(0) = \sum_{j=1}^{n} \sum_{k=1}^{n} \frac{\partial}{\partial x_k}\left(\frac{\partial f}{\partial x_j}(x^0 + th)\right)h_j h_k \Big|_{t=0}$$

$$= \sum_{j,k=1}^{n} \frac{\partial^2 f}{\partial x_k \partial x_j}(x^0 + th)h_j h_k \Big|_{t=0} = d^2 f(x^0 + th)\big|_{t=0}$$

$$\vdots$$

$$F^{(l+1)}(0) = d^{l+1} f(x^0 + th)\big|_{t=0}.$$

Since $F(1) = f(x)$ and $F(0) = f(x^0)$, we obtain

$$f(x) = \sum_{k=0}^{l} \frac{d^k f(x^0)}{k!} + \frac{d^{l+1} f(\xi)}{(l+1)!}.$$

Thus, Taylor's formula follows.

**Remark 13.70.** The remainder in this Taylor's expansion is said to be in the form of Lagrange.

**Corollary 13.71 (Lagrange's formula).** *Let a scalar function* $f : X \subset \mathbb{R}^n \to \mathbb{R}$ *be differentiable on a convex set* $X$*, i.e.,* $tx' + (1 - t)x'' \in X$ *for any* $x', x'' \in X$ *and for any* $0 \le t \le 1.$

*Then we have the multidimensional Lagrange formula*

$$f(x'') - f(x') = (\nabla f(\xi), x'' - x')_{\mathbb{R}^n},$$

*where* $\xi = x' + \theta(x'' - x'), 0 < \theta < 1.$

**Proof.** Let us define a function of one variable $t \in [0,1]$ as

$$F(t) := f(x' + t(x'' - x')), \quad x', x'' \in X.$$

Since $X$ is convex, $F(t)$ is well-defined. The function $F$ is also differentiable in $t$ since $f$ is differentiable on $X$. Applying the one-dimensional Lagrange formula we obtain

$$
\begin{aligned}
f(x'') - f(x') &= F(1) - F(0) = F'(\theta) \\
&= (\nabla f(x' + \theta(x'' - x')), x'' - x')_{\mathbb{R}^n} = (\nabla f(\xi), x'' - x')_{\mathbb{R}^n}.
\end{aligned}
$$

This concludes the proof.

**Corollary 13.72.** *Under the conditions of Theorem* 13.69 *we have the Taylor's formula with the remainder in integral form*

$$f(x) = \sum_{k=0}^{l} \frac{\mathrm{d}^k f(x^0)}{k!} + \frac{1}{l!} \int_0^1 \mathrm{d}^{l+1} f(x^0 + t(x - x^0))(1-t)^l \mathrm{d}t.$$

**Proof.** The proof is literally the same as in the one-dimensional case.

**Corollary 13.73 (Taylor's formula with remainder in Peano's form).** *Let a scalar function* $f : X \subset \mathbb{R}^n \to \mathbb{R}$ *be defined on an open set* $X$ *and be* $l$ *times differentiable at the point* $x^0 \in X$ *with* $l = 1, 2, \ldots$. *Then*

$$f(x) = \sum_{k=0}^{l} \frac{\mathrm{d}^k f(x^0)}{k!} + o(|x - x^0|^l), \quad x \to x^0.$$

**Proof.** We employ mathematical induction with respect to $l = 1, 2, \ldots$. If $l = 1$ then the differentiability of $f$ at $x^0$ leads to

$$f(x) - f(x^0) = (\nabla f(x^0), x - x^0)_{\mathbb{R}^n} + o(|x - x^0|),$$

so the statement holds for $l = 1$. Assuming now that the statement holds for any $l \geq 1$ we want to prove that it is true for $l + 1$ as well, i.e., we want to prove that

$$R_{l+1}(f, x) := f(x) - \sum_{k=0}^{l+1} \frac{\mathrm{d}^k f(x^0)}{k!} = o(|x - x^0|^{l+1}).$$

Recalling that $\mathrm{d}x = x - x^0$ and

$$\mathrm{d}^k f(x^0) = \sum_{|\alpha|=k} \frac{k!}{\alpha!} \partial^\alpha f(x^0)(x - x^0)^\alpha$$

we obtain that

$$
\frac{\partial R_{l+1}(f,x)}{\partial x_j} = \frac{\partial f}{\partial x_j}(x) - \sum_{k=1}^{l+1} \frac{1}{k!} \sum_{|\alpha|=k} \frac{k!}{\alpha!} \partial^\alpha f(x^0) \partial_j (x - x^0)^\alpha
$$

$$
= \frac{\partial f}{\partial x_j}(x) - \sum_{k=1}^{l+1} \frac{1}{k!} \sum_{|\alpha|=k} \frac{k!}{\alpha!} \partial^\alpha f(x^0) \alpha_j (x - x^0)^{\alpha-1\cdot\vec{e}_j}
$$

$$
= \frac{\partial f}{\partial x_j}(x) - \sum_{k=1}^{l+1} \frac{1}{k!} \sum_{|\alpha|=k} \frac{k!\alpha_j}{\alpha!} \partial^{\alpha-1\cdot\vec{e}_j} \frac{\partial f}{\partial x_j}(x^0)(x - x^0)^{\alpha-1\cdot\vec{e}_j}
$$

$$
= \frac{\partial f}{\partial x_j}(x) - \sum_{k=1}^{l+1} \frac{1}{k!} \sum_{|\beta|=k-1} \frac{k!}{\beta!} \partial^\beta \frac{\partial f}{\partial x_j}(x^0)(x - x^0)^\beta
$$

$$
= \frac{\partial f}{\partial x_j}(x) - \sum_{k=0}^{l} \frac{1}{(k+1)!} \sum_{|\beta|=k} \frac{(k+1)!}{\beta!} \partial^\beta \frac{\partial f}{\partial x_j}(x^0)(x - x^0)^\beta
$$

$$
= \frac{\partial f}{\partial x_j}(x) - \sum_{k=0}^{l} \frac{1}{k!} \sum_{|\beta|=k} \frac{k!}{\beta!} \partial^\beta \frac{\partial f}{\partial x_j}(x^0)(x - x^0)^\beta,
$$

where $\beta = \alpha - 1 \cdot \vec{e}_j = (\alpha_1, \alpha_2, \ldots, \alpha_j - 1, \ldots, \alpha_n)$ and

$$
\frac{\alpha_j}{\alpha!} = \frac{1}{(\alpha - 1 \cdot \vec{e}_j)!}.
$$

Applying now the induction hypothesis to the function $\frac{\partial f}{\partial x_j}$ we may conclude that

$$
\frac{\partial}{\partial x_j} R_{l+1}(f,x) = R_l\left(\frac{\partial f}{\partial x_j}, x\right) = o(|x - x^0|^l).
$$

Since $R_{l+1}(f, x^0) = 0$, by using Corollary 13.71 we obtain

$$
R_{l+1}(f,x) = R_{l+1}(f,x) - R_{l+1}(f,x^0)
$$
$$
= (\nabla R_{l+1}(f,\xi), x - x^0)_{\mathbb{R}^n} = o(|x - x^0|^l)|x - x_0| = o(|x - x^0|^{l+1}),
$$

where $\xi = x^0 + \theta(x - x^0)$ with $0 < \theta < 1$. Hence, this corollary is completely proved. $\blacksquare$

Taylor expansions and differentials of first and higher order allow one to study the question of maxima and minima for real-valued functions of several variables.

**Definition 13.74.** *Let a scalar function* $f : X \subset \mathbb{R}^n \to \mathbb{R}$ *be defined on an open set* $X$ *and let* $x^0 \in X$. *Then* $x^0$ *is called a point of* local minima (local maxima) *for* $f$ *if there is* $B_\delta(x^0) \subset X, \delta > 0$, *such that* $f(x) \geq f(x^0)$ $(f(x) \leq f(x^0))$ *for all* $x \in B_\delta(x^0)$.

**Theorem 13.75 (Necessary condition of local extrema).** *Let* $f : X \subset \mathbb{R}^n \to \mathbb{R}$, *where* $X$ *is an open set, and let* $x^0 \in X$. *If the gradient* $\nabla f(x^0)$ *exists and* $x^0$ *is a point of local extrema then* $\nabla f(x^0) = 0$.

**Proof.** Let us introduce for each $j = 1, 2, \ldots, n$ the function of one variable $t$ by

$$
g_j(t) := f(x^0 + te_j), \quad |t| < \delta.
$$

Then $t = 0$ is a one-dimensional point of local extrema for each function $g_j(t), j = 1, 2, \ldots, n$. Using a necessary condition of local extrema for the one-dimensional case we have that $g_j'(0) = 0$, if it exists. But $g_j'(0) = \frac{\partial f}{\partial x_j}(x^0)$, which exists. Thus $\nabla f(x^0) = 0$, and this theorem is proved.

**Example 13.76.** Let

$$f(x) = \frac{x_1 x_2}{x_1^2 + x_2^2}, \quad x^0 = (0,0), \quad f(x^0) = 0.$$

Then obviously

$$\frac{\partial f}{\partial x_1}(x^0) = \frac{\partial f}{\partial x_2}(x^0) = 0,$$

i.e., $\nabla f(x^0) = 0$. But $x^0$ is not a point of local extrema since $x_1 x_2$ has different sign in the neighborhood of $x^0 = (0,0)$.

If a function $f : X \subset \mathbb{R}^n \to \mathbb{R}$ defined on an open set $X$ has the second differential at the point $x^0 \in X$ then it can be represented as

$$d^2 f(x^0) = \sum_{|\alpha|=2} \frac{2}{\alpha!} \partial^\alpha f(x^0) h^\alpha = (Ah, h)_{\mathbb{R}^n}, \quad h = x - x^0,$$

where $A$ is the matrix $\{a_{jk}\}_{j,k=1}^n$ of order $n \times n$ such that

$$a_{jk} = \frac{\partial^2 f(x^0)}{\partial x_j \partial x_k} = \frac{\partial^2 f(x^0)}{\partial x_k \partial x_j} = a_{kj},$$

i.e., the matrix $A$ is symmetric and $d^2 f(x^0)$ is a symmetric quadratic form with respect to $h \in \mathbb{R}^n$. We recall that a quadratic form $(Ah, h)_{\mathbb{R}^n}$ is said to be

1. *positive* if $(Ah, h)_{\mathbb{R}^n} > 0$ for all $h \neq 0$,

2. *negative* if $(Ah, h)_{\mathbb{R}^n} < 0$ for all $h \neq 0$,

3. *alternating* if there are $h' \neq 0 \neq h''$ such that $(Ah'', h'')_{\mathbb{R}^n} < 0 < (Ah', h')_{\mathbb{R}^n}$.

**Remark 13.77.** There is the *Sylvester criterion* of the certainty (definiteness) of the quadratic form $(Ah, h)_{\mathbb{R}^n}$ in terms of minors of matrix $A$. Namely, the quadratic form $(Ah, h)_{\mathbb{R}^n}$ is positive (negative) if and only if $A_1 > 0, A_2 > 0, \ldots, A_n > 0$ ($A_1 < 0, A_2 > 0, \ldots, (-1)^n A_n > 0$), where $A_j$ are the major minors of order $j$ of the matrix $A$.

**Theorem 13.78 (Sufficient condition of local extrema).** *Let function* $f : X \subset \mathbb{R}^n \to \mathbb{R}$ *be defined on an open set* $X$, *and assume it is twice differentiable at the point* $x^0 \in$ *such that* $\nabla f(x^0) = 0$ *and* $d^2 f(x^0)$ *is sign-definite. Then* $x^0$ *is a point of local extrema. More precisely, if* $d^2 f(x^0)$ *is positive (negative) then* $x^0$ *is a point of local minima (local maxima). In addition, if* $d^2 f(x^0)$ *is alternating then there is no local extrema at* $x^0$.

***Proof.*** Since $f$ is twice differentiable at the point $x^0 \in X$, by using Corollary 13.73 we have that

$$f(x) = f(x^0) + df(x^0) + \frac{1}{2} d^2 f(x^0) + o(|h|^2), \quad h = x - x^0 \neq 0.$$

The conditions of this theorem imply that

$$f(x) - f(x^0) = \frac{1}{2}(Ah, h)_{\mathbb{R}^n} + o(|h|^2) = \frac{|h|^2}{2}\left((A\frac{h}{|h|}, \frac{h}{|h|})_{\mathbb{R}^n} + o_h(1)\right)$$

$$= \frac{|h|^2}{2}\left((A\theta, \theta)_{\mathbb{R}^n} + o_h(1)\right), \quad |\theta| = 1.$$

Considering continuous function $F(\theta) := (A\theta, \theta)_{\mathbb{R}^n}$ on the unit sphere we can conclude by the Weierstrass theorems that there exist

$$\min_{\theta \in S^{n-1}} F(\theta) = F(\theta'), \quad \max_{\theta \in S^{n-1}} F(\theta) = F(\theta'')$$

for some $\theta', \theta''$ on the unit sphere. If $\mathrm{d}^2 f(x^0)$ is positive (negative) then $F(\theta')$ is positive ($F(\theta'')$ is negative) and $f(x) - f(x^0) \geq \frac{|h|^2}{2}(F(\theta') + o_h(1))$ ($f(x) - f(x^0) \leq \frac{|h|^2}{2}(F(\theta'') + o_h(1))$). Choosing $h \neq 0$ small enough, we obtain for all $x \in B_\delta(x^0) \subset X$ (with $\delta > 0$ small enough) that $f(x) - f(x^0) > 0$ ($f(x) - f(x^0) < 0$). Hence, $x^0$ is a point of local minima (local maxima). Since there is a strict inequality in both cases, $x^0$ is a point of strict local extrema.

In the case when $\mathrm{d}^2 f(x^0)$ is alternating there are $h' \neq 0 \neq h''$ such that $(Ah'', h'')_{\mathbb{R}^n} < 0 < (Ah', h')_{\mathbb{R}^n}$. Denoting by $\theta' = h'/|h'|$ and $\theta'' = h''/|h''|$ the unit vectors we have first that $(A\theta', \theta')_{\mathbb{R}^n} > 0$ and $(A\theta'', \theta'')_{\mathbb{R}^n} < 0$, and second,

$$f(x^0 + t\theta') - f(x^0) = \frac{t^2}{2}\left((A\theta', \theta')_{\mathbb{R}^n} + o_t(1)\right) > 0$$

and

$$f(x^0 + t\theta'') - f(x^0) = \frac{t^2}{2}\left((A\theta'', \theta'')_{\mathbb{R}^n} + o_t(1)\right) < 0$$

for $t \in \mathbb{R}$ small enough. It shows that there is no local extrema at the point $x^0$. Theorem 13.78 is completely proved.

**Example 13.79.** Let

$$f(x_1, x_2) = x_1 x_2 + \frac{a}{x_1} + \frac{b}{x_2}, \quad a \neq 0 \neq b.$$

Then the candidates for the points of local extrema are the solutions of the system

$$\frac{\partial f}{\partial x_1} = x_2 - \frac{a}{x_1^2} = 0, \quad \frac{\partial f}{\partial x_2} = x_1 - \frac{b}{x_1^2} = 0$$

or

$$x_1^0 = \frac{a}{(ab)^{1/3}}, \quad x_2^0 = \frac{b}{(ab)^{1/3}}.$$

The second differential at this point $x^0 = (x_1^0, x_2^0)$ is

$$\mathrm{d}^2 f(x^0) = \frac{2a}{\left(\frac{a}{(ab)^{1/3}}\right)^3}h_1^2 + 2h_1 h_2 + \frac{2b}{\left(\frac{b}{(ab)^{1/3}}\right)^3}h_2^2 = \frac{2b}{a}\left(h_1^2 + \frac{a}{b}h_1 h_2 + \left(\frac{a}{b}\right)^2 h_2^2\right).$$

This implies that $\mathrm{d}^2 f(x^0) > 0$ ($\mathrm{d}^2 f(x^0) < 0$) if $b/a > 0$ ($b/a < 0$). Hence, for $b/a > 0$ ($b/a < 0$) a point $x^0$ is a point of local minima (local maxima).

**Exercise 13.80.**    1. Prove that in the two-dimensional case $x^0$ is a point of local extrema if and only if $B^2 - AC < 0$ and either $A > 0$ or $A < 0$, where

$$A = \frac{\partial^2 f}{\partial x_1^2}(x^0), \quad B = \frac{\partial^2 f}{\partial x_1 \partial x_2}(x^0), \quad C = \frac{\partial^2 f}{\partial x_2^2}(x^0).$$

2. Investigate the function

$$f(x_1, x_2) = ax_1^2 + bx_1 x_2 + cx_2^2$$

for a local extrema depending on the real parameters $a$, $b$, and $c$.

3. Investigate the functions

$$f(x_1, x_2) = ax_1^3 + bx_1^2 x_2 + cx_2^3$$

and

$$f(x_1, x_2) = ax_1^3 + bx_1 x_2^2 + cx_2^3$$

for a local extrema depending on the real parameters $a$, $b$, and $c$.

4. Investigate the following functions for local extremas:

(a) $f(x_1, x_2) = (4x_1^2 + x_2^2)e^{-x_1^2 - 4x_2^2}$.

(b) $f(x_1, x_2) = x_1^3 + x_2^3 - x_1 - x_2$.

(c) $f(x_1, x_2) = x_1^2 - x_2 + 1$.

(d) $f(x_1, x_2) = x_1^2 + \gamma \cos x_2$, where $\gamma$ is a real parameter.

(e) $f(x_1, x_2) = \sin(x_1^2 + x_2) + x_2$.

(f) $f(x_1, x_2) = \cos x_1 \cos x_2 e^{-x_1^2 - x_2^2}$.

(g) $f(x_1, x_2) = a \log x_1 + b \log x_2 + cx_1 + dx_2$, where $a, b, c, d$ are real parameters.

(h) $f(x_1, x_2) = a|x_1| + b|x_2|$, where $a, b$ are real parameters.

(i) $f(x_1, x_2) = ax_1^2 + b|x_1||x_2| + cx_2^2$, where $a, b$ are real parameters.

# Chapter 14

# Implicit functions

In multivariable analysis the concept of implicit function shows the relations (equations) to be converted to functions of several real variables. It does so by representing the relation as the graph of a function. There may not be a single function whose graph can represent the entire relation but there may be such a function on a restriction of the domain or relation. The implicit function theorem gives a sufficient condition to ensure that there is such a function. These types of functions generally cannot be expressed in closed form; they are implicitly defined by equations and this motivates the name of the theorem. In addition, this theorem shows when an inverse function exists and how the derivative of an inverse function can be calculated in terms of the derivative of given function. This theorem also allows us to investigate quite effectively the question of dependence (not necessarily linear) of differentiable functions.

**Theorem 14.1 (Implicit function theorem I).** *Let a scalar function $F : \widetilde{X} \subset \mathbb{R}^{n+1} \to \mathbb{R}, n \geq 1$, be defined on an open set $\widetilde{X}$ and differentiable in some neighborhood $B_{\widetilde{\delta}}(x^0, u_0) \subset \widetilde{X}$, where $x^0 \in \mathbb{R}^n, u_0 \in \mathbb{R}$. Assume that the derivative $\frac{\partial F}{\partial u}(x, u)$ is continuous at the point $(x^0, u_0)$. If $F(x^0, u_0) = 0$ and $\frac{\partial F}{\partial u}(x^0, u_0) \neq 0$ then there is a neighborhood $B_\delta(x^0)$ such that there exists a unique function $u = f(x)$ which converts the equation $F(x, u) = 0$ into the identity $F(x, f(x)) = 0$ for all $x \in B_\delta(x^0)$. Moreover, the function $f$ is differentiable in $B_\delta(x^0)$, and*

$$\frac{\partial f}{\partial x_j}(x) = -\frac{\frac{\partial F}{\partial x_j}(x, f(x))}{\frac{\partial F}{\partial u}(x, f(x))}, \quad x \in B_\delta(x^0),$$

*for all $j = 1, 2, \ldots, n$.*

***Proof.*** We accompany the proof with a geometric illustration shown in Figure 14.1.

We assume for definiteness that $\frac{\partial F}{\partial u}(x^0, u_0) > 0$. Then due to continuity of $\frac{\partial F}{\partial u}(x, u)$ at the point $(x^0, u_0)$ there is a neighborhood $B_{\widetilde{\delta}}(x^0, u_0)$ such that $\frac{\partial F}{\partial u}(x, u) > 0$ for all $(x, u) \in B_{\widetilde{\delta}}(x^0, u_0)$. Let us fix now $\varepsilon > 0$ such that $(x^0, u_0 - \varepsilon), (x^0, u_0 + \varepsilon) \in B_{\widetilde{\delta}}(x^0, u_0)$. Hence, any point $(x^0, u)$ with $u \in [u_0 - \varepsilon, u_0 + \varepsilon]$ belongs to $B_{\widetilde{\delta}}(x^0, u_0)$. For these values of $u$ we introduce a function $g$ of one variable as

$$g(u) := F(x^0, u), \quad u \in [u_0 - \varepsilon, u_0 + \varepsilon].$$

Since $g'(u) = \frac{\partial F}{\partial u}(x^0, u) > 0$ for all $u \in [u_0 - \varepsilon, u_0 + \varepsilon]$, $g(u)$ is increasing on this closed interval. Since $g(u_0) = F(x^0, u_0) = 0$, $g(u_0 - \varepsilon) < 0$ and $g(u_0 + \varepsilon) > 0$. Let us consider now

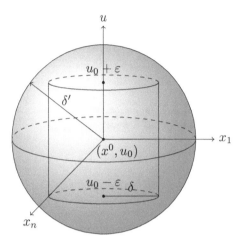

**Figure 14.1.** *Illustration of neighborhood $B_{\tilde{\delta}}(x^0, u_0)$.*

two multivariable functions $\varphi_1$ and $\varphi_2$ as

$$\varphi_1(x) := F(x, u_0 - \varepsilon), \quad \varphi_2(x) := F(x, u_0 + \varepsilon).$$

Due to differentiability of $F(x, u)$ in $B_{\tilde{\delta}}(x^0, u_0)$, functions $\varphi_1$ and $\varphi_2$ are continuous in $B_\delta(x^0)$. Moreover,

$$\varphi_1(x^0) = g(u_0 - \varepsilon) < 0, \quad \varphi_2(x^0) = g(u_0 + \varepsilon) > 0.$$

This implies that there is a neighborhood $B_{\delta_1}(x^0) \subset B_\delta(x^0)$ such that $\varphi_1(x) < 0$ and $\varphi_2(x) > 0$ for all $x \in B_{\delta_1}(x^0)$. Hence, for any fixed $x \in B_{\delta_1}(x^0)$ there exists a unique $u \in [u_0 - \varepsilon, u_0 + \varepsilon]$ such that $F(x, u) = 0$. Indeed, the existence of such a $u$ (for given $x$) follows from the property of continuous functions passing zero when changing sign, and uniqueness of such a $u$ follows from the monotonicity of $F(x, u)$ with respect to $u$. By this correspondence between $x$ and $u$ a function $u = f(x)$ is uniquely determined and converts the equation $F(x, u) = 0$ in $B_{\tilde{\delta}}(x^0, u_0)$ into the identity $F(x, f(x)) = 0$ in $B_{\delta_1}(x^0)$. It is clear by construction that the function $u = f(x)$ is continuous at $x^0$ since $|u - u_0| < \varepsilon$ with arbitrary $\varepsilon > 0$.

   In order to prove differentiability of $u = f(x)$ we consider $x, x + h \in B_{\delta_1}(x^0)$. Then the identity $F(x, f(x)) = 0$ implies

$$0 = F(x + h, u + H) - F(x, u) = \left( \frac{\partial F}{\partial x}(x, u), h \right)_{\mathbb{R}^n} + \frac{\partial F}{\partial u}(x, u)H + o(\sqrt{|h|^2 + H^2}),$$

where $H = f(x + h) - f(x)$. This equality can be rewritten as

$$\left( \frac{\partial F}{\partial u}(x, u) + o(1) \right) H = -\left( \frac{\partial F}{\partial x}(x, u), h \right)_{\mathbb{R}^n} + o(|h|)$$

because $H \to 0$ as $h \to 0$. Next,

$$f(x + h) - f(x) = H = -\frac{(\frac{\partial F}{\partial x}(x, u), h)_{\mathbb{R}^n} + o(|h|)}{\frac{\partial F}{\partial u}(x, u) + o(1)} = -\frac{(\frac{\partial F}{\partial x}(x, u), h)_{\mathbb{R}^n}}{\frac{\partial F}{\partial u}(x, u)} + o(|h|).$$

This means, by the definition of differentiability, that

$$\frac{\partial f}{\partial x}(x) = \nabla_x f(x) = - \left. \frac{\nabla_x F(x,u)}{\frac{\partial F}{\partial u}(x,u)} \right|_{u=f(x)}.$$

Theorem 14.1 is completely proved.

**Remark 14.2.** The latter formula can be obtained (formally) by the differentiation of the identity $F(x, f(x)) = 0$. Indeed,

$$0 = \frac{\partial}{\partial x_j}\left(F(x, f(x))\right) = \frac{\partial F}{\partial x_j}(x, f(x)) + \frac{\partial F}{\partial u}(x, f(x))\frac{\partial f}{\partial x_j},$$

which is equivalent to

$$\frac{\partial f(x)}{\partial x_j} = -\frac{\frac{\partial F}{\partial x_j}(x, f(x))}{\frac{\partial F}{\partial u}(x, f(x))}.$$

**Exercise 14.3.** Find the derivatives

$$\frac{\partial^2 f(x)}{\partial x_k \partial x_j}$$

of the implicit function using the procedure from the latter remark.

Implicit function theorem I can be generalized to system of equations, i.e., to the vector-valued functions. Namely, we consider a vector-valued function

$$\overrightarrow{F} : \widetilde{X} \subset \mathbb{R}^{n+m} \to \mathbb{R}^m,$$

where $\widetilde{X}$ is an open set of elements $(x, u), x \in \mathbb{R}^n, u \in \mathbb{R}^m$ and the relation $\overrightarrow{F}(x, u) = 0$ or $F_k(x, u) = 0, k = 1, 2, \ldots, m$. The main goal is to find (to prove existence of) a vector-valued function $u = \overrightarrow{f}(x)$ such that $\overrightarrow{f} : X \subset \mathbb{R}^n \to \mathbb{R}^m$ and $\overrightarrow{F}(x, \overrightarrow{f}(x)) = 0$. For these purposes we introduce the determinant

$$\det \frac{\partial \overrightarrow{F}}{\partial u} := \det \begin{pmatrix} \frac{\partial F_1}{\partial u_1} & \cdots & \frac{\partial F_1}{\partial u_m} \\ \vdots & \ddots & \vdots \\ \frac{\partial F_m}{\partial u_1} & \cdots & \frac{\partial F_m}{\partial u_m} \end{pmatrix} = \frac{\partial(F_1, \ldots, F_m)}{\partial(u_1, \ldots, u_m)}.$$

**Theorem 14.4 (Implicit function theorem II).** *Let a vector-valued function $\overrightarrow{F} : \widetilde{X} \subset \mathbb{R}^{n+m} \to \mathbb{R}^m$ be defined on an open set $\widetilde{X}$ and assume that it is continuously differentiable in some neighborhood $B_{\widetilde{\delta}}(x^0, u^0) \subset \widetilde{X}$. Let also $\overrightarrow{F}(x^0, u^0) = 0$ and $\det \frac{\partial \overrightarrow{F}}{\partial u}(x^0, u^0) \neq 0$. Then there is some neighborhood $B_\delta(x^0)$ of the point $x^0$ such that there exists a unique vector-valued function $u = \overrightarrow{f}(x)$ which converts the equation $\overrightarrow{F}(x, u) = 0$ into the identity $\overrightarrow{F}(x, \overrightarrow{f}(x)) = 0, x \in B_\delta(x^0)$. Moreover, the function $\overrightarrow{f}$ is differentiable and*

$$\frac{\partial f_k(x)}{\partial x_j} = -\frac{\frac{\partial(F_1, \ldots, F_m)}{\partial(u_1, \ldots, u_{k-1}, x_j, u_{k+1}, \ldots, u_m)}}{\frac{\partial(F_1, \ldots, F_m)}{\partial(u_1, \ldots, u_m)}}.$$

*for each $k = 1, 2, \ldots, m$ and $j = 1, 2, \ldots, n$.*

**Proof.** We employ mathematical induction with respect to $m$. For $m = 1$ the statement is true since this is just Theorem 14.1. Let us assume that the statement is valid for $m - 1$ with $m \geq 2$ and consider the statement for $m$. Due to conditions of this theorem we have

$$\det \frac{\partial \overrightarrow{F}}{\partial u}(x^0, u^0) = \begin{vmatrix} \frac{\partial F_1}{\partial u_1} & \cdots & \frac{\partial F_1}{\partial u_{m-1}} & \frac{\partial F_1}{\partial u_m} \\ \vdots & \ddots & \vdots & \vdots \\ \frac{\partial F_{m-1}}{\partial u_1} & \cdots & \frac{\partial F_{m-1}}{\partial u_{m-1}} & \frac{\partial F_{m-1}}{\partial u_m} \\ \frac{\partial F_m}{\partial u_1} & \cdots & \frac{\partial F_m}{\partial u_{m-1}} & \frac{\partial F_m}{\partial u_m} \end{vmatrix} \neq 0.$$

Since the determinant of order $m$ is not equal to zero, there is at least one minor of order $m - 1$ which is not equal to zero. We may assume without loss of generality that this nonzero minor of order $m - 1$ is a central (main) minor. Consider first $m - 1$ coordinates (equations) of the relation $\overrightarrow{F}(x, u) = 0$, i.e.,

$$\begin{cases} F_1(x, u_1, \ldots, u_{m-1}, u_m) = 0 \\ \vdots \\ F_{m-1}(x, u_1, \ldots, u_{m-1}, u_m) = 0 \end{cases}$$

with respect to $n + 1$ independent variables $(x, u_m)$. By the induction hypothesis there is a neighborhood $B_{\widetilde{\delta}}(x^0, u_m^0)$ of the point $(x^0, u_m^0)$ such that there exists a unique vector-valued function $\overrightarrow{\phi}(x, u_m)$ which converts the first $m - 1$ equations of $\overrightarrow{F}(x, u)$ into the identity

$$\begin{cases} F_1(x, \phi_1, \ldots, \phi_{m-1}, u_m) = 0 \\ \vdots \\ F_{m-1}(x, \phi_1, \ldots, \phi_{m-1}, u_m) = 0 \end{cases}$$

and the $m$th equation of $\overrightarrow{F}(x, u)$ into the function depending on $(x, u_m)$:

$$F_m(x, \phi_1, \ldots, \phi_{m-1}, u_m) =: \Psi(x, u_m).$$

To prove the statement it remains to solve the equation $\Psi(x, u_m) = 0$ with respect to $u_m$. In order to apply Theorem 14.1 we have to check its conditions. Indeed, we have the following:

1. $\Psi(x^0, u_m^0) = 0$ if and only if $F_m(x^0, u_m^0) = 0$ or
   $$F_m(x^0, \phi_1(x^0, u_m^0), \ldots, \phi_{m-1}(x^0, u_m^0), u_m^0) = 0.$$

2. $\Psi(x, u_m)$ is continuously differentiable as the superposition of continuously differentiable functions, and its derivative with respect to $u_m$ is equal to
   $$\frac{\partial \Psi}{\partial u_m} = \frac{\partial F_m}{\partial u_m} + \frac{\partial F_m}{\partial u_1}\frac{\partial \phi_1}{\partial u_m} + \cdots + \frac{\partial F_m}{\partial u_{m-1}}\frac{\partial \phi_{m-1}}{\partial u_m}.$$

3. That $\frac{\partial \Psi}{\partial u_m}(x^0, u_m^0) \neq 0$ can be checked as follows: differentiating the first $m - 1$ identities and $m$th equation with respect to $u_m$ one can obtain
   $$\begin{cases} \frac{\partial F_1}{\partial u_1}\frac{\partial \phi_1}{\partial u_m} + \cdots + \frac{\partial F_1}{\partial u_{m-1}}\frac{\partial \phi_{m-1}}{\partial u_m} + \frac{\partial F_1}{\partial u_m} = 0 \\ \vdots \\ \frac{\partial F_{m-1}}{\partial u_1}\frac{\partial \phi_1}{\partial u_m} + \cdots + \frac{\partial F_{m-1}}{\partial u_{m-1}}\frac{\partial \phi_{m-1}}{\partial u_m} + \frac{\partial F_{m-1}}{\partial u_m} = 0 \\ \frac{\partial F_m}{\partial u_1}\frac{\partial \phi_1}{\partial u_m} + \cdots + \frac{\partial F_m}{\partial u_{m-1}}\frac{\partial \phi_{m-1}}{\partial u_m} + \frac{\partial F_m}{\partial u_m} = \frac{\partial \Psi}{\partial u_m}. \end{cases}$$

Using shorter notation this system can be written as

$$
\begin{cases}
\dfrac{\partial \overrightarrow{F}}{\partial \widetilde{u}} \dfrac{\partial \overrightarrow{\phi}}{\partial u_m} + \dfrac{\partial \overrightarrow{F}}{\partial u_m} = 0, \\[2mm]
\dfrac{\partial F_m}{\partial \widetilde{u}} \dfrac{\partial \overrightarrow{\phi}}{\partial u_m} + \dfrac{\partial F_m}{\partial u_m} = \dfrac{\partial \Psi}{\partial u_m},
\end{cases}
$$

where $\overrightarrow{F} = (F_1, \ldots, F_{m-1})$, $\widetilde{u} = (u_1, \ldots, u_{m-1})$, and $\overrightarrow{\phi} = (\phi_1, \ldots, \phi_{m-1})$. Since $\det \dfrac{\partial \overrightarrow{F}}{\partial \widetilde{u}} \neq 0$ (by the conditions), the first vector-valued equation can be solved as

$$
\frac{\partial \overrightarrow{\phi}}{\partial u_m} = - \left( \frac{\partial \overrightarrow{F}}{\partial \widetilde{u}} \right)^{-1} \frac{\partial \overrightarrow{F}}{\partial u_m},
$$

which implies that

$$
\frac{\partial \Psi}{\partial u_m} = - \frac{\partial F_m}{\partial \widetilde{u}} \left( \frac{\partial \overrightarrow{F}}{\partial \widetilde{u}} \right)^{-1} \frac{\partial \overrightarrow{F}}{\partial u_m} + \frac{\partial F_m}{\partial u_m}.
$$

Denoting by $\Delta_1, \Delta_2, \ldots, \Delta_m$ the algebraic complement of the elements of the last column of given determinant $\Delta$ of order $m$ which is not equal to zero, multiplying the first $m - 1$ identities by $\Delta_1, \Delta_2, \ldots, \Delta_{m-1}$, respectively, and the $m$th equation by $\Delta_m$ and then summing one obtains

$$
\sum_{k=1}^{m-1} \frac{\partial \phi_k}{\partial u_m} \left( \Delta_1 \frac{\partial F_1}{\partial u_k} + \cdots + \Delta_m \frac{\partial F_m}{\partial u_k} \right) + \Delta_1 \frac{\partial F_1}{\partial u_m} + \cdots + \Delta_m \frac{\partial F_m}{\partial u_m} = \Delta_m \frac{\partial \Psi}{\partial u_m}
$$

or

$$
\Delta = \Delta_m \frac{\partial \Psi}{\partial u_m}
$$

or

$$
\frac{\partial \Psi}{\partial u_m} = \frac{\Delta}{\Delta_m} \neq 0.
$$

Hence, all conditions of Theorem 14.1 are satisfied with respect to $\Psi$ and $u_m$, and therefore there is a neighborhood $B_\delta(x^0)$ of the point $x^0$ such that there exists a unique differentiable function $u_m = f_m(x)$ which converts the equation $\Psi(x, u_m) = 0$ into the identity $\Psi(x, f_m(x)) = 0$. The latter fact, together with the induction hypothesis, implies that the functions

$$
u_k := \phi_k(x, f_m(x)) = f_k(x), \quad k = 1, 2, \ldots, m - 1,
$$

convert the first $m - 1$ relations into the identities

$$
\overrightarrow{F}(x, \overrightarrow{\phi}(x, f_m(x)), f_m(x)) = 0, \quad x \in B_\delta(x^0),
$$

and the $m$th relation into the identity

$$
F_m(x, \overrightarrow{\phi}(x, f_m(x)), f_m(x)) = \Psi(x, f_m(x)) = 0.
$$

In summary we can see that the vector-valued function $\overrightarrow{f}(x)$ from above solves the equation $\overrightarrow{F}(x, u) = 0$ of order $m$ so that $\overrightarrow{F}(x, \overrightarrow{f}(x)) = 0$ for $x \in B_\delta(x^0)$. It remains only to calculate the derivatives $\frac{\partial f_k}{\partial x_j}(x), j = 1, 2, \ldots, n, k = 1, 2, \ldots, m$. Differentiating these $m$ identities with respect to $x_j$ we obtain

$$\frac{\partial \overrightarrow{F}}{\partial x_j}(x, \overrightarrow{f}(x)) + \frac{\partial \overrightarrow{F}}{\partial u}(x, \overrightarrow{f}(x)) \frac{\partial \overrightarrow{f}(x)}{\partial x_j} = 0$$

or

$$\frac{\partial \overrightarrow{f}(x)}{\partial x_j} = -\left(\frac{\partial \overrightarrow{F}}{\partial u}(x, \overrightarrow{f}(x))\right)^{-1} \frac{\partial \overrightarrow{F}}{\partial x_j}(x, \overrightarrow{f}(x))$$

$$= -\frac{\frac{\partial(F_1, F_2, \ldots, F_m)}{\partial(u_1, \ldots, u_{k-1}, x_j, u_{k+1}, \ldots, u_m)}}{\frac{\partial(F_1, F_2, \ldots, F_m)}{\partial(u_1, u_2, \ldots, u_m)}},$$

which is just the well-known Cramer's rule from linear algebra. Thus, the theorem is completely proved.

**Corollary 14.5 (Existence of inverse function).** *Let a vector-valued function $\overrightarrow{f} : X \subset \mathbb{R}^n \to \mathbb{R}^n$ be defined on an open set $X$ and be continuously differentiable in some neighborhood $B_\delta(x^0) \subset X$ of a point $x^0$. If*

$$\det \frac{\partial \overrightarrow{f}}{\partial x}(x^0) \neq 0$$

*then there exists a unique function $(\overrightarrow{f})^{-1}$ which is inverse to $\overrightarrow{f}$ in $B_\delta(x^0)$, i.e.,*

$$x = (\overrightarrow{f})^{-1}(\overrightarrow{f}(x)), \quad x \in B_\delta(x^0),$$

*and*

$$u = \overrightarrow{f}((\overrightarrow{f})^{-1}(u)), \quad u \in \overrightarrow{f}(B_\delta(x^0)).$$

*Moreover, this inverse function $(\overrightarrow{f})^{-1}$ is continuously differentiable, and*

$$\frac{\partial (\overrightarrow{f})^{-1}(u)}{\partial u} = \left(\frac{\partial \overrightarrow{f}}{\partial x}\right)^{-1}$$

*or*

$$\frac{\partial \overrightarrow{f}(x)}{\partial x} = \left(\frac{\partial (\overrightarrow{f})^{-1}(u)}{\partial u}\right)^{-1}\Bigg|_{u = f(x)}$$

*in terms of corresponding matrices.*

***Proof.*** The proof follows straightforwardly from Theorem 14.4. Indeed, the equality $u = \overrightarrow{f}(x)$ can be rewritten as $\overrightarrow{F}(x, u) := \overrightarrow{f}(x) - u = 0$. Here $\overrightarrow{F}$ is continuously differentiable with respect to $x, u$ since $\overrightarrow{f}$ is continuously differentiable. Furthermore,

1. $\overrightarrow{F}(x^0, u^0) = 0$ if and only if $u^0 = \overrightarrow{f}(x^0)$,

2. since $\frac{\partial \overrightarrow{F}}{\partial x}(x, u) = \frac{\partial \overrightarrow{f}}{\partial x}(x)$ and $\det \frac{\partial \overrightarrow{f}}{\partial x}(x^0) \neq 0$, $\det \frac{\partial \overrightarrow{F}}{\partial x}(x^0, u^0) \neq 0$,

3. $\frac{\partial \overrightarrow{F}}{\partial x}(x, u)$ is continuous in $B_\delta(x^0)$ since $\frac{\partial \overrightarrow{f}}{\partial x}(x)$ is.

Applying Theorem 14.4 with respect to $x$ we obtain that in the neighborhood $V(u^0) = \overrightarrow{f}(B_\delta(x^0))$ there exists a unique continuously differentiable function $\overrightarrow{\phi}(u)$ such that $\overrightarrow{F}(\overrightarrow{\phi}(u), u) = 0$. The function $\overrightarrow{\phi}(u)$ is said to be an inverse function to $\overrightarrow{f}(x)$ and is denoted as $x = (\overrightarrow{f})^{-1}(u)$. It is clear that

$$\overrightarrow{f}((\overrightarrow{f})^{-1}(u)) - u \equiv 0, \quad (\overrightarrow{f})^{-1}(\overrightarrow{f}(x)) - x \equiv 0.$$

Moreover,

$$\frac{\partial}{\partial u}(\overrightarrow{F}(\overrightarrow{\phi}(u), u)) \equiv 0$$

or

$$\frac{\partial}{\partial u}(\overrightarrow{f}(\overrightarrow{\phi}(u)) - u) \equiv 0$$

or

$$\frac{\partial \overrightarrow{f}}{\partial x}\frac{\partial \overrightarrow{\phi}}{\partial u} - Id \equiv 0$$

or

$$\left.\frac{\partial \overrightarrow{\phi}}{\partial u}\right|_{u = \overrightarrow{f}(x)} = \left(\frac{\partial \overrightarrow{f}(x)}{\partial x}\right)^{-1}$$

or

$$\frac{\partial \overrightarrow{f}(x)}{\partial x} = \left.\left(\frac{\partial \overrightarrow{\phi}(u)}{\partial u}\right)^{-1}\right|_{u = \overrightarrow{f}(x)}.$$

This finishes the proof.

These theorems give a direction to investigate very applicable problems called "dependence of functions."

**Definition 14.6.** *Let a vector-valued function* $\overrightarrow{f} = (u_1, u_2, \ldots, u_m) : X \subset \mathbb{R}^n \to \mathbb{R}^m$ *be continuously differentiable on an open set $X$. Then*

1. *a function $u_{k_0}(x)$, $k_0 \in \{1, 2, \ldots, m\}$, is said to be* dependent *on the remaining functions $\{u_k(x)\}_{k=1}^m$ on $X$ if there is a continuously differentiable $\Phi : \mathbb{R}^{m-1} \to \mathbb{R}$ such that $u_{k_0}(x) = \Phi(u_1(x), \ldots, u_{k_0-1}(x), u_{k_0+1}(x), \ldots, u_m(x))$ for all $x \in X$;*

2. *the collection of functions $\{u_k(x)\}_{k=1}^m$ is said to be dependent on $X$ if there is $k_0$ such that $u_{k_0}(x)$ is dependent on the remaining functions $\{u_k(x)\}_{k=1}^m$;*

3. *the collection of functions $\{u_k(x)\}_{k=1}^m$ is said to be* independent *on $X$ if there is no continuously differentiable $\Phi : \mathbb{R}^{m-1} \to \mathbb{R}$ such that part 2 holds.*

**Theorem 14.7 (Sufficient condition of independence).** *Under the conditions of Definition 14.6 we assume that $n \geq m$. If the determinant*

$$\frac{\partial(u_1, u_2, \ldots, u_m)}{\partial(x_{j_1}, x_{j_2}, \ldots, x_{j_m})} \neq 0, \quad x \in B_\delta(x^0) \subset X,$$

*with respect to every $m$ variables of given $n$ variables then the collection of functions $\{u_k(x)\}_{k=1}^m$ is independent on $B_\delta(x^0)$.*

***Proof.*** We assume for definiteness and without loss of generality that

$$\frac{\partial(u_1, u_2, \ldots, u_m)}{\partial(x_1, x_2, \ldots, x_m)} \neq 0, \quad x \in B_\delta(x^0) \subset X.$$

Next, assume on the contrary that there exists a continuously differentiable function $\Phi : \mathbb{R}^{m-1} \to \mathbb{R}$ such that

$$u_{k_0}(x) = \Phi(u_1(x), \ldots, u_{k_0-1}(x), u_{k_0+1}(x), \ldots, u_m(x))$$

is an identity on $B_\delta(x^0)$. Differentiating this identity with respect to $x_j, j = 1, 2, \ldots, m$, we obtain that

$$\frac{\partial u_k}{\partial x_j} = \frac{\partial \Phi}{\partial u_1}\frac{\partial u_1}{\partial x_j} + \cdots + \frac{\partial \Phi}{\partial u_{k_0-1}}\frac{\partial u_{k_0-1}}{\partial x_j} + \frac{\partial \Phi}{\partial u_{k_0+1}}\frac{\partial u_{k_0+1}}{\partial x_j} + \cdots + \frac{\partial \Phi}{\partial u_m}\frac{\partial u_m}{\partial x_j}.$$

These equalities can be interpreted as follows: row vector $\frac{\partial u_k}{\partial x}$ of the determinant

$$\frac{\partial(u_1, u_2, \ldots, u_m)}{\partial(x_1, x_2, \ldots, x_m)}$$

is a linear combination of the remaining rows. This means that the determinant is equal to zero. This contradiction proves the theorem.

Let us now remove the condition $n \geq m$ (see Theorem 14.7). In that case we deal with the full derivative $\frac{\partial \vec{f}}{\partial x}(x)$ which is the matrix of order $m \times n$,

$$\frac{\partial \vec{f}}{\partial x} = \begin{pmatrix} \frac{\partial u_1}{\partial x_1} & \cdots & \frac{\partial u_1}{\partial x_n} \\ \vdots & \ddots & \vdots \\ \frac{\partial u_m}{\partial x_1} & \cdots & \frac{\partial u_m}{\partial x_n} \end{pmatrix}.$$

**Theorem 14.8 (Sufficient condition of dependence).** *Let a vector-valued function $\vec{f} : X \subset \mathbb{R}^n \to \mathbb{R}^m$ be defined on an open set $X$ and be continuously differentiable in $B_\delta(x^0) \subset X$ with some $x^0 \in X$. Assume that there is a minor of order $r \leq \min(m, n)$ of the matrix $\frac{\partial \vec{f}}{\partial x}(x^0)$ which is not equal to zero, and all minors of order $r + 1$ of the matrix $\frac{\partial \vec{f}}{\partial x}(x)$ are identically equal to zero in $B_\delta(x^0)$. Then $r$ functions that define the nonzero minor of order $r$ are independent in $B_\delta(x^0)$, but each of the other functions is dependent on these $r$ functions in $B_\delta(x^0)$.*

*Proof.* We assume without loss of generality that

$$\frac{\partial(u_1, u_2, \ldots, u_r)}{\partial(x_1, x_2, \ldots, x_r)} \neq 0, \quad x \in B_\delta(x^0), \quad r \leq \min(m, n).$$

Hence, the independence of $u_1, u_2, \ldots, u_r$ in $B_\delta(x^0)$ follows from Theorem 14.7. Next, assume that $r < \min(m, n)$ (the case $r = \min(m, n)$ will be considered below). It remains to show that each of the functions $u_{r+1}, \ldots, u_m$ is dependent on $u_1, \ldots, u_r$. Let us consider the system

$$F_k(x, u_1, \ldots, u_r) := u_k(x) - u_k = 0, \quad k = 1, 2, \ldots, r.$$

Since

$$\frac{\partial(F_1, F_2, \ldots, F_r)}{\partial(x_1, x_2, \ldots, x_r)} = \frac{\partial(u_1, u_2, \ldots, u_r)}{\partial(x_1, x_2, \ldots, x_r)} \neq 0,$$

this system can be solved with respect to $x_1, \ldots, x_r$ (see Theorem 14.4) such that the relations

$$\begin{cases} x_1 = \varphi_1(u_1, \ldots, u_r, x_{r+1}, \ldots, x_n), \\ x_2 = \varphi_2(u_1, \ldots, u_r, x_{r+1}, \ldots, x_n), \\ \vdots \\ x_r = \varphi_r(u_1, \ldots, u_r, x_{r+1}, \ldots, x_n) \end{cases}$$

convert the equations mentioned above into the identities

$$u_k(\varphi_1, \ldots, \varphi_r, x_{r+1}, \ldots, x_n) - u_k \equiv 0, \quad k = 1, 2, \ldots, r.$$

Differentiating these identities with respect to $x_j, j = r+1, \ldots, n$, we obtain (taking into account that $u_1, u_2, \ldots, u_r, x_{r+1}, \ldots, x_n$ are independent variables here) that

$$\frac{\partial u_k}{\partial x_1}\frac{\partial \varphi_1}{\partial x_j} + \cdots + \frac{\partial u_k}{\partial x_r}\frac{\partial \varphi_r}{\partial x_j} + \frac{\partial u_k}{\partial x_j} \equiv 0, \quad k = 1, 2, \ldots, r, j = r+1, \ldots, n.$$

Note further that for

$$u_{r+1} = u_{r+1}(\varphi_1, \ldots, \varphi_r, x_{r+1}, \ldots, x_n) =: \Phi(u_1, \ldots, u_r, x_{r+1}, \ldots, x_n)$$

we have that

$$\frac{\partial \Phi}{\partial x_j} = \frac{\partial u_{r+1}}{\partial x_1}\frac{\partial \varphi_1}{\partial x_j} + \cdots + \frac{\partial u_{r+1}}{\partial x_r}\frac{\partial \varphi_r}{\partial x_j} + \frac{\partial u_{r+1}}{\partial x_j}.$$

By the conditions of this theorem we have the following determinant of order $r + 1$:

$$\begin{vmatrix} \frac{\partial u_1}{\partial x_1} & \cdots & \frac{\partial u_1}{\partial x_r} & \frac{\partial u_1}{\partial x_j} \\ \vdots & \ddots & \vdots & \vdots \\ \frac{\partial u_r}{\partial x_1} & \cdots & \frac{\partial u_r}{\partial x_r} & \frac{\partial u_r}{\partial x_j} \\ \frac{\partial u_{r+1}}{\partial x_1} & \cdots & \frac{\partial u_{r+1}}{\partial x_r} & \frac{\partial u_{r+1}}{\partial x_j} \end{vmatrix} \equiv 0,$$

with a nonzero central minor. Thus, it is easy to see that

$$0 \equiv \frac{\partial \Phi}{\partial x_j}\Delta_{r+1},$$

where $\Delta_{r+1}$ is the algebraic complement of $\frac{\partial u_{r+1}}{\partial x_j}$ in this determinant, i.e., central nonzero minor of order $r$, and therefore $\frac{\partial \Phi}{\partial x_j} \equiv 0$ in $B_\delta(x^0)$ for $j = r+1, \ldots, n$. This means that $\Phi(u_1, \ldots, u_r, x_{r+1}, \ldots, x_n)$ is independent on $x_j, j = r+1, \ldots, n$, i.e.,

$$u_{r+1} = \Phi(u_1, \ldots, u_r).$$

A similar proof takes place for each $u_{r+1}, \ldots, u_m$.

Assuming now that $r = \min(m, n)$ we have three possibilities: $r = m < n, r = n < m$, and $r = m = n$. In the first case we have no $u_{r+1}, \ldots, u_m$ at all. In the second case we have no $x_{r+1}, \ldots, x_n$ and thus the above proof is valid. The third case is equivalent to Corollary 14.5. Hence the theorem is completely proved.

## 14.1 ▪ Conditional extrema

Let a scalar function $f : X' \subset \mathbb{R}^{n+m} \to \mathbb{R}$ be defined on an open set $X'$ and continuously differentiable in $B_\delta(x^0, u^0) \subset X', x^0 \in \mathbb{R}^n, u^0 \in \mathbb{R}^m$. At the same time the variables $x, u$ are interconnected through a vector-valued function $\overrightarrow{F} : X' \subset \mathbb{R}^{n+m} \to \mathbb{R}^m$ such that $\overrightarrow{F}(x, u) = 0$. These relations are called *communication conditions*.

**Definition 14.9.** *A scalar function $f(x, u)$ defined on an open set $X'$ is said to have a* local *conditional maxima (minima) at the point $(x^0, u^0) \in X'$ if there exists $B_{\delta'}(x^0, u^0) \subset X'$ such that $f(x, u) \leq f(x^0, u^0)$ ($f(x, u) \geq f(x^0, u^0)$) for all $(x, u) \in B_{\delta'}(x^0, u^0)$ with $\overrightarrow{F}(x, u) = 0$.*

The next steps will be considered under the condition

$$\det \frac{\partial \overrightarrow{F}}{\partial u}(x, u) \neq 0, \quad (x, u) \in B_{\delta'}(x^0, u^0).$$

In this case, due to Theorem 14.4 the equation $\overrightarrow{F}(x, u) = 0$ can be uniquely solved with respect to $u$ in the neighborhood $B_{\delta'}(x^0, u^0)$ such that there is a unique continuously differentiable function $\overrightarrow{\phi}(x)$ which transforms the equation into the identity $\overrightarrow{F}(x, \overrightarrow{\phi}) = 0$ for all $x \in B_\delta(x^0)$. Due to this fact the problem of finding conditional local extrema for $f(x, u)$ can be reduced (at least formally) to the problem of finding ordinary extrema for the function

$$g(x) := f(x, \overrightarrow{\phi}(x)).$$

This approach has a big disadvantage: the function $\overrightarrow{\phi}(x)$ is defined only implicitly and we can only prove its existence. That's why we might proceed as follows. First, we write the necessary condition for local extrema in terms of the first differential

$$\mathrm{d}f(x, u) = (\nabla_x f(x, u), \mathrm{d}x)_{\mathbb{R}^n} + (\nabla_u f(x, u), \mathrm{d}u)_{\mathbb{R}^m} = 0$$

and, second, we write also the first differential of the communication conditions $\overrightarrow{F}(x, u) \equiv 0$ as

$$\mathrm{d}\overrightarrow{F}(x, u) = \frac{\partial \overrightarrow{F}}{\partial x}(x, u)\mathrm{d}x + \frac{\partial \overrightarrow{F}}{\partial u}(x, u)\mathrm{d}u \equiv 0.$$

This implies that

$$\mathrm{d}u = -\left(\frac{\partial \overrightarrow{F}}{\partial u}\right)^{-1} \frac{\partial \overrightarrow{F}}{\partial x}\mathrm{d}x$$

and consequently that

$$(\nabla_x f(x, u), \mathrm{d}x)_{\mathbb{R}^n} - (\nabla_u f(x, u), \left(\frac{\partial \overrightarrow{F}}{\partial u}\right)^{-1} \frac{\partial \overrightarrow{F}}{\partial x}\mathrm{d}x)_{\mathbb{R}^m} = 0$$

or

$$\nabla_x f(x, u) - \left(\frac{\partial \overrightarrow{F}}{\partial x}\right)^T \left(\left(\frac{\partial \overrightarrow{F}}{\partial u}\right)^{-1}\right)^T \nabla_u f(x, u) = 0,$$

but we still have

$$\overrightarrow{F}(x, u) \equiv 0.$$

Hence we have $n + m$ equations with $n + m$ variables for defining the candidates for extrema points. The next step is to examine these points with respect to sign-definiteness of the second differential $\mathrm{d}^2 f(x, u)$, taking into account the relations

$$\mathrm{d}u = -\left(\frac{\partial \overrightarrow{F}}{\partial u}\right)^{-1} \frac{\partial \overrightarrow{F}}{\partial x}\mathrm{d}x, \quad \mathrm{d}^2 u = -\mathrm{d}\left(\left(\frac{\partial \overrightarrow{F}}{\partial u}\right)^{-1} \frac{\partial \overrightarrow{F}}{\partial x}\right)\mathrm{d}x$$

which follow from communication conditions.

**Example 14.10.** 1. Let

$$f(x_1, x_2, x_3) = x_1 x_2^2 x_3^3$$

with the communication condition

$$x_1 + 2x_2 + 3x_3 = a, \quad a > 0.$$

Writing this condition in the form

$$F(x_1, x_2, x_3) := x_1 + 2x_2 + 3x_3 - a \equiv 0$$

we have that

$$\frac{\partial F}{\partial x_3} = 3 \neq 0, \quad \mathrm{d}x_3 = -\frac{1}{3}\mathrm{d}x_1 - \frac{2}{3}\mathrm{d}x_2.$$

The system for defining the candidate points is

$$\mathrm{d}f = x_2^2 x_3^3 \mathrm{d}x_1 + 2x_1 x_2 x_3^3 \mathrm{d}x_2 + 3x_1 x_2^2 x_3^2 \mathrm{d}x_3 = 0, \quad \mathrm{d}x_3 = -\frac{1}{3}(\mathrm{d}x_1 + 2\mathrm{d}x_2).$$

This implies

$$x_2^2 x_3^3 \mathrm{d}x_1 + 2x_1 x_2 x_3^3 \mathrm{d}x_2 + 3x_1 x_2^2 x_3^2 \left( -\frac{1}{3}(\mathrm{d}x_1 + 2\mathrm{d}x_2) \right) = 0$$

or

$$x_2^2 x_3^2 (x_3 - x_1)\mathrm{d}x_1 + 2x_1 x_2 x_3 (x_3 - x_2)\mathrm{d}x_2 = 0.$$

The communication condition implies that

$$x_1 = x_2 = x_3 = a/6 \quad \text{or} \quad x_1 = x_2 = 0, x_3 = a/3$$
$$\text{or} \quad x_1 = x_3 = 0, x_2 = a/2 \quad \text{or} \quad x_2 = x_3 = 0, x_1 = a.$$

Next, using $\mathrm{d}^2 x_1 = \mathrm{d}^2 x_2 = \mathrm{d}^2 x_3 = 0$ and the previous relations we obtain

$$\begin{aligned}
\mathrm{d}^2 f &= \mathrm{d}(x_2^2 x_3^2 (x_3 - x_1)\mathrm{d}x_1) + 2\mathrm{d}(x_1 x_2 x_3 (x_3 - x_2)\mathrm{d}x_2) \\
&= 2x_2 x_3^2 (x_3 - x_1)\mathrm{d}x_1 \mathrm{d}x_2 + 2x_2^2 x_3 (x_3 - x_1)\mathrm{d}x_1 \mathrm{d}x_3 \\
&\quad + x_2^2 x_3^2 (\mathrm{d}x_3 - \mathrm{d}x_1)\mathrm{d}x_1 + 2x_2 x_3 (x_3 - x_2)\mathrm{d}x_1 \mathrm{d}x_2 \\
&\quad + 2x_1 x_3 (x_3 - x_2)\mathrm{d}x_1 \mathrm{d}x_2 + 2x_1 x_2 (x_3 - x_2)\mathrm{d}x_1 \mathrm{d}x_3 \\
&\quad + 2x_1 x_2 x_3 (\mathrm{d}x_3 - \mathrm{d}x_2)\mathrm{d}x_1.
\end{aligned}$$

It is easy to see that at the points $(0, 0, a/3)$, $(0, a/2, 0)$, and $(a, 0, 0)$ the second differential is equal to zero. Moreover, at these points the value of the function is equal to zero, and it is evident that there is no extrema at these points since this function changes the sign in the neighborhood of these points. But at the point $(a/6, a/6, a/6)$ the second differential is equal to

$$\begin{aligned}
\mathrm{d}^2 f(a/6, a/6, a/6) &= (a/6)^4 (\mathrm{d}x_3 - \mathrm{d}x_1)\mathrm{d}x_1 + 2(a/6)^4 (\mathrm{d}x_3 - \mathrm{d}x_2)\mathrm{d}x_2 \\
&= (a/6)^4 \left( -\frac{1}{3}\mathrm{d}x_1 - \frac{2}{3}\mathrm{d}x_2 - \mathrm{d}x_1 \right)\mathrm{d}x_1 \\
&\quad + 2(a/6)^4 \left( -\frac{1}{3}\mathrm{d}x_1 - \frac{2}{3}\mathrm{d}x_2 - \mathrm{d}x_2 \right)\mathrm{d}x_2 \\
&= -\frac{2}{3}(a/6)^4 (2(\mathrm{d}x_1)^2 + 2\mathrm{d}x_1 \mathrm{d}x_2 + 5(\mathrm{d}x_2)^2) < 0
\end{aligned}$$

which is clear if we look at the corresponding quadratic form. Thus, $(a/6, a/6, a/6)$ is a point of local maxima, and this local maxima is equal to $(a/6)^6$.

2. Let
$$f(x_1, x_2, x_3) = x_1 x_2 x_3$$

with the communication conditions

$$x_1^2 + x_2^2 + x_3^2 = 1, \quad x_1 + x_2 + x_3 = 0.$$

Then $\vec{F} = (F_1, F_2) = 0$, where

$$F_1(x_1, x_2, x_3) = x_1^2 + x_2^2 + x_3^2 - 1, \quad F_2(x_1, x_2, x_3) = x_1 + x_2 + x_3.$$

This implies that

$$\det \frac{\partial \vec{F}}{\partial(x_2, x_3)} = \begin{vmatrix} \frac{\partial F_1}{\partial x_2} & \frac{\partial F_1}{\partial x_3} \\ \frac{\partial F_2}{\partial x_2} & \frac{\partial F_2}{\partial x_3} \end{vmatrix} = \begin{vmatrix} 2x_2 & 2x_3 \\ 1 & 1 \end{vmatrix} = 2x_2 - 2x_3 \neq 0$$

if and only if $x_2 \neq x_3$. The candidate points satisfy the system

$$\begin{cases} \mathrm{d}f(x_1, x_2, x_3) = x_2 x_3 \mathrm{d}x_1 + x_1 x_3 \mathrm{d}x_2 + x_1 x_2 \mathrm{d}x_3 = 0, \\ x_1 \mathrm{d}x_1 + x_2 \mathrm{d}x_2 + x_3 \mathrm{d}x_3 = 0, \\ \mathrm{d}x_1 + \mathrm{d}x_2 + \mathrm{d}x_3 = 0 \end{cases}$$

or

$$\begin{cases} x_2 \mathrm{d}x_2 + x_3 \mathrm{d}x_3 = -x_1 \mathrm{d}x_1, \\ \mathrm{d}x_2 + \mathrm{d}x_3 = -\mathrm{d}x_1, \end{cases}$$

which is equivalent to $\mathrm{d}f(x_1, x_2, x_3) = 0$. So

$$\mathrm{d}x_2 = \frac{(x_1 - x_3)\mathrm{d}x_1}{x_3 - x_2}, \quad \mathrm{d}x_3 = \frac{(x_2 - x_1)\mathrm{d}x_1}{x_3 - x_2}.$$

Now $\mathrm{d}f(x_1, x_2, x_3) = 0$ implies

$$x_2 x_3 \mathrm{d}x_1 + x_1 x_3 \frac{x_1 - x_3}{x_3 - x_2}\mathrm{d}x_1 + x_1 x_2 \frac{x_2 - x_1}{x_3 - x_2}\mathrm{d}x_1 = 0$$

or

$$\frac{(x_2 - x_1)(2x_3^2 + x_1 x_2)}{x_3 - x_2}\mathrm{d}x_1 = 0.$$

Hence there are two possibilities:

(a) $x_2 = x_1 \neq x_3$,

(b) $x_1 \neq x_2 \neq x_3, x_3 = \pm\sqrt{-x_1 x_2/2}$ $(x_1 x_2 < 0)$.

In the first case we have that

$$x_1 = x_2, \quad x_3 = -2x_1, \quad x_1^2 + x_1^2 + 4x_1^2 = 1$$

or

$$x_1 = x_2 = \pm\sqrt{1/6}, \quad x_3 = \mp 2\sqrt{1/6}.$$

In the second case we have that

$$x_3 = \pm\sqrt{-x_1 x_2/2}$$

and

$$\begin{cases} x_1^2 + x_2^2 - x_1 x_2/2 = 1, \\ x_1 + x_2 = \mp\sqrt{-x_1 x_2/2}. \end{cases}$$

Solving the latter system yields $x_1 x_2 = -1/3$. Hence the system becomes

$$\begin{cases} x_1^2 + x_2^2 = 5/6, \\ x_1 + x_2 = -1/3. \end{cases}$$

Eliminating $x_2$ we get

$$x_1 = \pm\sqrt{2/3} \quad \text{or} \quad x_1 = \pm\sqrt{1/6}$$

implying

$$x_2 = \mp\frac{1}{\sqrt{6}} \quad \text{or} \quad x_2 = \mp\sqrt{2/3}$$

with $x_3 = \pm\sqrt{1/6}$. Out of the eight possibilities here only

$$\left(\frac{1}{\sqrt{6}}, -\sqrt{2/3}, \frac{1}{\sqrt{6}}\right) \quad \text{and} \quad \left(-\frac{1}{\sqrt{6}}, \sqrt{2/3}, -\frac{1}{\sqrt{6}}\right)$$

fit. Hence we have in total four critical points

$$\left(\frac{1}{\sqrt{6}}, \frac{1}{\sqrt{6}}, -\sqrt{2/3}\right), \left(-\frac{1}{\sqrt{6}}, -\frac{1}{\sqrt{6}}, \sqrt{2/3}\right),$$
$$\left(\frac{1}{\sqrt{6}}, -\sqrt{2/3}, \frac{1}{\sqrt{6}}\right), \quad \text{and} \quad \left(-\frac{1}{\sqrt{6}}, \sqrt{2/3}, -\frac{1}{\sqrt{6}}\right).$$

The first two points correspond to case (a), and second two points to case (b). Thus, for the first two points we have

$$dx_3 = 0, \quad dx_2 = -dx_1.$$

So

$$\begin{aligned} d^2 f &= d(x_2 x_3)dx_1 + d(x_1 x_3)dx_2 + d(x_1 x_2)dx_3 \\ &= x_3 dx_2 dx_1 + x_2 dx_3 dx_1 + x_1 dx_3 dx_2 + x_3 dx_1 dx_2 \\ &= x_3 dx_2 dx_1 + x_3 dx_1 dx_2 = 2x_3 dx_1 dx_2 \\ &= -2x_3(dx_1)^2 = \begin{cases} 2\sqrt{\frac{2}{3}}(dx_1)^2, \\ -2\sqrt{\frac{2}{3}}(dx_1)^2. \end{cases} \end{aligned}$$

This implies that $\left(\frac{1}{\sqrt{6}}, \frac{1}{\sqrt{6}}, -\sqrt{2/3}\right)$ is a point of minima and this minima equals $-2/(6\sqrt{6})$, and $\left(-\frac{1}{\sqrt{6}}, -\frac{1}{\sqrt{6}}, \sqrt{2/3}\right)$ is a point of maxima and this maxima equals $2/(6\sqrt{6})$. For the second two points we have

$$dx_2 = 0, \quad dx_3 = -dx_1.$$

So

$$d^2f = x_3 dx_2 dx_1 + x_2 dx_3 dx_1 + x_1 dx_3 dx_2$$
$$+ x_3 dx_1 dx_2 + x_1 dx_2 dx_3 + x_2 dx_1 dx_3$$
$$= x_2 dx_3 dx_1 + x_2 dx_1 dx_3 = 2x_2 dx_1 dx_3$$

$$= -2x_2(dx_1)^2 = \begin{cases} 2\sqrt{\frac{2}{3}}(dx_1)^2, \\ -2\sqrt{\frac{2}{3}}(dx_1)^2. \end{cases}$$

This implies that $\left(\frac{1}{\sqrt{6}}, -\sqrt{2/3}, \frac{1}{\sqrt{6}}\right)$ is a point of minima and this minima equals $-2/(6\sqrt{6})$ and $\left(-\frac{1}{\sqrt{6}}, \sqrt{2/3}, -\frac{1}{\sqrt{6}}\right)$ is a point of maxima equaling $2/(6\sqrt{6})$.

3. Let

$$f(x_1, x_2, x_3) = x_1 x_2 + x_3 x_2$$

with the communication conditions

$$x_1^2 + x_2^2 = 2, \quad x_2 + x_3 = 2.$$

Then $\overrightarrow{F} = (F_1, F_2) = 0$, where

$$F_1(x_1, x_2, x_3) = x_1^2 + x_2^2 - 2, \quad F_2(x_1, x_2, x_3) = x_2 + x_3 - 2.$$

This implies

$$\det \frac{\partial \overrightarrow{F}}{\partial(x_2, x_3)} = \begin{vmatrix} \frac{\partial F_1}{\partial x_2} & \frac{\partial F_1}{\partial x_3} \\ \frac{\partial F_2}{\partial x_2} & \frac{\partial F_2}{\partial x_3} \end{vmatrix} = \begin{vmatrix} 2x_2 & 0 \\ 1 & 1 \end{vmatrix} = 2x_2 \neq 0$$

and, in addition,

$$\begin{cases} 2x_1 dx_1 + 2x_2 dx_2 = 0, \\ dx_2 + dx_3 = 0 \end{cases}$$

or

$$\begin{cases} dx_2 = -\frac{x_1}{x_2} dx_1, \\ dx_3 = \frac{x_1}{x_2} dx_1. \end{cases}$$

Now

$$df = x_2 dx_1 + x_1 dx_2 + x_2 dx_3 + x_3 dx_2$$
$$= x_2 dx_1 - x_1 \frac{x_1}{x_2} dx_1 + x_2 \frac{x_1}{x_2} dx_1 - x_3 \frac{x_1}{x_2} dx_1$$
$$= \left( x_2 - \frac{x_1^2}{x_2} + x_1 - \frac{x_1 x_3}{x_2} \right) dx_1 = 0$$

if and only if

$$\left( x_1 + x_2 - \frac{x_1^2 + x_1 x_3}{x_2} \right) dx_1 = 0,$$

i.e., the system for critical points is

$$\begin{cases} x_1 + x_2 = \frac{x_1^2 + x_1 x_3}{x_2}, \\ x_1^2 + x_2^2 = 2, \\ x_2 + x_3 = 2 \end{cases}$$

or

$$\begin{cases} x_3 = 2 - x_2, \\ x_1^2 + x_2^2 = 2, \\ x_1^2 - 2x_1x_2 - x_2^2 + 2x_1 = 0. \end{cases}$$

If we eliminate $x_2$ from the latter two equations we obtain

$$(x_1^2 - 1)(2x_1^2 + 2x_1 - 1) = 0.$$

Therefore

$$x_1^{(1)} = 1, \quad x_1^{(2)} = -1, \quad x_1^{(3)} = \frac{-1 - \sqrt{3}}{2}, \quad x_1^{(4)} = \frac{-1 + \sqrt{3}}{2},$$

$$x_2^{(1)} = 1, \quad x_2^{(2)} = 1, \quad x_2^{(3)} = \frac{1}{1 + \sqrt{3}}, \quad x_2^{(4)} = \frac{-1}{\sqrt{3} - 1},$$

$$x_3^{(1)} = 1, \quad x_3^{(2)} = 1, \quad x_3^{(3)} = \frac{3 - \sqrt{3}}{2}, \quad x_3^{(4)} = \frac{5 + \sqrt{3}}{2}.$$

For simplicity, we will consider only the points

$$(1, 1, 1), \quad (-1, 1, 1).$$

To examine the second differential we have to remember that

$$\mathrm{d}x_2 = -\frac{x_1}{x_2}\mathrm{d}x_1, \quad \mathrm{d}x_3 = \frac{x_1}{x_2}\mathrm{d}x_1.$$

Hence

$$\begin{aligned} \mathrm{d}^2 f &= \mathrm{d}(x_2\mathrm{d}x_1) + \mathrm{d}(x_1\mathrm{d}x_2) + \mathrm{d}(x_2\mathrm{d}x_3) + \mathrm{d}(x_3\mathrm{d}x_2) \\ &= \mathrm{d}x_2\mathrm{d}x_1 + \mathrm{d}x_1\mathrm{d}x_2 + x_1\mathrm{d}^2x_2 + \mathrm{d}x_2\mathrm{d}x_3 + x_2\mathrm{d}^2x_3 + \mathrm{d}x_3\mathrm{d}x_2 \\ &= 2\mathrm{d}x_1\mathrm{d}x_2 + 2\mathrm{d}x_2\mathrm{d}x_3 + x_1\mathrm{d}^2x_2 + x_2\mathrm{d}^2x_3. \end{aligned}$$

Here

$$\mathrm{d}^2 x_2 = -\mathrm{d}\left(\frac{x_1}{x_2}\right)\mathrm{d}x_1 = -\frac{1}{x_2}(\mathrm{d}x_1)^2 + \frac{x_1}{x_2^2}\mathrm{d}x_1\mathrm{d}x_2 = -\frac{1}{x_2}(\mathrm{d}x_1)^2 - \frac{x_1^2}{x_2^3}(\mathrm{d}x_1)^2$$

and

$$\mathrm{d}^2 x_3 = \mathrm{d}\left(\frac{x_1}{x_2}\right)\mathrm{d}x_1 = \frac{1}{x_2}(\mathrm{d}x_1)^2 - \frac{x_1}{x_2^2}\mathrm{d}x_1\mathrm{d}x_2 = \frac{1}{x_2}(\mathrm{d}x_1)^2 + \frac{x_1^2}{x_2^3}(\mathrm{d}x_1)^2.$$

This leads to

$$\begin{aligned} \mathrm{d}^2 f &= 2\mathrm{d}x_1\left(-\frac{x_1}{x_2}\mathrm{d}x_1\right) + 2\left(-\frac{x_1}{x_2}\mathrm{d}x_1\right)\left(\frac{x_1}{x_2}\mathrm{d}x_1\right) \\ &\quad + x_1\left(-\frac{1}{x_2}(\mathrm{d}x_1)^2 - \frac{x_1^2}{x_2^3}(\mathrm{d}x_1)^2\right) + x_2\left(\frac{1}{x_2}(\mathrm{d}x_1)^2 + \frac{x_1^2}{x_2^3}(\mathrm{d}x_1)^2\right) \\ &= \left(1 - \frac{3x_1}{x_2} - \frac{x_1^2}{x_2^2} - \frac{x_1^3}{x_2^3}\right)(\mathrm{d}x_1)^2. \end{aligned}$$

Hence

$$\mathrm{d}^2 f(1, 1, 1) = -4(\mathrm{d}x_1)^2, \quad \mathrm{d}^2 f(-1, 1, 1) = 4(\mathrm{d}x_1)^2.$$

This means that $(1, 1, 1)$ is a point of local maxima equaling 2, and $(-1, 1, 1)$ is a point of local minima equaling 0.

4. Let

$$f(x_1, x_2) = x_1 + 2x_2^2$$

with the communication conditions given by

$$2x_1^2 + x_2^2 \leq 1.$$

This problem can be divided into two steps: to find the points of local extrema in open domain $\{(x_1, x_2) : 2x_1^2 + x_2^2 < 1\}$ and to find the points under the communication conditions $2x_1^2 + x_2^2 = 1$.

For the first problem we have

$$\nabla f(x_1, x_2) = (1, 4x_2)$$

and thus there are no critical points, i.e., there are no points of local extrema inside of this domain.

For the second problem we have

$$\begin{cases} \mathrm{d}f(x_1, x_2) = \mathrm{d}x_1 + 4x_2\mathrm{d}x_2 = 0, \\ 4x_1\mathrm{d}x_1 + 2x_2\mathrm{d}x_2 = 0. \end{cases}$$

The solution of this system is either $x_2 = 0$ and $x_1 = \pm\sqrt{1/2}$ or $x_1 = 1/8$ and $x_2 = \pm\sqrt{31/32}$. The second differential is equal to

$$\mathrm{d}^2 f = \mathrm{d}^2 x_1 + 4(\mathrm{d}x_2)^2,$$

where

$$\mathrm{d}^2 x_1 = -\mathrm{d}\left(\frac{x_2}{2x_1}\mathrm{d}x_2\right) = -\mathrm{d}\left(\frac{x_2}{2x_1}\right)\mathrm{d}x_2 = -\frac{1}{2}\frac{x_1\mathrm{d}x_2 - x_2\mathrm{d}x_1}{x_1^2}\mathrm{d}x_2$$

$$= -\frac{1}{2x_1}(\mathrm{d}x_2)^2 + \frac{1}{2}\frac{x_2}{x_1^2}\left(-\frac{x_2}{2x_1}\mathrm{d}x_2\right)\mathrm{d}x_2$$

$$= -\frac{1}{2x_1}(\mathrm{d}x_2)^2 - \frac{x_2^2}{4x_1^3}(\mathrm{d}x_2)^2.$$

That's why we have

$$\mathrm{d}^2 f = \left(-\frac{1}{2x_1} - \frac{x_2^2}{4x_1^3} + 4\right)(\mathrm{d}x_2)^2$$

so that

$$\mathrm{d}^2 f\left(\pm\frac{1}{\sqrt{2}}, 0\right) = \left(4 \mp \frac{1}{\sqrt{2}}\right)(\mathrm{d}x_2)^2 > 0$$

and

$$\mathrm{d}^2 f(1/8, \pm\sqrt{31/32}) = -\frac{31/32}{4(1/8)^3}(\mathrm{d}x_2)^2 < 0.$$

Therefore, the points $(\pm 1/\sqrt{2}, 0)$ are points of local minima equaling $\pm 1/\sqrt{2}$, and the points $(1/8, \pm\sqrt{31/32})$ are points of local maxima equaling $33/16$.

**Exercise 14.11.** Examine the points

$$\left(\frac{-1-\sqrt{3}}{2}, \frac{1}{\sqrt{3}+1}, \frac{3-\sqrt{3}}{2}\right), \quad \left(\frac{-1+\sqrt{3}}{2}, \frac{-1}{\sqrt{3}-1}, \frac{5+\sqrt{3}}{2}\right)$$

for local extrema from part 3 of Example 14.10.

## 14.2 ▪ Lagrange multipliers method

Let $f : X \subset \mathbb{R}^n \to \mathbb{R}$ be continuously differentiable on an open set $X$ and let $\overrightarrow{F} : X \subset \mathbb{R}^n \to \mathbb{R}^m$ define the communication conditions $\overrightarrow{F}(x) = 0$. We assume also that $\overrightarrow{F}$ is continuously differentiable, $m < n$, and rank $\frac{\partial \overrightarrow{F}}{\partial x} = m$, i.e., the equation $\overrightarrow{F}(x) = 0$ can be uniquely solved with respect to the first $m$ coordinates $(x_1, \ldots, x_m)$ of $(x_1, \ldots, x_n)$ (we may assume this without loss of generality).

Consider a function depending on $x$ and new variable $\lambda = (\lambda_1, \ldots, \lambda_m)$ such that $\Phi : X \times \Lambda \subset \mathbb{R}^{n+m} \to \mathbb{R}$ and

$$\Phi(x, \lambda) := f(x) + (\overrightarrow{F}(x), \lambda)_{\mathbb{R}^m}, \quad \lambda \in \Lambda.$$

The function $\Phi$ is said to be a *Lagrange function* and $\lambda$ are called *Lagrange multipliers*.

Now we forget the conditions $\overrightarrow{F}(x) = 0$ and investigate the function $\Phi(x, \lambda)$ for the usual local extrema. Thus, we need to first find the critical points (candidates), i.e., the solutions of the equation

$$d\Phi(x, \lambda) = (\nabla_x f(x), dx)_{\mathbb{R}^n} + \left( \lambda \frac{\partial \overrightarrow{F}}{\partial x}, dx \right)_{\mathbb{R}^n} + (\overrightarrow{F}, d\lambda)_{\mathbb{R}^m} = 0$$

or

$$\nabla_x f(x) + \lambda \frac{\partial \overrightarrow{F}}{\partial x} = 0, \quad \overrightarrow{F} = 0,$$

or

$$\left( \frac{\partial \overrightarrow{F}}{\partial x} \right)^T \lambda^T = -(\nabla f)^T, \quad \overrightarrow{F} = 0.$$

Since rank $\left( \frac{\partial \overrightarrow{F}}{\partial x} \right)^T$ = rank $\frac{\partial \overrightarrow{F}}{\partial x} = m$, $\lambda^T$ can be uniquely determined from the latter equation. Let us assume that $\lambda^0 = (\lambda_1^0, \ldots, \lambda_m^0)$ are chosen so that there is $x^0 \in X$ such that the latter system of $m + n$ equations is solvable, i.e., the necessary conditions are fulfilled. Then we need to examine the second differential. It is equal to

$$d^2\Phi(x^0, \lambda^0) = d_x^2\Phi(x^0, \lambda^0) + d_\lambda^2\Phi(x^0, \lambda^0) + \sum_{k=1}^{m} \sum_{j=1}^{n} \frac{\partial^2 \Phi(x^0, \lambda^0)}{\partial x_j \partial \lambda_k} dx_j d\lambda_k$$

$$= d_x^2\Phi(x^0, \lambda^0) + \sum_{j=1}^{n} \left( \sum_{k=1}^{m} \frac{\partial F_k}{\partial x_j} d\lambda_k \right) dx_j = d_x^2\Phi(x^0, \lambda^0).$$

**Example 14.12.**    1. Let

$$f(x) = a_1 x_1^2 + \cdots + a_n x_n^2,$$

where $a_1 > a_2 > \cdots > a_n, a_j \neq 0, j = 1, 2, \ldots, n$, and let the communication conditions be

$$x_1^2 + \cdots + x_n^2 \leq 1.$$

The problem is to examine this function for global extrema in the closed unit ball. First, we try to find possible points of local extrema in open ball $x_1^2 + \cdots + x_n^2 < 1$. Since we have the equations

$$\nabla_x f = (2a_1 x_1, \ldots, 2a_n x_n) = 0,$$

$x^0 = (0, 0, \ldots, 0)$ is the only critical point in this open ball. The second differential at this point is equal to

$$d^2 f(0) = 2 \sum_{j=1}^{n} a_j (dx_j)^2.$$

Therefore we have only three possibilities for the coefficients $a_j$:

(a) $0 > a_1 > \cdots > a_n$, whence $d^2 f(0) < 0$, and $x^0$ is a point of local maxima which equals 0.

(b) $a_1 > a_2 > \cdots > a_n > 0$ so that $d^2 f(0) > 0$, and $x^0$ is a point of local minima which equals 0.

(c) $a_1 > a_2 > \cdots > a_{j_0} > 0 > a_{j_0+1} > \cdots > a_n$. Then $d^2 f(x^0)$ is not sign-definite and therefore $x^0$ is not a point of local extrema.

Now we examine function $f$ for conditional extrema, i.e., with the communication condition $x_1^2 + \cdots + x_n^2 = 1$. Using the Lagrange multipliers method we have

$$\Phi(x, \lambda) = a_1 x_1^2 + \cdots + a_n x_n^2 + \lambda(x_1^2 + \cdots + x_n^2 - 1).$$

We get

$$\nabla_x \Phi(x, \lambda) = 2((a_1 - \lambda)x_1, \ldots, (a_n - \lambda)x_n) = 0$$

and

$$\partial_\lambda \Phi(x, \lambda) = x_1^2 + \cdots + x_n^2 - 1 = 0.$$

Since $a_1 > a_2 > \cdots > a_n$, all $x_j$ except one, say $x_{k_0}$, must be equal to zero and $\lambda = a_{k_0}$ in this case, i.e., we have

$$x_j = 0, \quad j = 1, 2, \ldots, n, j \neq k_0, \quad x_{k_0}^2 = 1, \quad \lambda^0 = a_{k_0} \neq 0.$$

The second differential is

$$d_x^2 \Phi(x^0, \lambda^0) = 2 d_x \left( \sum_{j=1}^{n} (a_j - \lambda) x_j dx_j \right)$$

$$= 2 \sum_{j=1, j \neq k_0}^{n} (a_j - \lambda)(dx_j)^2 + 2(a_{k_0} - \lambda) x_{k_0} d^2 x_{k_0}$$

$$= 2 \sum_{j=1, j \neq k_0}^{n} (a_j - a_{k_0})(dx_j)^2.$$

We have the following possibilities:

(a) $1 < k_0 < n$. Then $a_j - a_{k_0}$ have different sign and therefore $d^2 \Phi(x^0, \lambda^0)$ is not sign-definite, i.e., there is no local extrema in this case.

(b) $k_0 = 1$. Then $a_j - a_{k_0} < 0$ and $d^2 \Phi(x^0, \lambda^0) < 0$, meaning that the points $(\pm 1, 0, \ldots, 0)$ are the points of local maxima (conditional) and this maxima is equal to $a_1$.

(c) $k_0 = n$. Then $a_j - a_{k_0} > 0$ and $d^2 \Phi(x^0, \lambda^0) > 0$, meaning that the points $(0, \ldots, 0, \pm 1)$ are the points of local minima (conditional) and this minima is equal to $a_n$.

In conclusion,

$$\max_{|x|\leq 1} f(x) = \begin{cases} 0, & 0 > a_1 > \cdots > a_n, \\ a_1, & a_1 > \cdots > a_n > 0. \end{cases}$$

2. Let

$$f(x) = \frac{a_1}{x_1} + \frac{a_2}{x_2} + \cdots + \frac{a_n}{x_n}$$

with the communication condition

$$x_1^2 + \cdots + x_n^2 = 1.$$

For the gradient of $\Phi(x,\lambda) = f(x) + (\overrightarrow{F}(x),\lambda)_{\mathbb{R}^m}$ we obtain

$$\frac{\partial \Phi}{\partial x_j} = -\frac{a_j}{x_j^2} + 2\lambda x_j = 0, \quad j = 1, 2, \ldots, n,$$

and

$$\frac{\partial \Phi}{\partial \lambda} = x_1^2 + \cdots + x_n^2 - 1 = 0.$$

So

$$x_j = \sqrt[3]{\frac{a_j}{2\lambda}}, \quad j = 1, 2, \ldots, n,$$

and

$$\sqrt[3]{\frac{a_1^2}{(2\lambda)^2}} + \cdots + \sqrt[3]{\frac{a_n^2}{(2\lambda)^2}} = 1.$$

It follows that

$$a_1^{2/3} + \cdots + a_n^{2/3} = (2\lambda)^{2/3}$$

or

$$2\lambda^0 = \pm(a_1^{2/3} + \cdots + a_n^{2/3})^{3/2} =: \pm A_0.$$

(a) If $2\lambda^0 = A_0$ then

$$x_j^0 = \sqrt[3]{\frac{a_j}{A_0}}, \quad j = 1, 2, \ldots, n.$$

Since not all $a_j = 0$, there is $k_0 \in \{1, 2, \ldots, n\}$ such that $a_{k_0} \neq 0$ and so $A_0 \neq 0$. Solving the communication conditions for $x_{k_0}$ we obtain

$$x_{k_0} = \pm\sqrt{1 - x_1^2 - x_2^2 - \cdots - x_{k_0-1}^2 \cdots - x_n^2}.$$

Then $x_1, x_2, \ldots, x_{k_0-1}, x_{k_0+1}, \ldots, x_n$ are independent variables and $x_{k_0}$ is a dependent variable. It implies that

$$x_1 dx_1 + \cdots + x_n dx_n = 0$$

and so

$$d(x_1 dx_1 + \cdots + x_n dx_n) = 0.$$

Since
$$(\mathrm{d}x_1)^2 + \cdots + (\mathrm{d}x_n)^2 + x_{k_0}\mathrm{d}^2 x_{k_0} = 0,$$

we have
$$\mathrm{d}^2 x_{k_0} = -\frac{(\mathrm{d}x_1)^2 + \cdots + (\mathrm{d}x_n)^2}{x_{k_0}}.$$

We obtain

$$\mathrm{d}^2\Phi(x^0, \lambda^0) = 2\sum_{j=1}^{n}\frac{a_j}{(x_j^0)^3}(\mathrm{d}x_j)^2 + 2\lambda^0\sum_{j=1}^{n}(\mathrm{d}x_j)^2 + 2\lambda^0 x_{k_0}^0 \mathrm{d}^2 x_{k_0}$$

$$= 2\sum_{j=1}^{n}\left(\frac{a_j}{(x_j^0)^3} + \lambda^0\right)(\mathrm{d}x_j)^2 + 2\lambda^0 x_{k_0}^0 \mathrm{d}^2 x_{k_0}$$

$$= 2\sum_{j=1}^{n}\left(A_0 + \frac{1}{2}A_0\right)(\mathrm{d}x_j)^2 + A_0 x_{k_0}^0 \mathrm{d}^2 x_{k_0}$$

$$= 3A_0\sum_{j=1}^{n}(\mathrm{d}x_j)^2 + A_0\sqrt[3]{\frac{a_{k_0}}{A_0}}\left(\frac{-\sum_{j=1}^{n}(\mathrm{d}x_j)^2}{x_{k_0}}\right)$$

$$= 2A_0\sum_{j=1}^{n}(\mathrm{d}x_j)^2 > 0.$$

This means that the point $(\sqrt[3]{a_1/A_0}, \ldots, \sqrt[3]{a_n/A_0})$ is a point of local minima (conditional) and this minima is equal to $(a_1^{2/3} + \cdots + a_n^{2/3})^{3/2}$.

(b) If $2\lambda^0 = -A_0$ then

$$x_j^0 = -\sqrt[3]{\frac{a_j}{A_0}}$$

and we obtain similarly that

$$\mathrm{d}^2\Phi(x^0, \lambda^0) = -2A_0\sum_{j=1}^{n}(\mathrm{d}x_j)^2 < 0.$$

This means that the point $(-\sqrt[3]{a_1/A_0}, \ldots, -\sqrt[3]{a_n/A_0})$ is a point of local maxima (conditional) and this maxima is equal to $-(a_1^{2/3} + \cdots + a_n^{2/3})^{3/2}$.

3. Let
$$f(x_1, x_2) = x_1$$

with the communication conditions $x_1^3 = x_2^2$. Since $x_1 \geq 0$ necessarily, $x^0 = (0,0)$ is a point of local minima (conditional) of $f$. Let us try to obtain this fact using the Lagrange multipliers method. Indeed,

$$\Phi(x_1, x_2, \lambda) = x_1 + \lambda(x_1^3 - x_2^2)$$

and so

$$\frac{\partial\Phi}{\partial x_1} = 1 + 3\lambda x_1^2, \quad \frac{\partial\Phi}{\partial x_2} = -2\lambda x_2, \quad \frac{\partial\Phi}{\partial \lambda} = x_1^3 - x_2^2.$$

Equating these values to zero yields

$$\lambda = -\frac{1}{3x_1^2}, \quad x_2 = 0, \quad x_1 = 0,$$

i.e., there is a contradiction. It means that in this case the Lagrange multipliers method does not work. But there is a modification of this classical method and in this particular case it reads as

$$\Phi_M(x_1, x_2, \lambda_0, \lambda) = \lambda_0 x_1 + \lambda(x_1^3 - x_2^2).$$

**Exercise 14.13.** 1. Show that the latter modification does not work in this particular case.

2. Examine the applicability of the Lagrange multipliers method for

$$f(x_1, x_2) = (x_2 - x_1^2)(x_2 - 2x_1^2)$$

with the communication condition $y = kx, k \neq 0$.

# Chapter 15

# Multidimensional Riemann integrals

In this chapter we will define multidimensional proper Riemann integrals for Jordan measurable bounded domains as well as improper integrals for unbounded domains and Riemann surface integrals. In particular, the formulas of Gauss–Ostrogradskii, Green, and Stokes and their numerous applications are considered. The approach to defining all these integrals is based on the theory of Jordan measure presented in Chapter 12. A very important part of this current chapter is the proof of the Fubini theorem and its applications; also important is the proof of the change of variables formula for multidimensional Riemann integrals.

## 15.1 ▪ Proper multidimensional integrals

We consider bounded sets $X \subset \mathbb{R}^n$ that are Jordan measurable (see Chapter 12) with measure $\mu(X) > 0$. In this case, for any $\varepsilon > 0$ there exist elementary figures $F$ and $G$ such that

$$F \subset X \subset G, \quad F = \bigcup_{k=1}^{m} \Pi_k, \quad G = \bigcup_{k=1}^{m} \Pi'_k,$$

where $\Pi_k$ and $\Pi'_k$ are rectangular parallelepipeds satisfying

$$\operatorname{int} \Pi_k \cap \operatorname{int} \Pi_l = \emptyset, \quad \operatorname{int} \Pi'_k \cap \operatorname{int} \Pi'_l = \emptyset, \quad k \neq l,$$

with

$$\mu(\Pi_k) = \prod_{j=1}^{n}(b_j - a_j), \quad \mu(\Pi'_k) = \prod_{j=1}^{n}(b'_j - a'_j)$$

such that

$$\mu(G) - \mu(F) = \sum_{k=1}^{m}(\mu(\Pi'_k) - \mu(\Pi_k)) < \varepsilon.$$

The Jordan measure of $X$ can be obtained then as

$$\mu(X) = \inf_{X \subset G} \mu(G) = \sup_{F \subset X} \mu(F).$$

Alongside measurable sets $X$ we consider bounded functions $f$ defined on $X$. We denote

$$M^f := \sup_X f(x), \quad m^f := \inf_X f(x), \quad M_k^f := \sup_{\Pi_k} f(x), \quad m_k^f := \inf_{\Pi_k} f(x),$$

$$M_k^{'f} := \sup_{\Pi'_k} f(x), \quad m_k^{'f} := \inf_{\Pi'_k} f(x)$$

and introduce the lower and upper Darboux's sums as

$$L_F(f, X) := \sum_{k=1}^{m} m_k^f \mu(\Pi_k), \quad F = \bigcup_{k=1}^{m} \Pi_k,$$

and

$$U_G(f, X) := \sum_{k=1}^{m} M_k^{\prime f} \mu(\Pi_k'), \quad G = \bigcup_{k=1}^{m} \Pi_k',$$

under the assumption that $f$ is extended to be zero outside of $\overline{X}$. It can be proved similarly as in Chapter 12 that if

$$F_1 \subset F_2 \subset X, \quad X \subset G_1 \subset G_2$$

then

$$L_{F_1}(f, X) \leq L_{F_2}(f, X), \quad U_{G_1}(f, X) \leq U_{G_2}(f, X)$$

and so $L_{F_1}(f, X) \leq U_{G_2}(f, X)$, where $F_1, F_2, G_1$, and $G_2$ are elementary figures. These properties of Darboux's sums lead to the inequality

$$\sup_{F \subset X} L_F(f, X) \leq \inf_{X \subset G} U_G(f, X),$$

where both values exist.

**Exercise 15.1.** Prove all these assertions for Darboux's sums.

The latter exercise justifies the following definition.

**Definition 15.2.** *A bounded function $f$ defined on a bounded measurable set $X \subset \mathbb{R}^n$ is said to be* integrable *if*

$$\sup_{F \subset X} L_F(f, X) = \inf_{X \subset G} U_G(f, X),$$

*and this common value is denoted as the* proper multidimensional Riemann integral

$$\int_X f(x)\mathrm{d}x = \int \cdots \int_X f(x_1, x_2, \ldots, x_n)\mathrm{d}x_1\mathrm{d}x_2 \cdots \mathrm{d}x_n.$$

**Theorem 15.3 (Criterion of integrability).** *Let $X \subset \mathbb{R}^n$ be bounded and measurable with Jordan measure $\mu(X) > 0$. A bounded function $f$ defined on $X$ is integrable if and only if for any $\varepsilon > 0$ there exist elementary figures $F$ and $G$ such that*

$$F \subset X \subset G, \quad U_G(f, X) - L_F(f, X) < \varepsilon.$$

*Proof.* Let $f$ be integrable on $X$. Then

$$\int_X f(x)\mathrm{d}x = \sup_{F \subset X} L_F(f, X) = \inf_{X \subset G} U_G(f, X).$$

Hence, for any $\varepsilon > 0$ there are elementary figures $F$ and $G$ such that

$$\int_X f(x)\mathrm{d}x - L_F(f, X) < \varepsilon/2, \quad U_G(f, X) - \int_X f(x)\mathrm{d}x < \varepsilon/2.$$

This implies that for this $\varepsilon > 0$ and for $F \subset X \subset G$ we have

$$U_G(f, X) - L_F(f, X) < \varepsilon.$$

Conversely, let us assume that for any $\varepsilon > 0$ there exist two elementary figures $F$ and $G$ such that

$$F \subset X \subset G, \quad U_G(f, X) - L_F(f, X) < \varepsilon.$$

By Exercise 15.1 we get

$$0 \le \inf_{X \subset G} U_G(f, X) - \sup_{F \subset X} L_F(f, X) < \varepsilon.$$

Since $\varepsilon > 0$ is arbitrary, we obtain that

$$\inf_{X \subset G} U_G(f, X) = \sup_{F \subset X} L_F(f, X) = \int_X f(x) \mathrm{d}x.$$

This proves the theorem.

**Corollary 15.4.** *Let $X$ be as in Theorem 15.3. If $f$ is continuous on $\overline{X}$ then $f$ is integrable on $X$.*

**Proof.** Since $f$ is continuous on a bounded closed set $\overline{X}$, this function is bounded (see the Weierstrass theorem) and uniformly continuous (see the Cantor theorem) on $\overline{X}$. Hence, for any $\varepsilon > 0$ there exists $\delta > 0$ such that

$$|f(x') - f(x'')| < \frac{\varepsilon}{2\mu(X)}$$

for all $x', x'' \in X$ and $|x' - x''| < \delta$. Since $X$ is Jordan measurable with $\mu(X) > 0$, then (for this $\varepsilon > 0$) there exist two elementary figures $F$ and $G$ such that

$$F \subset X \subset G, \quad \mu(G) - \mu(F) < \frac{\varepsilon}{2M},$$

where $M = \max_{\overline{X}} |f(x)|$. Combining these facts yields

$$U_G(f, X) - L_F(f, X) = \sum_{k=1}^{m} M_k^{'f} \mu(\Pi_k') - \sum_{k=1}^{m} m_k^f \mu(\Pi_k)$$

$$= \sum_{k=1}^{m} M_k^{'f}(\mu(\Pi_k') - \mu(\Pi_k)) + \sum_{k=1}^{m} (M_k^{'f} - m_k^f)\mu(\Pi_k)$$

$$\le M(\mu(G) - \mu(F)) + \frac{\varepsilon}{2\mu(X)}\mu(F) < \varepsilon.$$

This proves the corollary.

**Theorem 15.5 (The properties of a proper multidimensional Riemann integral).** *Suppose $f_1$ and $f_2$ are integrable on a measurable set $X$ with $\mu(X) > 0$. Then*

1. *the function $c_1 f_1 + c_2 f_2$ is integrable on $X$ for arbitrary constants $c_1$ and $c_2$ and*

$$\int_X (c_1 f_1(x) + c_2 f_2(x)) \mathrm{d}x = c_1 \int_X f_1(x) \mathrm{d}x + c_2 \int_X f_2(x) \mathrm{d}x,$$

2. *the function $f_1 f_2$ is integrable on $X$,*

3. *the function $|f_1|$ (as well as $|f_2|$) is integrable on $X$ and*

$$\left| \int_X f_1(x)dx \right| \le \int_X |f_1(x)|\, dx.$$

**Proof.** The proof literally repeats the proof of corresponding properties in the one-dimensional case (see Theorems 9.19 and 9.25).

**Exercise 15.6.** Show that $f$ is integrable on $X$ if and only if there exist the special limits of the integral sums

$$\lim_{\mu(\Pi_k)\to 0} \sum_{k=1}^{m} f(\xi^{(k)})\mu(\Pi_k), \quad \xi^{(k)} \in \Pi_k,$$

and

$$\lim_{\mu(\Pi'_k)\to 0} \sum_{k=1}^{m} f(\xi^{(k)})\mu(\Pi'_k), \quad \xi^{(k)} \in \Pi'_k,$$

where $\xi^{(k)}$ are chosen arbitrarily and $F = \cup_{k=1}^{m}\Pi_k$ and $G = \cup_{k=1}^{m}\Pi'_k$ are arbitrary elementary figures such that

$$F \subset X \subset G, \quad \mu(G) - \mu(F) < \varepsilon$$

for arbitrary (small) $\varepsilon > 0$, and these limits are equal to each other.

**Remark 15.7.** For measurable set $X$ with $\mu(X) = 0$ and for arbitrary bounded function $f$ defined on $X$, by definition we set

$$\int_X f(x)dx = 0.$$

**Theorem 15.8 (Fubini).** *Suppose $X$ and $Y$ are bounded Jordan measurable sets in $\mathbb{R}^n$ and $\mathbb{R}^m$ with $\mu(X), \mu(Y) > 0$, respectively. If*

$$\int_{X\times Y} |f(x,y)|dxdy < \infty,$$

*where the integral is taken with respect to a product measure $\mu(X \times Y) = \mu(X)\mu(Y)$ on $\mathbb{R}^{n+m}$ then*

$$\int_X \left( \int_Y f(x,y)dy \right) dx = \int_Y \left( \int_X f(x,y)dx \right) dy = \int_{X\times Y} f(x,y)dxdy,$$

*where the first two integrals are iterated integrals with respect to two measures and the third integral is an integral with respect to the product of these two measures.*

**Proof.** Since $X$ and $Y$ are Jordan measurable in $\mathbb{R}^n$ and $\mathbb{R}^m$, respectively, there are elementary figures $F, G \subset \mathbb{R}^n$ and $\widetilde{F}, \widetilde{G} \subset \mathbb{R}^m$ such that

$$F \subset X \subset G, \quad \widetilde{F} \subset Y \subset \widetilde{G}$$

and

$$\mu(G) - \mu(F) < \frac{\varepsilon}{2\mu(Y)}, \quad \mu(\widetilde{G}) - \mu(\widetilde{F}) < \frac{\varepsilon}{4\mu(X)}.$$

It follows that $F \times \widetilde{F} \subset X \times Y \subset G \times \widetilde{G}$ and

$$\mu(G \times \widetilde{G}) - \mu(F \times \widetilde{F}) = \mu(G)\mu(\widetilde{G}) - \mu(F)\mu(\widetilde{F})$$
$$= \mu(G)(\mu(\widetilde{G}) - \mu(\widetilde{F})) + \mu(\widetilde{F})(\mu(G) - \mu(F))$$
$$< \mu(G)\frac{\varepsilon}{4\mu(X)} + \mu(Y)\frac{\varepsilon}{2\mu(Y)} < \varepsilon$$

if $G$ is chosen so close to $X$ that $\mu(G)/\mu(X) < 2$. Hence we may conclude that the set $X \times Y$ is Jordan measurable in $\mathbb{R}^{n+m}$ and we may define (see Exercise 15.6)

$$\int_{X \times Y} f(x,y) \mathrm{d}x\mathrm{d}y = \lim_{\mu(\Pi_k \times \widetilde{\Pi}_j) \to 0} \sum_{k=1}^{m_1} \sum_{j=1}^{m_2} f(\xi^{(k)}, \xi^{(j)}) \mu(\Pi_k \times \widetilde{\Pi}_j) =: L,$$

where $\xi^{(k)} \in \Pi_k, \xi^{(j)} \in \widetilde{\Pi}_j$ and

$$F = \bigcup_{k=1}^{m_1} \Pi_k, \quad \widetilde{F} = \bigcup_{j=1}^{m_2} \widetilde{\Pi}_j.$$

This limit exists due to the integrability of $f(x,y)$ on the set $X \times Y$. Moreover, this limit can be represented also as

$$L = \lim_{\mu(\Pi_k) \to 0} \lim_{\mu(\widetilde{\Pi}_j) \to 0} \sum_{k=1}^{m_1} \sum_{j=1}^{m_2} f(\xi^{(k)}, \xi^{(j)}) \mu(\Pi_k) \mu(\widetilde{\Pi}_j)$$

$$= \lim_{\mu(\Pi_k) \to 0} \sum_{k=1}^{m_1} \int_Y f(\xi^{(k)}, y) \mathrm{d}y \mu(\Pi_k) = \int_X \left( \int_Y f(x,y) \mathrm{d}y \right) \mathrm{d}x$$

and similarly

$$L = \int_Y \left( \int_X f(x,y) \mathrm{d}x \right) \mathrm{d}y.$$

Existence of the latter iterated integrals follow from the fact that $f(x,y)$ is integrable on $X \times Y$. Thus, the theorem is proved.

**Corollary 15.9.** *Under the conditions of Theorem* 15.8 *it is true that*

$$\int_{X \times Y} |f(x,y)| \mathrm{d}x\mathrm{d}y < \infty$$

*if and only if either of the integrals*

$$\int_X \left( \int_Y |f(x,y)| \mathrm{d}y \right) \mathrm{d}x, \quad \int_Y \left( \int_X |f(x,y)| \mathrm{d}x \right) \mathrm{d}y$$

*is finite.*

**Exercise 15.10.** Suppose that functions $g$ and $h$ are integrable on bounded measurable sets $X \subset \mathbb{R}^n$ and $Y \subset \mathbb{R}^m$, respectively. Prove that the function $f(x,y) := g(x)h(y)$ is integrable on the set $X \times Y$ and that

$$\int_{X \times Y} f(x,y) \mathrm{d}x\mathrm{d}y = \left( \int_X g(x) \mathrm{d}x \right) \left( \int_Y h(y) \mathrm{d}y \right).$$

**Exercise 15.11.** Evaluate the iterated integrals

$$\int_0^1 \left( \int_0^1 \frac{x^2 - y^2}{(x^2 + y^2)^2} \mathrm{d}x \right) \mathrm{d}y, \quad \int_0^1 \left( \int_0^1 \frac{x^2 - y^2}{(x^2 + y^2)^2} \mathrm{d}y \right) \mathrm{d}x$$

and show that they are not equal to each other. Conclude that

$$\int_0^1 \int_0^1 \left| \frac{x^2 - y^2}{(x^2 + y^2)^2} \right| \mathrm{d}x \mathrm{d}y = +\infty.$$

Explain this phenomenon with respect to Corollary 15.9.

**Exercise 15.12.** Evaluate the iterated integrals

$$\int_0^1 \left( \int_0^1 f(x, y) \mathrm{d}x \right) \mathrm{d}y, \quad \int_0^1 \left( \int_0^1 f(x, y) \mathrm{d}y \right) \mathrm{d}x$$

for the function

$$f(x, y) = \begin{cases} 1/y^2, & 0 < x < y/2, 0 < y < 1, \\ -1/y^2, & y/2 < x < y, 0 < y < 1, \\ 0, & 0 < y < x, 0 < x < 1, \end{cases}$$

and make the same conclusions as in Exercise 15.11.

**Theorem 15.13 (Change of variables).** *Let $X$ and $X'$ be bounded measurable sets in $\mathbb{R}^n$ with positive Jordan measures. Suppose that a function $\vec{\varphi} : \mathbb{R}^n \to \mathbb{R}^n$ is such that*

1. *$\vec{\varphi} : \overline{X} \to \overline{X'}$ is onto and one-to-one mapping;*

2. *$\vec{\varphi}$ is continuously differentiable on $\overline{X}$;*

3. *the Jacobian of transformation from $X'$ to $X$*

$$J(x) := \det \frac{\partial \vec{\varphi}(x)}{\partial x}$$

*does not change sign throughout $X$, i.e., either $J(x) > 0$ or $J(x) < 0$ everywhere on $X$.*

*Assume that $f$ is integrable on $X'$. Then the function $f(\vec{\varphi}(x))|J(x)|$ is integrable on $X$ and*

$$\int_X f(\vec{\varphi}(x))|J(x)| \mathrm{d}x = \int_{X'} f(x') \mathrm{d}x'.$$

**Proof.** According to Exercise 15.6 we have

$$\int_{X'} f(x') \mathrm{d}x' = \lim_{\mu(\widetilde{\Pi}_k) \to 0} \sum_{k=1}^m f((\xi')^{(k)}) \mu(\widetilde{\Pi}_k), \quad (\xi')^{(k)} \in \widetilde{\Pi}_k,$$

where $\widetilde{\Pi}_k$ are rectangular parallelepipeds from elementary figure $\widetilde{F} = \cup_{k=1}^m \widetilde{\Pi}_k$ such that $\{\widetilde{F}\}$ exhaust $X'$ as $\mu(\widetilde{\Pi}_k) \to 0$, i.e.,

$$\mu(X') - \mu(\widetilde{F}) < \varepsilon$$

for arbitrary (small) $\varepsilon > 0$. By the conditions of this theorem we have that

$$\widetilde{\Pi_k} = \overrightarrow{\varphi}(Q_k),$$

where $Q_k$ are curvilinear (in general) parallelepipeds in $X$ such that $Q = \cup_{k=1}^m Q_k$ exhaust $X$ as $\mu(Q_k) \to 0$, i.e.,

$$\mu(X) - \mu(Q) < \varepsilon$$

for arbitrary (small) $\varepsilon > 0$. Indeed, since $\overrightarrow{\varphi}$ is continuously differentiable, we have that

$$x' := \overrightarrow{\varphi}(x) = \overrightarrow{\varphi}(x^0) + \frac{\partial \overrightarrow{\varphi}}{\partial x}(x^0)(x - x^0) + o(|x - x^0|)$$

at any point $x^0 \in X$ or

$$x' - (x^0)' = \frac{\partial \overrightarrow{\varphi}}{\partial x}(x^0)(x - x^0) + o(|x - x^0|),$$

where $(x^0)' = \overrightarrow{\varphi}(x^0)$. This implies that $\widetilde{\Pi_k} \approx A(Q_k)$ is a linear transformation $A = \frac{\partial \overrightarrow{\varphi}}{\partial x}(x^0)$ of $Q_k$ up to infinitesimals of higher order of smallness than the length of the sides of the parallelepipeds. In that case we have

$$\sum_{k=1}^m f((\xi')^{(k)}) \mu(\widetilde{\Pi_k}) \approx \sum_{k=1}^m f(\overrightarrow{\varphi}(\xi^{(k)})) \mu(A(Q_k)) = \sum_{k=1}^m f(\overrightarrow{\varphi}(\xi^{(k)})) |J(\xi^{(k)})| \mu(Q_k)$$

as $\mu(Q_k) \to 0$, where $\mu(Q_k)$ is a Jordan measure of the parallelepiped (not necessarily rectangular). Consideration of the general (curvilinear) parallelepipeds instead of the rectangular allows us to construct the same multidimensional Riemann integrals as before. Letting a $m \to \infty$ ($\mu(Q_k) \to 0$) we obtain that

$$\int_{X'} f(x') \mathrm{d}x' = \lim_{\mu(Q_k) \to 0} \sum_{k=1}^m f(\overrightarrow{\varphi}(\xi^{(k)})) |J(\xi^{(k)})| \mu(Q_k) = \int_X f(\overrightarrow{\varphi}(x)) |J(x)| \mathrm{d}x.$$

This finishes the proof.

**Corollary 15.14.** *If a set $X \subset \mathbb{R}^n$ is bounded and measurable with Jordan measure $\mu(X) > 0$ then*

$$\mu(X) = \int_X 1 \mathrm{d}x =: \mathrm{Vol}(X).$$

*The value $\mathrm{d}x = \mathrm{d}x_1 \mathrm{d}x_2 \cdots \mathrm{d}x_n$ is said to be a volume element in $\mathbb{R}^n$.*

**Example 15.15.** 1. *Spherical coordinates* in $\mathbb{R}^3$. Let

$$\begin{cases} x_1 = r \cos \varphi \sin \theta, \\ x_2 = r \sin \varphi \sin \theta, \\ x_3 = r \cos \theta, \end{cases}$$

where $r \geq 0$ and the angles $\varphi$ and $\theta$ are so that $\varphi \in [0, 2\pi]$ and $\theta \in [0, \pi]$. These formulas define the spherical coordinates in $\mathbb{R}^3$. The Jacobian of the transformation from $(x_1, x_2, x_3)$ to $(r, \varphi, \theta)$ is

$$J(r, \varphi, \theta) = \det \begin{pmatrix} \frac{\partial x_1}{\partial r} & \frac{\partial x_2}{\partial r} & \frac{\partial x_3}{\partial r} \\ \frac{\partial x_1}{\partial \varphi} & \frac{\partial x_2}{\partial \varphi} & \frac{\partial x_3}{\partial \varphi} \\ \frac{\partial x_1}{\partial \theta} & \frac{\partial x_2}{\partial \theta} & \frac{\partial x_3}{\partial \theta} \end{pmatrix}$$

$$= \det \begin{pmatrix} \cos\varphi \sin\theta & \sin\varphi \sin\theta & \cos\theta \\ -r\sin\varphi \sin\theta & r\cos\varphi \sin\theta & 0 \\ r\cos\varphi \cos\theta & r\sin\varphi \cos\theta & -r\sin\theta \end{pmatrix}$$

$$= -r^2 \cos^2\varphi \sin^3\theta - r^2 \sin^2\varphi \sin\theta \cos^2\theta$$
$$- r^2 \cos^2\varphi \cos^2\theta \sin\theta - r^2 \sin^2\varphi \sin^3\theta = -r^2 \sin\theta$$

and its modulus is $|J| = r^2 \sin\theta$. Hence,

$$\int_{|x| \leq R} f(x) \mathrm{d}x$$

$$= \int_0^R \mathrm{d}r \int_0^{2\pi} \mathrm{d}\varphi \int_0^\pi f(r\cos\varphi \sin\theta, r\sin\varphi \sin\theta, r\cos\theta) r^2 \sin\theta \mathrm{d}\theta.$$

In particular for radial function $f$ we have

$$\int_{|x| \leq R} f(|x|) \mathrm{d}x = \int_0^R \mathrm{d}r \int_0^{2\pi} \mathrm{d}\varphi \int_0^\pi f(r) r^2 \sin\theta \mathrm{d}\theta$$

$$= \int_0^R f(r) r^2 \mathrm{d}r \int_0^{2\pi} \mathrm{d}\varphi \int_0^\pi \sin\theta \mathrm{d}\theta = 4\pi \int_0^R r^2 f(r) \mathrm{d}r.$$

2. *Cylindrical coordinates* in $\mathbb{R}^3$. Let

$$\begin{cases} x_1 = r\cos\varphi, \\ x_2 = r\sin\varphi, \\ x_3 = x_3, \end{cases}$$

where $r \geq 0$, $x_3 \in \mathbb{R}$, and $\varphi \in [0, 2\pi]$. These formulas define the cylindrical coordinates in $\mathbb{R}^3$. The Jacobian of the transformation from $(x_1, x_2, x_3)$ to $(r, \varphi, x_3)$ is

$$J(r, \varphi, x_3) = \det \begin{pmatrix} \cos\varphi & \sin\varphi & 0 \\ -r\sin\varphi & r\cos\varphi & 0 \\ 0 & 0 & 1 \end{pmatrix} = r.$$

Hence, for example,

$$\int_{x_1^2 + x_2^2 \leq R^2, 0 \leq x_3 \leq h} f(x_1, x_2, x_3) \mathrm{d}x_1 \mathrm{d}x_2 \mathrm{d}x_3$$

$$= \int_0^R \int_0^{2\pi} \int_0^h f(r\cos\varphi, r\sin\varphi, x_3) r \mathrm{d}r \mathrm{d}\varphi \mathrm{d}x_3.$$

3. *Spherical coordinates* in $\mathbb{R}^n, n \geq 2$. Let

$$\begin{cases} x_1 = r\sin\theta_1\sin\theta_2\cdots\sin\theta_{n-1}, \\ x_2 = r\cos\theta_1\sin\theta_2\cdots\sin\theta_{n-1}, \\ \vdots \\ x_k = r\cos\theta_{k-1}\prod_{j=k}^{n-1}\sin\theta_j, \qquad k = 3,\dots,n-1, \\ \vdots \\ x_n = r\cos\theta_{n-1}, \end{cases}$$

where $r \geq 0, \theta_1 \in [0,2\pi]$ and $\theta_j \in [0,\pi], j = 2,\dots,n-1$. These formulas define the spherical coordinates in $\mathbb{R}^n, n \geq 2$. The Jacobian of the transformation from $(x_1, x_2, \dots, x_n)$ to $(r, \theta_1, \theta_2, \dots, \theta_{n-1})$ is given in Figure 15.1.

$$J = \det \begin{pmatrix} \sin\theta_1\cdots\sin\theta_{n-1} & \cdots & \cos\theta_{k-1}\prod_{j=k}^{n-1}\sin\theta_j & \cdots & \cos\theta_1 \\ r\cos\theta_1\sin\theta_2\cdots\sin\theta_{n-1} & \cdots & 0 & \cdots & 0 \\ \vdots & \vdots & \vdots & \vdots & \vdots \\ r\sin\theta_1\cdots\cos\theta_{k-1}\cdots\sin\theta_{n-1} & \cdots & -r\sin\theta_{k-1}\prod_{j=1}^{k-1}\sin\theta_j & \cdots & 0 \\ \vdots & \vdots & \vdots & \vdots & \vdots \\ r\sin\theta_1\cdots\sin\theta_{n-2}\cos\theta_{n-1} & \cdots & r\cos\theta_{k-1}\prod_{j=k}^{n-2}\sin\theta_j\cos\theta_{n-1} & \cdots & -r\sin\theta_{n-1} \end{pmatrix}$$

**Figure 15.1.** *The Jacobian of $J = J(r, \theta_1, \theta_2, \dots, \theta_{n-1})$.*

It can be proved by induction that

$$J(r, \theta_1, \theta_2, \dots, \theta_{n-1}) = -r^{n-1}\prod_{j=1}^{n-1}\sin^{j-1}\theta_j.$$

Hence, for example, for radial function $f$ we have

$$\int_{|x|\leq R} f(|x|)\mathrm{d}x$$

$$= \int_0^R r^{n-1}f(r)\mathrm{d}r \int_0^{2\pi}\mathrm{d}\theta_1 \int_0^\pi \sin\theta_2\mathrm{d}\theta_2 \cdots \int_0^\pi \sin^{n-2}\theta_{n-1}\mathrm{d}\theta_{n-1}.$$

4. Let $X \subset \mathbb{R}^3$ be a bounded set with boundary

$$\partial X = \{x \in \mathbb{R}^3 : (x_1^2 + x_2^2 + x_3^2)^2 = a^3 x_3, a > 0\}.$$

Let us compute the volume of $X$. Due to symmetricity with respect to $x_1$ and $x_2$ and using spherical coordinates in $\mathbb{R}^3$ we obtain

$$\mathrm{Vol}(X) = 4 \int_{X\cap\{x_1,x_2,x_3>0\}} 1\mathrm{d}x_1\mathrm{d}x_2\mathrm{d}x_3$$

$$= 4 \int_0^{\pi/2} \mathrm{d}\varphi \int_0^{\pi/2} \mathrm{d}\theta \int_0^{a\sqrt[3]{\cos\theta}} r^2\sin\theta\mathrm{d}r$$

$$= 2\pi \int_0^{\pi/2} \sin\theta\mathrm{d}\theta \int_0^{a\sqrt[3]{\cos\theta}} r^2\mathrm{d}r$$

$$= \frac{2\pi}{3}a^3 \int_0^{\pi/2} \sin\theta\cos\theta\mathrm{d}\theta = \frac{\pi}{3}a^3 \int_0^{\pi/2} \sin(2\theta)\mathrm{d}\theta = \frac{a^3\pi}{3}.$$

**Exercise 15.16.**    1. Evaluate the integral

$$\iint_X \frac{\sin x_1}{x_1} \mathrm{d}x_1 \mathrm{d}x_2,$$

where $X$ is the triangle in the $(x_1, x_2)$-plane bounded by the $x_1$-axis, the line $x_2 = x_1$, and the line $x_1 = 1$.

2. Evaluate the integral

$$\int_0^\pi \left( \int_{x_1}^\pi \frac{\sin x_2}{x_2} \mathrm{d}x_2 \right) \mathrm{d}x_1.$$

Hint: Use the Fubini theorem.

**Exercise 15.17.** Calculate the area of the two-dimensional set bounded by the curve

$$\frac{x_1^2}{a^2} + \frac{x_2^2}{b^2} = \frac{x_1}{h} + \frac{x_2}{k}, \quad a, b, h, k > 0.$$

Hint: Using the angle $\varphi_0$ with

$$\sin \varphi_0 = \frac{a/h}{\sqrt{a^2/h^2 + b^2/k^2}}, \quad \cos \varphi_0 = \frac{b/k}{\sqrt{a^2/h^2 + b^2/k^2}}$$

reduces this curve to

$$r = \sqrt{a^2/h^2 + b^2/k^2} \sin(\varphi + \varphi_0).$$

Here the following modified polar coordinates might be used:

$$x_1 = ar \cos \varphi, \quad x_2 = br \sin \varphi, \quad \varphi \in [0, 2\pi].$$

**Exercise 15.18.** Suppose that $f$ is continuous on a closed bounded set (i.e., compact set) $\Omega = \overline{\Omega} \subset \mathbb{R}^n$. Show that

1.

$$m \operatorname{Vol}(\Omega) \le \int_\Omega f(x)\mathrm{d}x \le M \operatorname{Vol}(\Omega),$$

where $m = \min_\Omega f(x)$ and $M = \max_\Omega f(x)$;

2. there is $\xi \in \Omega$ such that

$$\int_\Omega f(x)\mathrm{d}x = f(\xi) \operatorname{Vol}(\Omega);$$

3. $f(x) \equiv 0$ in $\Omega$ if we assume in addition that $f(x) \ge 0$ in $\Omega$ and $\int_\Omega f(x)\mathrm{d}x = 0$.

## 15.2 ▪ Improper multidimensional integrals

Let $X \subset \mathbb{R}^n$ be an open set. Let $\{X_k\}_{k=1}^\infty$ be a monotone sequence of open, bounded, and Jordan measurable sets such that

$$\overline{X_k} \subset X_{k+1}, \quad k = 1, 2, \ldots, \quad X = \bigcup_{k=1}^\infty X_k,$$

i.e., the sequence $\{X_k\}_{k=1}^\infty$ exhausts the set $X$.

**Definition 15.19.** *Let* $f : X \subset \mathbb{R}^n \to \mathbb{R}$ *be integrable on any closed, bounded, and Jordan measurable subset of* $X$. *If for any monotone sequence* $\{X_k\}_{k=1}^\infty$ *that exhausts the set* $X$ *the limit*

$$\lim_{k \to \infty} \int_{X_k} f(x) \mathrm{d}x$$

*exists then this limit is said to be a* convergent improper integral *of* $f$ *on* $X$ *and is denoted as*

$$\int_X f(x) \mathrm{d}x = \lim_{k \to \infty} \int_{X_k} f(x) \mathrm{d}x.$$

**Remark 15.20.** It is clear that this limit, if it exists for any such sequence $\{X_k\}_{k=1}^\infty$, is unique.

**Exercise 15.21.** Let $f$ be nonnegative on a set $X$. Prove that the integral

$$\int_X f(x) \mathrm{d}x$$

is convergent if and only if the number sequence $\{\int_{X_k} f(x) \mathrm{d}x\}_{k=1}^\infty$ is bounded for one monotone exhausting sequence $\{X_k\}_{k=1}^\infty$.

**Theorem 15.22 (Equivalence of convergence and absolute convergence for improper multidimensional integrals).** *The integral*

$$\int_X f(x) \mathrm{d}x$$

*is convergent if and only if the integral*

$$\int_X |f(x)| \mathrm{d}x$$

*is convergent.*

*Proof.* Let us first prove that the convergence of the integral

$$\int_X |f(x)| \mathrm{d}x$$

implies the convergence of the integral

$$\int_X f(x) \mathrm{d}x.$$

Indeed, let $\{X_k\}_{k=1}^\infty$ be an arbitrary monotone sequence that exhausts $X$. Then

$$\int_{X_k} |f(x)| \mathrm{d}x = \int_{X_k} f_+(x) \mathrm{d}x + \int_{X_k} f_-(x) \mathrm{d}x,$$

where

$$f_+(x) := \frac{|f(x)| + f(x)}{2} \geq 0, \quad f_-(x) := \frac{|f(x)| - f(x)}{2} \geq 0.$$

Since $|f|$ is integrable on each bounded Jordan measurable subset of $X$, so are the functions $f_+$ and $f_-$. Thus, the integral

$$\int_{X_k} f(x) \mathrm{d}x = \int_{X_k} f_+(x) \mathrm{d}x - \int_{X_k} f_-(x) \mathrm{d}x$$

exists also. The convergence of the integral $\int_X |f(x)|\mathrm{d}x$ is equivalent to the fact that the limits

$$\lim_{k\to\infty} \int_{X_k} f_+(x)\mathrm{d}x, \quad \lim_{k\to\infty} \int_{X_k} f_-(x)\mathrm{d}x$$

exist too due to positiveness of $f_+$ and $f_-$. This implies that the limit

$$\lim_{k\to\infty} \int_{X_k} f(x)\mathrm{d}x = \lim_{k\to\infty} \int_{X_k} f_+(x)\mathrm{d}x - \lim_{k\to\infty} \int_{X_k} f_-(x)\mathrm{d}x$$

exists, i.e., the integral $\int_X f(x)\mathrm{d}x$ converges.

Conversely, let us assume on the contrary that the integral $\int_X f(x)\mathrm{d}x$ converges but the integral $\int_X |f(x)|\mathrm{d}x$ does not converge. This means (see Exercise 15.21) that for any monotone sequence $\{X_k\}_{k=1}^\infty$ which exhausts $X$ it holds that

$$\lim_{k\to\infty} \int_{X_k} |f(x)|\mathrm{d}x = +\infty.$$

Due to this fact we can choose a sequence $\{X_k\}_{k=1}^\infty$ such that

$$\int_{X_{k+1}} |f(x)|\mathrm{d}x > 3 \int_{X_k} |f(x)|\mathrm{d}x + 2k.$$

Then we also have that

$$\int_{X_{k+1}\setminus \overline{X_k}} |f(x)|\mathrm{d}x > 2 \int_{X_k} |f(x)|\mathrm{d}x + 2k$$

and then (for example)

$$\int_{X_{k+1}\setminus \overline{X_k}} f_+(x)\mathrm{d}x > \int_{X_k} |f(x)|\mathrm{d}x + k.$$

Up to an arbitrarily small $\varepsilon > 0$ we may substitute the latter inequality by lower sums to obtain

$$L_F(f_+, X_{k+1}\setminus \overline{X_k}) = \sum_{l=1}^m m_l\mu(\Pi_l) > \int_{X_k} |f(x)|\mathrm{d}x + k - \varepsilon,$$

where $m_l = \inf_{\Pi_l} f_+ \geq 0$ and $F = \cup_{l=1}^m \Pi_l$ is an elementary figure such that $F \subset X_{k+1}\setminus\overline{X_k}$. Consider now only such parts of $\{\Pi_l\}_{l=1}^m$, where $m_l > 0$. It means that $f_+(x) = f(x)$ in these parallelepipeds and thus

$$\sideset{}{'}\sum_{l=1}^m m_l\mu(\Pi_l) > \int_{X_k} |f(x)|\mathrm{d}x + k - \varepsilon.$$

This leads to the inequality

$$\int_{X_{k+1}\setminus \overline{X_k}} f(x)\mathrm{d}x \geq \int_{X_k} |f(x)|\mathrm{d}x + k - 1.$$

At the same time we obviously have

$$\int_{X_k} f(x)\mathrm{d}x \geq - \int_{X_k} |f(x)|\mathrm{d}x.$$

Adding the latter two inequalities we obtain that

$$\int_{X_{k+1}} f(x)\mathrm{d}x \geq k - 1.$$

This implies that for this choice of monotone sequence $\{X_k\}_{k=1}^{\infty}$ that exhausts $X$ it holds that

$$\lim_{k\to\infty} \int_{X_{k+1}} f(x)\mathrm{d}x = +\infty.$$

This contradiction proves the theorem.

In addition to convergence and absolute convergence of improper multidimensional integrals (see Theorem 15.22) there is one special type of convergence that is very practical and applicable.

**Definition 15.23.** *Let* $f : \mathbb{R}^n \to \mathbb{R}$ *be integrable on each ball* $B_R(0), R > 0$. *If the limit*

$$\lim_{R\to+\infty} \int_{B_R(0)} f(x)\mathrm{d}x$$

*exists then this limit is called a* principal value integral *and is denoted as*

$$\mathrm{p.\,v.} \int_{\mathbb{R}^n} f(x)\mathrm{d}x := \lim_{R\to+\infty} \int_{B_R(0)} f(x)\mathrm{d}x.$$

**Example 15.24.** Let $f$ be of the form

$$f(x) = h(r)g(\theta_1, \theta_2, \ldots, \theta_{n-1}),$$

where $(r, \theta_1, \theta_2, \ldots, \theta_{n-1})$ are spherical coordinates in $\mathbb{R}^n$ and functions $h$ and $g$ are continuous. Assuming that

$$\int_0^{2\pi} \mathrm{d}\theta_1 \int_0^{\pi} \mathrm{d}\theta_2 \cdots \int_0^{\pi} \mathrm{d}\theta_{n-1} g(\theta_1, \theta_2, \ldots, \theta_{n-1}) \prod_{j=1}^{n-1} \sin^{j-1}\theta_j = 0$$

we can easily obtain that

$$\mathrm{p.\,v.} \int_{\mathbb{R}^n} f(x)\mathrm{d}x = 0.$$

**Exercise 15.25.**     1. Define real numbers $\lambda$ and $\mu$ for which the integral

$$\int_{\mathbb{R}^n} \frac{1}{|x|^{\mu}(1+|x|)^{\lambda}}\mathrm{d}x$$

converges.

2. Define real numbers $\alpha$ and $\beta$ for which the integral

$$\int_{\mathbb{R}^n} \frac{1}{|x|^{\alpha} \log^{\beta}(1+|x|)}\mathrm{d}x$$

converges.

3. Prove that the integral

$$\prod_{j=1}^{n} \int_{x_j \geq 1} \frac{1}{x_1^\alpha + x_2^\beta + x_3^\gamma + \cdots + x_n^\lambda} \mathrm{d}x$$

converges if $\frac{1}{\alpha} + \frac{1}{\beta} + \frac{1}{\gamma} + \cdots + \frac{1}{\lambda} < 1$.

4. Prove that

$$\mathrm{p.\,v.} \int_{\mathbb{R}^n} \frac{|x|^2 - n x_j^2}{(|x|^2 + \varepsilon^2)^{(n+1)/2}} \mathrm{d}x = 0, \quad \varepsilon > 0,$$

for each $j = 1, 2, \ldots, n$.

5. Prove that

$$\lim_{\varepsilon \to +0, R \to +\infty} \int_{\varepsilon < |x| < R} \frac{x_j}{|x|^{n+1}} \mathrm{d}x = 0$$

for each $j = 1, 2, \ldots, n$.

6. Prove that the integral

$$\int_{\mathbb{R}^n} \frac{1}{|x|^\lambda} \mathrm{d}x$$

diverges for any real $\lambda$.

7. Find real $\alpha$ and $\beta$ such that the integral

$$\int_{\mathbb{R}^n} \frac{\sin(|x|^\beta)}{|x|^\alpha} \mathrm{d}x$$

converges.

8. Formulate the Fubini theorem (see Theorem 15.8) for the case of improper multidimensional integrals.

**Example 15.26.** Let us consider the double integral

$$I := \int_1^\infty \int_{e^{-x}}^1 \frac{1}{x^3 y} \mathrm{d}y \mathrm{d}x.$$

We will calculate it using the Fubini theorem as an iterated integral. The set of integration on the plane is depicted in Figure 15.2. Thus, we have (iterated integral)

$$I = \int_0^{e^{-1}} \mathrm{d}y \int_{\log(1/y)}^\infty \frac{\mathrm{d}x}{x^3 y} + \int_{e^{-1}}^1 \mathrm{d}y \int_1^\infty \frac{\mathrm{d}x}{x^3 y}$$

$$= \frac{1}{2} \int_0^{e^{-1}} \frac{\mathrm{d}y}{y \log^2 y} + \frac{1}{2} \int_{e^{-1}}^1 \frac{\mathrm{d}y}{y} = -\frac{1}{2} \frac{1}{\log(e^{-1})} - \frac{1}{2} \log(e^{-1}) = 1.$$

**Exercise 15.27.**     1. Prove that

$$\int_0^\infty e^{-x^2} \mathrm{d}x = \frac{\sqrt{\pi}}{2}.$$

Hint: Use the fact that

$$\left( \int_0^\infty e^{-x^2} \mathrm{d}x \right)^2 = \int_0^\infty \int_0^\infty e^{-x^2 - y^2} \mathrm{d}x \mathrm{d}y.$$

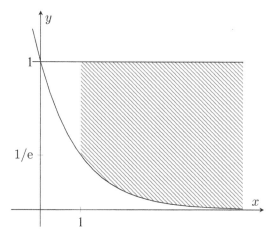

**Figure 15.2.** *Region of integration in Example* 15.26.

2. Evaluate the integral

$$\int_0^\infty \frac{e^{-ax} - e^{-bx}}{x} dx, \quad a, b > 0.$$

Hint: Use the relation

$$\frac{e^{-ax} - e^{-bx}}{x} = \int_a^b e^{-xy} dy$$

and use the Fubini theorem.

## 15.3 ▪ Surface integrals

**Definition 15.28.** *A set $S \subset \mathbb{R}^n$ is called a* surface *of class $C^k, k = 1, 2, \ldots,$ if for any point $x^0 \in S$ there is an open set $V \subset \mathbb{R}^n$ containing $x^0$ and a real-valued function $\varphi \in C^k(V)$ such that*

$$S \cap V = \{x \in V : \varphi(x) = 0, \nabla\varphi(x) \neq 0\}.$$

*These surfaces are called* regular.

**Remark 15.29.** Since $\nabla\varphi(x) \neq 0$, by the implicit function theorem (see Theorem 14.1) we can solve the equation $\varphi(x) = 0$ near the point $x^0$ with respect to $x_n$ (for example) to obtain

$$x_n = \psi(x'), \quad x' = (x_1, x_2, \ldots, x_{n-1}),$$

with some function $\psi \in C^k$. In this case a neighborhood of the point $x^0$ can be mapped into a piece of the hyperplane $\widetilde{x_n} = 0$, where

$$x \mapsto (x', \widetilde{x_n}) \equiv (x', x_n - \psi(x')).$$

For given regular surface $S$ the vector $\nabla\varphi(x) \neq 0$ is perpendicular to $S$ at the point $x \in S$ since $\nabla\varphi(x)$ is a normal vector of the corresponding hyperplane at $x$ (see Theorem 13.30).

**Example 15.30.**    1. Let $f : X \subset \mathbb{R}^n \to \mathbb{R}$ be continuously differentiable on open bounded set $X$. Then the graph

$$\Gamma(f) = \{(x, y) \in \mathbb{R}^{n+1} : x \in X, y = f(x)\}$$

is a regular surface of class $C^1$ in $\mathbb{R}^{n+1}$. Indeed, considering $C^1$-function $\varphi(x, y)$ given by

$$\varphi(x, y) := f(x) - y, \quad x \in X,$$

we obtain that a set $S \subset \mathbb{R}^{n+1}$ defined as

$$S := \{(x, y) \in \mathbb{R}^{n+1} : \varphi(x, y) = 0, x \in X\} = \Gamma(f)$$

is a regular surface of class $C^1$ since

$$\nabla_{(x,y)}\varphi(x, y) = (\nabla_x \varphi(x, y), -1) \neq 0.$$

2. Let $\gamma \subset \mathbb{R}^2$ be a curve (it is a surface on the plane) defined by the equations

$$x_1 = \varphi_1(t), \quad x_2 = \varphi_2(t), \quad t \in [\alpha, \beta],$$

with continuously differentiable functions $\varphi_1$ and $\varphi_2$. Assuming that, for example, equation $x_1 = \varphi_1(t)$ is uniquely solvable with respect to $t$, i.e., $\varphi_1$ has an inverse function $\varphi_1^{-1}$ such that $t = \varphi_1^{-1}(x_1)$ with $x_1$ from some interval $[a, b]$ (this can occur if $\varphi_1'(t) < 0$ or $\varphi_1'(t) > 0$ everywhere on the interval $[\alpha, \beta]$), we obtain that

$$x_2 = \varphi_2(t) = \varphi_2(\varphi_1^{-1}(x_1)) =: g(x_1)$$

and the graph of $g$ defines (uniquely) this curve from class $C^1$ since $g$ is continuously differentiable with

$$\nabla_{(x_1,x_2)}(g(x_1) - x_2) = (g'(x_1), -1) \neq 0.$$

3. Consider a system of three equations in two variables $(u, v) \in \Omega \subset \mathbb{R}^2$, where $\Omega$ is an open set, as

$$x_1 = \varphi_1(u, v), \quad x_2 = \varphi_2(u, v), \quad x_3 = \varphi_3(u, v)$$

with real-valued continuously differentiable functions $\varphi_1$, $\varphi_2$, and $\varphi_3$. Let us assume that the determinant (for example)

$$\begin{vmatrix} \frac{\partial\varphi_1}{\partial u} & \frac{\partial\varphi_2}{\partial u} \\ \frac{\partial\varphi_1}{\partial v} & \frac{\partial\varphi_2}{\partial v} \end{vmatrix} \neq 0$$

for all $(u, v) \in \Omega$. Due to the fact that $\varphi_1$ and $\varphi_2$ are continuously differentiable in $\Omega$ this determinant is either positive or negative everywhere in $\Omega$. Under these conditions the system

$$\begin{cases} x_1 - \varphi_1(u, v) = 0, \\ x_2 - \varphi_2(u, v) = 0 \end{cases}$$

can be uniquely solved (see Theorem 14.4) with respect to $u$ and $v$ to obtain

$$u = \psi_1(x_1, x_2), \quad v = \psi_2(x_1, x_2).$$

Hence, we have that

$$x_3 = \varphi_3(u, v) = \varphi_3(\psi_1(x_1, x_2), \psi_2(x_1, x_2)) =: g(x_1, x_2)$$

and the graph of $g$ defines a regular surface $S$ in $\mathbb{R}^3$.

**Definition 15.31.** *Let $S \subset \mathbb{R}^n$ be a closed, i.e., compact without boundary, and regular surface of class $C^1$. If a normal vector*

$$\nu(x) = \frac{\nabla\varphi(x)}{|\nabla\varphi(x)|}$$

*of $S$, where $\varphi$ defines $S$, is continuous everywhere throughout $S$ then this surface is said to be* bilateral *(or double-sided). Such a surface is called* positively oriented *with respect to outward normal vector.*

**Remark 15.32.** The surface defined in Definition 15.31 has the following property: for any point $x^0 \in S$ there is a neighborhood of $x^0$ in $S$ that can be uniquely mapped (projected) onto a tangent hyperplane at the point $x^0$. This property follows from the geometric meaning of differentiability (see Theorem 13.47). Finite union of such surfaces will be considered also later.

Let $S \subset \mathbb{R}^n$ be a regular surface and assume that it is divided into a finite number of subsurfaces $\{S_k\}_{k=1}^m$ such that

$$S = \bigcup_{k=1}^m S_k, \quad \text{int } S_k \cap \text{int } S_l = \emptyset, k \neq l,$$

and each subsurface $S_k$ is uniquely projected onto the tangent hyperplane at any point of $S_k$. Denoting by $\Delta$ the maximal diameter of $S_k$ as

$$\Delta = \max_{1 \leq k \leq n} \left\{ \max_{x,y \in S_k} |x - y| \right\}$$

and by $\sigma_k(x^{(k)})$ the area of the projection of $S_k$ onto the tangent hyperplane at some point $x^{(k)} \in S_k$ one defines the sums

$$\sigma_m(S, S_k; x^{(k)}) := \sum_{k=1}^m \sigma_k(x^{(k)}).$$

**Definition 15.33.**

1. *A number $\sigma$ is said to be a limit of the sums $\sigma_m(S, S_k; x^{(k)})$ as $\Delta \to 0$ if for any $\varepsilon > 0$ there is $\delta > 0$ such that $|\sigma_m(S, S_k; x^{(k)}) - \sigma| < \varepsilon$ for all partitions of $S$ into $\{S_k\}_{k=1}^m$ with $\Delta < \delta$ and for arbitrary choice of $x^{(k)} \in S_k$.*

2. *A regular surface $S$ is called* squarable *if the limit*

$$\lim_{\Delta \to 0} \sigma_m(S, S_k; x^{(k)}) =: \sigma$$

*exists. The number $\sigma$ is called the surface area of $S$.*

**Remark 15.34.** Since for each $S_k$ it is assumed that $S_k$ is uniquely projected onto the tangent hyperplane at any point of $S_k$, we may assume without loss of generality that $S_k$ can be uniquely projected onto every coordinate plane, i.e., onto the hyperplane defined by the normal vector $e_j = (0, \ldots, 0, 1, 0, \ldots, 0)$. By $\theta_j(x^{(k)})$ we denote the angle between $\nu(x^{(k)})$ and $e_j$ so that

$$(\nu(x^{(k)}), e_j) = \cos(\theta_j(x^{(k)}))|\nu(x^{(k)})||e_j| = \cos(\theta_j(x^{(k)})) =: \alpha_j$$

and $\nu(x^{(k)}) = \alpha_1 e_1 + \cdots + \alpha_j e_j + \cdots + \alpha_n e_n$, i.e., $\alpha_j = \cos(\theta_j(x^{(k)}))$ are the coordinates of the normal vector $\nu(x^{(k)})$ with respect to the orthonormal basis $\{e_j\}_{j=1}^n$ in $\mathbb{R}^n$; see Figure 15.3.

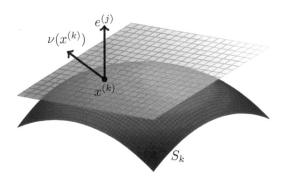

**Figure 15.3.** *Illustration of tangent hyperplane.*

For arbitrary continuous function $f$ defined on regular surface $S$ of class $C^1$ one can consider the sums

$$\sum_{k=1}^{m} f(x^{(k)})\sigma_k(x^{(k)}), \quad \sum_{k=1}^{m} f(x^{(k)})\sigma_k(x^{(k)}) \cos(\theta_j(x^{(k)})),$$

where $S = \cup_{k=1}^{m} S_k$ and $x^{(k)} \in S_k$. Under these conditions for $f$ and $S$ it can be proved that the limits

$$\lim_{\Delta \to 0} \sum_{k=1}^{m} f(x^{(k)})\sigma_k(x^{(k)}), \quad \lim_{\Delta \to 0} \sum_{k=1}^{m} f(x^{(k)})\sigma_k(x^{(k)}) \cos(\theta_j(x^{(k)}))$$

exist. These limits are denoted as

$$\int_S f(x)\mathrm{d}\sigma(x), \quad \int_S f(x) \cos(\theta_j(x))\mathrm{d}\sigma(x),$$

respectively, and they are called the *surface integrals* of $f$ of the *first and second kinds*. For a vector-valued continuous function $\overrightarrow{f}$ on $S$ we will have then that

$$\sum_{j=1}^{n} \int_S f_j(x) \cos(\theta_j(x))\mathrm{d}\sigma(x) = \int_S (\overrightarrow{f}(x), \nu(x))_{\mathbb{R}^n} \mathrm{d}\sigma(x).$$

If we denote by $\Omega_j$ a projection of surface $S$ onto the coordinate hyperplane

$$x^{(j)} := (x_1, \ldots, x_{j-1}, x_{j+1}, \ldots, x_n)$$

then the surface integral of the second kind can be rewritten as

$$\int_S f(x)\nu_j(x)\mathrm{d}\sigma(x) = \int_S f(x) \cos(\theta_j(x))\mathrm{d}\sigma(x) = \int_{\Omega_j} f(x)\mathrm{d}x^{(j)}.$$

We are now in position to prove the main theorem of surface integration. Here we denote

$$\mathrm{div}\, \overrightarrow{F}(x) = \sum_{j=1}^{n} \frac{\partial F_j}{\partial x_j}(x).$$

**Theorem 15.35 (Divergence theorem).** *Let* $\Omega \subset \mathbb{R}^n$ *be a bounded open set with boundary* $S = \partial \Omega$ *that is a regular closed surface of class* $C^1$ *(or piecewise* $C^1$*) such that any line which is parallel to any coordinate axes intersects* $S$ *in (at most) two points. Suppose that* $\overrightarrow{F}(x)$ *is a vector-valued continuously differentiable function defined on* $\overline{\Omega} = \Omega \cup S$. *Then*

$$\int_\Omega \operatorname{div} \overrightarrow{F}(x)\mathrm{d}x \equiv \int_\Omega \sum_{j=1}^n \frac{\partial F_j}{\partial x_j}(x)\mathrm{d}x$$

$$= \int_S (\overrightarrow{F}(x), \nu(x))_{\mathbb{R}^n}\mathrm{d}\sigma(x) \equiv \sum_{j=1}^n \int_{\Omega_j} F_j(x)\mathrm{d}x^{(j)}.$$

*This formula is called the* Gauss–Ostrogradskii formula.

*Proof.* Since

$$\int_\Omega \operatorname{div} \overrightarrow{F}(x)\mathrm{d}x \equiv \sum_{j=1}^n \int_\Omega \frac{\partial F_j}{\partial x_j}(x)\mathrm{d}x,$$

it suffices to consider only each term of this sum, i.e.,

$$\int_\Omega \frac{\partial F_j}{\partial x_j}(x)\mathrm{d}x.$$

Due to the conditions of this theorem we have that for any line that is parallel to any coordinate axes there are (at most) two points $x^+(x^{(j)})$ and $x^-(x^{(j)})$ intersecting $S$ such that $x^+(x^{(j)})$ belongs to the positive part $S^+$ of $S$ and $x^-(x^{(j)})$ belongs to the negative part $S^-$ of $S$ with respect to orientation chosen on $S$; see Figure 15.4.

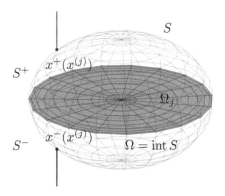

**Figure 15.4.** *Positive and negative parts of surface $S$.*

Hence, by the one-dimensional Newton's formula, we have

$$\int_\Omega \frac{\partial F_j}{\partial x_j}(x)\mathrm{d}x = \int_{\Omega_j} [F_j(x_1, \dots, x_{j-1}, x^+(x^{(j)}), x_{j+1}, \dots, x_n)$$

$$- F_j(x_1, \dots, x_{j-1}, x^-(x^{(j)}), x_{j+1}, \dots, x_n)]\mathrm{d}x^{(j)}$$

$$= \int_{S^+} F_j(x)\nu_j(x)\mathrm{d}\sigma(x) + \int_{S^-} F_j(x)\nu_j(x)\mathrm{d}\sigma(x)$$

taking into account the orientation (or the normal vector $\nu$ on $S$). Thus, we obtain that

$$\int_\Omega \frac{\partial F_j}{\partial x_j}(x)\mathrm{d}x = \int_S F_j(x)\nu_j(x)\mathrm{d}\sigma(x)$$

and hence

$$\int_\Omega \operatorname{div} \vec{F}(x)\mathrm{d}x = \int_S (\vec{F}(x), \nu(x))_{\mathbb{R}^n}\,\mathrm{d}\sigma(x).$$

This finished the proof.

**Corollary 15.36.** *Let us assume that open bounded set $\Omega \subset \mathbb{R}^n$ is divided into a finite number of subdomains $\Omega_l, l = 1, 2, \ldots, m$, such that*

$$\Omega = \bigcup_{l=1}^m \Omega_l$$

*and each $\Omega_l$ satisfies all conditions of the divergence theorem. Then the Gauss–Ostrogradskii formula holds in this case also.*

**Exercise 15.37.**    1. Suppose that two-dimensional domain $\Omega$ is defined as

$$\Omega := \{(x_1, x_2) \in \mathbb{R}^2 : x_1 \in (a, b), f(a) < x_2 < f(x_1)\},$$

where $f$ is monotone increasing. Suppose also that functions $P(x_1, x_2)$ and $Q(x_1, x_2)$ are continuously differentiable on $\overline{\Omega}$. Prove that

$$\int_\Omega \left(\frac{\partial P}{\partial x_1}(x_1, x_2) - \frac{\partial Q}{\partial x_2}(x_1, x_2)\right)\mathrm{d}x_1\mathrm{d}x_2$$
$$= \int_{\partial\Omega} Q(x_1, x_2)\mathrm{d}x_1 + \int_{\partial\Omega} P(x_1, x_2)\mathrm{d}x_2.$$

2. Suppose that a domain $\Omega \subset \mathbb{R}^2$ satisfies all conditions of the divergence theorem (Theorem 15.35). Suppose also that functions $P(x_1, x_2)$ and $Q(x_1, x_2)$ are continuously differentiable on $\overline{\Omega}$. Prove that

$$\int_\Omega \left(\frac{\partial P}{\partial x_1}(x_1, x_2) - \frac{\partial Q}{\partial x_2}(x_1, x_2)\right)\mathrm{d}x_1\mathrm{d}x_2$$
$$= \int_{\partial\Omega} Q(x_1, x_2)\mathrm{d}x_1 + \int_{\partial\Omega} P(x_1, x_2)\mathrm{d}x_2.$$

This result is called *Green's theorem* (or *Green's formula*).

3. Under the conditions of part 2 prove that

$$\operatorname{Vol}(\Omega) = \frac{1}{2}\int_{\partial\Omega} (x_1\mathrm{d}x_2 - x_2\mathrm{d}x_1),$$

where $\partial\Omega$ is a closed curve $\gamma$ such that $\operatorname{int}\gamma = \Omega$.

4. Using the divergence theorem show that

$$\operatorname{Vol}(\Omega) = \frac{1}{n}\int_{\partial\Omega} (x, \nu(x))_{\mathbb{R}^n}\,\mathrm{d}\sigma(x),$$

where $\Omega \subset \mathbb{R}^n$ is a Jordan measurable set with boundary $\partial\Omega$ that satisfies all conditions of the divergence theorem. In particular,

$$\mathrm{Vol}(B_R(0)) = \frac{R^n \omega_n}{n},$$

where $\omega_n$ is the area of the unit sphere in $\mathbb{R}^n$.

5. Using Green's theorem from part 2 prove that

$$Q(x_1, x_2)\mathrm{d}x_1 + P(x_1, x_2)\mathrm{d}x_2$$

is an exact differential form of some function $u(x_1, x_2)$, i.e., $Q = \partial_x u$ and $P = \partial_y u$ if and only if

$$\frac{\partial Q}{\partial x_2}(x_1, x_2) = \frac{\partial P}{\partial x_1}(x_1, x_2), \quad (x_1, x_2) \in \Omega.$$

6. Let $S \subset \mathbb{R}^3$ be a surface defined by the system

$$x_1 = \varphi_1(u, v), \quad x_2 = \varphi_2(u, v), \quad x_3 = \varphi_3(u, v), \quad (u, v) \in \Omega \subset \mathbb{R}^2,$$

where $\Omega$ is a two-dimensional smooth domain. Assuming that $S$ is a regular closed surface of class $C^1$ prove that its area $\sigma(S)$ can be calculated as

$$\sigma(S) = \int_\Omega \sqrt{\left|\frac{\partial \vec{r}}{\partial u}\right|^2 \left|\frac{\partial \vec{r}}{\partial v}\right|^2 - \left(\frac{\partial \vec{r}}{\partial u}, \frac{\partial \vec{r}}{\partial v}\right)_{\mathbb{R}^3}^2}\, \mathrm{d}u\mathrm{d}v,$$

where $\vec{r} = (\varphi_1, \varphi_2, \varphi_3)$.

7. Let $S \subset \mathbb{R}^3$ be a regular surface defined by the equation

$$\varphi(x_1, x_2, x_3) = 0, \quad \nabla\varphi(x_1, x_2, x_3) \neq 0.$$

Prove that its area $\sigma(S)$ can be calculated as

$$\sigma(S) = \int_\Omega \frac{|\nabla\varphi(x_1, x_2, x_3)|}{\left|\frac{\partial\varphi}{\partial x_3}(x_1, x_2, x_3)\right|}\Bigg|_{\varphi(x_1, x_2, x_3) = 0} \mathrm{d}x_1\mathrm{d}x_2,$$

where $\Omega$ is a projection of $S$ to the $(x_1, x_2)$-plane.

8. Under the conditions of part 6 prove that for any continuous function $f$ on the surface $S$ we have that

$$\int_S f(x)\mathrm{d}\sigma(x) = \int_\Omega f(\vec{r}(u, v))\sqrt{\left|\frac{\partial \vec{r}}{\partial u}\right|^2 \left|\frac{\partial \vec{r}}{\partial v}\right|^2 - \left(\frac{\partial \vec{r}}{\partial u}, \frac{\partial \vec{r}}{\partial v}\right)_{\mathbb{R}^3}^2}\, \mathrm{d}u\mathrm{d}v.$$

**Remark 15.38.** Returning to Green's formula (see Exercise 15.37)

$$\int_\Omega \left(\frac{\partial P}{\partial x_1}(x_1, x_2) - \frac{\partial Q}{\partial x_2}(x_1, x_2)\right)\mathrm{d}x_1\mathrm{d}x_2$$

$$= \int_{\partial\Omega} Q(x_1, x_2)\mathrm{d}x_1 + \int_{\partial\Omega} P(x_1, x_2)\mathrm{d}x_2,$$

where $\partial\Omega = \gamma$ is a closed Jordan curve on the plane defined by the parametrization

$$x_1 = \varphi(t), \quad x_2 = \psi(t), \quad t \in [\alpha, \beta], \quad \varphi(\alpha) = \varphi(\beta), \quad \psi(\alpha) = \psi(\beta)$$

we obtain that the right-hand side is equal to

$$\int_\alpha^\beta [Q(\varphi(t), \psi(t))\varphi'(t) + P(\varphi(t), \psi(t))\psi'(t)]\mathrm{d}t$$

$$= \int_\alpha^\beta \left[ Q(\varphi(t), \psi(t))\frac{\varphi'(t)}{\sqrt{\varphi'(t)^2 + \psi'(t)^2}} + P(\varphi(t), \psi(t))\frac{\psi'(t)}{\sqrt{\varphi'(t)^2 + \psi'(t)^2}} \right] \mathrm{d}l$$

$$= \int_\gamma [-Q(\varphi(t), \psi(t))\nu_2 + P(\varphi(t), \psi(t))\nu_1]\mathrm{d}l,$$

where

$$\nu = (\nu_1, \nu_2) := \left( \frac{\psi'(t)}{\sqrt{\varphi'(t)^2 + \psi'(t)^2}}, -\frac{\varphi'(t)}{\sqrt{\varphi'(t)^2 + \psi'(t)^2}} \right)$$

and $\mathrm{d}l = \sqrt{\varphi'(t)^2 + \psi'(t)^2}\mathrm{d}t$. It can be interpreted in such a way that the vector $\nu$ is an outward normal vector at the boundary of $\Omega$; see Figure 15.5.

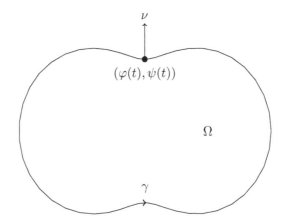

**Figure 15.5.** *Schematic presentation of outward normal vector $\nu$.*

Indeed, the curve $\gamma$ can be defined by the equation

$$\Phi(x_1, x_2) := \psi(\varphi^{-1}(x_1)) - x_2 = 0,$$

which implies that

$$\nu = \frac{\nabla\Phi}{|\nabla\Phi|} = \frac{(\psi'(t)/\varphi'(t), -1)}{\sqrt{1 + \psi'(t)^2/\varphi'(t)^2}} = \frac{(\psi'(t), -\varphi'(t))}{\sqrt{\varphi'(t)^2 + \psi'(t)^2}}.$$

This fact allows us to rewrite Green's formula as

$$\int_\Omega \mathrm{div}(P, -Q)\mathrm{d}x_1\mathrm{d}x_2 = \int_\gamma (P(x_1, x_2)\nu_1 - Q(x_1, x_2)\nu_2)\mathrm{d}l.$$

In other words, Green's formula is a particular case of the Gauss–Ostrogradskii formula (see the divergence theorem). Moreover, it is a particular case of the three-dimensional Stokes theorem (see Theorem 15.39).

We consider now the Stokes formula for two and three dimensions. Let us denote by rot $\overrightarrow{F}$ (or curl $\overrightarrow{F}$) for $\overrightarrow{F} = (F_1, F_2, F_3)$ in three dimensions the vector

$$\operatorname{rot} \overrightarrow{F} := \begin{vmatrix} F_1 & F_2 & F_3 \\ \overrightarrow{i} & \overrightarrow{j} & \overrightarrow{k} \\ \partial_1 & \partial_2 & \partial_3 \end{vmatrix}$$

$$= \left( \frac{\partial F_3}{\partial x_2} - \frac{\partial F_2}{\partial x_3} \right) \overrightarrow{i} + \left( \frac{\partial F_1}{\partial x_3} - \frac{\partial F_3}{\partial x_1} \right) \overrightarrow{j} + \left( \frac{\partial F_2}{\partial x_1} - \frac{\partial F_1}{\partial x_2} \right) \overrightarrow{k},$$

where $(\overrightarrow{i}, \overrightarrow{j}, \overrightarrow{k})$ is the standard normal basis in $\mathbb{R}^3$ and vector-valued function $\overrightarrow{F}(x_1, x_2, x_3)$ is differentiable. In the two-dimensional case we define

$$\operatorname{rot} \overrightarrow{F} = \frac{\partial F_2}{\partial x_1} - \frac{\partial F_1}{\partial x_2}.$$

**Theorem 15.39 (Stokes formula).** *Let $S \subset \mathbb{R}^3$ be a surface of class $C^1$ with boundary $\partial S$ which is a closed curve of class $C^1$ with a positive direction of orientation with respect to one side of $S$. Let also $\overrightarrow{F} : \Omega \subset \mathbb{R}^3 \to \mathbb{R}^3$ be continuously differentiable on some open set $\Omega \subset \mathbb{R}^3$ such that $S \subset \Omega$. Then*

$$\int_S (\operatorname{rot} \overrightarrow{F}, \overrightarrow{\nu})_{\mathbb{R}^3} \mathrm{d}\sigma(x) = \oint_{\partial S} (\overrightarrow{F}, \mathrm{d}x)_{\mathbb{R}^3}.$$

*This formula is called the* Stokes formula *in the three-dimensional case.*

**Proof.** To prove the theorem it suffices to show that

$$\int_S \left( \frac{\partial F_1}{\partial x_3} \nu_2 - \frac{\partial F_1}{\partial x_2} \nu_3 \right) \mathrm{d}\sigma(x) = \int_{\partial S} F_1(x) \mathrm{d}x_1,$$

$$\int_S \left( \frac{\partial F_2}{\partial x_1} \nu_3 - \frac{\partial F_2}{\partial x_3} \nu_1 \right) \mathrm{d}\sigma(x) = \int_{\partial S} F_2(x) \mathrm{d}x_2,$$

$$\int_S \left( \frac{\partial F_3}{\partial x_2} \nu_1 - \frac{\partial F_3}{\partial x_1} \nu_2 \right) \mathrm{d}\sigma(x) = \int_{\partial S} F_3(x) \mathrm{d}x_3.$$

We prove only the first equality since the other equalities can be proved similarly. Let us assume for the moment that the surface $S$ can be uniquely projected on each of the three planes $(x_1, x_2)$, $(x_1, x_3)$, and $(x_2, x_3)$. We may also assume without loss of generality that the normal vectors on $S$ form acute angles with the coordinate axes $x_1$, $x_2$, and $x_3$. By these conditions the surface $S$ is uniquely projected to the $(x_1, x_2)$-plane, and thus $S$ is a graph of a continuously differentiable function $x_3 = \psi(x_1, x_2)$ such that the surface $S$ is defined by the equation

$$\varphi(x_1, x_2, x_3) := x_3 - \psi(x_1, x_2) = 0.$$

In that case the normal vector $\overrightarrow{\nu} = (\nu_1, \nu_2, \nu_3)$ is given by

$$\nu_1 = -\frac{\dfrac{\partial \psi}{\partial x_1}}{\sqrt{1 + \left( \dfrac{\partial \psi}{\partial x_1} \right)^2 + \left( \dfrac{\partial \psi}{\partial x_2} \right)^2}}, \quad \nu_2 = -\frac{\dfrac{\partial \psi}{\partial x_2}}{\sqrt{1 + \left( \dfrac{\partial \psi}{\partial x_1} \right)^2 + \left( \dfrac{\partial \psi}{\partial x_2} \right)^2}},$$

and

$$\nu_3 = \frac{1}{\sqrt{1 + \left( \dfrac{\partial \psi}{\partial x_1} \right)^2 + \left( \dfrac{\partial \psi}{\partial x_2} \right)^2}}.$$

That's why we have that

$$\int_S \left( \frac{\partial F_1}{\partial x_3} \nu_2 - \frac{\partial F_1}{\partial x_2} \nu_3 \right) d\sigma(x)$$

$$= -\int_S \left( \frac{\partial F_1}{\partial x_2} + \frac{\partial \psi}{\partial x_2} \frac{\partial F_1}{\partial x_3} \right) \frac{d\sigma(x)}{\sqrt{1 + \left( \frac{\partial \psi}{\partial x_1} \right)^2 + \left( \frac{\partial \psi}{\partial x_2} \right)^2}}$$

$$= -\int_S \frac{\partial}{\partial x_2} [F_1(x_1, x_2, \psi(x_1, x_2)] \nu_3 d\sigma(x).$$

Let domain $\Omega \subset \mathbb{R}^2$ be a projection of $S$ to the $(x_1, x_2)$-plane, i.e., $\Omega$ is the domain of function $\psi(x_1, x_2)$ with graph $S$. Hence the latter integral equals

$$-\int_\Omega \frac{\partial}{\partial x_2} [F_1(x_1, x_2, \psi(x_1, x_2)] dx_1 dx_2.$$

Next, using the divergence theorem for the two-dimensional case with scalar function $F_1$ (integration by parts) we obtain

$$-\int_\Omega \frac{\partial}{\partial x_2} [F_1(x_1, x_2, \psi(x_1, x_2)] dx_1 dx_2 = \int_{\partial \Omega} F_1(x_1, x_2, \psi(x_1, x_2)) \tilde{\nu}_2 dl(x_1, x_2),$$

where $\tilde{\nu}_2$ is the second coordinate of the outward normal vector $\overrightarrow{\nu}$ to the curve $\partial \Omega$. But this is just the integral (see Remark 15.34 after Definition 15.33)

$$\int_{\partial S} F_1(x_1, x_2, x_3) dx_1.$$

If we consider the sum of these three equalities we obtain the Stokes formula in this particular case, i.e.,

$$\int_S (\text{rot } \overrightarrow{F}, \overrightarrow{\nu})_{\mathbb{R}^3} d\sigma(x) = \int_{\partial S} (\overrightarrow{F}, dx)_{\mathbb{R}^3}.$$

The general case with respect to surfaces can be considered using the partition of the surface with small parts of $S$ such that each "small" part satisfies the previous conditions (see Figure 15.6).

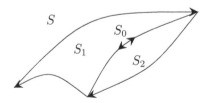

**Figure 15.6.** *Schematic representation of partition of surface.*

Now applying the Stokes formula for $S = S_1 \cup S_2$, for example, we obtain the same formula as before since integrals over $\partial S = \partial(S_1 \cup S_2)$ with respect to their common boundaries $S_0$ are running twice in the opposite directions and therefore they cancel each other. This completes the proof.

**Corollary 15.40.** *Let surface* $S \subset \mathbb{R}^2$ *be located on the* $(x_1, x_2)$-plane, i.e., $S = \Omega \subset \mathbb{R}^2$ *such that* $\Omega$ *is a bounded domain with the boundary (curve)* $\partial\Omega$ *of class* $C^1$. *Let also function* $\overrightarrow{F} = (F_1, F_2)$ *depend only on* $(x_1, x_2) \in \Omega$. *Then the Stokes formula reduces to*

$$\int_S (\text{rot }\overrightarrow{F}, \overrightarrow{\nu})\text{d}\sigma(x) = \int_\Omega \left(\frac{\partial F_2}{\partial x_1} - \frac{\partial F_1}{\partial x_2}\right)\text{d}x_1\text{d}x_2 = \int_{\partial\Omega} F_1(x)\text{d}x_1 + \int_{\partial\Omega} F_2(x)\text{d}x_2.$$

***Proof.*** The statement follows straightforwardly from the Stokes formula in the three-dimensional case since $\overrightarrow{\nu} = (0, 0, 1)$, and rot $\overrightarrow{F}$ can be associated (in $\mathbb{R}^3$) with the vector

$$\left(0, 0, \frac{\partial F_2}{\partial x_1} - \frac{\partial F_1}{\partial x_2}\right).$$

It is easy to see that in this case it is just Green's theorem in the two-dimensional case.

**Exercise 15.41.**     1. Under the conditions of the divergence theorem prove the *Green's identities*

$$\int_\Omega (f(x)\nabla^2 g(x) - g(x)\nabla^2 f(x))\text{d}x$$

$$= \int_{\partial\Omega} (f(x)\nabla g(x) - g(x)\nabla f(x), \overrightarrow{\nu}(x))_{\mathbb{R}^n}\,\text{d}\sigma(x)$$

and

$$\int_\Omega (f(x)\nabla^2 g(x) + (\nabla f(x), \nabla g(x))_{\mathbb{R}^n})\text{d}x$$

$$= \int_{\partial\Omega} f(x)\,(\nabla g(x), \overrightarrow{\nu}(x))_{\mathbb{R}^n}\,\text{d}\sigma(x).$$

2. Prove that if function $f(x)$, $x \in \mathbb{R}^3$ is twice continuously differentiable then $\text{rot}(\nabla f(x)) = 0$.

3. Prove that the differential form $(\overrightarrow{F}, \text{d}x)_{\mathbb{R}^3}$ in $\mathbb{R}^3$ is exact, i.e., $(\overrightarrow{F}, \text{d}x)_{\mathbb{R}^3} = \text{d}f(x)$ for some twice continuously differential function $f$ if and only if $\text{rot }\overrightarrow{F} = 0$.

4. Let $\gamma$ be a closed curve on the $(x_1, x_3)$-plane such that it is a straight line from $(0, 1, 0)$ to $(0, 0, 0)$, followed by a straight line to $(0, 0, 1)$ and ending with a quarter of unit circle to $(0, 1, 0)$ with a positive direction of orientation. Let also $\overrightarrow{F}(x) = (x_2, x_3, x_1)$ be a vector-valued function. Show that

$$\int_\gamma (\overrightarrow{F}, \text{d}x)_{\mathbb{R}^3} = \frac{\pi}{4}.$$

5. Let $\gamma$ be the closed curve $x_3^2 = x_1^2 + x_2^2$ intersecting the plane $x_3 = 1$ and let $\overrightarrow{F}(x) = (\sin x_1 - x_2^3/3, \cos x_2 + x_1^3/3, x_1 x_2 x_3)$ be a vector-valued function. Show that

$$\int_S (\text{rot }\overrightarrow{F}, \overrightarrow{\nu})_{\mathbb{R}^3}\text{d}\sigma(x) = \frac{\pi}{2},$$

where $S = \text{int }\gamma$ on this plane.

6. Let $\gamma$ be the closed curve obtained by intersecting the cylinder $x_1^2 + x_2^2 = 1$ with the plane $x_2 + x_3 = 2$, and let $\overrightarrow{F}(x) = (-x_2^2, x_1, x_3^2)$ be a vector-valued function. Show that

$$\int_\gamma (\overrightarrow{F}, \mathrm{d}x)_{\mathbb{R}^3} = \pi.$$

7. Let $S$ be the surface

$$S = \{x \in \mathbb{R}^3 : x_3 = 4 - x_1^2 - x_2^2, x_3 + 3 \geq 0\}$$

and let $\overrightarrow{F}(x) = (2x_1x_2x_3 + 3x_3, x_1^2x_2, \cos(x_1x_2x_3)\mathrm{e}^{x_1})$ be a vector-valued function. Show that

$$\int_S (\mathrm{rot}\,\overrightarrow{F}, \overrightarrow{\nu})_{\mathbb{R}^3} \mathrm{d}\sigma(x) = 0.$$

8. Let $S$ be the part of the surface $x_3 = 5 - x_1^2 - x_2^2$ above the plane $x_3 = 1$. Let $\overrightarrow{F}(x) = (x_3^2, -3x_1x_2, x_1^3x_2^3)$ be a vector-valued function. Show that

$$\int_S (\mathrm{rot}\,\overrightarrow{F}, \overrightarrow{\nu})_{\mathbb{R}^3} \mathrm{d}\sigma(x) = 0.$$

9. Let $\gamma$ be the closed curve defined by the triangle having the vertices $(1,0,0)$, $(0,1,0)$, and $(0,0,1)$ and let $\overrightarrow{F}(x) = (x_3^2, x_2^2, x_1)$ be a vector-valued function. Show that

$$\int_\gamma (\overrightarrow{F}, \mathrm{d}x)_{\mathbb{R}^3} = -\frac{1}{6}.$$

10. Let $\overrightarrow{F}(x) = (x_3, x_1, x_2)$ be a vector-valued function and let $\gamma$ be the closed curve obtained by the intersection of the plane $x_3 = 2x_1 + 2x_2 - 1$ with the paraboloid $x_3 = x_1^2 + x_2^2$. Show that

$$\int_\gamma (\overrightarrow{F}, \mathrm{d}x)_{\mathbb{R}^3} = -3\pi.$$

11. Let $\overrightarrow{F}(x) = (x_1x_2^2, -x_1^2x_2, x_1x_2x_3)$ be a vector-valued function and let $S$ be the portion of the surface $x_3 = 1 - x_1^2 - x_2^2$ above the $(x_1, x_2)$-plane. Show that

$$\int_S (\mathrm{rot}\,\overrightarrow{F}, \overrightarrow{\nu})_{\mathbb{R}^3} \mathrm{d}\sigma(x) = 0.$$

12. Using the Stokes formula compute

$$\int_\gamma x_1^2 x_3 \mathrm{d}x_1 + 3x_1 \mathrm{d}x_2 - x_2^2 \mathrm{d}x_3,$$

where $\gamma$ is the unit circle $x_1^2 + x_2^2 = 1$.

13. Let $\overrightarrow{F}(x) = (f_1(x_1), f_2(x_2), f_3(x_3))$ be a continuously differentiable vector-valued function. Show that

$$\int_\gamma (\overrightarrow{F}, \mathrm{d}x)_{\mathbb{R}^3} = 0,$$

where $\gamma$ is an arbitrary closed curve of class $C^1$.

14. Let $S$ be the portion of

$$\{x \in \mathbb{R}^3 : x_3 = px_1 + qx_2\}$$

over a region in the $(x_1, x_2)$-plane with area $A$ and let $\overrightarrow{F}(x) = (a(x_1 + x_2) + cx_3, a(x_1 + x_2) + cx_3, a(x_1 + x_2) + cx_3)$ be a vector-valued function. Show that

$$\int_\gamma (\overrightarrow{F}, \mathrm{d}x)_{\mathbb{R}^3} = A(p - q)(c - a),$$

where $\gamma$ is the boundary of this region on the $(x_1, x_2)$-plane.

15. Let $f(x)$ and $g(x)$ be two arbitrary twice continuously differentiable scalar functions. Show that

$$\int_\gamma (f(x)\nabla g(x) + g(x)\nabla f(x), \mathrm{d}x)_{\mathbb{R}^3} = 0,$$

where $\gamma$ is an arbitrary closed curve of class $C^1$.

16. Prove that if function $\overrightarrow{F}$ is twice differentiable then $\mathrm{div}(\mathrm{rot}\,\overrightarrow{F}) = 0$.

17. Let functions $f$ and $g$ be twice continuously differentiable on a neighborhood of surface $S$ which satisfies all conditions of the Stokes theorem. Prove that

$$\iint_S ((\nabla f \times \nabla g), \overrightarrow{\nu})_{\mathbb{R}^3}\mathrm{d}\sigma(x) = \int_{\partial S} (f\nabla g, \mathrm{d}x)_{\mathbb{R}^3},$$

where $\nabla f \times \nabla g$ is understood as

$$\nabla f \times \nabla g = \det \begin{pmatrix} \frac{\partial f}{\partial x_1} & \frac{\partial f}{\partial x_2} & \frac{\partial f}{\partial x_3} \\ \frac{\partial g}{\partial x_1} & \frac{\partial g}{\partial x_2} & \frac{\partial g}{\partial x_3} \\ \overrightarrow{i} & \overrightarrow{j} & \overrightarrow{k} \end{pmatrix}.$$

## 15.4 ▪ Uniform convergence and integrals dependent on a parameter

We consider a sequence of real-valued functions $\{f_k\}_{k=1}^\infty$ defined on a set $X \subset \mathbb{R}^n$. We assume that for each $x \in X$ the number sequence $\{f_k(x)\}_{k=1}^\infty$ converges to some value denoted as $f(x)$ which is called the limiting function $f$ defined on $X$. This convergence of $\{f_k(x)\}_{k=1}^\infty$ is said to be *pointwise convergence*. But we are further interested in the uniform convergence of this sequence of functions. The uniform convergence is required for the study of termwise limit, termwise integration, and termwise differentiation of sequences (series) of functions and, in particular, for integrals dependent on a parameter.

**Definition 15.42.** *A sequence $\{f_k\}_{k=1}^\infty$ of functions defined on a set $X \subset \mathbb{R}^n$ converges uniformly on $X$ to a limiting function $f$ if for any $\varepsilon > 0$ there exists $k_0 \in \mathbb{N}$ such that*

$$|f_k(x) - f(x)| < \varepsilon$$

*for all $k \geq k_0$ and for all $x \in X$.*

**Remark 15.43.** It is clear that the uniform convergence implies pointwise convergence, but the converse is not true. Indeed, considering the sequence of functions

$$f_k(x) := \begin{cases} 1 - kx, & 0 \le x \le 1/k, \\ 0, & 1/k < x \le 1, \end{cases}$$

defined on the interval $[0, 1]$ we can see that the limiting function $f$ with respect to pointwise convergence is

$$f(x) = \begin{cases} 1, & x = 0, \\ 0, & 0 < x \le 1. \end{cases}$$

The convergence is not uniform on $[0, 1]$ since for the sequence $x_k = 1/(2k)$, we have that

$$|f_k(x_k) - f(x_k)| = 1/2.$$

One should note also here that functions $f_k$ are continuous on the interval $[0, 1]$, but the limiting function $f$ is not continuous there.

**Exercise 15.44.** Prove that a sequence of functions $\{f_k\}_{k=1}^{\infty}$ converges uniformly on $X \subset \mathbb{R}^n$ to a limiting function $f$ if and only if the number sequence

$$r_k := \sup_X |f_k(x) - f(x)|$$

converges to zero, i.e., $\lim_{k \to \infty} r_k = 0$.

**Exercise 15.45 (Cauchy criterion).** Prove that a sequence of functions $\{f_k\}_{k=1}^{\infty}$ converges uniformly on $X$ to a limiting function $f$ if and only if for any $\varepsilon > 0$ there exists $k_0 \in \mathbb{N}$ such that

$$|f_k(x) - f_m(x)| < \varepsilon$$

for all $k, m \ge k_0$ and for all $x \in X$. It implies also that the limiting function $f$ is continuous on $X$. Hint: Use the Cauchy criterion for number sequences.

There is one special case of pointwise convergence which implies uniform convergence.

**Theorem 15.46 (Dini test).** *Let a sequence of functions* $\{f_k\}_{k=1}^{\infty}$ *converge pointwise to a limiting function* $f$ *on a compact set* $X \subset \mathbb{R}^n$. *Let also the number sequence* $\{f_k(x)\}_{k=1}^{\infty}$ *be nondecreasing or nonincreasing for each* $x \in X$. *If all functions* $f_k, k = 1, 2, \ldots,$ *and* $f$ *are continuous on* $X$ *then the sequence* $\{f_k\}_{k=1}^{\infty}$ *converges to* $f$ *uniformly on* $X$.

**Proof.** We assume for definiteness and without loss of generality that the sequence $\{f_k(x)\}_{k=1}^{\infty}$ is nondecreasing for each $x \in X$. Then the sequence $r_k := f - f_k$ satisfies the following properties:

1. All functions $r_k$ are continuous and $r_k(x) \ge 0$,

2. $\{r_k(x)\}_{k=1}^{\infty}$ is nonincreasing for each $x \in X$,

3. $\lim_{k \to \infty} r_k(x) = 0$ pointwise on $X$.

Let us prove that the latter convergence is uniform on $X$.

Assume on the contrary that it is not true. Then there is $\varepsilon_0 > 0$ such that there exists a sequence $\{x_k\}_{k=1}^{\infty} \subset X$ for which $r_k(x_k) \ge \varepsilon_0$ for $k = 1, 2, \ldots$. Since $\{x_k\}_{k=1}^{\infty}$ is bounded, by the Bolzano–Weierstrass principle there is a convergent subsequence $\{x_{j_k}\}_{k=1}^{\infty}$ of $\{x_k\}_{k=1}^{\infty}$ with limit $x^0 \in X$. Since all functions $r_k, k = 1, 2, \ldots$, are continuous on $X$,

$$\lim_{k \to \infty} r_m(x_{j_k}) = r_m(x^0), \quad m = 1, 2, \ldots.$$

Due to monotonicity of $r_m$ at each point we conclude that

$$r_m(x_{j_k}) \geq r_{j_k}(x_{j_k}), \quad j_k \geq m.$$

But this implies that

$$r_m(x^0) \geq \varepsilon_0 > 0$$

for all $m$. This contradiction proves the theorem.

**Remark 15.47.** The study of uniform convergence of series of functions is clearly reduced to the study of uniform convergence of the sequence of partial sums.

**Exercise 15.48.**   1. Prove the *Weierstrass test*: Let $\sum_{k=1}^{\infty} g_k(x)$ be a series of functions defined on a set $X \subset \mathbb{R}^n$. If there is a number sequence $\{a_k\}_{k=1}^{\infty}$ such that

$$|g_k(x)| \leq a_k, \quad x \in X,$$

for all $k = 1, 2, \ldots$ and the number series $\sum_{k=1}^{\infty} a_k$ converges then the series of functions $\sum_{k=1}^{\infty} g_k(x)$ converges uniformly on $X$.

  2. Prove the *Dirichlet–Abel test*: Let $\{u_k\}_{k=1}^{\infty}$ and $\{v_k\}_{k=1}^{\infty}$ be two sequences of functions defined on a set $X \subset \mathbb{R}^n$. Suppose that the following conditions are fulfilled:

   (a) $\{v_k(x)\}_{k=1}^{\infty}$ is nondecreasing for each $x \in X$, and $\lim_{k \to \infty} v_k(x) = 0$ uniformly on $X$.

   (b) $\{\sum_{k=1}^{m} u_k(x)\}_{m=1}^{\infty}$ is uniformly bounded in $x \in X$ and $m \in \mathbb{N}$.

   Then the series of functions $\sum_{k=1}^{\infty} u_k(x) v_k(x)$ converges uniformly on $X$. Hint: Use the proofs of Theorems 4.37 and 4.38.

Let $x^0$ be a limiting point of a set $X \subset \mathbb{R}^n$, i.e., $x^0 \in X'$. Let also a sequence of functions $\{f_k\}_{k=1}^{\infty}$ converge pointwise on $X$ to a limiting function $f$ defined on $X$. We are interested in the question, when $f$ has a limit at $x^0 \in X'$, whether all functions $f_k, k = 1, 2, \ldots$, have this limit. The following theorem answers this question.

**Theorem 15.49 (Termwise limit).** *Let a sequence of functions $\{f_k\}_{k=1}^{\infty}$ converge uniformly on $X$ to a limiting function $f$. Let $x^0 \in X$ and assume that the limit*

$$\lim_{x \to x^0} f_k(x) =: b_k$$

*exists for all $k = 1, 2, \ldots$. Then $f$ has a limit at this point and this limit can be calculated as*

$$\lim_{x \to x^0} f(x) = \lim_{k \to \infty} b_k = \lim_{k \to \infty} (\lim_{x \to x^0} f_k(x)).$$

***Proof.*** Let us first prove that the limit $\lim_{k \to \infty} b_k$ exists. Indeed, since $\{f_k\}_{k=1}^{\infty}$ converges to $f$ uniformly on $X$, by the Cauchy criterion (Exercise 15.45) for any $\varepsilon > 0$ there exists $k_0 \in \mathbb{N}$ such that

$$|f_m(x) - f_k(x)| < \varepsilon$$

for all $m, k \geq k_0$ and for all $x \in X$. Passing here to the limit $x \to x^0$ we obtain $|b_m - b_k| \leq \varepsilon$. Since $\varepsilon > 0$ is arbitrary, we may conclude that the number sequence $\{b_k\}_{k=1}^\infty$ is a Cauchy sequence. Hence $\lim_{k\to\infty} b_k =: b$ exists.

We may now estimate the difference between $f(x)$ and $b$ as

$$|f(x) - b| \leq |f_k(x) - f(x)| + |f_k(x) - b_k| + |b_k - b|.$$

Due to uniform convergence of $\{f_k\}_{k=1}^\infty$ and existence of $\lim_{k\to\infty} b_k$, for given $\varepsilon > 0$ we can find $k_0 \in \mathbb{N}$ such that

$$|f_{k_0}(x) - f(x)| < \varepsilon/3, \quad |b_{k_0} - b| < \varepsilon/3.$$

Since $\lim_{x\to x^0} f_{k_0}(x) = b_{k_0}$, we can find (for the same $\varepsilon > 0$) $\delta > 0$ such that

$$|f_{k_0}(x) - b_{k_0}| < \varepsilon/3$$

for all $x \in U'_\delta(x^0)$. Thus, for this value of $x$ we have

$$|f(x) - b| < \varepsilon$$

and the proof is finished.

**Corollary 15.50.** *Under the same conditions of Theorem* 15.49 *for the sequence of functions* $\{\sum_{k=1}^m f_k\}_{m=1}^\infty$ *we have*

$$\lim_{x\to x^0} \sum_{k=1}^\infty f_k(x) = \sum_{k=1}^\infty \lim_{x\to x^0} f_k(x).$$

**Corollary 15.51.** *Suppose that the functions* $f_k, k = 1, 2, \ldots,$ *are continuous on a set* $X \subset \mathbb{R}^n$ *and the sequence of functions* $\{f_k\}_{k=1}^\infty$ *(the series* $\sum_{k=1}^\infty f_k$*) converges uniformly on* $X$. *Then the limiting function* $f$ *(the sum of the series* $\sum_{k=1}^\infty f_k$*) is continuous on* $X$.

**Example 15.52.** Let us consider again the sequence of functions

$$f_k(x) := \begin{cases} 1 - kx, & 0 \leq x \leq 1/k, \\ 0, & 1/k < x \leq 1, \end{cases}$$

defined on the interval $[0, 1]$. For each $k = 1, 2, \ldots$ we have that $\lim_{x\to+0} f_k(x) = 1$. The limiting function is

$$f(x) = \begin{cases} 1, & x = 0, \\ 0, & 0 < x \leq 1. \end{cases}$$

Since

$$\lim_{x\to+0} f(x) = 0 \neq \lim_{k\to\infty} (\lim_{x\to+0} f_k(x)) = 1,$$

it is impossible to use the termwise limit in this case. The reason is that the sequence $\{f_k\}_{k=1}^\infty$ does not converge uniformly. What is more, each $f_k$ is continuous on $[0, 1]$ but the limiting function is not.

Another application of uniform convergence concerns integration.

**Theorem 15.53 (Termwise integration).** *Let all functions of the sequence $\{f_k\}_{k=1}^{\infty}$ be integrable in proper sense on a bounded and Jordan measurable set $X \subset \mathbb{R}^n$ with $\mu(X) > 0$. If the limit*

$$\lim_{k \to \infty} f_k(x) = f(x)$$

*holds uniformly on $X$ then the limiting function $f$ is integrable on $X$ and*

$$\lim_{k \to \infty} \int_X f_k(x)\mathrm{d}x = \int_X \lim_{k \to \infty} f_k(x)\mathrm{d}x = \int_X f(x)\mathrm{d}x.$$

*Proof.* Since the sequence of functions $\{f_k\}_{k=1}^{\infty}$ converges to $f$ uniformly on $X$, for any $\varepsilon > 0$ there exists $k_0 \in \mathbb{N}$ such that

$$\sup_X |f_k(x) - f(x)| < \frac{\varepsilon}{2\mu(X)}$$

for all $k \geq k_0$ (see Exercise 15.44). Let us assume for the moment that $f$ is integrable on $X$. Then we will have

$$\left| \int_X f_k(x)\mathrm{d}x - \int_X f(x)\mathrm{d}x \right| \leq \int_X |f_k(x) - f(x)|\mathrm{d}x < \varepsilon/2.$$

This justifies termwise integration for a uniformly convergent sequence of integrable functions. So, it remains to prove that $f$ is integrable. Indeed, due to uniform convergence we have

$$|f(x') - f(x'')| \leq |f_k(x') - f(x')| + |f_k(x'') - f(x'')| + |f_k(x') - f_k(x'')|$$
$$< \frac{\varepsilon}{2\mu(X)} + \frac{\varepsilon}{2\mu(X)} + |f_k(x') - f_k(x'')|$$

for any $x', x'' \in X$ and $k \geq k_0$ as above. This implies that for any elementary figures $F$ and $G$ such that $F \subset X \subset G$ we have

$$U_G(f, X) - L_F(f, X) < U_G(f_k, X) - L_F(f_k, X) + \varepsilon, \quad k \geq k_0.$$

Since $f_k$ are integrable for each $k = 1, 2, \ldots$, due to the criterion of integrability (see Theorem 15.3) for any $\varepsilon > 0$ there exist elementary figures $F$ and $G$ such that $F \subset X \subset G$ and

$$U_G(f_{k_0}, X) - L_F(f_{k_0}, X) < \varepsilon.$$

It means that for these elementary figures we have

$$U_G(f, X) - L_F(f, X) < 2\varepsilon.$$

Since $\varepsilon > 0$ was arbitrary, $f$ is integrable on $X$. Theorem 15.53 is proved.

**Exercise 15.54.**    1. Formulate and prove the analogue of the latter theorem for uniformly convergent series of integrable functions.

2. Simplify the proof of the latter theorem for the sequence of functions which are continuous on $X$.

**Theorem 15.55 (Termwise differentiation).** *Let all functions of the sequence $\{f_k\}_{k=1}^\infty$ be defined on an open bounded convex set $X \subset \mathbb{R}^n$ with partial derivatives $\frac{\partial f_k}{\partial x_j}(x), x \in X, j = 1, 2, \ldots, n$. If the sequences $\{\frac{\partial f_k}{\partial x_j}\}_{k=1}^\infty, j = 1, 2, \ldots, n$, converge uniformly on $X$ and the sequence $\{f_k\}_{k=1}^\infty$ converges at some point $x^0 \in X$ then the sequence $\{f_k\}_{k=1}^\infty$ converges uniformly on $X$ to a limiting function $f$ such that $f$ has partial derivatives $\frac{\partial f}{\partial x_j}(x), j = 1, 2, \ldots, n$, on $X$ and*

$$\frac{\partial f}{\partial x_j}(x) = \lim_{k \to \infty} \frac{\partial f_k}{\partial x_j}(x), \quad j = 1, 2, \ldots, n,$$

*i.e., the sequence $\{f_k\}_{k=1}^\infty$ admits termwise differentiation.*

**Proof.** Since the sequences $\{f_k(x^0)\}_{k=1}^\infty$ and $\{\frac{\partial f_k}{\partial x_j}(x)\}_{k=1}^\infty$ converge (the latter uniformly), for any $\varepsilon > 0$ there is $k_0 \in \mathbb{N}$ such that

$$|f_m(x^0) - f_k(x^0)| < \varepsilon/2$$

for all $k, m \geq k_0$ and

$$\left| \frac{\partial f_m}{\partial x_j}(x) - \frac{\partial f_k}{\partial x_j}(x) \right| < \frac{\varepsilon}{2\sqrt{n}\,\mathrm{diam}\, X}$$

for any $j = 1, 2, \ldots, n$ and for all $x \in X$, where $\mathrm{diam}\, X > 0$ denotes the diameter of Jordan measurable set $X$. Now applying Lagrange's formula (Corollary 13.71) we obtain

$$(f_m(x) - f_k(x)) - (f_m(x^0) - f_k(x^0)) = (\nabla(f_m - f_k)(\xi), x - x^0)_{\mathbb{R}^n}.$$

This implies that

$$|f_m(x) - f_k(x)| < \varepsilon/2 + |\nabla(f_m - f_k)(\xi)||x - x^0| < \varepsilon.$$

The Cauchy criterion yields now that the sequence of functions $\{f_k\}_{k=1}^\infty$ converges uniformly on $X$ to a limiting function $f$. It remains only to show that $f$ has partial derivatives $\frac{\partial f}{\partial x_j}, j = 1, 2, \ldots, n$, and

$$\frac{\partial f}{\partial x_j}(x) = \lim_{k \to \infty} \frac{\partial f_k}{\partial x_j}(x), \quad x \in X.$$

Indeed, let $x \in X$ be arbitrary and fixed. Let us denote

$$\varphi_k^{(j)}(t) := \frac{f_k(x + te_j) - f_k(x)}{t}, \quad j = 1, 2, \ldots, n,$$

where $t > 0$ small enough and $\{e_j\}_{j=1}^n$ is the standard basis in $\mathbb{R}^n$. Applying again Lagrange's formula we obtain

$$\varphi_k^{(j)}(t) - \varphi_m^{(j)}(t) = \frac{(f_k(x + te_j) - f_m(x + te_j)) - (f_k(x) - f_m(x))}{t}$$

$$= \frac{\partial}{\partial x_j}(f_k(x + \theta t e_j) - f_m(x + \theta t e_j)),$$

where $0 < \theta < 1$. Hence, for any $\varepsilon > 0$ there exists $k_0 \in \mathbb{N}$ such that

$$|\varphi_k^{(j)}(t) - \varphi_m^{(j)}(t)| < \varepsilon$$

for all $k, m \geq k_0$ and for all $t$ with $0 < t < \delta$. Therefore the sequence $\{\varphi_k^{(j)}(t)\}_{k=1}^\infty$ satisfies the Cauchy criterion. By Theorem 15.49 we see that the limit $\lim_{k \to \infty} \varphi_k^{(j)}(t)$ exists and is equal to

$$\lim_{k \to \infty} \varphi_k^{(j)}(t) = \frac{f(x + te_j) - f(x)}{t}.$$

Moreover, by this theorem

$$\lim_{t \to 0} ( \lim_{k \to \infty} \varphi_k^{(j)}(t)) = \lim_{k \to \infty} (\lim_{t \to 0} \varphi_k^{(j)}(t))$$

or

$$\frac{\partial f}{\partial x_j}(x) = \lim_{k \to \infty} \frac{\partial f_k}{\partial x_j}(x), \quad j = 1, 2, \ldots, n.$$

This finishes the proof.

**Corollary 15.56.** *Under the conditions of Theorem* 15.55 *for the sequence* $\{\sum_{k=1}^m f_k(x)\}_{m=1}^\infty$ *we have*

$$\frac{\partial}{\partial x_j} \sum_{k=1}^\infty f_k(x) = \sum_{k=1}^\infty \frac{\partial}{\partial x_j} f_k(x), \quad j = 1, 2, \ldots, n.$$

**Example 15.57.** Let us consider the series of functions

$$\sum_{k=1}^\infty \frac{\cos(kx)}{k^\alpha}, \quad \alpha > 0, x \in [0, 2\pi].$$

Using the Dirichlet–Abel test (see Exercise 15.48, part 2) we may conclude that this series converges uniformly on the interval $[\delta, 2\pi - \delta]$ with some $\delta > 0$ small enough if $\alpha > 0$. Indeed, the sequence $1/k^\alpha$ monotonically tends to zero as $k \to \infty$, and the partial sums (see Example 4.40)

$$\left| \sum_{k=1}^m \cos(kx) \right| = \left| \frac{\sin((m + 1/2)x) - \sin(x/2)}{2 \sin(x/2)} \right| \leq \frac{1}{\sin(x/2)}, \quad 0 < x < 2\pi,$$

are uniformly bounded for $x \in [\delta, 2\pi - \delta]$. Moreover, if $\alpha > 1$ then this series converges uniformly on $[0, 2\pi]$ by the Weierstrass test since

$$\left| \sum_{k=1}^\infty \frac{\cos(kx)}{k^\alpha} \right| \leq \sum_{k=1}^\infty \frac{|\cos(kx)|}{k^\alpha} \leq \sum_{k=1}^\infty \frac{1}{k^\alpha} < \infty, \quad \alpha > 1.$$

Hence we may conclude that for any $0 < \alpha \leq 1$ this series defines a continuous function on the interval $[\delta, 2\pi - \delta]$ for any $\delta > 0$ small enough, and for $\alpha > 1$ it defines a continuous function on the whole interval $[0, 2\pi]$. Due to periodicity of $\cos(kx)$ this result can be extended to the whole line. Next, formally differentiating this series we obtain

$$\left( \sum_{k=1}^\infty \frac{\cos(kx)}{k^\alpha} \right)' = - \sum_{k=1}^\infty \frac{\sin(kx)}{k^{\alpha-1}}.$$

Since

$$\left| \sum_{k=1}^m \sin(kx) \right| = \left| \frac{\cos((m + 1/2)x) - \cos(x/2)}{2 \sin(x/2)} \right| \leq \frac{1}{\sin(x/2)}, \quad 0 < x < 2\pi,$$

the partial sums are uniformly bounded for $x \in [\delta, 2\pi - \delta]$ with $\delta > 0$ arbitrarily small and we may conclude (repeating the same arguments as above) that for $1 < \alpha \leq 2$ the series

$$\sum_{k=1}^\infty \frac{\cos(kx)}{k^\alpha}$$

defines a continuously differentiable function on the interval $[\delta, 2\pi - \delta]$ with $\delta > 0$ arbitrarily small and for any $\alpha > 2$ this function is continuously differentiable for all $x \in [0, 2\pi]$.

**Exercise 15.58.** Find the values of $\alpha > 0$ for which the series from Example 15.57 admits termwise integration.

**Exercise 15.59.** Let $x \in [0, 1]$ and define the function $g$ as

$$g(x) = \begin{cases} x^2 \cos(1/x), & x \neq 0, \\ 0, & x = 0, \end{cases}$$

so that its derivative is

$$g'(x) = \begin{cases} \sin(1/x) + 2x \cos(1/x), & x \neq 0, \\ 0, & x = 0. \end{cases}$$

Let $\{x_k\}_{k=1}^{\infty}$ be the sequence of all rational numbers from the interval $[0, 1]$. Prove that the series

$$\sum_{k=1}^{\infty} \frac{g(x - x_k)}{k^2}, \quad x \in [0, 1],$$

defines a function which is differentiable everywhere on $[0, 1]$ but its derivative has a breakpoint of the second kind at each $x_k$.

One of the most important results of classical analysis is the famous Ascoli–Arzelà theorem. To formulate and prove this result we need some new notations.

**Definition 15.60.** *A collection $F$ of functions defined on a set $X \subset \mathbb{R}^n$ is said to be*

1. *uniformly bounded on $X$ if there exists a constant $M > 0$ such that $|f(x)| \leq M$ for all $x \in X$ and for all $f \in F$,*

2. *equicontinuous on $X$ if for any $\varepsilon > 0$ there exists $\delta > 0$ such that $|f(x) - f(y)| < \varepsilon$ for all $x, y \in X$ with $|x - y| < \delta$ and for all $f \in F$.*

**Theorem 15.61 (Ascoli–Arzelà).** *Let $X \subset \mathbb{R}^n$ be compact and let $\{f_k\}_{k=1}^{\infty}$ be a sequence of real-valued continuous functions defined on $X$. If the family $F = \{f_k\}_{k=1}^{\infty}$ is uniformly bounded and equicontinuous on $X$ then there exists a subsequence $\{f_{j_k}\}_{k=1}^{\infty}$ of $\{f_k\}_{k=1}^{\infty}$ that converges uniformly on $X$ to a continuous function.*

**Proof.** Since the set $X$ is compact in $\mathbb{R}^n$, there exists a countable subset $D = \{d_1, d_2, \ldots\}$ of $X$ such that $\overline{D} = X$ (for example, due to the fact that rational numbers form an everywhere dense set). Consider the sequence $\{f_k(d_1)\}_{k=1}^{\infty}$ of real numbers. Since $\{f_k\}_{k=1}^{\infty}$ is uniformly bounded, the sequence $\{f_k(d_1)\}_{k=1}^{\infty}$ is a bounded sequence of real numbers. By the Bolzano–Weierstrass principle (see Theorem 13.8) there exists a convergent subsequence denoted as $\{f_k^{(1)}(d_1)\}_{k=1}^{\infty}$ which converges to the number $f(d_1)$. Now consider the sequence $\{f_k^{(1)}(d_2)\}_{k=1}^{\infty}$ of real numbers. This sequence is also bounded and contains a convergent subsequence denoted as $\{f_k^{(2)}(d_2)\}_{k=1}^{\infty}$ that converges to $f(d_2)$.

We continue to construct convergent subsequences in this manner. We obtain countably many subsequences such that

$$f_1^{(1)}(d_1), f_2^{(1)}(d_1), \ldots, f_k^{(1)}(d_1), \ldots \to f(d_1),$$
$$f_1^{(2)}(d_2), f_2^{(2)}(d_2), \ldots, f_k^{(2)}(d_2), \ldots \to f(d_2),$$

$$\vdots$$

$$f_1^{(k)}(d_k), f_2^{(k)}(d_k), \ldots, f_k^{(k)}(d_k), \ldots \to f(d_k),$$

$$\vdots$$

Now we define a new sequence of functions $g_k(x) := f_k^{(k)}(x)$. Then for each $d_j \in D$ we have that the number sequence $\{g_k(d_j)\}_{k=1}^{\infty}$ converges to $f(d_j)$ by construction. We aim to show that actually $\{g_k\}_{k=1}^{\infty}$ is a Cauchy sequence with respect to uniform convergence on $X$. Indeed, for any $\varepsilon > 0$ there exists $k_0^{(j)} \in \mathbb{N}$ such that

$$|g_k(d_j) - g_m(d_j)| < \varepsilon/3$$

for all $k, m \geq k_0^{(j)}$. Furthermore, since $\{f_k\}_{k=1}^{\infty}$ is equicontinuous, for this given $\varepsilon > 0$ there exists $\delta > 0$ such that

$$|g_k(x) - g_k(y)| < \varepsilon/3$$

for all $x, y \in X$ with $|x - y| < \delta$ and for all $k = 1, 2, \ldots$.

The open balls $\{B_\delta(d_j)\}_{j=1}^{\infty}$ form an open cover of $X$ since the set $D$ is dense in $X$. But $X$ is compact and therefore by the Heine–Borel lemma there is a finite open subcover of $X$ denoted as

$$B_\delta(r_{j_1}), B_\delta(r_{j_2}), \ldots, B_\delta(r_{j_l}).$$

For each $r_{j_1}, \ldots, r_{j_l}$ there are corresponding numbers $k_0^{(j_1)}, \ldots, k_0^{(j_l)}$ (defined above). Now let

$$k_0 := \max(k_0^{(j_1)}, \ldots, k_0^{(j_l)}).$$

Then for $k, m \geq k_0$ and $x \in X$ we have that $x \in B_\delta(r_{j_i})$ for some $i \in \{1, 2, \ldots, l\}$ and

$$|g_m(x) - g_k(x)| \leq |g_m(x) - g_m(r_{j_i})| + |g_k(x) - g_k(r_{j_i})| + |g_m(r_{j_i}) - g_k(r_{j_i})| < \varepsilon$$

due to the choices of $k_0$ and $\delta$ above. This inequality is uniform in $x \in X$, and therefore by the Cauchy criterion the sequence of continuous functions $\{g_k\}_{k=1}^{\infty}$ is uniformly convergent. That's why the limiting function $f$ is continuous.

**Remark 15.62.** The proof of the latter theorem shows that instead of uniform boundedness of the sequence $\{f_k(x)\}_{k=1}^{\infty}$ on $X$ it is enough to assume the boundedness of this sequence only at one point $x \in X$.

**Remark 15.63.** There is one sufficient and simple condition which guarantees the equicontinuity of the sequence $\{f_k\}_{k=1}^{\infty}$. In fact, it is enough to assume that there exists a constant $A > 0$ such that

$$|f_k(x') - f_k(x'')| \leq A|x' - x''|$$

for all $k = 1, 2, \ldots$ and for all $x', x'' \in X$.

Integrals that depend on a parameter (or parameters) and their properties are closely related to the concept of uniform convergence. That is why we study these questions together.

Let $X$ and $Y$ be compact sets in $\mathbb{R}^m$ and $\mathbb{R}^n$, respectively, with positive Jordan measures $\mu_m(X)$ and $\mu_n(Y)$. Let $f(x, y)$ be a function defined on $X \times Y \subset \mathbb{R}^m \times \mathbb{R}^n$ which is integrable in a proper sense with respect to $y$ on $Y$ for each $x \in X$. Then the function

$$F(x) := \int_Y f(x, y)\,\mathrm{d}y$$

is well-defined. This function is called an *integral that depends on the parameter $x \in X$*.

The theorem below provides a sufficient condition for the continuity (and therefore integrability) of $F(x)$ on $X$.

**Theorem 15.64 (Continuity).** *Let $f : X \times Y \subset \mathbb{R}^m \times \mathbb{R}^n \to \mathbb{R}$ be a continuous function. Then $F$ is continuous and therefore integrable on $X$. Moreover,*

$$\int_X F(x)\mathrm{d}x = \int_Y \left( \int_X f(x,y)\mathrm{d}x \right) \mathrm{d}y.$$

***Proof.*** Since $X \times Y$ is compact in $\mathbb{R}^{m+n} = \mathbb{R}^m \times \mathbb{R}^n$, by the Cantor theorem (see Theorem 13.33) the continuous function $f$ is uniformly continuous there. Hence, for any $\varepsilon > 0$ there exists $\delta > 0$ such that

$$|f(x',y) - f(x'',y)| < \frac{\varepsilon}{\mu_n(Y)}$$

uniformly in $y \in Y$ for all $x', x'' \in X$ with $|x' - x''| < \delta$. This implies that

$$|F(x') - F(x'')| \le \int_Y |f(x',y) - f(x'',y)|\mathrm{d}y < \varepsilon.$$

The integrability of $F$ on $X$ follows from its continuity on $X$. The claimed equality concerning integrals follows from the Fubini theorem (see Theorem 15.8). This finishes the proof.

The next theorem shows when we may differentiate the function $F$. For this purpose we assume that $X \subset \mathbb{R}^m$ is the closure of an open bounded set.

**Theorem 15.65 (Differentiation).** *Let functions $f(x,y)$ and $\frac{\partial f}{\partial x_j}(x,y), j = 1, 2, \ldots, n$, be continuous on $X \times Y$. Then $F$ has a continuous derivative $\frac{\partial F}{\partial x_j}$ on $X$ and*

$$\frac{\partial F}{\partial x_j}(x) = \int_Y \frac{\partial f}{\partial x_j}(x,y)\mathrm{d}y.$$

***Proof.*** Let $x \in X$ be fixed and let $t \in \mathbb{R}$ be chosen so small that $x + te_j \in X$, where $e_j$ is the standard basis of $\mathbb{R}^m$. Applying Lagrange's formula (Corollary 13.71 of Theorem 13.69) we have

$$\frac{1}{t}\Delta_{te_j}F(x) = \int_Y \frac{f(x + te_j, y) - f(x,y)}{t}\mathrm{d}y = \int_Y \frac{\partial f}{\partial x_j}(x + \theta te_j, y)\mathrm{d}y, \quad 0 < \theta < 1.$$

Theorem 15.64 implies that the partial derivative $\frac{\partial F}{\partial x_j}(x)$ exists and equals the expression claimed in this theorem. Continuity of the partial derivative is also a consequence of this theorem.

**Exercise 15.66.** Let two real-valued functions $\varphi$ and $\psi$ be defined on a set $X \subset \mathbb{R}^m$ with $\varphi(x) \le \psi(x), x \in X$, and with continuous derivatives $\frac{\partial \varphi}{\partial x_j}$ and $\frac{\partial \psi}{\partial x_j}, j = 1, 2, \ldots, m$. Let also function $f(x,y)$ be defined on the set $X \times [\varphi(x), \psi(x)]$ with continuous derivative $\frac{\partial f}{\partial x_j}(x,y), y \in [\varphi(x), \psi(x)]$. Prove that

$$F(x) := \int_{\varphi(x)}^{\psi(x)} f(x,y)\mathrm{d}y$$

has a derivative $\frac{\partial F}{\partial x_j}(x)$ and

$$\frac{\partial F}{\partial x_j}(x) = \int_{\varphi(x)}^{\psi(x)} \frac{\partial f}{\partial x_j}(x,y)\mathrm{d}y + f(x,\psi(x))\frac{\partial \psi}{\partial x_j}(x) - f(x,\varphi(x))\frac{\partial \varphi}{\partial x_j}(x).$$

Let us consider now the improper integral

$$F(x) = \int_Y f(x,y)\mathrm{d}y, \quad x \in X,$$

having only one singular point $y^0 \in Y$, where $Y$ is compact in $\mathbb{R}^n$ and $X \subset \mathbb{R}^m$ is Jordan measurable (not necessarily bounded).

**Definition 15.67.** *The integral defined above is said to be uniformly convergent with respect to* $x \in X$ *if it is convergent for any* $x \in X$ *and if, given* $\varepsilon > 0$, *there is* $\delta_0 > 0$ *such that*

$$\left| \int_{Y \cap B_\delta(y^0)} f(x,y)\mathrm{d}y \right| < \varepsilon$$

*holds for any* $0 < \delta < \delta_0$ *and uniformly in* $x \in X$.

**Remark 15.68.** The latter definition can be regarded in the following equivalent form. Denote

$$F_\delta(x) := \int_{Y \cap B_\delta(y^0)} f(x,y)\mathrm{d}y.$$

Then we obtain from Definition 15.67 that

$$|F(x) - F_\delta(x)| < \varepsilon$$

for all $x \in X$ and for all $0 < \delta < \delta_0$, i.e., the limit

$$\lim_{\delta \to 0} F_\delta(x) = F(x)$$

holds uniformly in $x \in X$.

**Theorem 15.69 (Continuity of improper integral).** *Suppose that the sets* $X \subset \mathbb{R}^m$ *and* $Y \subset \mathbb{R}^n$ *are compact and the function* $f(x,y)$ *is continuous on* $X \times Y$ *except at the point* $(x, y^0)$. *If the integral defining* $F$ *is uniformly convergent on* $X$ *then* $F$ *is continuous on* $X$.

**Proof.** It follows from the conditions of this theorem that the function $f(x,y)$ is continuous on the compact set $X \times \{Y \setminus B_\delta(y^0)\}$. Hence, Theorem 15.64 yields that $F_\delta$ is continuous on $X$ and

$$\lim_{\delta \to 0} F_\delta(x) = F(x)$$

holds uniformly in $x \in X$. Then Corollary 15.51 implies that $F$ is continuous on $X$.

**Corollary 15.70.** *Under the conditions of Theorem 15.69 the function* $F$ *is integrable on* $X$ *and*

$$\int_X F(x)\mathrm{d}x = \int_Y \left( \int_X f(x,y)\mathrm{d}x \right) \mathrm{d}y.$$

**Proof.** The integrability of $F$ follows from continuity. In order to prove the equality concerning integrals we denote

$$\eta_\delta := \max_{x \in X} |F_\delta(x) - F(x)|.$$

By Theorem 15.69 we have

$$\lim_{\delta \to 0} \eta_\delta = 0.$$

Next,

$$\left| \int_X F_\delta(x)\mathrm{d}x - \int_X F(x)\mathrm{d}x \right| \le \int_X |F_\delta(x) - F(x)|\mathrm{d}x \le \eta_\delta \mu_m(X) \to 0$$

as $\delta \to 0$. Theorem 15.64 leads to the equality

$$\int_X F_\delta(x)\mathrm{d}x = \int_{Y \setminus B_\delta(y^0)} \left( \int_X f(x,y)\mathrm{d}x \right) \mathrm{d}y \to \int_X F(x)\mathrm{d}x$$

as $\delta \to 0$. This proves corollary.

**Theorem 15.71 (Differentiability of an improper integral).** *Let all conditions of Theorem* 15.69 *be fulfilled. Assume in addition that $X$ is the closure of a bounded open set in $\mathbb{R}^n$ and that function $f(x,y)$ has a continuous derivative $\frac{\partial f}{\partial x_j}(x,y), j = 1, 2, \ldots, m$, everywhere on $X \times Y$ except possibly at point $(x, y^0)$. If the integral defining $F$ is convergent at each point $x \in X$ and if the integral*

$$\int_Y \frac{\partial f}{\partial x_j}(x,y)\mathrm{d}y$$

*is uniformly convergent on $X$ then $\frac{\partial F}{\partial x_j}(x)$ exists and*

$$\frac{\partial F}{\partial x_j}(x) = \int_Y \frac{\partial}{\partial x_j} f(x,y)\mathrm{d}y.$$

***Proof.*** Applying Theorem 15.65 to $F_\delta$ from above we obtain

$$\frac{\partial F_\delta}{\partial x_j}(x) = \int_{Y \setminus B_\delta(y^0)} \frac{\partial f}{\partial x_j}(x,y)\mathrm{d}y.$$

By the hypothesis we have

$$\lim_{\delta \to 0} F_\delta(x) = F(x)$$

pointwise on $X$ and

$$\lim_{\delta \to 0} \frac{\partial F_\delta}{\partial x_j}(x) = \lim_{\delta \to 0} \int_{Y \setminus B_\delta(y^0)} \frac{\partial f}{\partial x_j}(x,y)\mathrm{d}y = \int_Y \frac{\partial f}{\partial x_j}(x,y)\mathrm{d}y$$

uniformly in $x \in X$. This proves the theorem.

**Exercise 15.72.** Let the integral defining $F$ have only one singularity at $y^0 \in Y$. Assume also that there exists a function $\varphi(y) \ge 0$ such that

$$|f(x,y)| \le \varphi(y), \quad (x,y) \in X \times Y.$$

Prove that if the improper integral

$$\int_Y \varphi(y)\mathrm{d}y$$

converges then the integral defining $F$ converges uniformly in $x \in X$.

There is very practical interest in integrals of the form

$$F(x) := \int_X f(x,y)g(y)\mathrm{d}y, \quad x \in X \tag{15.1}$$

(i.e., the case $Y = X \subset \mathbb{R}^n$), where the function $f(x, y)$ is continuous everywhere on $X \times X$ except at the diagonal $x = y$, and function $g$ is Jordan measurable and bounded. In addition, we assume that $X$ is the closure of an open bounded set.

**Definition 15.73.** *The integral* (15.1) *is said to be convergent uniformly at a point* $x^0 \in X$ *if given* $\varepsilon > 0$ *there exists* $\delta_0 > 0$ *such that*

$$\left| \int_{X \cap B_\delta(x^0)} f(x, y) g(y) \mathrm{d}y \right| < \varepsilon$$

*for all* $x \in B_{\delta_0}(x^0) \cap X$ *and all* $0 < \delta \le \delta_0$.

**Remark 15.74.** Actually the latter definition is concerned with uniform convergence of this integral in the neighborhood of the point.

**Theorem 15.75 (Continuity).** *If the integral defining* $F$ *converges uniformly at* $x^0 \in X$ *then it is continuous at* $x^0$ *(and in its neighborhood).*

***Proof.*** Definition 15.73 implies that for any $\varepsilon > 0$ there exists $\delta > 0$ such that

$$\left| \int_{X \cap B_\delta(x^0)} f(x, y) g(y) \mathrm{d}y \right| < \varepsilon/3$$

for all $x \in B_\delta(x^0) \cap X$. We note that the function $f(x, y)$ is uniformly continuous for $y \in X \setminus B_\delta(x^0)$ and $x \in \overline{B_{\delta/2}(x^0)} \cap X$ since

$$|x - y| > |y - x^0| - |x - x^0| > \delta - \delta/2 = \delta/2 > 0.$$

Hence, there is $0 < \delta_1 < \delta/2$ such that

$$|f(x, y) - f(x^0, y)| < \frac{\varepsilon}{3M\mu_n(X)}, \quad M = \sup_X g(x) > 0,$$

for all $|x - x^0| < \delta_1$. In this case we have

$$\left| \int_{X \setminus B_\delta(x^0)} f(x, y) g(y) \mathrm{d}y - \int_{X \setminus B_\delta(x^0)} f(x^0, y) g(y) \mathrm{d}y \right|$$

$$\le M \int_{X \setminus B_\delta(x^0)} |f(x, y) - f(x^0, y)| \mathrm{d}y < \frac{\varepsilon}{3}.$$

Moreover, for all $x$ with $|x - x^0| < \delta_1$ we have that

$$\left| \int_X f(x, y) g(y) \mathrm{d}y - \int_X f(x^0, y) g(y) \mathrm{d}y \right|$$

$$\le \left| \int_{X \cap B_\delta(x^0)} f(x, y) g(y) \mathrm{d}y \right| + \left| \int_{X \cap B_\delta(x^0)} f(x^0, y) g(y) \mathrm{d}y \right|$$

$$+ \left| \int_{X \setminus B_\delta(x^0)} (f(x, y) - f(x^0, y)) g(y) \mathrm{d}y \right| < \varepsilon/3 + \varepsilon/3 + \varepsilon/3 = \varepsilon.$$

This proves the theorem.

**Exercise 15.76.** Let $f(x, y)$ from the latter theorem satisfy the condition

$$|f(x, y)| \le C|x - y|^{-\lambda}, \quad x, y \in X,$$

with some constants $C > 0$ and $0 < \lambda < n$. Prove that $F$ is continuous on $X$.

**Theorem 15.77 (Differentiability).** *Let function $g$ from above be continuous on $X$. Suppose that the following conditions are satisfied:*

1. *A partial derivative $\frac{\partial f}{\partial x_j}(x, y), j = 1, 2, \ldots, n$ exists and is continuous on $X \times X$ except at the diagonal $x = y$;*

2. *the integral*

$$\int_X f(x, y)g(y)\mathrm{d}y$$

   *converges pointwise in $x \in B_\delta(x^0) \cap X$ for some $\delta > 0$;*

3. *the integral*

$$\int_X \frac{\partial}{\partial x_j} f(x, y)g(y)\mathrm{d}y$$

   *converges uniformly at $x^0$.*

*Then the equality*

$$\frac{\partial}{\partial x_j} \int_X f(x, y)g(y)\mathrm{d}y = \int_X \frac{\partial}{\partial x_j} f(x, y)g(y)\mathrm{d}y$$

*holds everywhere in the neighborhood of $x^0$.*

**Proof.** Let us prove this theorem for $x = x^0$. To this end we consider

$$F_\delta(x) := \int_{|y - x^0| \ge 2\delta} f(x, y)g(y)\mathrm{d}y$$

and

$$\frac{\partial}{\partial x_j} F_\delta(x) = \int_{|y - x^0| \ge 2\delta} \frac{\partial}{\partial x_j} f(x, y)g(y)\mathrm{d}y.$$

If $|x - x^0| < \delta$ and $|y - x^0| \ge 2\delta$ then $|x - y| > \delta$. It means that $F_\delta$ and $\frac{\partial}{\partial x_j} F_\delta$ are continuous, since $g$ is continuous by hypothesis. Differentiation under the integral sign is justified by Theorem 15.71. We may conclude also that for $x \in B_\delta(x^0) \cap X$ the limits

$$\lim_{\delta \to 0} F_\delta(x) = F(x), \quad \lim_{\delta \to 0} \frac{\partial F_\delta}{\partial x_j}(x) =: \Psi(x)$$

exist. Furthermore, due to conditions of this theorem we have

$$\frac{F_\delta(x^0 + te_j) - F_\delta(x^0)}{t} = \frac{1}{t} \int_{|y - x^0| \ge 2\delta} (f(x^0 + te_j, y) - f(x^0, y))g(y)\mathrm{d}y$$

$$= \int_{|y - x^0| \ge 2\delta} \left( \frac{\partial}{\partial x_j} f(x^0 + \theta te_j, y) + o_t(1) \right) g(y)\mathrm{d}y$$

$$\to \int_{|y - x^0| \ge 2\delta} \frac{\partial f}{\partial x_j}(x^0, y)g(y)\mathrm{d}y$$

as $t \to 0$. Therefore we obtain that for any $\varepsilon > 0$ there exists $\delta_1 < \delta$ such that

$$\left| \frac{F_{\delta_1}(x^0 + te_j) - F_{\delta_1}(x^0)}{t} - \Psi(x^0) \right| < \varepsilon$$

for $t$ small enough. Passing to the limit $\delta \to 0$ allows us to conclude that

$$\left| \frac{F(x^0 + te_j) - F(x^0)}{t} - \Psi(x^0) \right| \le \varepsilon$$

for $t$ small enough. This means that in fact

$$\Psi(x^0) = \frac{\partial F}{\partial x_j}(x^0).$$

Similarly this fact can be proved for any $x \in B_\delta(x^0) \cap X$. Thus, this theorem is proved.

We will consider now the integral

$$F(x) := \int_Y f(x,y) \mathrm{d}y$$

taken over an unbounded closed Jordan measurable set $Y$ such that the point at infinity is the only singularity of $f(x,y)$ for any $x \in X$.

**Definition 15.78.** *Let a set $X \subset \mathbb{R}^m$ be compact. The integral defining $F$ is said to be uniformly convergent with respect to $x \in X$ if it is pointwise convergent in $x \in X$ and if, for any $\varepsilon > 0$, there is a number $R_0 > 0$ (sufficiently large) such that*

$$\left| \int_{Y \setminus B_R(0)} f(x,y) \mathrm{d}y \right| < \varepsilon$$

*for all $R \ge R_0$ and for all $x \in X$.*

In complete analogy with the proofs of Theorems 15.69 and 15.71 we obtain the following result.

**Theorem 15.79 (Improper integral).**

1. *Let function $f(x,y)$ be continuous on the set $X \times Y$ and let the integral defining $F$ be uniformly convergent on $X$. Then $F$ is continuous on $X$ and Riemann integrable on $X$ and*

$$\int_X F(x) \mathrm{d}x = \int_Y \left( \int_X f(x,y) \mathrm{d}x \right) \mathrm{d}y.$$

2. *Let $X \subset \mathbb{R}^m$ be the closure of an open bounded set and let function $f(x,y)$ and its partial derivative $\frac{\partial f}{\partial x_j}, j = 1, 2, \ldots, n$, be continuous. If the integral defining $F$ converges pointwise in $x \in X$ and the integral*

$$\int_Y \frac{\partial}{\partial x_j} f(x,y) \mathrm{d}y$$

*converges uniformly in $x \in X$ then $\frac{\partial F}{\partial x_j}$ exists and*

$$\frac{\partial F}{\partial x_j}(x) = \int_Y \frac{\partial}{\partial x_j} f(x,y) \mathrm{d}y.$$

**Exercise 15.80.** Let function $g$ be continuous on a compact set $X \subset \mathbb{R}^n$. Consider the integral

$$F(x) = \int_X \frac{g(y)}{|x-y|^\lambda} dy, \quad x \in X.$$

Determine the value of parameter $\lambda$ for which

1. $F$ is continuous on $X$, or

2. $\frac{\partial F}{\partial x_j}$ exists and is continuous on $X$. Compute also $\frac{\partial F}{\partial x_j}(x), j = 1, 2, \ldots, n$.

**Exercise 15.81 (One-dimensional case).**    1. Prove that if $f(x,y)$ is continuous on the set $[a,b] \times [c, \infty)$ and the integral

$$I(x) := \int_c^\infty f(x,y) dy$$

converges uniformly in $x \in [a,b]$ then $I$ is continuous on $[a,b]$.

2. Prove the *Dini test for an improper integral*: Suppose that the function $f(x,y) \geq 0$ is continuous on the set $[a,b] \times [c, \infty)$. If the integral

$$I(x) := \int_c^\infty f(x,y) dy$$

converges pointwise in $x \in [a,b]$ and if it is continuous then this integral converges uniformly in $x \in [a,b]$.

3. Prove the *Dirichlet–Abel test for improper integral*: Suppose that the function $f(x,y)$ is integrable with respect to $y \in [c, R]$ for any $R > c$ for each $x \in [a,b]$. If there is a constant $M > 0$ such that

$$\left| \int_c^A f(x,y) dy \right| \leq M$$

uniformly in $x \in [a,b]$ and $A > c$ and if the function $g$ is monotone decreasing and vanishing as $y \to \infty$ then the integral

$$I(x) := \int_c^\infty f(x,y) dy$$

converges uniformly in $x \in [a,b]$. If, in addition, $f$ and $g$ are continuous then $I$ is also continuous.

4. Let function $f(x,y)$ and its derivative $\frac{\partial f}{\partial x}$ be continuous on the set $[a,b] \times [c, \infty)$. Prove that if the integral

$$I(x) := \int_c^\infty f(x,y) dy$$

converges pointwise in $x \in [a,b]$ and if the integral

$$\int_c^\infty \frac{\partial}{\partial x} f(x,y) dy$$

converges uniformly in $x \in [a,b]$ then $I$ is continuously differentiable and

$$I'(x) = \int_c^\infty \frac{\partial}{\partial x} f(x,y) dy$$

for all $x \in [a,b]$.

5. Prove the *Fubini theorem for improper integrals dependent on parameter*: Let function $f(x, y) \geq 0$ be continuous on the set $[a, \infty) \times [c, \infty)$. Let also the integrals

$$I(x) := \int_c^\infty f(x, y) \mathrm{d}y, \quad K(y) := \int_a^\infty f(x, y) \mathrm{d}x$$

be continuous with respect to $x \geq a$ and $y \geq c$, respectively. Then the convergence of one of the integrals

$$\int_a^\infty I(x) \mathrm{d}x, \quad \int_c^\infty K(y) \mathrm{d}y$$

implies the convergence of the other and

$$\int_a^\infty I(x) \mathrm{d}x = \int_a^\infty \left( \int_c^\infty f(x, y) \mathrm{d}y \right) \mathrm{d}x$$

$$= \int_c^\infty K(y) \mathrm{d}y = \int_c^\infty \left( \int_a^\infty f(x, y) \mathrm{d}x \right) \mathrm{d}y.$$

6. Prove that the integral

$$\int_0^\infty x \sin(x^3 - ax) \mathrm{d}x$$

converges uniformly in $a \in [-R, R]$ for any fixed $R > 0$.

**Example 15.82.** Using the integral of Dirichlet (see Example 10.20) we will show that

$$J_1(\alpha) := \int_0^\infty \frac{\sin^2(\alpha x)}{x^2} \mathrm{d}x = \frac{\pi}{2} |\alpha|.$$

Since $J_1(\alpha) = J_1(-\alpha)$ and $J_1(0) = 0$, it is enough to consider $\alpha > 0$. The integral of Dirichlet converges uniformly in $\alpha \in [\alpha_1, \alpha_2] \subset \mathbb{R}_+$. This fact allows us to differentiate $J_1(\alpha)$ with respect to $\alpha$ under the integral sign to obtain

$$J_1'(\alpha) = 2 \int_0^\infty \frac{\sin(\alpha x) \cos(\alpha x)}{x} \mathrm{d}x = \int_0^\infty \frac{\sin(2\alpha x)}{x} \mathrm{d}x = \frac{\pi}{2}, \quad \alpha > 0.$$

Thus, $J_1(\alpha) = \frac{\pi}{2}\alpha + C$ for $\alpha > 0$. But $J_1(0) = 0$ implies $C = 0$. Hence $J_1(\alpha) = \frac{\pi}{2}|\alpha|$. Similarly one sees that

$$\int_0^\infty \frac{\sin^3(\alpha x)}{x^3} \mathrm{d}x = \frac{3\pi}{8} \alpha |\alpha|.$$

**Exercise 15.83.**  1. Show that the integral

$$\int_0^1 \frac{x^\alpha - 1}{\log x} \mathrm{d}x$$

converges for any $\alpha > -1$ and is equal to $\log(1 + \alpha)$.

2. Show that

$$\int_0^\infty \frac{\cos x}{1 + x^2} \mathrm{d}x = \frac{\pi}{2e}.$$

Hint: Use the integral

$$I(\alpha) := \int_0^\infty \frac{\cos(\alpha x)}{1 + x^2} \mathrm{d}x, \quad \alpha > 0,$$

and differentiate twice in $\alpha > 0$.

3. Show that

$$\int_0^\infty \frac{\sin^2 x}{x^2(1+x^2)}\,dx = \frac{\pi}{4}(e^{-2}+1).$$

Hint: Use the integral

$$I(\alpha) := \int_0^\infty \frac{\sin^2(\alpha x)}{x^2(1+x^2)}\,dx, \quad \alpha > 0,$$

and differentiate three times in $\alpha > 0$ to obtain an ordinary differential equation of order two for $I'(\alpha)$.

4. Let $x > 0$. Prove that

$$\int_0^\infty \frac{e^{-t} - e^{-xt}}{t}\,dt = \log x.$$

# Chapter 16

# Lebesgue integration

In this chapter we will extend the class of Jordan measurable sets in $\mathbb{R}^n$ (see Chapter 12) to a much wider class of measurable sets which are called Lebesgue measurable sets with the corresponding Lebesgue measure. We will consider then measurable functions and will extend the notion of the Riemann integral to the Lebesgue integral. Consequently, we will consider the central part of Lebesgue's theory, which is closeness with respect to the operation of passage to the limit in measure theory and in Lebesgue integration. We shall also consider some classes of Lebesgue integrable functions and related theorems which concern the representation of linear bounded functionals, in particular, the theorems of Radon and Nikodym and F. Riesz.

## 16.1 ▪ Lebesgue measure in $\mathbb{R}^n$

Our approach is based on the notion of a rectangular parallelepiped and an elementary figure in $\mathbb{R}^n, n \geq 1$, introduced in Chapter 12 (see Definition 12.28).

**Proposition 16.1.** *Let $F$ and $F_j, j = 1, 2, \ldots$, be elementary figures such that*

$$F \subset \bigcup_{j=1}^{\infty} F_j,$$

*where the family $\{F_j\}_{j=1}^{\infty}$ is at most countable (it might be finite). Then*

$$\mu'(F) \leq \sum_{j=1}^{\infty} \mu'(F_j),$$

*where $\mu'$ denotes Jordan's measure of an elementary figure.*

**Proof.** Elementary figures $F$ and $F_j, j = 1, 2, \ldots$, are closed and bounded sets by definition. Next, for every $F_j$ and for any $\varepsilon > 0$ one can find an open set $G_j$ such that $G_j$ is an elementary figure and

$$\mu'(G_j) \leq \mu'(F_j) + \varepsilon/2^j.$$

Thus

$$F \subset \bigcup_{j=1}^{\infty} G_j$$

and this union is an open cover of closed and bounded set $F$. Applying the classical Heine–Borel lemma (see Theorem 13.10) we conclude that there is a finite subcover $\{G_{j_k}\}_{k=1}^l$ such that

$$F \subset \bigcup_{k=1}^{l} G_{j_k}, \quad \mu'(F) \leq \sum_{k=1}^{l} \mu'(G_{j_k}).$$

This implies that

$$\mu'(F) \leq \sum_{k=1}^{l}(\mu'(F_{j_k}) + \varepsilon/2^{j_k}) \leq \sum_{j=1}^{\infty} \mu'(F_j) + \sum_{j=1}^{\infty} \varepsilon/2^j = \sum_{j=1}^{\infty} \mu'(F_j) + \varepsilon.$$

Since $\varepsilon > 0$ was arbitrary, we obtain

$$\mu'(F) \leq \sum_{j=1}^{\infty} \mu'(F_j)$$

and this proposition is proved.

**Corollary 16.2.** *Let elementary figure $F$ be the union of mutually disjoint elementary figures $F_j$, i.e.,*

$$F = \bigcup_{j=1}^{\infty} F_j, \quad F_j \cap F_k = \emptyset, j \neq k.$$

*Then*

$$\mu'(F) = \sum_{j=1}^{\infty} \mu'(F_j).$$

***Proof.*** The properties of Jordan's measure (see Chapter 12) give that for any $m \in \mathbb{N}$ we have that

$$\mu'(F) \geq \mu'(\cup_{j=1}^{m} F_j) = \sum_{j=1}^{m} \mu'(F_j).$$

Letting $m \to +\infty$ we obtain that

$$\mu'(F) \geq \sum_{j=1}^{\infty} \mu'(F_j).$$

The opposite inequality is the essence of Proposition 16.1. Hence this corollary is proved.

**Remark 16.3.** In order to avoid problems with infinite numbers we assume that we consider first the case when the sets are bounded and are contained (without loss of generality) in the parallelepiped $\Pi_R = [-R, R]^n$ with $R > 0$ fixed and big enough.

**Definition 16.4.** *Let $X \subset \mathbb{R}^n$ be a bounded set. The* outer Lebesgue measure *of $X$, denoted by $\mu^*(X)$, or* outer measure *for short, is defined as*

$$\mu^*(X) := \inf_{\cup_{k=1}^{\infty}\Pi_k \supset X} \sum_{k=1}^{\infty} \mu'(\Pi_k),$$

*where $\Pi_k, k = 1, 2, \ldots,$ are rectangular parallelepipeds and the infimum is taken over all such covers of $X$.*

**Remark 16.5.** One can obtain the same value for $\mu^*(X)$ if we will consider in Definition 16.4 the covering of $X$ by elementary figures (instead of parallelepipeds) since any elementary figure (see Definition 12.28) is the finite union of mutually disjoint rectangular parallelepipeds. Moreover, if $X \subset \mathbb{R}^n$ is an elementary figure then obviously $\mu^*(X) = \mu'(X)$.

**Theorem 16.6 (Properties of outer measure).**

1. *If $X$ is the empty set then $\mu^*(X) = 0$.*

2. *If $X \subset Y$ then $\mu^*(X) \leq \mu^*(Y)$.*

3. *If $X \subset \cup_{k=1}^{\infty} X_k$ then $\mu^*(X) \leq \sum_{k=1}^{\infty} \mu^*(X_k)$.*

4. *If $X, Y$ are two bounded sets in $\mathbb{R}^n$ then*

$$|\mu^*(X) - \mu^*(Y)| \leq \mu^*(X \Delta Y).$$

*Proof.*

1. If $X$ is empty then every collection of rectangular parallelepipeds covers $X$ and, therefore, the infimum in Definition 16.4 is equal to zero.

2. If $X \subset Y$ then any cover of $Y$ covers $X$ and thus

$$\mu^*(Y) = \inf_{\cup_{k=1}^{\infty} \Pi_k \supset Y} \sum_{k=1}^{\infty} \mu'(\Pi_k) = \inf_{\cup_{k=1}^{\infty} \Pi_k \supset Y \supset X} \sum_{k=1}^{\infty} \mu'(\Pi_k)$$

$$\geq \inf_{\cup_{k=1}^{\infty} \widetilde{\Pi}_k \supset X} \sum_{k=1}^{\infty} \mu'(\widetilde{\Pi}_k) = \mu^*(X).$$

3. If $\sum_{k=1}^{\infty} \mu^*(X_k) = +\infty$ then there is nothing to prove, so we may assume that $\sum_{k=1}^{\infty} \mu^*(X_k) < \infty$. Consequently, $\mu^*(X_k) < \infty$ for each $k = 1, 2, \ldots$. By the definition of outer measure for every $X_k$ there is a cover $\cup_{j=1}^{\infty} \Pi_j^{(k)}$ such that

$$X_k \subset \bigcup_{j=1}^{\infty} \Pi_j^{(k)}$$

and

$$\sum_{j=1}^{\infty} \mu'(\Pi_j^{(k)}) \leq \mu^*(X_k) + \varepsilon/2^k.$$

Hence

$$X \subset \bigcup_{k=1}^{\infty} X_k \subset \bigcup_{k,j=1}^{\infty} \Pi_j^{(k)}$$

and

$$\mu^*(X) \leq \sum_{k,j=1}^{\infty} \mu'(\Pi_j^{(k)}) \leq \sum_{k=1}^{\infty} \mu^*(X_k) + \varepsilon.$$

Since $\varepsilon > 0$ was arbitrary, we obtain the statement.

4. Since $X \subset Y \cup (X \Delta Y)$ (see Exercise 1.10), parts 2 and 3 of this theorem lead to

$$\mu^*(X) \leq \mu^*(Y) + \mu^*(X \Delta Y).$$

Similarly $Y \subset X \cup (X \Delta Y)$ implies

$$\mu^*(Y) \leq \mu^*(X) + \mu^*(X \Delta Y).$$

Combining these two inequalities we obtain the needed estimate.

Theorem 16.6 is completely proved.

**Definition 16.7.** *Let $X \subset \mathbb{R}^n$ be bounded. Then $X$ is said to be* Lebesgue measurable, *or* measurable *for short, if for any $\varepsilon > 0$ there is an elementary figure $F$ such that $\mu^*(X \Delta F) < \varepsilon$. The function $\mu^*$ (the outer measure) considered only on Lebesgue measurable sets is called the* Lebesgue measure *and is denoted by $\mu$.*

**Remark 16.8.** Any set $N \subset \mathbb{R}^n$ with $\mu^*(N) = 0$ is Lebesgue measurable and $\mu(N) = 0$. Indeed, since empty set $\emptyset$ can be considered as an elementary figure (see Definition 12.28), we have that

$$\mu^*(N \Delta \emptyset) = \mu^*(N) = 0 < \varepsilon.$$

**Theorem 16.9 (Properties of Lebesgue measure).**

1. *Let $X \subset \mathbb{R}^n$ be measurable. Then the set $\Pi_R \setminus X$ is also measurable.*

2. *If $X_1, X_2, \ldots, X_m$ are measurable sets then their union and intersection are measurable and if they are mutually disjoint then the additivity property*

$$\mu \left( \bigcup_{k=1}^{m} X_k \right) = \sum_{k=1}^{m} \mu(X_k)$$

*holds.*

3. *The difference and symmetric difference of two measurable sets are also measurable.*

4. *If $X \subset \mathbb{R}^n$ is measurable then for any $h \in \mathbb{R}^n$ the set $X_h := \{x + h : x \in X\}$ is also measurable and $\mu(X_h) = \mu(X)$.*

*Proof.*

1. Since (see Exercise 1.9)

$$(\Pi_R \setminus X) \Delta (\Pi_R \setminus \operatorname{int} F) = X \Delta \operatorname{int} F$$

and since $\widetilde{F} := \Pi_R \setminus \operatorname{int} F$ is an elementary figure, we have that

$$\mu^*((\Pi_R \setminus X) \Delta \widetilde{F}) = \mu^*(X \Delta \operatorname{int} F) = \mu^*(X \Delta F) < \varepsilon.$$

Hence $\Pi_R \setminus X$ is measurable.

2. It suffices to prove these statements for two measurable sets $X_1$ and $X_2$. Then for any $\varepsilon > 0$ there are elementary figures $F_1$ and $F_2$ such that

$$\mu^*(X_1 \Delta F_1) < \varepsilon/2, \quad \mu^*(X_2 \Delta F_2) < \varepsilon/2.$$

But since (see Exercise 1.10)

$$(X_1 \cup X_2)\Delta(F_1 \cup F_2) \subset (X_1\Delta F_1) \cup (X_2\Delta F_2), \tag{16.1}$$

Theorem 16.6 implies that

$$\mu^*((X_1 \cup X_2)\Delta(F_1 \cup F_2)) \leq \mu^*(X_1\Delta F_1) + \mu^*(X_2\Delta F_2) < \varepsilon.$$

It proves that $X_1 \cup X_2$ is measurable since $F_1 \cup F_2$ is an elementary figure. For measurability of the intersection $X_1 \cap X_2$ we use the equality

$$X_1 \cap X_2 = \Pi_R \setminus ((\Pi_R \setminus X_1) \cup (\Pi_R \setminus X_2))$$

and parts 1 and 2 of this theorem. To prove the additivity for measure $\mu$ we find for any $\varepsilon > 0$ elementary figures $F_1$ and $F_2$ such that

$$\mu^*(X_1\Delta F_1) < \varepsilon/2, \quad \mu^*(X_2\Delta F_2) < \varepsilon/2.$$

Since $X_1 \cap X_2 = \emptyset$,

$$F_1 \cap F_2 \subset (X_1\Delta F_1) \cup (X_2\Delta F_2)$$

and consequently

$$\mu'(F_1 \cap F_2) = \mu^*(F_1 \cap F_2) \leq \mu^*(X_1\Delta F_1) + \mu^*(X_2\Delta F_2) < \varepsilon.$$

Moreover, Theorem 16.6 (part 4) gives that

$$|\mu^*(X_1) - \mu^*(F_1)| = |\mu^*(X_1) - \mu'(F_1)| \leq \mu^*(X_1\Delta F_1) < \varepsilon/2$$

and

$$|\mu^*(X_2) - \mu^*(F_2)| = |\mu^*(X_2) - \mu'(F_2)| \leq \mu^*(X_2\Delta F_2) < \varepsilon/2.$$

Due to additivity of measure $\mu'$ for elementary figures (see Chapter 12) we obtain

$$\mu'(F_1 \cup F_2) = \mu'(F_1) + \mu'(F_2) - \mu'(F_1 \cap F_2) \geq \mu^*(X_1) + \mu^*(X_2) - 2\varepsilon.$$

Using (16.1) we obtain

$$\mu^*(X_1 \cup X_2) \geq \mu'(F_1 \cup F_2) - \mu^*((X_1 \cup X_2)\Delta(F_1 \cup F_2))$$
$$\geq \mu'(F_1 \cup F_2) - \varepsilon \geq \mu^*(X_1) + \mu^*(X_2) - 3\varepsilon.$$

Letting $\varepsilon \to 0$ we have

$$\mu^*(X_1 \cup X_2) \geq \mu^*(X_1) + \mu^*(X_2).$$

But the opposite inequality is always valid due to Theorem 16.6 (part 3). So

$$\mu^*(X_1 \cup X_2) = \mu^*(X_1) + \mu^*(X_2).$$

Since $X_1, X_2$ and $X_1 \cup X_2$ are measurable, we may substitute here the Lebesgue measure $\mu$.

3. This statement follows from the equalities (see Exercise 1.9)

$$X_1 \setminus X_2 = X_1 \cap (\Pi_R \setminus X_2)$$

and

$$X_1\Delta X_2 = (X_1 \setminus X_2) \cup (X_2 \setminus X_1)$$

and from part 1 of this theorem.

4. Let us first notice that for any bounded set $X \subset \mathbb{R}^n$ it follows that $\mu^*(X_h) = \mu^*(X)$. This fact is a consequence of Definition 16.4 of outer measure and the fact that for any cover $\{\Pi_k\}_{k=1}^{\infty}$ of $X$ the family $\{\Pi_k + h\}_{k=1}^{\infty}$ is a cover of $X_h$ and vice versa. Second, if $X$ is measurable then for any $\varepsilon > 0$ there is an elementary figure $F$ such that

$$\mu^*(X \Delta F) < \varepsilon$$

or

$$\mu^*(X_h \Delta F_h) = \mu^*((X \Delta F)_h) < \varepsilon.$$

Since $F_h$ is an elementary figure, $X_h$ is measurable and $\mu(X_h) = \mu(X)$.

**Theorem 16.10 ($\sigma$-additivity of measure).** *Let $\{X_j\}_{j=1}^{\infty}$ be a countable family of measurable sets. Then the sets $\cup_{j=1}^{\infty} X_j$ and $\cap_{j=1}^{\infty} X_j$ are also measurable. Moreover, if the family $\{X_j\}_{j=1}^{\infty}$ is mutually disjoint then the $\sigma$-additivity*

$$\mu \left( \bigcup_{j=1}^{\infty} X_j \right) = \sum_{j=1}^{\infty} \mu(X_j) \qquad \text{.}$$

*holds.*

***Proof.*** Let

$$X_1' := X_1, \quad X_k' := X_k \setminus \bigcup_{j=1}^{k-1} X_j, \quad k = 2, 3, \ldots.$$

Then

$$\bigcup_{k=1}^{\infty} X_k' = \bigcup_{j=1}^{\infty} X_j =: X$$

and $\{X_k'\}_{k=1}^{\infty}$ are mutually disjoint. Due to Theorem 16.9 the sets $X_k'$ are measurable and for any finite $m \in \mathbb{N}$ we have

$$\mu \left( \bigcup_{k=1}^{m} X_k' \right) = \sum_{k=1}^{m} \mu(X_k') \leq \mu^*(X) < \infty.$$

That's why the series $\sum_{k=1}^{\infty} \mu(X_k')$ converges, and for any $\varepsilon > 0$ there is $m_0 \in \mathbb{N}$ such that

$$\sum_{k=m_0+1}^{\infty} \mu(X_k') < \varepsilon/2.$$

On the other hand, since $\cup_{k=1}^{m_0} X_k'$ is measurable, for this $\varepsilon > 0$ there exists an elementary figure $F$ such that

$$\mu^* \left( \bigcup_{k=1}^{m_0} X_k' \Delta F \right) < \varepsilon/2.$$

The latter two facts imply that

$$X \Delta F \subset \left( \left( \bigcup_{k=1}^{m_0} X_k' \right) \Delta F \right) \cup \left( \left( \bigcup_{k=m_0+1}^{\infty} X_k' \right) \Delta F \right)$$

and therefore

$$\mu^*(X\Delta F) \leq \mu^* \left( \left( \bigcup_{k=1}^{m_0} X_k' \right) \Delta F \right) + \mu^* \left( \left( \bigcup_{k=m_0+1}^{\infty} X_k' \right) \Delta F \right)$$

$$< \varepsilon/2 + \sum_{k=m_0+1}^{\infty} \mu(X_k) < \varepsilon,$$

i.e., $X$ is measurable. Next, since

$$\bigcap_{j=1}^{\infty} X_j = \Pi_R \setminus \bigcup_{j=1}^{\infty} (\Pi_R \setminus X_j),$$

the measurability of $\cap_{j=1}^{\infty} X_j$ also follows. The $\sigma$-additivity of Lebesgue measure $\mu$ can be obtained as follows. For any $m_0 \in \mathbb{N}$ we have that (see Theorem 16.9)

$$\mu \left( \bigcup_{j=1}^{m_0} X_j \right) = \sum_{j=1}^{m_0} \mu(X_j) \leq \mu(X),$$

where $\{X_j\}_{j=1}^{\infty}$ are mutually disjoint. Thus,

$$\sum_{j=1}^{\infty} \mu(X_j) \leq \mu(X) < \infty.$$

On the other hand, due to Theorem 16.6

$$\mu(X) = \mu^*(X) \leq \sum_{j=1}^{\infty} \mu^*(X_j) = \sum_{j=1}^{\infty} \mu(X_j).$$

This proves the theorem.

**Corollary 16.11.** *If* $X_1 \supset X_2 \supset \cdots \supset X_j \supset \cdots$ *is a sequence of measurable closed sets and*

$$X = \bigcap_{j=1}^{\infty} X_j$$

*then* $\mu(X) = \lim_{j \to \infty} \mu(X_j)$.

**Proof.** Let us assume first that $X = \emptyset$. Next, for any $k = 1, 2, \ldots$

$$X_k = \bigcup_{j=k}^{\infty} (X_j \setminus X_{j+1}),$$

where the sets $\{X_j \setminus X_{j+1}\}_{j=1}^{\infty}$ are measurable and mutually disjoint. Hence, Theorem 16.10 gives that

$$\mu(X_1) = \sum_{j=1}^{\infty} \mu(X_j \setminus X_{j+1}) < \infty$$

and

$$\mu(X_k) = \sum_{j=k}^{\infty} \mu(X_j \setminus X_{j+1})$$

with $\mu(X_k) \to 0$ as $k \to \infty$ due to the convergence of the series which represents $\mu(X_1)$. This proves that claim for the empty set. For general $X$ one may consider $X'_j := X_j \setminus X$.

**Corollary 16.12.** *If $X_1 \subset X_2 \subset \cdots \subset X_j \subset \cdots$ is a sequence of measurable sets and*

$$X = \bigcup_{j=1}^{\infty} X_j$$

*then $\mu(X) = \lim_{j\to\infty} \mu(X_j)$.*

**Proof.** Since

$$\Pi_R \setminus X = \Pi_R \setminus \bigcup_{j=1}^{\infty} X_j = \bigcap_{j=1}^{\infty} (\Pi_R \setminus X_j),$$

the sets satisfy

$$(\Pi_R \setminus X_1) \supset (\Pi_R \setminus X_2) \supset \cdots .$$

Applying Corollary 16.11 and Theorem 16.9, part 2, we obtain

$$\mu(\Pi_R \setminus X) = \lim_{j\to\infty} \mu(\Pi_R \setminus X_j) = (2R)^n - \lim_{j\to\infty} \mu(X_j)$$

or

$$(2R)^n - \mu(X) = (2R)^n - \lim_{j\to\infty} \mu(X_j).$$

This concludes the proof.

We want to show now that any bounded open set and any bounded closed set (compact) are measurable. In the one-dimensional case it is well known that every open set can be represented as a union of at most countable disjoint open intervals. In the multidimensional case it is not true that every open set is a union of at most countable disjoint open parallelepipeds. But it is almost true.

**Proposition 16.13.** *Every open set in $\mathbb{R}^n$ is a union of not more than countable almost disjoint parallelepipeds, meaning that their internals are not intersecting.*

**Proof.** Let $G \subset \mathbb{R}^n$ be open. We construct a family of disjoint cubes $Q_j, j \in \mathbb{N}$ (parallelepipeds of equal sides) with integer coordinates. If $Q_j \subset G$ we include it in the family; otherwise we exclude it, i.e., we include in this family only cubes $Q_j \subset G$. Next, we bisect the sides of $Q_j$ to obtain $2^n$ almost disjoint cubes of side one-half and repeat the procedure for the rest of $G$. Iterating this process arbitrarily many times we obtain not more than a countable family of almost disjoint cubes. The union of the cubes in this family is contained in $G$ since we include only cubes that are contained in $G$.

Conversely, if $x \in G$ then since $G$ is open, some sufficiently small cube in this bisection procedure that contains $x$ is entirely contained in $G$ and such a cube is included in this family. Hence the union of the family contains $G$ and is therefore equal to $G$.

**Remark 16.14.** As mentioned, in the one-dimensional case this statement can be clarified more precisely. Namely, every open set $X$ on the line is a union of not more than countable mutually disjoint intervals, i.e.,

$$X = \bigcup_{j=1}^{\infty} (a_j, b_j), \quad (a_j, b_j) \cap (a_k, b_k) = \emptyset, j \neq k.$$

**Theorem 16.15 (Measurability of open and closed sets).** *Every open bounded set and every closed bounded set in $\mathbb{R}^n$ are measurable.*

*Proof.* Let $G \subset \mathbb{R}^n$ be open and bounded. Then Proposition 16.13 implies that

$$G = \bigcup_{j=1}^{\infty} \Pi_j, \quad \text{int } \Pi_j \cap \text{int } \Pi_k = \emptyset, j \neq k.$$

Due to Theorem 16.10 we have that $G$ is measurable (since $\Pi_j$ are measurable) and

$$\mu(G) = \sum_{j=1}^{\infty} \mu(\Pi_j) < \infty.$$

Now let $K \subset \mathbb{R}^n$ be a closed bounded set. Then the set $\text{int } \Pi_R \setminus K$ is open and bounded and therefore measurable. Moreover,

$$\mu(K) = (2R)^n - \mu(\text{int } \Pi_R \setminus K).$$

This proves the theorem.

**Theorem 16.16 (Criterion of measurability for bounded sets).** *A bounded set $X \subset \mathbb{R}^n$ is measurable if and only if for any $\varepsilon > 0$ there is an open set $G$ and a closed (compact) set $K$ such that $K \subset X \subset G$ and $\mu(G \setminus K) < \varepsilon$.*

*Proof.* Let us assume that for any $\varepsilon > 0$ there are two sets $K$ and $G$ such that $K \subset X \subset G$ and $\mu(G \setminus K) < \varepsilon/2$. Then, for any elementary figure $F \subset X$ we have

$$\mu^*(X \Delta F) = \mu^*(((X \setminus K) \cup K) \Delta F) \leq \mu^*(((G \setminus K) \Delta F) \cup (K \Delta F))$$
$$\leq \mu^*(G \setminus K) + \mu^*(K \Delta F) = \mu(G \setminus K) + \mu^*(K \Delta F) < \varepsilon/2 + \mu^*(K \Delta F).$$

Since $K$ is measurable, we may find elementary figure $F$ such that $\mu^*(K \Delta F) < \varepsilon/2$. This proves the criterion in one direction.

Conversely, let $X$ be measurable. Then $X^c := \Pi_R \setminus X$ is also measurable. Due to Definition 16.4, for any $\varepsilon > 0$ there are two elementary figures $F_1$ and $F_2$ such that

$$\mu^*(X \Delta F_1) < \varepsilon/2, \quad \mu^*(X^c \Delta F_2) < \varepsilon/2.$$

Consider now only these parts of $F_1$ and $F_2$, denoted by $\widetilde{F_1}$ and $\widetilde{F_2}$, respectively, such that they are elementary and belong to $X$ and $\Pi_R \setminus X$, respectively. Then the sets

$$K := \widetilde{F_1} \subset X, \quad G := \text{int } \Pi_R \setminus \widetilde{F_2} \supset X$$

are closed and open, respectively. Moreover,

$$\varepsilon/2 > \mu^*(X \Delta F_1) \geq \mu^*(X \setminus \widetilde{F_1}) = \mu(X \setminus K)$$

and
$$\varepsilon/2 > \mu^*(X^c \Delta F_2) \geq \mu^*(X^c \setminus \widetilde{F_2}) \geq \mu^*(G \setminus X) = \mu(G \setminus X).$$

Combining these inequalities we obtain
$$\mu(G \setminus K) \leq \mu(X \setminus K) + \mu(G \setminus X) < \varepsilon.$$

This proves the theorem.

So far we have considered only bounded measurable sets since we assumed that they belong to the paralellepiped $\Pi_R$ with fixed $R > 0$ big enough. It is not difficult to get rid of this requirement. Indeed, let us represent the whole space as

$$\mathbb{R}^n = \bigcup_{k_1, k_2, \ldots, k_n = -\infty}^{\infty} F_{k_1 k_2 \cdots k_n},$$

where the elementary sets $F_{k_1 k_2 \cdots k_n}$ are given by

$$F_{k_1 k_2 \cdots k_n} = \prod_{j=1}^{n} [k_j, k_j + 1], \quad k_j \in \mathbb{Z}.$$

**Definition 16.17.** *A set $X \subset \mathbb{R}^n$ is said to be measurable if each of the sets*

$$X_{k_1 k_2 \cdots k_n} := X \cap F_{k_1 k_2 \cdots k_n}$$

*is measurable. In this case the value*

$$\mu(X) := \sum_{k_1, k_2, \ldots, k_n = -\infty}^{\infty} \mu(X_{k_1 k_2 \cdots k_n})$$

*is called the* Lebesgue measure *of $X$. This series either converges to a finite nonnegative number or diverges to $+\infty$. In both cases this value is called the Lebesgue measure of $X$.*

**Exercise 16.18.** 1. Prove that every countable set $X \subset \mathbb{R}^n$ is measurable with $\mu(X) = 0$. In particular, the set

$$X = \{x \in \mathbb{R}^n : x = (x_1, x_2, \ldots, x_n), x_j \in \mathbb{Q}\}$$

is measurable with measure zero.

2. Let $K \subset \mathbb{R}^n$ be compact. Prove that

$$\mu(K) = \mu(G) - \mu(G \setminus K),$$

where $G$ is an open bounded set such that $K \subset G$. Prove also that the value $\mu(K)$ does not depend on the choice of such $G$.

3. Prove that every bounded set $X \subset \mathbb{R}^n$ is measurable if and only if for any $\varepsilon > 0$ there is a compact set $K \subset X$ such that $\mu^*(X) - \mu(K) < \varepsilon$.

4. Prove that the statement of part 3 does not hold if compact set $K \subset X$ is substituted by an open set $G \supset X$ with $\mu^*(X) < \mu(G) + \varepsilon$.

5. Let $K \subset \mathbb{R}^n$ be compact with $\mu(K) > 0$. Let $f : K \to \mathbb{R}$ be continuous. Prove that the set

$$X = \{(x, y) \in \mathbb{R}^{n+1} : x \in K, y = f(x)\}$$

has measure zero.

**Definition 16.19.** *The collection of sets in $\mathbb{R}^n$ that are countable intersections of open sets is denoted by $G_\delta(\mathbb{R}^n)$ and the collection of sets in $\mathbb{R}^n$ that are a countable union of closed sets is denoted by $F_\sigma(\mathbb{R}^n)$.*

**Theorem 16.20 (Property of $G_\delta$ and $F_\sigma$).** *Suppose that $X \subset \mathbb{R}^n$ is Lebesgue measurable. Then there are two sets $G \in G_\delta(\mathbb{R}^n)$ and $F \in F_\sigma(\mathbb{R}^n)$ such that*

$$F \subset X \subset G, \quad \mu(G) = \mu(X) = \mu(F),$$

*i.e., $\mu(G \setminus X) = \mu(X \setminus F) = 0$.*

**Proof.** Assume first that $X$ is bounded. Then Theorem 16.16 allows us to choose for any $k \in \mathbb{N}$ an open set $G_k$ and closed set $F_k$ such that

$$F_k \subset X \subset G_k, \quad \mu(G_k \setminus F_k) < 1/k.$$

Now the sets

$$G := \bigcap_{k=1}^{\infty} G_k, \quad F := \bigcap_{k=1}^{\infty} F_k$$

belong to $G_\delta(\mathbb{R}^n)$ and $F_\sigma(\mathbb{R}^n)$, respectively, and

$$\mu(X \setminus F) \le \mu(X \setminus F_k) < 1/k$$

and

$$\mu(G \setminus X) \le \mu(G_k \setminus X) < 1/k.$$

Since $k$ was arbitrary, we obtain $\mu(G \setminus X) = \mu(X \setminus F) = 0$.

In the case when $X$ is not bounded the proof follows by using Definition 16.17 and evident changes.

**Exercise 16.21.** 1. Let $X \subset \mathbb{R}^n$ be an arbitrary set with outer Lebesgue measure $\mu^*(X) < \infty$. Prove that the following are equivalent:

(a) $X$ is Lebesgue measurable.

(b) $\mu^*(X) = \sup_K \{\mu(K) : K \subset X, K \text{ is compact}\}$.

(c) $\mu^*(X) = \inf_G \{\mu(G) : X \subset G, G \text{ is open}\}$.

2. Prove that for arbitrary set $X \subset \mathbb{R}^n$ the following are equivalent:

(a) $X$ is Lebesgue measurable.

(b) There are compact sets $\{K_j\}_{j=1}^{\infty}$ and open sets $\{G_j\}_{j=1}^{\infty}$ such that

$$\bigcup_{j=1}^{\infty} K_j \subset X \subset \bigcup_{j=1}^{\infty} G_j$$

and the difference

$$\bigcup_{j=1}^{\infty} G_j \setminus \bigcup_{j=1}^{\infty} K_j$$

has outer measure zero.

3. Let $\{x_k\}_{k=1}^{\infty}$ be a sequence of all rational numbers from $[0,1]$. For some $\varepsilon > 0$ (small enough) consider the open set

$$G = \bigcup_{k=1}^{\infty} \left( x_k - \frac{\varepsilon}{2^{k+1}}, x_k + \frac{\varepsilon}{2^{k+1}} \right) \in G_\delta(\mathbb{R}).$$

Prove that

(a) $\mu(G) \leq \varepsilon$,

(b) $\mu(K) \geq 1 - \varepsilon$,

(c) int $K = \emptyset$,

where $K = [0,1] \setminus G$.

4. Show that there is a set $X \subset \mathbb{R}^n$ such that $\mu(X) = 0$ but $X \notin F_\sigma(\mathbb{R}^n)$.

5. Assume $X \subset \mathbb{R}^n$ is not measurable. Suppose that $X_1 \subset \mathbb{R}^n$ is measurable with $\mu(X_1) > 0$ and $X \cap X_1$ is measurable. Does it follow that $\mu(X \cap X_1) = 0$?

6. Under the conditions of part 5 we assume that $X \cap X_1 \neq \emptyset$. Does it follow that $X \cap X_1$ is not measurable?

Recalling that a linear map $T : \mathbb{R}^n \to \mathbb{R}^n$ is called *orthogonal* if $T^t = T^{-1}$, i.e., $(Tx, Ty)_{\mathbb{R}^n} = (x, y)$ for all $x, y \in \mathbb{R}^n$, we obtain the following result.

**Theorem 16.22 (On orthogonal transformation of measurable sets).** *If $X \subset \mathbb{R}^n$ is bounded and $T : \mathbb{R}^n \to \mathbb{R}^n$ is a linear orthogonal map then*

$$\mu^*(TX) = \mu^*(X)$$

*and $X$ is measurable if and only if $TX$ is measurable.*

**Proof.** Let us denote $\widetilde{X} := TX$. Given $\varepsilon > 0$ there is a cover $\cup_{k=1}^{\infty} \Pi_k \supset \widetilde{X}$ such that

$$\mu^*(\widetilde{X}) + \varepsilon/2 > \sum_{k=1}^{\infty} \mu'(\Pi_k).$$

Next, for each $k \in \mathbb{N}$ we can find a cover $\cup_{j=1}^{\infty} \widetilde{\Pi_{k_j}}$ of $\Pi_k$ such that

$$\sum_{j=1}^{\infty} \mu'(\widetilde{\Pi_{k_j}}) \leq \mu'(\Pi_k) + \varepsilon/2^{k+1}.$$

This implies that

$$\sum_{k,j=1}^{\infty} \mu'(\widetilde{\Pi_{k_j}}) \leq \sum_{k=1}^{\infty} \mu'(\Pi_k) + \varepsilon/2 < \mu^*(\widetilde{X}) + \varepsilon.$$

If $\Pi_{k_j} = T^t \widetilde{\Pi_{k_j}}$ then $\cup_{k,j=1}^\infty \Pi_{k_j}$ covers $X$ and

$$\mu^*(X) \le \sum_{k,j=1}^\infty \mu'(\Pi_{k_j}).$$

But $T$ is orthogonal and hence

$$\mu'(\Pi_{k_j}) = \mu'(\widetilde{\Pi_{k_j}}).$$

Therefore

$$\mu^*(X) \le \sum_{k,j=1}^\infty \mu'(\widetilde{\Pi_{k_j}}) < \mu^*(\widetilde{X}) + \varepsilon.$$

Since $\varepsilon > 0$ was arbitrary, by letting $\varepsilon \to +0$ we obtain that

$$\mu^*(X) \le \mu^*(\widetilde{X}).$$

Applying the same argument to the inverse mapping $X = T^{-1}\widetilde{X} = T^t\widetilde{X}$ we get the reverse inequality. So $\mu^*(X) = \mu^*(\widetilde{X})$. The last part of this theorem follows from Definition 16.7 and Theorem 16.9.

**Exercise 16.23.** Let $X \subset \mathbb{R}^n$ be bounded and let $\Lambda : \mathbb{R}^n \to \mathbb{R}^n$ be a linear mapping such that

$$\Lambda x := (\lambda_1 x_1, \dots, \lambda_n x_n), \quad x \in \mathbb{R}^n, \lambda_j > 0, j = 1, 2, \dots, n.$$

Prove that

$$\mu^*(\Lambda X) = \lambda_1 \lambda_2 \cdots \lambda_n \mu^*(X).$$

**Corollary 16.24.** *Suppose that $A : \mathbb{R}^n \to \mathbb{R}^n$ is a linear transformation with $\det A \ne 0$ and $X$ is a bounded set in $\mathbb{R}^n$. Then*

$$\mu^*(AX) = |\det A| \mu^*(X),$$

*and $AX$ is measurable if $X$ is measurable.*

**Proof.** According to the polar decomposition (known from linear algebra) the map $A$ may be written as $A = T \circ U$, where $T$ is orthogonal and $U := \sqrt{A^t A}$ is positive symmetric. Any positive symmetric map in turn can be diagonalized as

$$U = T_1^t \circ \Lambda \circ T_1,$$

where $T_1$ is orthogonal and

$$\Lambda x = (\lambda_1 x_1, \dots, \lambda_n x_n), \quad \lambda_j > 0, j = 1, 2, \dots, n,$$

is diagonal. According to Exercise 16.23 we have

$$\mu^*(\Lambda X) = \lambda_1 \lambda_2 \cdots \lambda_n \mu^*(X).$$

Since $|\det T| = |\det T_1| = 1$, we have that

$$|\det A| = \det \Lambda = \lambda_1 \lambda_2 \cdots \lambda_n.$$

That's why we have finally that

$$\mu^*(AX) = \mu^*(\Lambda X) = \det \Lambda \mu^*(X) = |\det A| \mu^*(X).$$

This finishes the proof.

**Exercise 16.25.** Prove that $X \subset \mathbb{R}^n$ is measurable if and only if

1. $X = F \cup F_1$, where $F \in F_\sigma(\mathbb{R}^n)$ and $\mu(F_1) = 0$, or

2. $X = G \setminus G_1$, where $G \in G_\delta(\mathbb{R}^n)$ and $\mu(G_1) = 0$.

**Exercise 16.26.** Considering the family of all measurable sets (up to equivalent sets), we introduce a function

$$\rho(X, Y) := \mu(X \Delta Y).$$

Prove that this family is a complete metric space if the convergence is defined as follows: $\{X_k\}_{k=1}^\infty$ converges to $X$ if and only if

$$\lim_{k \to \infty} \rho(X_k, X) = 0.$$

Two measurable sets $X_1$ and $X_2$ are said to be *equivalent* if $\mu(X_1 \Delta X_2) = 0$.

## 16.2 ▪ Measurable functions

For this section it is useful to consider the extended real line, i.e.,

$$\overline{\mathbb{R}} := \{x : -\infty \le x \le \infty\},$$

by adding two new elements $-\infty$ and $+\infty$ such that the following arithmetic operations are fulfilled:

1. For any $x \in \mathbb{R}$ we set

$$x + (+\infty) = +\infty, \quad x + (-\infty) = -\infty, \quad +\infty + (+\infty) = +\infty$$
$$-\infty + (-\infty) = -\infty, \quad +\infty - (-\infty) = +\infty;$$

2. for any $x \in \mathbb{R}_+$ we set

$$x \cdot (+\infty) = +\infty, \quad x \cdot (-\infty) = -\infty$$

and for any $x \in \mathbb{R}_-$ we set

$$x \cdot (+\infty) = -\infty, \quad x \cdot (-\infty) = +\infty;$$

3. we also set

$$0 \cdot (+\infty) = 0, \quad (+\infty) \cdot (+\infty) = +\infty,$$
$$(+\infty) \cdot (-\infty) = -\infty, \quad (-\infty) \cdot (-\infty) = +\infty;$$

4. for $x \in \mathbb{R} \setminus \{0\}$ we set (see part 3)

$$\frac{\pm\infty}{x} = \frac{1}{x} \cdot (\pm\infty), \quad \frac{x}{\pm\infty} = 0.$$

**Remark 16.27.** The values

$$(+\infty) + (-\infty), \quad (+\infty) - (+\infty), \quad (-\infty) - (-\infty), \quad \frac{\pm\infty}{\pm\infty}$$

are not defined.

These new notations allow us to consider real-valued functions defined on any measurable set $X \subset \mathbb{R}^n$ with the range $R(f) = f(X) \subset \overline{\mathbb{R}}$.

**Definition 16.28.** *Let $f : X \subset \mathbb{R}^n \to \overline{\mathbb{R}}$ be a real-valued function defined on a measurable set $X$. Then $f$ is said to be* measurable *if the set*

$$X_a := \{x \in X : f(x) \geq a\}$$

*is measurable for any $a \in \mathbb{R}$.*

**Theorem 16.29 (Equivalence of measurability).** *Let $X \subset \mathbb{R}^n$ be a measurable set. Then $f : X \to \mathbb{R}$ is measurable if and only if one of the following sets is measurable for any $a \in \mathbb{R}$:*

$$\{x \in X : f(x) > a\}, \quad \{x \in X : f(x) < a\}, \quad \{x \in X : f(x) \leq a\}.$$

*Proof.* The statement follows immediately from the representations

$$\{x \in X : f(x) > a\} = \bigcup_{k=1}^{\infty} \{x \in X : f(x) \geq a + 1/k\},$$
$$\{x \in X : f(x) < a\} = X \setminus \{x \in X : f(x) \geq a\},$$
$$\{x \in X : f(x) \leq a\} = X \setminus \{x \in X : f(x) > a\},$$

and Theorems 16.9 and 16.10.

**Remark 16.30.** The measurability of any of the three sets can be considered as a new definition of measurability of function $f$ on the set $X$ equivalently to the original one (Definition 16.28).

One says that some property is true *almost everywhere* (a.e.) on the set $X \subset \mathbb{R}^n$ if it is valid on $X$ except for a subset of $X$ of measure zero.

**Definition 16.31.** *Let $f$ and $g$ be two functions defined on a measurable set $X \subset \mathbb{R}^n$. They are said to be* equivalent *on $X$, in short $f \approx g$, if*

$$\mu(\{x \in X : f(x) \neq g(x)\}) = 0.$$

**Theorem 16.32 (Main properties of measurable functions).** *Let $X \subset \mathbb{R}^n$ be a measurable set. Then the following hold:*

1. *Arbitrary function $f$ is measurable on a set of measure zero.*

2. *If $f : X \to \mathbb{R}$ is measurable then it is measurable on any measurable subset $X' \subset X$.*

3. *If $f \approx g$ on $X$ and $f$ is measurable on $X$ then $g$ is also measurable and vice versa.*

4. *If $f$ is continuous a.e. on $X$ then $f$ is measurable on $X$.*

5. *If $f$ is measurable on $X$ then*

$$|f|, \quad f + c, \quad c \cdot f, \quad c \in \mathbb{R} \setminus \{0\}$$

*are measurable on $X$ too.*

6. *If $f$ and $g$ are measurable on $X$ then the set*

$$\{x \in X : f(x) > g(x)\}$$

   *is measurable.*

7. *If $f, g : X \to \mathbb{R}$ are measurable then*

$$f \pm g, \quad f \cdot g, \quad \frac{f}{g}, \quad g \neq 0$$

   *are also measurable on $X$.*

***Proof.***

1. This follows from the evident embedding

$$X_a = \{x \in X : f(x) \geq a\} \subset X$$

   and from the inequality $\mu(X_a) \leq \mu(X) = 0$.

2. This part is also clear since

$$X_a' = \{x \in X' : f(x) \geq a\} = X' \cap X_a$$

   and $X_a'$ is measurable as the intersection of two measurable sets.

3. By Definition 16.31 it follows that the sets

$$\{x \in X : f(x) \geq a\}, \quad \{x \in X : g(x) \geq a\}$$

   may differ only by some set of measure zero and, therefore, if one of these two sets is measurable then the other is also measurable.

4. It suffices to consider only the continuous function defined on $X$. Indeed, let us first assume that $X$ is closed. Then, due to continuity of $f$, it follows that the set

$$X_a = \{x \in X : f(x) \geq a\}$$

   is also closed and therefore measurable. If $X$ is an arbitrary measurable set then there is a closed set $K \subset X$ (see Theorem 16.16) such that $\mu(X \setminus K) < \varepsilon$. Thus, $X_a \cap K$ is closed and

$$\mu^*(X_a \Delta (X_a \cap K)) \leq \mu^*(X \setminus K) = \mu(X \setminus K) < \varepsilon.$$

   This implies that $X_a$ is measurable.

5. Measurability of $|f|$, $f + c$, and $cf$ follow from the equalities

$$\{x \in X : |f(x)| \geq a\} = \{x \in X : f(x) \geq a\} \cup \{x \in X : f(x) \leq -a\},$$
$$\{x \in X : f(x) + c \geq a\} = \{x \in X : f(x) \geq a - c\},$$
$$\{x \in X : cf(x) \geq a\} = \{x \in X : f(x) \geq a/c, c > 0\}$$
$$\cup \{x \in X : f(x) \leq a/c, c < 0\}$$

   and Theorem 16.16.

6. To prove that the set

$$\{x \in X : f(x) > g(x)\}$$

is measurable one can use the representation

$$\{x \in X : f(x) > g(x)\} = \bigcup_{k=1}^{\infty} \{x \in X : f(x) > r_k\} \cap \{x \in X : g(x) < r_k\},$$

where $\{r_k\}_{k=1}^{\infty}$ denotes the set of all rational numbers numbered in any order. It is clear that the set

$$\{x \in X : f(x) \geq g(x)\}$$

is also measurable (see the proof of Theorem 16.29).

7. From parts 5 and 6 we get that the set

$$\{x \in X : f(x) > a \pm g(x)\} = \{x \in X : f(x) \mp g(x) > a\}$$

is measurable, i.e., $f \pm g$ is measurable. Let us prove next that $f^2$ is measurable if $f$ is measurable. Indeed,

$$\{x \in X : f^2(x) \geq a\} = \{x \in X : a < 0\} \cup \{x \in X : f(x) \geq \sqrt{a}, a \geq 0\}$$
$$\cup \{x \in X : f(x) \leq -\sqrt{a}, a \geq 0\}.$$

This shows that $f^2$ is measurable. The measurability of $fg$ now follows from the identity

$$fg = \frac{1}{4}((f+g)^2 - (f-g)^2).$$

If $f$ is measurable and $f(x) \neq 0$ on $X$ then $1/f$ is also measurable since

$$\{x \in X : 1/f(x) > a\} = \{x \in X : f(x) < 1/a, f(x) > 0, a > 0\}$$
$$\cup \{x \in X : f(x) > 0, a < 0\}$$
$$\cup \{x \in X : f(x) > 1/a, f(x) < 0, a < 0\}$$
$$\cup \{x \in X : f(x) > 0, a = 0\}.$$

The measurability of $f/g, g \neq 0$ follows from the representation

$$\frac{f(x)}{g(x)} = f(x)\frac{1}{g(x)}$$

and the previous considerations.

Theorem 16.32 is completely proved.

**Remark 16.33.** It should be noted that continuity of some function a.e. on a measurable set is not the same as the equivalence (see Definition 16.31) with some continuous function on this set. For example, the Dirichlet function is equivalent to the continuous function $f(x) \equiv 0$ on any measurable set on the line. But the Dirichlet function is not continuous a.e. on this set since it is discontinuous everywhere.

**Exercise 16.34.**    1. Prove that if $f$ is measurable on each measurable set $X_j, j = 1, 2, \dots$, then it is measurable on $\cup_{j=1}^{\infty} X_j$.

2. Prove that the superposition $h = f \circ g$, where $f$ is continuous and $g$ is measurable, is also measurable. Show that the superposition $h = g \circ f$, where $f$ and $g$ are as above, is not necessarily measurable. Hint: Use the statement of Exercise 16.41 below.

3. Let $f, g : X \subset \mathbb{R}^n \to \mathbb{R}$ be continuous on a measurable set $X$. Prove that $f \approx g$ if and only if $f(x) = g(x)$ for each $x \in X$.

**Exercise 16.35 (One-dimensional case).**  Prove that

1. the Dirichlet function is measurable on any measurable set on the real line,

2. the Riemann function is measurable on any measurable set on the real line,

3. any monotone function is measurable on an interval $[a, b]$,

4. the derivative of some function is measurable if it is finite at any point on an interval $[a, b]$,

5. any piecewise continuous function is measurable on an interval $[a, b]$.

**Theorem 16.36 (Sequences of measurable functions).** *Let $\{f_j\}_{j=1}^{\infty}$ be a sequence of measurable functions defined on a measurable set $X \subset \mathbb{R}^n$. Then*

1. *the functions*

$$\overline{f}(x) := \varlimsup_{j \to \infty} f_j(x), \quad \underline{f}(x) := \varliminf_{j \to \infty} f_j(x)$$

*are measurable on $X$,*

2. *if the limit*

$$f(x) := \lim_{j \to \infty} f_j(x)$$

*exists a.e. on $X$ then $f$ is measurable on $X$.*

*Proof.*

1. We first note that the functions

$$\varphi(x) := \sup_k g_k(x), \quad \psi(x) := \inf_k g_k(x)$$

are measurable if the functions $g_k$ are measurable for each $k = 1, 2, \dots$. This follows from the representations

$$\{x \in X : \varphi(x) > a\} = \bigcup_{k=1}^{\infty} \{x \in X : g_k(x) > a\}$$

and

$$\{x \in X : \psi(x) < a\} = \bigcup_{k=1}^{\infty} \{x \in X : g_k(x) < a\}$$

for any $a \in \mathbb{R}$. But

$$\varlimsup_{j \to \infty} f_j(x) = \inf_{j \geq 1} (\sup_{k \geq j} f_k(x)), \quad \varliminf_{j \to \infty} f_j(x) = \sup_{j \geq 1} (\inf_{k \geq j} f_k(x)).$$

These facts imply the first statement.

2. This follows immediately from part 1 since $\lim_{j\to\infty} f_j(x)$ exists a.e. on $X$ if and only if

$$\overline{\lim_{j\to\infty}} f_j(x) = \underline{\lim_{j\to\infty}} f_j(x)$$

a.e. on $X$.

For understanding the Lebesgue integral, which will be considered below, the convergence of sequences of measurable functions in measure plays an important role.

**Definition 16.37.** *Let functions* $f_j, j = 1, 2, \ldots,$ *and* $f$ *be measurable on a measurable set* $X \subset \mathbb{R}^n$ *and take finite values a.e. on* $X$. *Then the sequence* $\{f_j\}_{j=1}^\infty$ *is said to be convergent to* $f$ *in measure on* $X$ *if, for any* $\varepsilon > 0$,

$$\lim_{j\to\infty} \mu(\{x \in X : |f_j(x) - f(x)| \geq \varepsilon\}) = 0.$$

*Equivalently, for any* $\varepsilon > 0$ *and for any* $\delta > 0$ *there is* $N \in \mathbb{N}$ *such that for all* $j \geq N$ *it follows that*

$$\mu(\{x \in X : |f_j(x) - f(x)| \geq \varepsilon\}) < \delta.$$

**Theorem 16.38 (Convergence in measure and a.e.).** *Let* $X \subset \mathbb{R}^n$ *be a measurable set with* $\mu(X) < \infty$. *Then*

1. *if the sequence* $\{f_j\}_{j=1}^\infty$ *of measurable functions converges to* $f$ *a.e. on* $X$ *then* $\{f_j\}_{j=1}^\infty$ *converges to* $f$ *in measure on* $X$,

2. *if the sequence* $\{f_j\}_{j=1}^\infty$ *of measurable functions converges to* $f$ *in measure on* $X$ *then there is a subsequence* $\{f_{k_j}\}_{j=1}^\infty$ *which converges to* $f$ *a.e. on* $X$.

*Proof.* From Theorem 16.36 it follows that the limiting function $f$ is measurable on $X$ in both cases. Let

$$X_j(\varepsilon) = \{x \in X : |f_j(x) - f(x)| \geq \varepsilon\}, \quad \varepsilon > 0,$$

and

$$E = \bigcap_{k=1}^\infty \left( \bigcup_{j=k}^\infty X_j(\varepsilon) \right).$$

Then the sequence $\{\cup_{j=k}^\infty X_j(\varepsilon)\}_{k=1}^\infty$ is a sequence of measurable closed sets. Corollary 16.11 implies that

$$\lim_{k\to\infty} \cup_{j=k}^\infty X_j(\varepsilon) = \mu(E).$$

Let $X_0 \subset X$ denote the set of measure zero where

$$\lim_{j\to\infty} f_j(x) \neq f(x), \quad x \in X_0.$$

One can check now that $E \subset X_0$. Indeed, if $x_0 \notin X_0$, i.e.,

$$\lim_{j\to\infty} f_j(x_0) = f(x_0),$$

then for given $\varepsilon > 0$ there is $N \in \mathbb{N}$ such that for all $j \geq N$ it holds that

$$|f_j(x_0) - f(x_0)| < \varepsilon.$$

Hence $x_0 \notin \cup_{j=N}^{\infty} X_j(\varepsilon)$ and therefore $x_0 \notin E$. But $\mu(X_0) = 0$ implies $\mu(E) = 0$ too. Thus

$$\lim_{j\to\infty} \mu(X_j(\varepsilon)) = 0.$$

This proves part 1.

Let $\{\varepsilon_j\}_{j=1}^{\infty}$ be a sequence of positive numbers with $\lim_{j\to\infty} \varepsilon_j = 0$ and let $\{\eta_j\}_{j=1}^{\infty}$ be a sequence of positive numbers such that

$$\sum_{j=1}^{\infty} \eta_j < \infty.$$

Let a sequence $\{k_j\}_{j=1}^{\infty}$ of integers be chosen such that

$$0 < k_1 < k_2 < \cdots < k_j < \cdots$$

and

$$\mu(\{x \in X : |f_{k_j}(x) - f(x)| \ge \varepsilon_j\}) < \eta_j.$$

The existence of such a sequence can be proved by induction with respect to the conditions of part 2. We show that the subsequence $\{f_{k_j}\}_{j=1}^{\infty}$ satisfies the conditions of part 2. Indeed, let a set $Y$ be defined as

$$Y := \bigcap_{m=1}^{\infty} \left( \bigcup_{j=m}^{\infty} \{x \in X : |f_{k_j}(x) - f(x)| \ge \varepsilon_j\} \right).$$

Since the sequence

$$\left\{ \bigcup_{j=m}^{\infty} \{x \in X : |f_{k_j}(x) - f(x)| \ge \varepsilon_j\} \right\}_{m=1}^{\infty}$$

is a sequence of measurable closed sets, Corollary 16.11 implies that

$$\lim_{m\to\infty} \mu\left( \bigcup_{j=m}^{\infty} \{x \in X : |f_{k_j}(x) - f(x)| \ge \varepsilon_j\} \right) = \mu(Y).$$

But on the other hand,

$$\mu\left( \bigcup_{j=m}^{\infty} \{x \in X : |f_{k_j}(x) - f(x)| \ge \varepsilon_j\} \right) < \sum_{j=m}^{\infty} \eta_j.$$

Due to convergence of this series we obtain

$$\lim_{m\to\infty} \mu\left( \bigcup_{j=m}^{\infty} \{x \in X : |f_{k_j}(x) - f(x)| \ge \varepsilon_j\} \right) = 0,$$

i.e., $\mu(Y) = 0$. It remains to check that

$$\lim_{j\to\infty} f_{k_j}(x) = f(x)$$

for all $x \in X \setminus Y$. Indeed, let $x_0 \in X \setminus Y$. Then there is $N \in \mathbb{N}$ such that

$$x_0 \notin \bigcup_{j=N}^{\infty} \{x \in X : |f_{k_j}(x) - f(x)| \geq \varepsilon_j\}.$$

It means that

$$x_0 \notin \{x \in X : |f_{k_j}(x_0) - f(x_0)| \geq \varepsilon_j\}$$

for all $j \geq N$, i.e.,

$$|f_{k_j}(x_0) - f(x_0)| < \varepsilon_j$$

for all $j \geq N$. By the choice of the sequence $\{\varepsilon_j\}_{j=1}^{\infty}$ we have that

$$\lim_{j \to \infty} f_{k_j}(x_0) = f(x_0).$$

This finishes the proof of part 2 and the theorem is completely proved.

**Example 16.39.** Consider the sequence

$$f_j^{(k)}(x) := \begin{cases} 1, & \frac{j-1}{k} < x \leq \frac{j}{k}, \\ 0, & \text{otherwise}, \end{cases} \quad x \in (0, 1],$$

where $j = 1, 2, \ldots, k$ and $k = 1, 2, \ldots$. Let us renumber these functions as follows:

$$f_1^{(1)}, f_1^{(2)}, f_2^{(2)}, \ldots, f_1^{(k)}, \ldots, f_k^{(k)}, \ldots.$$

Then it is not difficult to see that this new sequence converges to zero in measure on $(0, 1]$. But at the same time this sequence is not convergent at any fixed point $x \in (0, 1]$. This example shows that part 2 of Theorem 16.38 does not hold for sequences.

**Theorem 16.40 (Egorov's theorem).** *Let $X \subset \mathbb{R}^n$ be a measurable set with $\mu(X) < \infty$ and let $\{f_j\}_{j=1}^{\infty}$ be a sequence of measurable functions which converge to $f$ a.e. on $X$. Then for any $\delta > 0$ there exists a measurable set $X_\delta \subset X$ such that $\mu(X_\delta) > \mu(X) - \delta$, and the limit*

$$\lim_{j \to \infty} f_j(x) = f(x)$$

*holds uniformly on $X_\delta$.*

**Proof.** From Theorem 16.36 it follows that the limiting function $f$ is measurable on $X$. Let us introduce the sets

$$X_k^m := \bigcap_{j \geq k} \{x \in X : |f_j(x) - f(x)| < 1/m\}, \quad m, k = 1, 2, \ldots.$$

Thus, for fixed $m$ and $k$ and for all $j \geq k$ and for all $x \in X_k^m$ we have

$$|f_j(x) - f(x)| < \frac{1}{m}.$$

Denoting $X^m := \cup_{k=1}^{\infty} X_k^m$ we obtain for fixed $m$ that

$$X_1^m \subset X_2^m \subset \cdots \subset X_k^m \subset \cdots \subset X^m.$$

The $\sigma$-additivity of the Lebesgue measure and its continuity (see Corollary 16.12) implies that for any $m \in \mathbb{N}$ and $\delta > 0$ there is a number $m_0 \in \mathbb{N}$ (depending on $m$) such that

$$\mu(X^m \setminus X_{m_0}^m) < \frac{\delta}{2^m}.$$

Let us show that $X_\delta := \cap_{m=1}^\infty X_{m_0}^m$ satisfies the conditions of Egorov's theorem. Indeed, if $x \in X_\delta$ then for each $m$ and for all $j \geq m_0$ it follows that

$$|f_j(x) - f(x)| < \frac{1}{m}$$

and this inequality is uniform in $x \in X_\delta$. It means that the sequence $\{f_j\}_{j=1}^\infty$ converges to $f$ uniformly in $x \in X_\delta$. Let us investigate the measure of $X \setminus X_\delta$. We first note that $\mu(X \setminus X^m) = 0$ for each $m$. Indeed, if $x_0 \in X \setminus X^m$ then there is $j$ big enough such that

$$|f_j(x_0) - f(x_0)| \geq \frac{1}{m},$$

i.e., the sequence $\{f_j(x_0)\}_{j=1}^\infty$ does not converge to $f(x_0)$. But the sequence $\{f_j\}_{j=1}^\infty$ converges to $f$ a.e. on $X$ and so $\mu(X \setminus X^m) = 0$. This also implies that

$$\mu(X \setminus X_{m_0}^m) = \mu(X^m \setminus X_{m_0}^m) < \frac{\delta}{2^m}$$

and therefore

$$\mu(X \setminus X_\delta) = \mu\left(X \setminus \bigcap_{m=1}^\infty X_{m_0}^m\right) = \mu\left(\bigcup_{m=1}^\infty (X \setminus X_{m_0}^m)\right) \leq \sum_{m=1}^\infty \mu(X \setminus X_{m_0}^m) < \delta.$$

This proves the theorem.

**Exercise 16.41 (Simple functions).**  1. Let $f : X \subset \mathbb{R}^n \to \mathbb{R}$ be a function which takes no more than a countable number of values $y_1, y_2, \ldots$. Such functions are said to be *simple functions*. Prove that $f$ is measurable on $X$ if and only if the sets

$$\{x \in X : f(x) = y_k\}, \quad k = 1, 2, \ldots,$$

are measurable.

2. Let $f$ be a function defined on a measurable set $X$. Prove that $f$ is measurable on $X$ if and only if it is a uniform limit of the sequence of simple functions.

3. Let $F : \mathbb{R}^n \to \mathbb{R}$ be a continuous function and $f_j : \mathbb{R} \to \mathbb{R}$ be a measurable function for $j = 1, 2, \ldots, n$. Prove that the superposition $h(t) := F(f_1(t), f_2(t), \ldots, f_n(t))$ is measurable on the line.

**Exercise 16.42 (One-dimensional case).**  1. Prove the following *Frechet theorem*: Let $f : [a, b] \to \mathbb{R}$ be a measurable function. Then there is a sequence $\{f_j\}_{j=1}^\infty$ such that $f_j \in C[a, b], j = 1, 2, \ldots,$ and

$$\lim_{j \to \infty} f_j(x) = f(x)$$

a.e. on $[a, b]$.

2. Prove *Luzin's theorem*: A real-valued function $f$ defined on an interval $[a, b]$ is measurable if and only if for any $\varepsilon > 0$ there exists function $g$ such that $g \in C[a, b]$ and

$$\mu(\{x \in [a, b] : f(x) \neq g(x)\}) < \varepsilon.$$

3. Let $f : [a, b] \to \mathbb{R}$ be a measurable function. Prove that there is a decreasing function $g$ on the interval $[a, b]$ such that

$$\mu(\{t \in [a, b] : f(t) > x\}) = \mu(\{t \in [a, b] : g(t) > x\})$$

for any $x \in [a, b]$.

## 16.3 ▪ Lebesgue integral

To introduce multidimensional Lebesgue integral we use an approach similar to that for the Riemann integral (see Chapters 8, 9, 10, and 15). We consider first measurable sets $X \subset \mathbb{R}^n$ with $\mu(X) < \infty$.

**Definition 16.43.** *The family* $Q = \{X_j\}_{j=1}^m$ *is said to be a* partition *of measurable set* $X$ *if*

$$X = \bigcup_{j=1}^m X_j, \quad X_j \cap X_k = \emptyset, j \neq k,$$

*and all* $X_j$ *are measurable.*

Let function $f : X \subset \mathbb{R}^n \to \mathbb{R}$ be bounded. For any partition $Q$ of $X$ we introduce the finite values

$$M_j = \sup_{x \in X_j} f(x), \quad m_j = \inf_{x \in X_j} f(x), \quad M = \sup_{x \in X} f(x), \quad m = \inf_{x \in X} f(x).$$

**Definition 16.44.** *For partition* $Q$ *of* $X$ *and bounded function* $f$ *the values*

$$U(Q, f) = \sum_{j=1}^m M_j \mu(X_j), \quad L(Q, f) = \sum_{j=1}^m m_j \mu(X_j)$$

*are said to be* upper *and* lower *integral sums of* $f$, *respectively.*

It is not difficult to see that for any partition $Q$ and any bounded function $f$ the integral sums satisfy the following properties:

1. $m\mu(X) \leq L(Q, f) \leq U(Q, f) \leq M\mu(X)$,

2. $\sup_Q L(Q, f) < \infty$ and $\inf_Q U(Q, f) < \infty$.

**Definition 16.45.** *The values*

$$\overset{*}{\int_X} f(x)\mathrm{d}\mu(x) := \inf_Q U(Q, f), \quad \int_X{}_* f(x)\mathrm{d}\mu(x) := \sup_Q L(Q, f)$$

*are called the* upper *and* lower Lebesgue integrals *of function* $f$ *on the set* $X$, *respectively.*

**Definition 16.46.** *A partition* $Q' = \{X'_j\}_{j=1}^{m'}$ *of measurable set* $X$ *is called a* refinement *of partition* $Q = \{X_j\}_{j=1}^{m}$ *if for any* $X'_j \in Q'$ *there is* $X_k \in Q$ *such that* $X'_j \subset X_k$. *If* $Q'$ *and* $Q''$ *are two arbitrary partitions of* $X$ *then partition* $Q$ *is called their* product *if* $Q = \{X'_j \cap X''_k\}_{j,k=1}^{m',m''}$.

**Remark 16.47.** It is clear that the product $Q$ of partitions $Q'$ and $Q''$ is their common refinement.

**Theorem 16.48 (Properties of integral sums).** *Let partition* $Q'$ *be a refinement of partition* $Q$. *Then*

$$L(Q, f) \leq L(Q', f), \quad U(Q', f) \leq U(Q, f).$$

**Proof.** From Definition 16.46 it follows that for each $k = 1, 2, \ldots, n$ we have

$$X_k = \bigcup_{j \in J(k)} X'_j$$

for some set $J(k)$ of indices. Therefore clearly

$$M'_j \leq M_k, \quad m'_j \geq m_k, \quad j \in J(k).$$

These inequalities imply that

$$U(Q', f) = \sum_{j=1}^{m'} M'_j \mu(X'_j) = \sum_{k=1}^{m} \sum_{j \in J(k)} M'_j \mu(X'_j)$$

$$\leq \sum_{k=1}^{m} M_k \sum_{j \in J(k)} \mu(X'_j) = \sum_{k=1}^{m} M_k \mu(X_k) = U(Q, f).$$

The proof for lower sums is similar.

**Corollary 16.49.** *Let* $Q'$ *and* $Q''$ *be two arbitrary partitions of the set* $X$. *Then*

$$L(Q', f) \leq U(Q'', f)$$

*and consequently*

$$\int_{*X} f(x) \mathrm{d}\mu(x) \leq \int_X^{*} f(x) \mathrm{d}\mu(x).$$

**Proof.** Denoting by $Q$ the product of $Q'$ and $Q''$ we have by Theorem 16.48 that

$$L(Q', f) \leq L(Q, f) \leq U(Q, f) \leq U(Q'', f).$$

Next, we have

$$\int_{*X} f(x) \mathrm{d}\mu(x) = \sup_{Q'} L(Q', f) \leq U(Q'', f)$$

and

$$\int_X^{*} f(x) \mathrm{d}\mu(x) = \inf_{Q''} U(Q'', f) \geq \int_{*X} f(x) \mathrm{d}\mu(x).$$

This concludes the proof.

**Definition 16.50.** *A bounded function* $f : X \subset \mathbb{R}^n \to \mathbb{R}$ *is said to be* Lebesgue integrable *on a measurable set* $X$, *denoted by* $f \in \mathcal{L}(X)$, *if*

$$\int_{X_*} f(x)\mathrm{d}\mu(x) = \int_X^* f(x)\mathrm{d}\mu(x).$$

*This value is called the* Lebesgue integral *of* $f$ *on the set* $X$ *and is denoted as*

$$\int_X f(x)\mathrm{d}\mu(x).$$

Similarly to the multidimensional Riemann integral one can prove the following criterion.

**Theorem 16.51 (Criterion of Lebesgue integrability).** *Let* $X \subset \mathbb{R}^n$ *be measurable with* $\mu(X) < \infty$. *A bounded function* $f : X \to \mathbb{R}$ *is Lebesgue integrable on* $X$ *if and only if for any* $\varepsilon > 0$ *there is a partition* $Q$ *of* $X$ *such that*

$$U(Q, f) - L(Q, f) < \varepsilon.$$

*Proof.* The proof literally repeats the proof of Theorem 15.3.

**Theorem 16.52 (Some properties of Lebesgue integral).** *Let* $f_1, f_2 \in \mathcal{L}(X)$ *and* $\mu(X) < \infty$. *Then*

1. *the functions* $c_1 f_1 + c_2 f_2, c_1, c_2 \in \mathbb{R}$ *and* $f_1 f_2$ *are integrable and*

$$\int_X (c_1 f_1 + c_2 f_2)(x)\mathrm{d}\mu(x) = c_1 \int_X f_1(x)\mathrm{d}\mu(x) + c_2 \int_X f_2(x)\mathrm{d}\mu(x),$$

2. *if* $f_1(x) \leq f_2(x)$ *a.e. on* $X$ *then*

$$\int_X f_1(x)\mathrm{d}\mu(x) \leq \int_X f_2(x)\mathrm{d}\mu(x).$$

*Proof.* The proof of part 1 literally repeats the proof of Theorem 9.19 based on Definitions 16.43–16.46 and Theorems 16.48 and 16.51.

To prove part 2 let us denote by $X' \subset X$ the set of all $x \in X$, where the inequality $f_1(x) \leq f_2(x)$ does not hold, i.e., $\mu(X') = 0$. Thus the latter inequality is valid for all $x \in X \setminus X'$. Denoting

$$f(x) := f_2(x) - f_1(x), \quad x \in X \setminus X',$$

we obtain for any partition $Q$ of $X \setminus X'$ that

$$0 \leq L(Q, f) \leq U(Q, f) \leq M_1 \mu(X \setminus X') = M_1 \mu(X),$$

where $M_1 = \sup_{X \setminus X'} f(x)$. This implies that

$$\int_{X \setminus X'} f(x)\mathrm{d}\mu(x) \geq 0.$$

The general case follows from

$$\int_X f_1(x)\mathrm{d}\mu(x) = \int_{X \setminus X'} f_1(x)\mathrm{d}\mu(x) \leq \int_{X \setminus X'} f_2(x)\mathrm{d}\mu(x) = \int_X f_2(x)\mathrm{d}\mu(x).$$

This finishes the proof.

**Exercise 16.53.**  1. Prove that any bounded function $f \in \mathcal{L}(X)$ if $\mu(X) = 0$ and that in this case

$$\int_X f(x)\mathrm{d}\mu(x) = 0.$$

2. Prove that

$$\int_X 1\mathrm{d}\mu(x) = \mu(X).$$

3. Prove that if $f \in \mathcal{L}(X_1)$ and $f \in \mathcal{L}(X_2)$ and $X_1 \cap X_2 = \emptyset$ then $f \in \mathcal{L}(X_1 \cup X_2)$ and

$$\int_{X_1 \cup X_2} f(x)\mathrm{d}\mu(x) = \int_{X_1} f(x)\mathrm{d}\mu(x) + \int_{X_2} f(x)\mathrm{d}\mu(x).$$

4. Prove that if $f \in \mathcal{L}(X)$ then $f \in \mathcal{L}(X')$ for any measurable $X' \subset X$.

**Theorem 16.54 (Criterion of Lebesgue integrability II).**

1. *Let $f : X \subset \mathbb{R}^n \to \mathbb{R}$ be a bounded and measurable function on $X$ with $\mu(X) < \infty$. Then $f \in \mathcal{L}(X)$.*

2. *Let $f : X \subset \mathbb{R}^n \to \mathbb{R}$ with $\mu(X) < \infty$. Then $f \in \mathcal{L}(X)$ if and only if there is a sequence $\{f_j\}_{j=1}^{\infty}$ of simple functions such that*

$$\lim_{j \to \infty} f_j(x) = f(x)$$

*uniformly on $X$ and there exists the finite limit*

$$\lim_{j \to \infty} \int_X f_j(x)\mathrm{d}\mu(x) =: \int_X f(x)\mathrm{d}\mu(x).$$

*Proof.*

1. Let

$$m = \inf_X f(x), \quad M = \sup_X f(x).$$

We divide the interval $[m, M]$ by the points

$$m = y_0 < y_1 < \cdots < y_k = M.$$

Let $\delta = \max_{1 \leq j \leq k}(y_j - y_{j-1}) > 0$. This partition of the interval $[m, M]$ induces the partition $Q$ of $X$ such that

$$X = \bigcup_{j=1}^{k} X_j, \quad X_j \cap X_i = \emptyset, i \neq j,$$

where

$$X_1 = \{x \in X : y_0 \leq f(x) \leq y_1\}$$

and

$$X_j = \{x \in X : y_{j-1} < f(x) \leq y_j\}, \quad j = 2, \ldots, k.$$

Since $f$ is measurable, all these sets $X_j$ are also measurable. For this partition $Q$ we have

$$\sum_{j=1}^{k} y_{j-1}\mu(X_j) \leq L(Q,f) \leq U(Q,f) \leq \sum_{j=1}^{k} y_j\mu(X_j).$$

Thus,

$$0 \leq U(Q,f) - L(Q,f) \leq \sum_{j=1}^{k}(y_j - y_{j-1})\mu(X_j) \leq \delta\sum_{j=1}^{k}\mu(X_j) = \delta\mu(X) \to 0$$

as $\delta \to 0$. Therefore

$$\int_{*X} f(x)\mathrm{d}\mu(x) = \int_X^* f(x)\mathrm{d}\mu(x)$$

and this part is proved.

2. Let sequence $\{f_k\}_{k=1}^{\infty}$ be defined by

$$f_k(x) := \sum_{j=1}^{k} y_j\chi_j(x), \quad k = k(\delta),$$

where $\chi_j(x), j = 1, 2, \ldots, k$, are characteristic functions of the sets $X_j$ which were defined in part 1. Then

$$|f(x) - f_k(x)| = \left|\sum_{j=1}^{k} f(x)\chi_j(x) - \sum_{j=1}^{k} y_j\chi_j(x)\right|$$

$$\leq \sum_{j=1}^{k}|y_j - f(x)|\chi_j(x) \leq \delta\sum_{j=1}^{k}\chi_j(x) = \delta.$$

This means that $\{f_k\}_{k=1}^{\infty}$ converges to $f$ uniformly on $X$ if $f \in \mathcal{L}(X)$.

Conversely, let $\{f_j\}_{j=1}^{\infty}$ be a sequence of simple functions such that

$$\lim_{j\to\infty} f_j(x) = f(x)$$

uniformly on $X$. Assume that the limit

$$\lim_{j\to\infty} \int_X f_j(x)\mathrm{d}\mu(x)$$

is finite. Since $f_j$ are simple (see Exercise 16.41, part 1), each $f_j$ takes at most a countable number of values

$$f_j(x) \in \{y_1^{(j)}, y_2^{(j)}, \ldots, y_k^{(j)}, \ldots\}, \quad j = 1, 2, \ldots,$$

and the sets

$$X_k^{(j)} = \{x \in X : f_j(x) = y_k^{(j)}\}$$

are measurable. Moreover,

$$\int_X f_j(x)\mathrm{d}\mu(x) = \sum_{k=1}^{\infty} y_k^{(j)}\mu(X_k^{(j)})$$

and this series converges. Next, for any $\varepsilon > 0$ there is $j_0(\varepsilon) > 0$ such that for all $x \in X$ and for all $j \geq j_0$ it follows that

$$|f_j(x) - f(x)| < \varepsilon$$

or

$$-\varepsilon - f_j(x) \leq f(x) \leq f_j(x) + \varepsilon.$$

This implies that for the partition $Q = \{X_k^{(j)}\}_k$ we have (due to convergence of the corresponding series) that

$$U(Q, f) \leq U(Q, f_{j_0}) + \varepsilon\mu(X)$$

and

$$L(Q, f) \geq L(Q, -f_{j_0}) - \varepsilon\mu(X) = -U(Q, f_{j_0}) - \varepsilon\mu(X).$$

Hence

$$U(Q, f) - L(Q, f) \leq 2\varepsilon\mu(X).$$

Since $\mu(X) < \infty$, this inequality means that $f \in \mathcal{L}(X)$ (see Theorem 16.51). Finally,

$$\left| \int_X f_j(x)\mathrm{d}\mu(x) - \int_X f(x)\mathrm{d}\mu(x) \right| \leq \int_X |f_j(x) - f(x)|\mathrm{d}\mu(x) < \varepsilon\mu(X).$$

**Corollary 16.55.** *If $g \in \mathcal{L}(X)$ and $|f(x)| \leq g(x)$ a.e. on $X$ then $f \in \mathcal{L}(X)$ also and*

$$\left| \int_X f(x)\mathrm{d}\mu(x) \right| \leq \int_X g(x)\mathrm{d}\mu(x).$$

**Proof.** We consider first simple functions $f$ and $g$ and exclude from $X$ the set of measure zero, where the inequality $|f(x)| \leq g(x)$ does not hold. Then the remaining $X'$ of $X$ is the union of not more than countable sets $X_j, j = 1, 2, \ldots$, such that $f$ and $g$ take the values $a_j$ and $b_j$, respectively, and

$$|a_j| \leq b_j, \quad j = 1, 2, \ldots .$$

Without loss of generality we may assume that these sets $X_j$ are the same for these functions and that

$$X_j = \{x \in X : f(x) = a_j, g(x) = b_j\}.$$

Since $g \in \mathcal{L}(X)$, we have

$$\sum_{j=1}^{\infty} |a_j|\mu(X_j) \leq \sum_{j=1}^{\infty} b_j\mu(X_j) = \int_{X'} g(x)\mathrm{d}\mu(x) = \int_X g(x)\mathrm{d}\mu(x).$$

Thus $f$ is also Lebesgue integrable and

$$\left| \int_X f(x)\mathrm{d}\mu(x) \right| = \left| \int_{X'} f(x)\mathrm{d}\mu(x) \right| = \left| \sum_{j=1}^{\infty} a_j\mu(X_j) \right|$$

$$\leq \sum_{j=1}^{\infty} |a_j|\,\mu(X_j) = \int_X |f(x)|\mathrm{d}\mu(x)$$

$$\leq \sum_{j=1}^{\infty} b_j\mu(X_j) = \int_X g(x)\mathrm{d}\mu(x).$$

The general case can be proved by the limiting process using part 2 of Theorem 16.54.

**Corollary 16.56.** *The Lebesgue integrals*

$$\int_X f(x)\mathrm{d}\mu(x), \quad \int_X |f(x)|\mathrm{d}\mu(x)$$

*exist or do not exist simultaneously.*

**Remark 16.57.** The latter theorem and its corollaries might be considered as one of the most important results of Lebesgue integration.

**Exercise 16.58.**     1. Prove Corollary 16.56.

  2. Let $f : X \subset \mathbb{R}^n \to \mathbb{R}$ be measurable on $X$ with $\mu(X) < \infty$. Prove that there is a measurable function $g(x) \geq 0$ such that $fg \in \mathcal{L}(X)$.

**Theorem 16.59 (Connection between Riemann and Lebesgue integrals).** *Let $X \subset \mathbb{R}^n$ be Jordan measurable with measure $0 < \mu'(X) < \infty$. If $f : X \to \mathbb{R}$ is bounded and Riemann integrable then $f \in \mathcal{L}(X)$ and*

$$(R) \int_X f(x)\mathrm{d}x = \int_X f(x)\mathrm{d}\mu(x),$$

*where the left-hand side is a Riemann integral and $\mathrm{d}x = \mathrm{d}\mu'(x)$.*

*Proof.* First, we note that if $X$ is Jordan measurable then it is Lebesgue measurable and these measures are equal (see Theorem 12.31 and Theorem 16.16). Next, assuming that $f \geq 0$ and denoting the lower and upper Riemann integrals of $f$ by $\underline{I}_R$ and $\overline{I}_R$ (see Definition 15.2), respectively, we obtain that

$$\underline{I}_R \leq \int_{*X} f(x)\mathrm{d}\mu(x) \leq \int_X^* f(x)\mathrm{d}\mu(x) \leq \overline{I}_R.$$

This implies that Riemann integrability leads to Lebesgue integrability and to the equality of the corresponding integrals. In the general case we use the representation

$$f = f_+ - f_-, \quad f_+ = \frac{f + |f|}{2}, \quad f_- = \frac{|f| - f}{2}$$

and Theorems 15.5, 16.52, and 16.54.

**Example 16.60.** If we consider the Dirichlet function $\mathcal{D}(x)$ on some interval $[a, b]$ then (see Exercise 9.16) this function is not Riemann integrable. But it is Lebesgue integrable since $\mathcal{D} \approx 0$ on $[a, b]$.

**Remark 16.61.** Definition 16.46 of Lebesgue integrability does not assume (formally) that $f$ is measurable. But later we will see that this is necessary.

Until now we have assumed that measurable function $f$ was bounded and it was defined on a measurable set $X$ with $\mu(X) < \infty$. We assume now that measurable function $f$, defined on the set $X$ with $\mu(X) < \infty$, is no longer bounded. Assuming first that $f \geq 0$ we introduce for any $N \in \mathbb{N}$ the function

$$f_N(x) := \begin{cases} f(x), & f(x) \leq N, \\ N, & \text{otherwise.} \end{cases}$$

The function $f_N$ is called the *cut-off function* of $f$. This cut-off function $f_N$ is measurable and integrable since it is bounded (see Theorem 16.54). Thus, the integrals

$$I_N(f) := \int_X f_N(x)\mathrm{d}\mu(x)$$

are well-defined and $\{I_N(f)\}_{N=1}^{\infty}$ is a sequence of nonnegative numbers which is nondecreasing with respect to $N$.

**Definition 16.62.** *If there exists a finite limit (meaning that this sequence is bounded)*

$$\lim_{N\to\infty} I_N(f) = \lim_{N\to\infty} \int_X f_N(x)\mathrm{d}\mu(x)$$

*then $f$ is said to be* Lebesgue integrable *(in short, integrable) and this limit is said to be the integral of $f$ on $X$, i.e.,*

$$\int_X f(x)\mathrm{d}\mu(x) := \lim_{N\to\infty} \int_X f_N(x)\mathrm{d}\mu(x).$$

**Example 16.63.** Let $f : X \subset \mathbb{R}^n \to \mathbb{R}$ be defined as follows:

$$f(x) = \frac{1}{\sqrt{1 - |x|^2}}, \quad x \in X = \{x \in \mathbb{R}^n : |x| < 1\}.$$

Then the cut-off function will be

$$f_N(x) = \begin{cases} \frac{1}{\sqrt{1-|x|^2}}, & |x| \le (1 - 1/N^2)^{1/2}, \\ N, & |x| > (1 - 1/N^2)^{1/2}. \end{cases}$$

Using polar coordinates in $\mathbb{R}^n$ we have that

$$\begin{aligned} I_N(f) &= \int_{|x|\le(1-1/N^2)^{1/2}} (1 - |x|^2)^{-1/2}\mathrm{d}\mu(x) + N\int_{1>|x|>(1-1/N^2)^{1/2}} \mathrm{d}\mu(x) \\ &= \int_0^{(1-1/N^2)^{1/2}} r^{n-1}(1-r^2)^{-1/2}\mathrm{d}r \int_{|\theta|=1} \mathrm{d}\theta + N\int_{(1-1/N^2)^{1/2}}^1 r^{n-1}\mathrm{d}r \int_{|\theta|=1} \mathrm{d}\theta \\ &= \frac{\omega_n}{2}\int_0^{1-1/N^2} t^{n/2-1}(1-t)^{-1/2}\mathrm{d}t + N\omega_n \left.\frac{r^n}{n}\right|_{(1-1/N^2)^{1/2}}^1, \end{aligned}$$

where $\omega_n = 2\pi^{n/2}/\Gamma(n/2)$ is the area of unit sphere in $\mathbb{R}^n$. This implies that

$$\lim_{N\to\infty} I_N(f) = \frac{\omega_n}{2}B(n/2, 1/2) = \frac{2\pi^{n/2}}{2\Gamma(n/2)}\frac{\Gamma(n/2)\Gamma(1/2)}{\Gamma((n+1)/2)} = \frac{\pi^{(n+1)/2}}{\Gamma((n+1)/2)}.$$

Hence $f \in \mathcal{L}(X)$ and

$$\int_{|x|<1} \frac{1}{\sqrt{1 - |x|^2}}\mathrm{d}\mu(x) = \frac{\pi^{(n+1)/2}}{\Gamma((n+1)/2)}, \quad n \ge 1.$$

**Exercise 16.64.** Let $f : X \subset \mathbb{R}^n \to \mathbb{R}$ be nonnegative and $\mu(X) < \infty$. Prove that

1. if $f \in \mathcal{L}(X)$ then
$$\mu(\{x \in X : f(x) = +\infty\}) = 0;$$

2. if $\mu(X) = 0$ then any function $f \in \mathcal{L}(X)$ and
$$\int_X f(x)\mathrm{d}\mu(x) = 0;$$

3. if $f \in \mathcal{L}(X)$ then for any $\sigma > 0$ we have the *Chebyshev inequality*
$$\mu(\{x \in X : f(x) \geq \sigma\}) \leq \frac{1}{\sigma}\int_X f(x)\mathrm{d}\mu(x);$$

4. if $f \in \mathcal{L}(X)$ and
$$\int_X f(x)\mathrm{d}\mu(x) = 0$$
then $f \approx 0$ on $X$, i.e., $f = 0$ a.e. on $X$;

5. if $f$ is measurable then $f \in \mathcal{L}(X)$ if and only if the series
$$\sum_{k=0}^{\infty} 2^k \mu(\{x \in X : f(x) \geq 2^k\})$$
converges;

6. if $f$ is measurable then $f \in \mathcal{L}(X)$ if and only if the series
$$\sum_{k=0}^{\infty} k\mu(\{x \in X : k \leq f(x) < k+1\})$$
converges.

**Theorem 16.65 ($\sigma$-additivity of the integral).** *Let*
$$X = \bigcup_{j=1}^{\infty} X_j, \quad X_j \cap X_k = \emptyset, j \neq k,$$

*where $X_j$ are measurable and $\mu(X) < \infty$. Then*

1. *if $f \geq 0$ and $f \in \mathcal{L}(X)$ then $f \in \mathcal{L}(X_j)$ for each $j = 1, 2, \dots$ and*
$$\int_X f(x)\mathrm{d}\mu(x) = \sum_{j=1}^{\infty} \int_{X_j} f(x)\mathrm{d}\mu(x),$$

2. *if $f \geq 0$ and $f \in \mathcal{L}(X_j)$ for each $j = 1, 2, \dots$ and the series*
$$\sum_{j=1}^{\infty} \int_{X_j} f(x)\mathrm{d}\mu(x)$$
*converges then $f \in \mathcal{L}(X)$ and*
$$\int_X f(x)\mathrm{d}\mu(x) = \sum_{j=1}^{\infty} \int_{X_j} f(x)\mathrm{d}\mu(x).$$

*Proof.*

1. Let us denote

$$R_k := \bigcup_{j=k+1}^{\infty} X_j.$$

Then due to Theorem 16.10 we have

$$\mu(R_k) = \sum_{j=k+1}^{\infty} \mu(X_j) \to 0$$

as $k \to \infty$. Using Exercise 16.53 we obtain

$$\int_X f(x)\mathrm{d}\mu(x) = \int_{X \setminus R_k} f(x)\mathrm{d}\mu(x) + \int_{R_k} f(x)\mathrm{d}\mu(x),$$

i.e.,

$$0 \le \int_X f(x)\mathrm{d}\mu(x) - \sum_{j=1}^{k} \int_{X_j} f(x)\mathrm{d}\mu(x) = \int_{R_k} f(x)\mathrm{d}\mu(x) = \lim_{N \to \infty} \int_{R_k} f_N(x)\mathrm{d}\mu(x).$$

Thus, for any $\varepsilon > 0$ there exists $N_0 \in \mathbb{N}$ such that for all $N \ge N_0$ it holds that

$$0 \le \int_X f(x)\mathrm{d}\mu(x) - \sum_{j=1}^{k} \int_{X_j} f(x)\mathrm{d}\mu(x)$$

$$< \int_{R_k} f_N(x)\mathrm{d}\mu(x) + \varepsilon \le N\mu(R_k) + \varepsilon.$$

Letting $k \to +\infty$ (for some fixed $N \ge N_0$) we get

$$0 \le \int_X f(x)\mathrm{d}\mu(x) - \sum_{j=1}^{\infty} \int_{X_j} f(x)\mathrm{d}\mu(x) \le \varepsilon.$$

Since $\varepsilon > 0$ was arbitrary, we may conclude that

$$\int_X f(x)\mathrm{d}\mu(x) = \sum_{j=1}^{\infty} \int_{X_j} f(x)\mathrm{d}\mu(x).$$

2. For any $N \in \mathbb{N}$ and for the set $R_k$ from above we have

$$0 \le \int_X f_N(x)\mathrm{d}\mu(x) - \sum_{j=1}^{k} \int_{X_j} f_N(x)\mathrm{d}\mu(x) = \int_{R_k} f_N(x)\mathrm{d}\mu(x) \le N\mu(R_k).$$

This implies that

$$\int_X f_N(x)\mathrm{d}\mu(x) = \sum_{j=1}^{\infty} \int_{X_j} f_N(x)\mathrm{d}\mu(x) \le \sum_{j=1}^{\infty} \int_{X_j} f(x)\mathrm{d}\mu(x),$$

since $0 \le f_N(x) \le f(x)$. It shows that the monotone number sequence $I_N(f)$ is bounded and therefore convergent. Hence $f \in \mathcal{L}(X)$. The corresponding equality for integrals follows from the proof of part 1.

The theorem is completely proved.

The next theorem concerns one of the most important properties of the Lebesgue integral, namely, its absolute continuity.

**Theorem 16.66 (Absolute continuity of the integral).** *Let $f \geq 0$ and $f \in \mathcal{L}(X)$ with $\mu(X) < \infty$. Then for any $\varepsilon > 0$ there exists $\delta > 0$ such that for any $X' \subset X$ with $\mu(X') < \delta$ it follows that*

$$0 \leq \int_{X'} f(x)\mathrm{d}\mu(x) < \varepsilon.$$

*This property of the Lebesgue integral is called* absolute continuity.

**Proof.** Definition 16.62 implies that for any $\varepsilon > 0$ there is $N_0 \in \mathbb{N}$ such that for all $N \geq N_0$ we have

$$0 \leq \int_X (f(x) - f_N(x))\mathrm{d}\mu(x) < \varepsilon/2.$$

Thus, for any set $X' \subset X$ with $\mu(X') < \delta$ and for fixed $N = N_0$ it holds that

$$0 \leq \int_{X'} f(x)\mathrm{d}\mu(x) = \int_{X'} (f(x) - f_{N_0}(x))\mathrm{d}\mu(x) + \int_{X'} f_{N_0}(x)\mathrm{d}\mu(x)$$
$$< \varepsilon/2 + N_0\mu(X') \leq \varepsilon/2 + N_0\delta.$$

If we choose now $\delta < \varepsilon/(2N_0)$ then we obtain the needed property.

We assume now that measurable function $f$ is no longer nonnegative (and not bounded). But we assume still that $\mu(X) < \infty$. In that case we use nonnegative functions $f_+$ and $f_-$ such that

$$f = f_+ - f_-, \quad |f| = f_+ + f_-.$$

**Definition 16.67.** *Let $f : X \subset \mathbb{R}^n \to \mathbb{R}$ be measurable and $\mu(X) < \infty$. Then $f$ is said to be integrable on $X$ if both $f_+$ and $f_-$ are integrable and*

$$\int_X f(x)\mathrm{d}\mu(x) := \int_X f_+(x)\mathrm{d}\mu(x) - \int_X f_-(x)\mathrm{d}\mu(x)$$

*and*

$$\int_X |f(x)|\mathrm{d}\mu(x) = \int_X f_+(x)\mathrm{d}\mu(x) + \int_X f_-(x)\mathrm{d}\mu(x).$$

*In particular, $f$ is integrable on $X$ if and only if $|f|$ is integrable. We use the same symbol in this case, i.e., $f \in \mathcal{L}(X)$.*

This definition allows us to extend Theorems 16.65 and 16.66 (and some others) for general $f$ when $\mu(X) < \infty$.

**Theorem 16.68 ($\sigma$-additivity of the integral).** *Let*

$$X = \bigcup_{j=1}^{\infty} X_j, \quad X_j \cap X_k = \emptyset, j \neq k,$$

*where $X_j$ are measurable and $\mu(X) < \infty$. Then*

1. *if $f \in \mathcal{L}(X)$ then $f \in \mathcal{L}(X_j)$ for each $j = 1, 2, \ldots$ and*

$$\int_X f(x)\mathrm{d}\mu(x) = \sum_{j=1}^{\infty} \int_{X_j} f(x)\mathrm{d}\mu(x),$$

2. *if $f \in \mathcal{L}(X_j)$ for each $j = 1, 2, \ldots$ and the series*

$$\sum_{j=1}^{\infty} \int_{X_j} |f(x)| \mathrm{d}\mu(x)$$

*converges then $f \in \mathcal{L}(X)$ and*

$$\int_X f(x) \mathrm{d}\mu(x) = \sum_{j=1}^{\infty} \int_{X_j} f(x) \mathrm{d}\mu(x).$$

**Theorem 16.69 (Absolute continuity of the integral).** *Let $f \in \mathcal{L}(X)$ with $\mu(X) < \infty$. Then for any $\varepsilon > 0$ there exists $\delta > 0$ such that for any $X' \subset X$ with $\mu(X') < \delta$ it follows that*

$$\left| \int_{X'} f(x) \mathrm{d}\mu(x) \right| < \varepsilon.$$

**Proof.** It suffices to apply Theorem 16.66 to function $|f|$ and use the inequality

$$\left| \int_{X'} f(x) \mathrm{d}\mu(x) \right| \leq \int_{X'} |f(x)| \mathrm{d}\mu(x).$$

**Exercise 16.70.**     1. Prove that

$$f(x) = \begin{cases} \dfrac{1}{x^\alpha} \sin \dfrac{1}{x^\beta}, & 0 < x \leq 1, \\ 1, & x = 0, \end{cases} \qquad \alpha \geq 0, \beta > 0,$$

belongs to $\mathcal{L}([0, 1])$ if and only if $\beta > 0, 0 \leq \alpha < 1$.

2. Prove that the derivative of the function from part 1 belongs to $\mathcal{L}([0, 1])$ if and only if $\beta > 0$ and $\alpha < -\beta$.

3. Prove that

$$f(x_1, x_2) = \begin{cases} \dfrac{x_1 x_2}{(x_1^2 + x_2^2)^2}, & (x_1, x_2) \neq 0, \\ 0, & (x_1, x_2) = 0, \end{cases}$$

does not belong to $\mathcal{L}([-1, 1] \times [-1, 1])$.

4. Prove that

$$f(x_1, x_2) = \begin{cases} \dfrac{x_1^2 - x_2^2}{(x_1^2 + x_2^2)^2}, & (x_1, x_2) \neq 0, \\ 0, & (x_1, x_2) = 0, \end{cases}$$

does not belong to $\mathcal{L}([0, 1] \times [0, 1])$.

5. Define parameter $\alpha > 0$ such that

$$f(x_1, x_2) = \frac{x_1 x_2}{(x_1^2 + x_2^2)^\alpha}$$

belongs to $\mathcal{L}([-1, 1] \times [-1, 1])$.

Now we are in position to extend the Lebesgue integral for the case when $\mu(X) = \infty$, in particular when $X = \mathbb{R}^n$.

**Definition 16.71.** *Let $X \subset \mathbb{R}^n$ be measurable with $\mu(X) = \infty$.*

1. *Then $f \geq 0$ is said to be integrable on $X$ if there exists the limit*

$$\lim_{R \to +\infty} \int_{X \cap \{x \in \mathbb{R}^n : |x| \leq R\}} f(x) \mathrm{d}\mu(x).$$

*This limit is called the integral of $f \geq 0$ on $X$ and is denoted as*

$$\int_X f(x) \mathrm{d}\mu(x) := \lim_{R \to +\infty} \int_{X \cap \{x \in \mathbb{R}^n : |x| \leq R\}} f(x) \mathrm{d}\mu(x)$$

*and we write in this case that $f \in \mathcal{L}(X)$.*

2. *If $f$ is of arbitrary sign then it is said to be integrable on $X$ if $f_+, f_- \in \mathcal{L}(X)$ as two nonnegative functions.*

Definitions 16.62, 16.67, and 16.71 allow us to extend all previous results and Theorems 16.48–16.66 (including Theorems 16.68–16.69) to the general case, i.e., for functions of arbitrary sign, not necessarily bounded and which are defined on a set $X \subset \mathbb{R}^n$ with $\mu(X) \leq \infty$, in particular when $X = \mathbb{R}^n$.

**Example 16.72.** Let $f : \mathbb{R}^n \to \mathbb{R}$ be defined as

$$f(x) = \frac{1}{(1 + |x|)^\alpha}.$$

We will determine $\alpha > 0$ such that $f \in \mathcal{L}(\mathbb{R}^n)$. Using polar coordinates we obtain

$$\lim_{R \to +\infty} \int_{|x| \leq R} \frac{1}{(1 + |x|)^\alpha} \mathrm{d}\mu(x) = \omega_n \lim_{R \to +\infty} \int_0^R \frac{r^{n-1}}{(1+r)^\alpha} \mathrm{d}r = \omega_n \int_0^\infty \frac{r^{n-1}}{(1+r)^\alpha} \mathrm{d}r$$

$$= \omega_n \int_0^1 (1-t)^{n-1} t^{\alpha-n-1} \mathrm{d}t = \omega_n B(n, \alpha - n).$$

Hence $f \in \mathcal{L}(\mathbb{R}^n)$ if and only if $\alpha > n$.

**Exercise 16.73.**    1. Let $X \subset \mathbb{R}^n$ be measurable with $\mu(X) = \infty$. Prove that measurable $f \geq 0$ belongs to $\mathcal{L}(X)$ if and only if the series

$$\sum_{k=0}^\infty 2^{-k} \mu(\{x \in X : f(x) \geq 2^{-k}\})$$

converges.

2. Prove that the following functions are not integrable on $X$:

   (a)

$$f(x_1, x_2) = \frac{x_1^2 - x_2^2}{(x_1^2 + x_2^2)^2}, \quad X = [1, \infty) \times [1, \infty),$$

(b)

$$f(x_1, x_2) = \sin(x_1^2 + x_2^2), \quad X = \mathbb{R}^2,$$

(c)

$$f(x_1, x_2) = \frac{\sin \sqrt{\frac{1}{x_1^2 + x_2^2}}}{x_1^2 + x_2^2}, \quad X = \mathbb{R}^2,$$

(d)

$$f(x) = \frac{\sin x}{x}, \quad X = [0, \infty).$$

3. Determine the parameters $\alpha, \beta > 0$ that guarantee the integrability of

(a)

$$f(x_1, x_2) = \frac{1}{(1 + |x_1|^\alpha)(1 + |x_2|^\beta)},$$

(b)

$$f(x_1, x_2) = \frac{1}{1 + |x_1|^\alpha + |x_2|^\beta}$$

on the set $X = \mathbb{R}^2$.

4. Determine the parameters $\alpha, \beta$ such that $f(x) = x^\alpha \sin x^\beta$ belongs to $\mathcal{L}([1, \infty))$.

## 16.4 ▪ Limiting process for integrable functions

**Definition 16.74.** *The linear space of all integrable functions on a measurable set $X$ with $\mu(X) \leq \infty$ is said to be the* Lebesgue space *of integrable functions and is denoted as $L^1(X)$.*

**Remark 16.75.** It must be mentioned here that in the case $\mu(X) = \infty$ and $f \equiv$ constant we have $f \in L^1(X)$ if and only if this constant is equal to zero.

**Definition 16.76.** *Let $\{f_j\}_{j=1}^\infty$ be a sequence of functions from $L^1(X)$ with $\mu(X) \leq \infty$. The sequence is called* convergent in $L^1(X)$ *to a function $f \in L^1(X)$ if*

$$\lim_{j \to \infty} \int_X |f_j(x) - f(x)| \mathrm{d}\mu(x) = 0.$$

**Remark 16.77.** The convergence of $\{f_j\}_{j=1}^\infty$ in $L^1(X)$ gives the possibility to integrate this sequence such that

$$\lim_{j \to \infty} \int_X f_j(x) \mathrm{d}\mu(x) = \int_X f(x) \mathrm{d}\mu(x).$$

This follows immediately from the fact that

$$\left| \int_X f_j(x) \mathrm{d}\mu(x) - \int_X f(x) \mathrm{d}\mu(x) \right| \leq \int_X |f_j(x) - f(x)| \mathrm{d}\mu(x) \to 0$$

as $j \to \infty$.

**Remark 16.78.** The convergence of $\{f_j\}_{j=1}^{\infty} \subset L^1(X)$ to $f \in L^1(X)$ implies that this sequence converges to $f$ in measure on $X$. Indeed, let $\varepsilon > 0$ and let $X_j$ be defined as

$$X_j = \{x \in X : |f_j(x) - f(x)| > \varepsilon\}.$$

Then we obtain

$$\int_X |f_j(x) - f(x)| \mathrm{d}\mu(x) \geq \int_{X_j} |f_j(x) - f(x)| \mathrm{d}\mu(x) > \varepsilon \mu(X_j)$$

and hence $\lim_{j \to \infty} \mu(X_j) = 0$.

The latter remark means that the convergence in measure on $X$ is weaker than convergence in $L^1(X)$. But under some additional conditions these two types of convergence are equivalent.

**Theorem 16.79 (Lebesgue theorem on the dominated convergence).** *Let $\{f_j\}_{j=1}^{\infty}$ be a sequence of measurable functions on a set $X \subset \mathbb{R}^n$ with $\mu(X) \leq \infty$. If this sequence converges to $f$ in measure $\mu$ on $X$ and if there is a function $F \in L^1(X)$ such that*

$$|f_j(x)| \leq F(x)$$

*a.e. on $X$ for each $j = 1, 2, \dots$ then*

$$\lim_{j \to \infty} \int_X |f_j(x) - f(x)| \mathrm{d}\mu(x) = 0.$$

***Proof.*** Let us first assume that $\mu(X) < \infty$. Then applying Theorem 16.38 we obtain that there is a subsequence $\{f_{k_j}\}_{j=1}^{\infty}$ which converges to $f$ a.e. on $X$. Passing to the limit in the inequality

$$|f_{k_j}(x)| \leq F(x)$$

we obtain that $|f(x)| \leq F(x)$ a.e. on $X$. This implies (see Theorem 16.54) that $f \in L^1(X)$. Next, fixing $\varepsilon > 0$ and considering the sets

$$X_j = \{x \in X : |f_j(x) - f(x)| > \varepsilon\}$$

we have

$$\int_X |f_j(x) - f(x)| \mathrm{d}\mu(x) = \int_{X \setminus X_j} |f_j(x) - f(x)| \mathrm{d}\mu(x) + \int_{X_j} |f_j(x) - f(x)| \mathrm{d}\mu(x)$$

$$< \varepsilon \mu(X \setminus X_j) + 2 \int_{X_j} F(x) \mathrm{d}\mu(x)$$

$$\leq \varepsilon \mu(X) + 2 \int_{X_j} F(x) \mathrm{d}\mu(x).$$

But due to the conditions of this theorem we get $\mu(X_j) \to 0$ as $j \to \infty$. By Theorem 16.66 the latter integral converges to zero as $j \to \infty$. Thus, we obtain that $f_j$ converges to $f$ in $L^1(X)$ since $\varepsilon > 0$ was arbitrary.

In the case $\mu(X) = \infty$ we proceed as follows. Given $\varepsilon > 0$ we use Definition 16.71 to find $R > 0$ so large that

$$\int_X |f_j(x) - f(x)| \mathrm{d}\mu(x) < \int_{X_R = X \cap \{x \in \mathbb{R}^n : |x| \leq R\}} |f_j(x) - f(x)| \mathrm{d}\mu(x) + \varepsilon/2$$

$$\leq 2 \int_{X_j} F(x) \mathrm{d}\mu(x) + \varepsilon \mu(X_j) + \varepsilon/2,$$

where $X_j := \{x \in X_R : |f_j(x) - f(x)| > \varepsilon\}$. Letting $j \to +\infty$ and $\varepsilon \to 0$ we obtain the needed result.

**Corollary 16.80.** *If a sequence $\{f_j\}_{j=1}^{\infty}$ of measurable functions converges to $f$ a.e. on $X$ and if there is a function $F \in L^1(X)$ such that*

$$|f_j(x)| \le F(x)$$

*a.e. on $X$ then $f \in L^1(X)$ and*

$$\lim_{j \to \infty} \int_X |f_j(x) - f(x)| \mathrm{d}\mu(x) = 0.$$

**Proof.** The proof follows from Theorems 16.38 and 16.79.

**Theorem 16.81 (Theorem of B. Levi).** *Let $\{f_j\}_{j=1}^{\infty}$ be a sequence of functions from $L^1(X)$ with $\mu(X) \le \infty$ such that*

$$f_j(x) \le f_{j+1}(x), \quad j = 1, 2, \ldots,$$

*a.e. on $X$. Suppose that the number sequence $\{\int_X f_j(x) \mathrm{d}\mu(x)\}_{j=1}^{\infty}$ is bounded. Then there is a limit*

$$\lim_{j \to \infty} f_j(x) =: f(x)$$

*a.e. on $X$ such that $f \in L^1(X)$ and*

$$\lim_{j \to \infty} \int_X f_j(x) \mathrm{d}\mu(x) = \int_X f(x) \mathrm{d}\mu(x).$$

**Proof.** We may assume without loss of generality that $f_j \ge 0$ for each $j = 1, 2, \ldots$ (for otherwise we consider the sequence $g_j(x) := f_j(x) - f_1(x) \ge 0$). Due to monotonicity of $\{f_j\}_{j=1}^{\infty}$ a.e. on $X$, there is a limit (finite or infinite)

$$f(x) := \lim_{j \to \infty} f_j(x)$$

a.e. on $X$. We show that $f \in L^1(X)$. Indeed, let us consider for each $N \in \mathbb{N}$ the cut-off functions $(f_j)_N$. Then this sequence converges to $f_N$ a.e. on $X$ which is bounded. Applying Corollary 16.80 we obtain

$$\lim_{j \to \infty} \int_X (f_j(x))_N \mathrm{d}\mu(x) = \int_X f_N(x) \mathrm{d}\mu(x).$$

Using now the inequality

$$\int_X (f_j(x))_N \mathrm{d}\mu(x) \le \int_X f_j(x) \mathrm{d}\mu(x)$$

and the latter limit we conclude that

$$\int_X (f(x))_N \mathrm{d}\mu(x) \le \lim_{j \to \infty} \int_X f_j(x) \mathrm{d}\mu(x).$$

Since the number sequence $\{\int_X f_j(x) \mathrm{d}\mu(x)\}_{j=1}^{\infty}$ is monotone (nondecreasing) and bounded,

$$\lim_{N \to \infty} \int_X (f(x))_N \mathrm{d}\mu(x) < \infty$$

and therefore $f \in L^1(X)$. The equality

$$\lim_{j \to \infty} \int_X f_j(x)\mathrm{d}\mu(x) = \int_X f(x)\mathrm{d}\mu(x)$$

follows now from Corollary 16.80.

**Corollary 16.82.** *Let $f_j \geq 0$ for each $j = 1, 2, \ldots$ and $f_j \in L^1(X)$ with $\mu(X) \leq \infty$. Let also the series*

$$\sum_{j=1}^{\infty} \int_X f_j(x)\mathrm{d}\mu(x)$$

*converge. Then the series*

$$\sum_{j=1}^{\infty} f_j(x)$$

*converges a.e. on $X$ and belongs to $L^1(X)$ and*

$$\int_X \sum_{j=1}^{\infty} f_j(x)\mathrm{d}\mu(x) = \sum_{j=1}^{\infty} \int_X f_j(x)\mathrm{d}\mu(x).$$

**Theorem 16.83 (Fatou's lemma).** *Let $\{f_j\}_{j=1}^{\infty}$ be a sequence of functions from $L^1(X)$ with $\mu(X) \leq \infty$. Suppose that*

1. *there is a limit*

$$f(x) := \lim_{j \to \infty} f_j(x)$$

   *a.e. on $X$, and*

2. *there is a constant $M > 0$ such that*

$$\int_X |f_j(x)|\mathrm{d}\mu(x) \leq M.$$

*Then the limiting function $f$ belongs to $L^1(X)$ and*

$$\int_X |f(x)|\mathrm{d}\mu(x) \leq M.$$

***Proof.*** Let us introduce the sequence

$$g_k(x) := \inf_{j \geq k} |f_j(x)|.$$

Then $g_k$ is measurable for each $k = 1, 2, \ldots$, nondecreasing a.e. on $X$, $g_k(x) \leq |f_k(x)|$ and

$$\lim_{k \to \infty} g_k(x) = |f(x)|$$

a.e. on $X$. These properties allow us to conclude that $g_k \in L^1(X)$ for each $k = 1, 2, \ldots$ and

$$0 \leq \int_X g_k(x)\mathrm{d}\mu(x) \leq M.$$

B. Levi's theorem (Theorem 16.81) gives that

$$\lim_{k \to \infty} \int_X g_k(x) \mathrm{d}\mu(x) = \int_X |f(x)| \mathrm{d}\mu(x)$$

and

$$\int_X |f(x)| \mathrm{d}\mu(x) \leq M.$$

This completes the proof.

**Exercise 16.84.**     1. Let $f_j \geq 0$ and $f_j \in L^1(X)$ for each $j = 1, 2, \ldots$ with $\mu(X) \leq \infty$. Let

$$f(x) := \lim_{j \to \infty} f_j(x)$$

a.e. on $X$. Prove that

$$\int_X f(x) \mathrm{d}\mu(x) \leq \lim_{j \to \infty} \int_X f_j(x) \mathrm{d}\mu(x),$$

where the integrals might be infinite.

2. Let $\{f_j\}_{j=1}^\infty$ be a sequence of nonnegative measurable functions on the set $X \subset \mathbb{R}^n$. Prove that if there exists a function $g \in L^1(X)$ such that $f_j(x) \leq g(x)$ a.e. on $X$ for all $j = 1, 2, \ldots$ then

$$\overline{\lim_{j \to \infty}} \int_X f_j(x) \mathrm{d}\mu(x) \leq \int_X \overline{\lim_{j \to \infty}} f_j(x) \mathrm{d}\mu(x) \leq \int_X g(x) \mathrm{d}\mu(x).$$

3. Let $\{f_j\}_{j=1}^\infty \subset L^1(X)$ with $\mu(X) < \infty$. Assume that

$$\lim_{j \to \infty} f_j(x) = f(x)$$

uniformly in $x \in X$. Prove that $f \in L^1(X)$ and

$$\lim_{j \to \infty} \int_X |f_j(x) - f(x)| \mathrm{d}\mu(x) = 0.$$

Does the statement hold if $\mu(X) = \infty$?

4. Let $\mu(X) \leq \infty$. Construct a sequence $\{f_j\}_{j=1}^\infty \subset L^1(X)$ such that $f_j \geq 0$ and

$$\lim_{j \to \infty} f_j(x) = f(x)$$

pointwise on $X$ but

$$\lim_{j \to \infty} \int_X f_j(x) \mathrm{d}\mu(x) = +\infty.$$

5. Let all conditions of Fatou's lemma be satisfied. Show that the limits

$$\lim_{j \to \infty} \int_X |f_j(x) - f(x)| \mathrm{d}\mu(x) = 0$$

and

$$\lim_{j \to \infty} \int_X f_j(x) \mathrm{d}\mu(x) = \int_X f(x) \mathrm{d}\mu(x)$$

do not follow necessarily.

6. Let $f \in L^1(\mathbb{R})$. Prove that the series

$$\sum_{j=-\infty}^{\infty} f(x + 2\pi j)$$

converges a.e. on $\mathbb{R}$.

**Theorem 16.85 (Criterion of Lebesgue integrability III).** *Let $f : X \subset \mathbb{R}^n \to \mathbb{R}$ be bounded on a measurable set $X$ with $\mu(X) < \infty$. Then $f \in L^1(X)$ if and only if $f$ is measurable on $X$.*

**Proof.** The sufficiency is proved in Theorem 16.54 (see part 1). In order to prove necessity let us assume that $f \in L^1(X)$. We note here that the definition of integrability does not assume that $f$ is measurable. Then there exists a partition $Q_m$ of $X$, $m = 1, 2, \ldots$, such that

$$U(Q_m, f) - L(Q_m, f) < 1/m,$$

where $Q_m = \{X_j^{(m)}\}_{j=1}^m$ (see Definition 16.43). We may assume without loss of generality that $Q_m$ is a refinement of $Q_{m-1}$ (see Definition 16.46) for $m = 2, 3, \ldots$. Now, with respect to the sequence $\{Q_m\}_{m=1}^{\infty}$ we introduce the functions defined on $X$ as

$$u_m(x) := M_j^{(m)}, \quad v_m(x) := m_j^{(m)}, \quad x \in X_j^{(m)},$$

where

$$M_j^{(m)} = \sup_{X_j^{(m)}} f(x), \quad m_j^{(m)} = \inf_{X_j^{(m)}} f(x).$$

For each $m = 1, 2, \ldots$ these functions are measurable as linear combinations of measurable functions and

$$v_m(x) \leq f(x) \leq u_m(x), \quad x \in X.$$

Moreover, these functions satisfy the monotonicity conditions

$$v_m(x) \leq v_{m+1}(x), \quad u_m(x) \geq u_{m+1}(x), \quad x \in X.$$

Thus the limits

$$v(x) := \lim_{m \to \infty} v_m(x), \quad u(x) := \lim_{m \to \infty} u_m(x), \quad x \in X,$$

exist and

$$v(x) \leq f(x) \leq u(x), \quad x \in X.$$

The functions $u$ and $v$ are measurable as the limits of measurable functions (see Theorem 16.36). Using B. Levi's theorem (see Theorem 16.81) we obtain that

$$\lim_{m \to \infty} \int_X (u_m(x) - v_m(x)) \mathrm{d}\mu(x) = \int_X (u(x) - v(x)) \mathrm{d}\mu(x).$$

But on the other hand,

$$\int_X (u_m(x) - v_m(x)) \mathrm{d}\mu(x) = U(Q_m, f) - L(Q_m, f) < 1/m.$$

Hence

$$\int_X (u(x) - v(x)) \mathrm{d}\mu(x) = 0.$$

This implies that $u(x) = f(x) = v(x)$ a.e. on $X$ and the measurability of $f$ on $X$.

**Corollary 16.86.** *Under the conditions of Theorem* 16.85 *a function $f$ is Riemann integrable on $X$ if and only if it is continuous a.e. on $X$.*

**Proof.** Let us introduce the so-called Baire functions

$$m(x) := \varliminf_{y \to x} f(y), \quad M(x) := \varlimsup_{y \to x} f(y)$$

which both exist since $f$ is assumed to be bounded. It is clear that $f$ is continuous at $x_0$ if and only if $m(x_0) = M(x_0)$. Using now the functions $u_m$ and $v_m$ defined in the proof of Theorem 16.85 we may conclude that

$$\lim_{m \to \infty} v_m(x) = m(x), \quad \lim_{m \to \infty} u_m(x) = M(x)$$

a.e. on $X$. Since $f$ is Riemann integrable, it is Lebesgue integrable also (see Theorem 16.59). Repeating now the proof of Theorem 16.85 we obtain that

$$\int_X (M(x) - m(x)) \mathrm{d}\mu(x) = 0.$$

So $M(x) = m(x)$ a.e. on $X$ and therefore $f$ is continuous a.e. on $X$.

**Remark 16.87.** The latter theorem and its corollary can be extended to the case $\mu(X) = \infty$. For these purposes Definition 16.71 and Theorem 16.81 can be used.

**Theorem 16.88 (Fubini).** *Let $f : X \times Y \subset \mathbb{R}^{n+m} \to \mathbb{R}$ belong to $L^1(X \times Y)$. Then $f_y(x) := f(x, y)$, as a function of $x$, is integrable on $X$ a.e. in $y$, $f_x(y) := f(x, y)$, as a function of $y$, is integrable on $Y$ a.e. in $x$, and the following equalities hold:*

$$\int_Y \left( \int_X f_y(x) \mathrm{d}\mu_n(x) \right) \mathrm{d}\mu_m(y) = \int_X \left( \int_Y f_x(y) \mathrm{d}\mu_m(y) \right) \mathrm{d}\mu_n(x)$$

$$= \int_{X \times Y} f(x, y) \mathrm{d}\mu_{n+m}(x, y),$$

*where $\mu_n(x)$, $\mu_m(y)$, and $\mu_{n+m}(x, y)$ are the Lebesgue measures on $\mathbb{R}^n$, $\mathbb{R}^m$, and $\mathbb{R}^{n+m}$, respectively.*

**Proof.** Assume first that $f(x, y) \geq 0$. Let us introduce the set

$$U := \{(x, y, z) \in \mathbb{R}^{n+m+1} : (x, y) \in X \times Y, 0 \leq z \leq f(x, y)\}.$$

Let $\lambda$ be the Lebesgue measure on the line. Then for Lebesgue measure $\mu_{n+m+1}$ on $\mathbb{R}^{n+m+1}$ we have that $\mu_{n+m+1}(x, y, z) = \mu_{n+m}(x, y)\lambda(z)$ and

$$\mu_{n+m+1}(U) = \int_{X \times Y} f(x, y) \mathrm{d}\mu_{n+m}(x, y).$$

But on the other hand,

$$\mu_{n+m+1}(U) = \int_X \xi(U_y)\mathrm{d}\mu_n(x),$$

where

$$U_y = \{(x,z) \in \mathbb{R}^{n+1} : (x,y,z) \in U\}$$

and

$$\xi(U_y) = \int_Y f(x,y)\mathrm{d}\mu_m(y).$$

This means that

$$\int_{X \times Y} f(x,y)\mathrm{d}\mu_{n+m}(x,y) = \int_X \left(\int_Y f(x,y)\mathrm{d}\mu_m(y)\right)\mathrm{d}\mu_n(x).$$

If we repeat this consideration interchanging $x$ and $y$ we obtain the result of the Fubini theorem in the case $f(x,y) \geq 0$. The general case can be obtained using the functions

$$f_+(x,y) = \frac{|f(x,y)| + f(x,y)}{2} \geq 0, \quad f_-(x,y) = \frac{|f(x,y)| - f(x,y)}{2} \geq 0.$$

This finishes the proof.

**Exercise 16.89.** Prove that

1. $\mu_{n+m}(x,y) = \mu_n(x)\mu_m(y),$

2. $\mu_{n+m+1}(x,y,z) = \mu_{n+m}(x,y)\lambda(z),$

3.

$$\mu_{n+m+1}(U) = \int_{X \times Y} f(x,y)\mathrm{d}\mu_{n+m}(x,y),$$

where $U$ is as in the proof of Theorem 16.88.

**Remark 16.90.** Fubini theorem is also valid for arbitrary measurable set $\widetilde{X} \subset \mathbb{R}^{n+m}$. In that case $\widetilde{X}$ can be represented as

$$\widetilde{X} = \widetilde{X}_y \times \widetilde{X}_x, \quad \widetilde{X}_y \subset \mathbb{R}^n, \quad \widetilde{X}_x \subset \mathbb{R}^m,$$

where

$$\widetilde{X}_y = \{x \in \mathbb{R}^n : (x,y) \in \widetilde{X}\}, \quad \widetilde{X}_x = \{y \in \mathbb{R}^m : (x,y) \in \widetilde{X}\}.$$

**Example 16.91.**    1. Let $X = Y = [-1,1] \subset \mathbb{R}^2$ and

$$f(x_1,x_2) = \begin{cases} \frac{x_1 x_2}{(x_1^2 + x_2^2)^2}, & x_1^2 + x_2^2 > 0, \\ 0, & (x_1,x_2) = (0,0). \end{cases}$$

Since $f$ is odd in $x_1$ and in $x_2$,

$$\int_{-1}^1 \left(\int_{-1}^1 f(x_1,x_2)\mathrm{d}\mu(x_1)\right)\mathrm{d}\mu(x_2) = \int_{-1}^1 \left(\int_{-1}^1 f(x_1,x_2)\mathrm{d}\mu(x_2)\right)\mathrm{d}\mu(x_1) = 0.$$

But using polar coordinates we obtain

$$\int_{X \times Y} |f(x_1, x_2)| d\mu(x_1, x_2) \geq \int_{x_1^2 + x_2^2 \leq 1} |f(x_1, x_2)| d\mu(x_1, x_2)$$

$$= \int_0^1 r dr \int_0^{2\pi} r^{-2} |\sin \theta| |\cos \theta| d\theta$$

$$= 4 \int_0^1 r^{-1} dr \int_0^{\pi/2} \sin \theta \cos \theta d\theta = 2 \int_0^1 r^{-1} dr = +\infty.$$

This shows that the Fubini theorem is not applicable even if the repeated integrals are equal to each other.

2. Let $X = Y = [0,1]$ and

$$f(x_1, x_2) = \begin{cases} \frac{x_1^2 - x_2^2}{(x_1^2 + x_2^2)^2}, & x_1^2 + x_2^2 > 0, \\ 0, & (x_1, x_2) = (0,0). \end{cases}$$

Then

$$\int_0^1 \left( \int_0^1 \frac{x_1^2 - x_2^2}{(x_1^2 + x_2^2)^2} d\mu(x_1) \right) d\mu(x_2) = \int_0^1 \left( \int_0^1 \frac{x_1^2 + x_2^2}{(x_1^2 + x_2^2)^2} d\mu(x_1) \right) d\mu(x_2)$$

$$- 2 \int_0^1 x_2^2 \left( \int_0^1 \frac{d\mu(x_1)}{(x_1^2 + x_2^2)^2} \right) d\mu(x_2)$$

$$= \int_0^1 \frac{1}{x_2} \arctan \frac{x_1}{x_2} \bigg|_0^1 d\mu(x_2)$$

$$- 2 \int_0^1 x_2^2 \left( \int_0^1 \frac{d\mu(x_1)}{(x_1^2 + x_2^2)^2} \right) d\mu(x_2)$$

$$= \int_1^\infty \frac{1}{v} \arctan v d\mu(v)$$

$$- 2 \int_0^1 x_2^2 \left( \int_0^1 \frac{d\mu(x_1)}{(x_1^2 + x_2^2)^2} \right) d\mu(x_2).$$

Due to antisymmetry of $f$ with respect to $x_1$ and $x_2$ we have that

$$\int_0^1 \left( \int_0^1 \frac{x_1^2 - x_2^2}{(x_1^2 + x_2^2)^2} d\mu(x_2) \right) d\mu(x_1) = - \int_1^\infty \frac{1}{v} \arctan v d\mu(v)$$

$$+ 2 \int_0^1 x_1^2 \left( \int_0^1 \frac{d\mu(x_2)}{(x_1^2 + x_2^2)^2} \right) d\mu(x_1).$$

So these two repeated integrals have different sign (they might be infinite). This shows that $f \notin L^1(X \times Y)$.

**Exercise 16.92.**    1. Prove that if at least one of the integrals

$$\int_Y \left( \int_X |f(x, y)| d\mu_n(x) \right) d\mu_m(y), \quad \int_X \left( \int_Y |f(x, y)| d\mu_m(y) \right) d\mu_n(x)$$

exists then $f \in L^1(X \times Y)$ and the equality from the Fubini theorem is also valid.

2. Prove *Tonelli's theorem*: Let $f \geq 0$ be measurable on $X' = X \times Y \subset \mathbb{R}^{n+m}$. Then

$$\int_Y \left( \int_X f(x,y) \mathrm{d}\mu_n(x) \right) \mathrm{d}\mu_m(y) = \int_X \left( \int_Y f(x,y) \mathrm{d}\mu_m(y) \right) \mathrm{d}\mu_n(x).$$

If, in addition,

$$\varphi(y) := \int_X f(x,y) \mathrm{d}\mu_n(x)$$

belongs to $L^1(Y)$ or

$$\psi(x) := \int_Y f(x,y) \mathrm{d}\mu_m(y)$$

belongs to $L^1(X)$, then $f \in L^1(X \times Y)$.

3. Let $\{f_j\}_{j=1}^\infty$ be a sequence defined on a set $X' = X \times Y \subset \mathbb{R}^{n+m}$ such that

    (a) $f_j(x,y) \geq 0, j = 1, 2, \ldots,$
    (b) $\sum_{j=1}^\infty f_j(x,y) \leq g(x,y)$ a.e. on $X'$,
    (c) $f_j$ and $g$ satisfy all conditions of the Fubini theorem.

    Prove that

$$f(x,y) := \sum_{j=1}^\infty f_j(x,y)$$

satisfies all conditions of the Fubini theorem.

4. Let $X' = (0,1) \times (0,1)$ and

$$f(x_1, x_2) = \begin{cases} \frac{1}{x_2^2}, & 0 < x_1 < x_2 < 1, \\ -\frac{1}{x_1^2}, & 0 < x_2 < x_1 < 1. \end{cases}$$

Does the Fubini theorem work for this function?

5. Let $X' = [-1,1] \times [-1,1]$ and

$$f_1(x_1, x_2) = \begin{cases} \frac{x_1^2 - x_2^2}{x_1^2 + x_2^2}, & x_1^2 + x_2^2 > 0, \\ 0, & (x_1, x_2) = (0,0), \end{cases}$$

and

$$f_2(x_1, x_2) = \begin{cases} \frac{x_1 x_2}{x_1^2 + x_2^2}, & x_1^2 + x_2^2 > 0, \\ 0, & (x_1, x_2) = (0,0). \end{cases}$$

Does the Fubini theorem work for these functions?

## 16.5 ▪ Lebesgue spaces $L^p$

We consider the collection of all functions $f$ defined on a measurable set $X \subset \mathbb{R}^n$ with $\mu(X) \leq \infty$ such that

$$\int_X |f(x)|^p \mathrm{d}\mu(x) < \infty, \quad 1 \leq p < \infty.$$

This collection is a linear space, i.e.,

1. if $f_1, f_2$ are from this collection then $\alpha_1 f_1 + \alpha_2 f_2$ is also from this collection for arbitrary constants $\alpha_1, \alpha_2 \in \mathbb{R}$;

2. to each element $f$ from this collection one can assign the number

$$\|f\|_{L^p(X)} = \|f\|_p := \left( \int_X |f(x)|^p d\mu(x) \right)^{1/p},$$

which is called a *norm* and it satisfies the following conditions:

(a) $\|f\|_p \geq 0$ and $\|f\|_p = 0$ if and only in $f = 0$ a.e. on $X$,

(b) $\|\alpha f\|_p = |\alpha| \|f\|_p, \alpha \in \mathbb{R}$,

(c) $\|f_1 + f_2\|_p \leq \|f_1\|_p + \|f_2\|_p$ (triangle inequality).

**Exercise 16.93.** Prove that

1. the collection of all functions such that $|f|^p \in L^1(X), 1 \leq p < \infty$, is a linear space,

2. the value

$$\|f\|_p = \left( \int_X |f(x)|^p d\mu(x) \right)^{1/p},$$

is a norm.

Hint: Use the Minkovskii inequality (see Corollary 9.43 and its generalization to the Lebesgue integral).

**Definition 16.94.** *A linear space of all functions $f$ such that $|f|^p \in L^1(X)$ with $\mu(X) \leq \infty$ and $1 \leq p < \infty$ equipped with the norm $\|f\|_p$ is called the* normed Lebesgue space $L^p(X)$.

**Definition 16.95.** *A sequence $\{f_j\}_{j=1}^\infty \subset L^p(X), 1 \leq p < \infty$, is said to be*

1. *a* Cauchy sequence *in $L^p(X)$ if for any $\varepsilon > 0$ there exists $N \in \mathbb{N}$ such that for all $k, j \geq N$ we have*

$$\|f_j - f_k\|_p < \varepsilon,$$

2. *a* convergent sequence *in $L^p(X)$ if there is $f \in L^p(X)$ such that*

$$\lim_{j \to \infty} \|f_j - f\|_p = 0.$$

**Remark 16.96.** It is clear that any convergent sequence in $L^p(X), 1 \leq p < \infty$, is a Cauchy sequence since

$$\|f_j - f_k\|_p \leq \|f_j - f\|_p + \|f_k - f\|_p \to 0$$

as $j, k \to \infty$.

**Theorem 16.97 (Completeness of $L^p$).** *The normed space $L^p(X), 1 \leq p < \infty$, with $\mu(X) \leq \infty$ is complete, i.e., any Cauchy sequence in $L^p(X)$ is convergent.*

***Proof.*** We assume first that $\mu(X) < \infty$. Let us introduce a number sequence

$$\varepsilon_k := \sup_{j \geq k} \|f_j - f_k\|_p.$$

Since $\{f_j\}_{j=1}^\infty$ is a Cauchy sequence, $\varepsilon_k \to 0$ as $k \to +\infty$. Hence, there is a subsequence $\{\varepsilon_{m_k}\}_{k=1}^\infty$ such that

$$\sum_{k=1}^\infty \varepsilon_{m_k} < \infty$$

(one may choose, for example, $\varepsilon_{m_k} \leq 2^{-k}$). Considering now the subsequence $\{f_{m_k}\}_{k=1}^\infty$ and using Hölder's inequality (see Corollary 9.43 and its generalization to the Lebesgue integral) we obtain that

$$\int_X |f_{m_k}(x) - f_{m_{k+1}}(x)| d\mu(x) \leq \|f_{m_k} - f_{m_{k+1}}\|_p (\mu(X))^{1/p'}, \quad 1/p + 1/p' = 1.$$

This inequality implies that

$$\sum_{k=1}^\infty \int_X |f_{m_k}(x) - f_{m_{k+1}}(x)| d\mu(x) \leq \sum_{k=1}^\infty \varepsilon_{m_k} (\mu(X))^{1/p'} < \infty.$$

Next, Theorem 16.81 (B. Levi) and its corollary for series give that

$$\sum_{k=1}^\infty |f_{m_k}(x) - f_{m_{k+1}}(x)|$$

converges a.e. on $X$ and therefore the series

$$f(x) := f_{m_1}(x) + \sum_{k=1}^\infty (f_{m_{k+1}}(x) - f_{m_k}(x))$$

converges a.e. on $X$ also. So we obtain that

$$f_{m_1}(x) + \sum_{k=1}^N (f_{m_{k+1}}(x) - f_{m_k}(x)) \equiv f_{m_{N+1}}(x)$$

converges to $f$ a.e. on $X$. Hence,

$$\lim_{N \to +\infty} (f_k(x) - f_{m_{N+1}}(x)) = f_k(x) - f(x)$$

a.e. on $X$. Applying Fatou's lemma (Theorem 16.83) we get for any $k \in \mathbb{N}$ that

$$\|f_k - f\|_p \leq \varepsilon_k \to 0$$

as $k \to \infty$. This proves the theorem when $\mu(X) < \infty$.

Let now $\mu(X) = \infty$. We consider the sets

$$X_R := X \cap \{x \in \mathbb{R}^n : |x| \leq R\}, \quad R > 0.$$

Applying the above procedure for sets $X_R, \mu(X_R) < \infty$ we obtain that

$$\lim_{k \to \infty} \left\| f_k - f^{(R_0)} \right\|_{L^p(X_{R_0})} = 0$$

for some $R_0 > 0$ which can be chosen later. Indeed, since $\{f_j\}_{j=1}^{\infty}$ is a Cauchy sequence then it is bounded in $L^p(X)$, i.e., there is a constant $M > 0$ such that

$$\|f_j\|_{L^p(X)} \leq M$$

for all $j = 1, 2, \ldots$. Hence, for any $\varepsilon > 0$ there is $R_0 > 0$ such that

$$\|f_j\|_{L^p(X \setminus X_R)} < \varepsilon/2$$

for all $R \geq R_0$ and for all $j \geq 1$. For given $\varepsilon > 0$ and $R_0$ from above let us introduce

$$f(x) := \begin{cases} f^{(R_0)}(x), & x \in X_{R_0}, \\ 0, & x \in X \setminus X_{R_0}. \end{cases}$$

Let us choose also $N \in \mathbb{N}$ such that

$$\left\| f_k - f^{(R_0)} \right\|_{L^p(X_{R_0})} < \varepsilon/2$$

for all $k \geq N$. Combining now these two facts we have that for given $\varepsilon > 0$ and $R_0 > 0, k \geq N$ we have

$$\|f_k - f\|_{L^p(X)} = \left( \left\| f_k - f^{(R_0)} \right\|_{L^p(X_{R_0})}^p + \|f_k\|_{L^p(X \setminus X_{R_0})}^p \right)^{1/p} < \varepsilon.$$

This finishes the proof.

**Corollary 16.98.** *If $\{f_j\}_{j=1}^{\infty}$ converges to $f$ in $L^p(X)$ then there is a subsequence $\{f_{m_j}\}_{j=1}^{\infty}$ which converges to $f$ a.e. on $X$.*

***Proof.*** The subsequence $\{f_{m_j}\}_{j=1}^{\infty}$ that satisfies the conditions of this corollary is obtained in the proof of Theorem 16.97.

**Remark 16.99.** We may list some other properties of the sequence $\{f_j\}_{j=1}^{\infty} \subset L^p(X)$ which converges to $f \in L^p(X)$:

1. $\|f_j\|_{L^p(X)} \to \|f\|_{L^p(X)}$ as $j \to +\infty$. This follows from the triangle inequalities

$$\|f_j\|_{L^p(X)} \leq \|f_j - f\|_{L^p(X)} + \|f\|_{L^p(X)}$$

and

$$\|f\|_{L^p(X)} \leq \|f_j - f\|_{L^p(X)} + \|f_j\|_{L^p(X)}$$

after rearranging.

2. $\{f_j\}_{j=1}^{\infty}$ converges to $f$ in measure on $X$. This fact follows from the Chebyshev inequality

$$\mu(\{x \in X : |f_j(x) - f(x)| > \sigma\}) \leq \frac{1}{\sigma^p} \int_X |f_j(x) - f(x)|^p \mathrm{d}\mu(x) \to 0$$

as $j \to \infty$.

3. It does not follow that $\{f_j\}_{j=1}^\infty$ converges to $f$ a.e. on $X$. A counterexample in the one-dimensional case is the sequence

$$f_{2^m+k}(x) = m\chi_{[k/2^m,(k+1)/2^m]}(x), \quad k = 0, 1, 2, \ldots, 2^m - 1.$$

Then

$$\|f_{2^m+k}\|_{L^p(\mathbb{R})} = m2^{-m/p} \to 0$$

as $m \to \infty$. This implies that

$$\|f_j\|_{L^p(\mathbb{R})} \to 0$$

and is equivalent that $f_j \to 0$. However, the sequence $\{f_j\}_{j=1}^\infty$ fails to converge for any $x \in [0,1] \subset \mathbb{R}$ since

$$\overline{\lim_{j\to\infty}} f_j(x) = +\infty, \quad \underline{\lim_{j\to\infty}} f_j(x) = 0.$$

4. The convergence of $\{f_j\}_{j=1}^\infty$ to $f$ a.e. on $X$ does not imply that $\{f_j\}_{j=1}^\infty$ converges to $f$ in $L^p(X)$. A counterexample in the one-dimensional case is

$$f_j(x) = j^2\chi_{(0,1/j)}(x), \quad j = 1, 2, \ldots.$$

Then $f_j$ converges to 0 at any point $x \in \mathbb{R}$ but

$$\|f_j\|_{L^p(\mathbb{R})} = j^2\left(\int_0^{1/j} 1\mathrm{d}\mu(x)\right)^{1/p} = j^{2-1/p} \to +\infty$$

as $j \to \infty$.

The following theorem clarifies the difference between pointwise convergence (or convergence in measure) and convergence in $L^p$.

**Theorem 16.100 (Convergence a.e. and $L^p$-convergence).** *Let $\{f_j\}_{j=1}^\infty$ be a sequence from $L^p(X)$ and let $f$ be a function from $L^p(X)$, $1 \le p < \infty$, with $\mu(X) \le \infty$. If $\{f_j\}_{j=1}^\infty$ converges to $f$ a.e. on $X$ and*

$$\lim_{j\to\infty} \|f_j\|_{L^p(X)} = \|f\|_{L^p(X)}$$

*then*

$$\lim_{j\to\infty} \|f_j - f\|_{L^p(X)} = 0.$$

*Proof.* Since

$$|f_j(x) - f(x)|^p \le 2^p(|f_j(x)|^p + |f(x)|^p)$$

a.e. on $X$ and

$$\lim_{j\to\infty}\left(2^p(|f_j(x)|^p + |f(x)|^p) - |f_j(x) - f(x)|^p\right) = 2^{p+1}|f(x)|^p$$

a.e. on $X$, applying Fatou's lemma (Theorem 16.81) we obtain

$$\int_X 2^{p+1}|f(x)|^p\mathrm{d}\mu(x) \le \underline{\lim_{j\to\infty}}\int_X \left(2^p(|f_j(x)|^p + |f(x)|^p) - |f_j(x) - f(x)|^p\right)\mathrm{d}\mu(x)$$

$$= 2^{p+1}\int_X |f(x)|^p\mathrm{d}\mu(x) - \overline{\lim_{j\to\infty}}\int_X |f_j(x) - f(x)|^p\mathrm{d}\mu(x).$$

This obviously leads to the inequality

$$\varlimsup_{j\to\infty} \int_X |f_j(x) - f(x)|^p \mathrm{d}\mu(x) \le 0.$$

Therefore

$$\lim_{j\to\infty} \left( \int_X |f_j(x) - f(x)|^p \mathrm{d}\mu(x) \right)^{1/p} = 0.$$

Theorem 16.100 is proved.

**Corollary 16.101.** *The statement of this theorem remains true if one assumes that $\{f_j\}_{j=1}^{\infty}$ converges to $f$ in measure (instead of convergence a.e. on $X$).*

**Theorem 16.102 (Density of continuous functions in $L^p$).** *Let $f \in L^p(X), 1 \le p < \infty$, be an arbitrary function and $\mu(X) \le \infty$. Then for any $\varepsilon > 0$ there is a continuous function $g$ defined on $X$ such that*

$$\|f - g\|_{L^p(X)} < \varepsilon.$$

***Proof.*** It is clear (see Definitions 16.67 and 16.71) that the proof of this theorem can be reduced to the case when $\mu(X) < \infty$.

The first step is that any function $f \in L^p(X), 1 \le p < \infty, \mu(X) < \infty$, can be approximated by simple functions, i.e., for any $\varepsilon > 0$ there is a simple function $g$ such that

$$\int_X |f(x) - g(x)|^p \mathrm{d}\mu(x) < \varepsilon.$$

This fact is a consequence of Theorem 16.54 (see part 2) and Theorem 16.100.

The second step is that any simple function which belongs to $L^p(X)$ can be approximated in the sense of $L^p$-convergence by the simple functions taking a finite number of values.

The third step is that any simple function taking only a finite number of values can be approximated in the sense of $L^p$-convergence by continuous functions. Indeed, since this simple function is a linear combination of characteristic functions $\chi_A(x)$, where $A$ is a measurable set, it is enough to consider only this function $\chi_A(x)$. For measurable set $A$ with $\mu(A) < \infty$ there is a closed set $F$ and an open set $G$ such that

$$F \subset A \subset G, \quad \mu(G) - \mu(F) < \varepsilon.$$

Let us define a function $g_\varepsilon$ on $X$ as

$$g_\varepsilon(x) := \frac{\rho(x, X \setminus G)}{\rho(x, X \setminus G) + \rho(x, X \setminus F)},$$

where $\rho(x, M) := \inf_{y \in M} |x - y|$. It is clear that $g_\varepsilon(x) = 0$ if $x \in X \setminus G$ and $g_\varepsilon(x) = 1$ if $x \in F$. Since $\inf_{y \in M} |x - y|$ is continuous, $g_\varepsilon$ is also continuous. Moreover,

$$\int_X |\chi_A(x) - g_\varepsilon(x)|^p \mathrm{d}\mu(x) \le \int_{G \setminus F} \mathrm{d}\mu(x) = \mu(G) - \mu(F) < \varepsilon.$$

This finishes the proof.

In what follows we consider the *support* of a function defined by

$$\operatorname{supp} f := \overline{\{x : f(x) \ne 0\}}.$$

**Corollary 16.103.** *The set of all continuous functions with compact support in $X$, denoted $C_0(X)$, is dense in $L^p(X)$ for $1 \le p < \infty$.*

**Exercise 16.104.**     1. Prove the latter corollary.

2. Prove that $L^p(X), 1 \leq p < \infty, \mu(X) \leq \infty$, is *separable normed space*, i.e., there is a countable set which is dense in $L^p(X)$. Hint: Consider the set of polynomials with rational coefficients.

3. Prove that for any $f \in L^p(X), 1 \leq p < \infty, \mu(X) \leq \infty$, we have

$$\lim_{h \to 0} \|f(\cdot + h) - f(\cdot)\|_{L^p(X_h)} = 0,$$

where $X_h = \{x \in X : x + h \in X\}, h \in \mathbb{R}^n$.

4. Prove that if $f \in L^{p_1}(X) \cap L^{p_2}(X)$ then $f \in L^p(X)$ for any $p_1 \leq p \leq p_2 < \infty$.

5. Prove that if $\mu(X) < \infty$ then $L^{p_1}(X) \subset L^{p_2}(X)$ for $1 \leq p_2 < p_1 < \infty$.

6. Let $L^p_\sigma(\mathbb{R}^n)$ denote the *weighted Lebesgue space* with the norm

$$\|f\|_{L^p_\sigma(\mathbb{R}^n)} := \left( \int_{\mathbb{R}^n} (1 + |x|)^{\sigma p} |f(x)|^p d\mu(x) \right)^{1/p}, \quad 1 \leq p < \infty, \sigma \in \mathbb{R}.$$

Prove that

(a) $L^p_\sigma(\mathbb{R}^n) \subset L^1(\mathbb{R}^n) \cap L^p(\mathbb{R}^n)$ if $\sigma > n - n/p$,

(b) $L^{p_1}_{\sigma_1}(\mathbb{R}^n) \subset L^{p_2}_{\sigma_2}(\mathbb{R}^n)$ if $p_1 > p_2 \geq 1$ and $\sigma_1 > \sigma_2 + n(1/p_2 - 1/p_1)$.

7. Prove the Minkovskii inequality for the weighted Lebesgue space $L^p_\sigma(\mathbb{R}^n)$.

We want to generalize the space $L^p(X)$ for $p = \infty$. Instead of integration in the case $1 \leq p < \infty$ we will have to resort to boundedness almost everywhere.

**Definition 16.105.** *Let $X \subset \mathbb{R}^n$ be a measurable set and let $f : X \to \mathbb{R}$ be a measurable function. Then we say that $f \in L^\infty(X)$ if there exists a constant $M \geq 0$ such that*

$$|f(x)| \leq M$$

*a.e. on $X$. Such functions are said to be* essentially bounded. *The value*

$$\operatorname*{ess\,sup}_{x \in X} |f(x)| := \inf\{M \geq 0 : |f(x)| \leq M \text{ a.e. on } X\}$$

*is said to be a norm in the linear space of essentially bounded functions and $L^\infty(X)$ equipped with this norm is said to be the Lebesgue space $L^\infty(X)$.*

**Exercise 16.106.**     1. Prove that $\|f\|_{L^\infty(X)} = \operatorname{ess\,sup}_{x \in X} |f(x)|$ is a norm.

2. Prove that if $f \in L^\infty(X)$ then $|f(x)| \leq \|f\|_{L^\infty(X)}$ a.e. on $X$.

3. Let $f \in L^\infty(X)$ with $0 < \mu(X) < \infty$. Prove that

$$\lim_{p \to \infty} \|f\|_{L^p(X)} = \|f\|_{L^\infty(X)}$$

and

$$\lim_{p \to \infty} \left( \frac{1}{\mu(X)} \int_X |f(x)|^p d\mu(x) \right)^{1/p} = \|f\|_{L^\infty(X)}.$$

4. Let $f \in L^p(X)$ for all $1 \le p < \infty$ with $\mu(X) \le \infty$. Prove that

$$\|f\|_{L^\infty(X)} = \lim_{p \to \infty} \|f\|_{L^p(X)},$$

where both values might be infinite.

5. Prove Hölder's and Minkovskii's inequalities for $p = 1, p' = \infty$.

**Theorem 16.107 (Completeness of $L^\infty$).** *The Lebesgue space $L^\infty(X)$ is complete with respect to the $L^\infty$-norm.*

**Proof.** We need to show that if $\{f_j\}_{j=1}^\infty \subset L^\infty(X)$ is a Cauchy sequence, i.e.,

$$\lim_{j,k \to \infty} \|f_j - f_k\|_{L^\infty(X)} = 0,$$

then there is a function $f \in L^\infty(X)$ such that

$$\lim_{j \to \infty} \|f_j - f\|_{L^\infty(X)} = 0.$$

For any $\varepsilon > 0$ there exists $N \in \mathbb{N}$ such that

$$\|f_j - f_k\|_{L^\infty(X)} < \varepsilon$$

for all $k, j \ge N$. Introducing the sets

$$F_{jk} := \{x \in X : |f_j(x) - f_k(x)| \ge \|f_j - f_k\|_{L^\infty(X)}\}$$

we can see that $\mu(F_{jk}) = 0$. Let

$$F := \bigcup_{j,k=1}^\infty F_{jk}, \quad E := \mathbb{R}^n \setminus F.$$

Note that $\mu(F) = 0$. Moreover,

$$E = \{x \in X : |f_j(x) - f_k(x)| \le \|f_j - f_k\|_{L^\infty(X)} \text{ for all } j, k \in \mathbb{N}\}$$
$$= \bigcap_{j,k=1}^\infty \{x \in X : |f_j(x) - f_k(x)| \le \|f_j - f_k\|_{L^\infty(X)}\}.$$

Hence, for any fixed $x \in E$ the number sequence $\{f_j(x)\}_{j=1}^\infty$ is a Cauchy sequence on the line. Since $\mathbb{R}$ is a complete space with the norm $|\cdot|$, there is a limit

$$f(x) := \lim_{j \to \infty} f_j(x), \quad x \in E.$$

Due to this limit $f(x)$ is a well-defined measurable function as a pointwise limit of measurable functions. Since $\mu(F) = 0$, we can put $f(x) = 0$ for $x \in F$. Thus, for all $j, k \ge N$ and a.e. on $X$ we have

$$|f_j(x) - f_k(x)| < \varepsilon.$$

Letting $k \to +\infty$ we get

$$|f_j(x) - f(x)| \le \varepsilon$$

a.e. on $X$. This shows that

$$\lim_{j \to \infty} \|f_j - f\|_{L^\infty(X)} = 0.$$

Finally, $f \in L^\infty(X)$ follows from the triangle inequality

$$\|f\|_{L^\infty(X)} \leq \|f_j\|_{L^\infty(X)} + \varepsilon < \infty$$

for any fixed $j \geq N$. This concludes the proof.

**Remark 16.108.** The proof of the latter theorem shows that actually the limit

$$\lim_{j \to \infty} f_j(x) = f(x)$$

is uniform on $X \setminus F$, where $F$ is the same as in the proof of Theorem 16.107.

**Example 16.109.** Let $\{f_j\}_{j=1}^\infty$ be a sequence on the line such that

$$f_j(X) = \begin{cases} 0, & x < 0, \\ jx, & 0 \leq x < 1/j, \\ 1, & x > 1/j, \end{cases}$$

and let $f(x) = \chi_{[0,+\infty)}(x)$. Then

$$\lim_{j \to \infty} f_j(x) = f(x)$$

pointwise on $\mathbb{R}$ and

$$\lim_{j \to \infty} \|f_j\|_{L^\infty(\mathbb{R})} = 1 = \|f\|_{L^\infty(\mathbb{R})}.$$

But

$$\lim_{j \to \infty} \|f_j - f\|_{L^\infty(\mathbb{R})} = 1.$$

This shows that a.e. convergence and convergence for norms (Theorem 16.100) do not imply convergence in the $L^\infty$-norm as they did for the spaces $L^p, 1 \leq p < \infty$.

**Remark 16.110.** Density of continuous functions does not hold in $L^\infty(X)$ as it did for the spaces $L^p, 1 \leq p < \infty$. Indeed, if a sequence $\{f_j\}_{j=1}^\infty$ of continuous functions converges to a function $f$ in $L^\infty(X)$ then the limiting function must necessarily be continuous due to uniform convergence (see Definition 16.95). This would imply that all functions from $L^\infty(X)$ are continuous. But this is not the case. There is also another reason why this is not true. The constant function cannot be approximated by compactly supported functions in $L^\infty(X)$. Nevertheless the following result holds.

**Theorem 16.111 (Density of simple functions in $L^\infty$).** *Let $f \in L^\infty(X)$. Then there is a sequence $\{f_j\}_{j=1}^\infty$ of simple functions such that*

$$\lim_{j \to \infty} \|f_j - f\|_{L^\infty(X)} = 0.$$

***Proof.*** The proof follows similarly to the proof of Theorem 16.102 using Exercise 16.106, parts 3 and 4.

**Remark 16.112.** The Lebesgue space $L^\infty$ is not separable in contrast to spaces $L^p$, $1 \leq p < \infty$. To see this, let us consider the family of functions

$$f_\alpha(x) := \begin{cases} 1, & |x| \leq \alpha, \\ 0, & |x| > \alpha, \end{cases} \quad \alpha \in \mathbb{R}_+,$$

defined on the set $X = \mathbb{R}^n$. Then for $\alpha \neq \beta$ we have

$$\|f_\alpha - f_\beta\|_{L^\infty(\mathbb{R}^n)} = 1.$$

Since this family is not countable, $L^\infty$ cannot be separable.

**Exercise 16.113.**    1. Prove that if $f \in L^\infty(X)$ with $\mu(X) \leq \infty$ then there is a sequence $\{f_j\}_{j=1}^\infty \subset C_0(X)$ such that

$$\lim_{j \to \infty} f_j(x) = f(x)$$

a.e. on $X$ and

$$|f_j(x)| \leq \|f\|_{L^\infty(X)}$$

a.e. on $X$ for each $j = 1, 2, \ldots$.

   2. Prove that if $fg \in L^1(X)$ for all $f \in L^1(X)$ then necessarily $g \in L^\infty(X)$.

It turns out that the property of absolute continuity of the Lebesgue integral and set functions defined on measurable sets are very related to each other. This is the meaning of the Rado–Nikodym theory which is discussed below.

**Definition 16.114.** *Let $\Phi$ be a nonnegative real-valued $\sigma$-additive function defined on measurable sets $X \subset \mathbb{R}^n$ with $\mu(X) < \infty$. Such a function is called a* function of sets. *This function $\Phi$ is said to be* absolutely continuous *with respect to Lebesgue measure $\mu$ if for any set $X$ with $\mu(X) = 0$ it follows that $\Phi(X) = 0$.*

**Example 16.115.** Let $f \geq 0$ and $f \in L^1(\mathbb{R}^n)$. Then $\Phi$ defined as

$$\Phi(X) := \int_X f(x)\mathrm{d}\mu(x), \quad X \subset \mathbb{R}^n,$$

is an absolutely continuous function of sets.

The following theorem shows that actually this example exhausts all such functions of sets.

**Theorem 16.116 (Radon–Nikodym).** *Let $\Phi$ be an arbitrary absolutely continuous function of sets. Then there is $f \geq 0$ with $f \in L^1(\mathbb{R}^n)$ such that*

$$\Phi(X) = \int_X f(x)\mathrm{d}\mu(x), \quad X \subset \mathbb{R}^n,$$

*and the function $f$ is uniquely determined up to $\mu$-equivalency.*

*Proof.* Let $E$ denote the set of all functions $f \geq 0$ and $f \in L^1(\mathbb{R}^n)$ such that

$$\int_X f(x)\mathrm{d}\mu(x) \leq \Phi(X)$$

for any measurable set $X \subset \mathbb{R}^n$ with $\mu(X) < \infty$. Let also

$$M := \sup_{f \in E} \int_{\mathbb{R}^n} f(x) \mathrm{d}\mu(x).$$

Then there is a sequence $\{f_j\}_{j=1}^{\infty} \subset E$ such that

$$\lim_{j \to \infty} \int_{\mathbb{R}^n} f_j(x) \mathrm{d}\mu(x) = M.$$

Next, setting

$$g_j(x) := \max_{1 \le k \le j} f_k(x), \quad x \in \mathbb{R}^n,$$

one can conclude that $g_j \in E$ and

$$\int_X g_j(x) \mathrm{d}\mu(x) \le \Phi(X)$$

for any measurable set $X \subset \mathbb{R}^n$. Indeed, let us represent $X$ as

$$X = \bigcup_{k=1}^{j} X_k, \quad X_k \cap X_l = \emptyset, k \ne l,$$

and for all $x \in X_k$ it holds that $g_j(x) = f_k(x)$. Then

$$\int_X g_j(x) \mathrm{d}\mu(x) = \sum_{k=1}^{j} \int_{X_k} f_k(x) \mathrm{d}\mu(x) \le \sum_{k=1}^{j} \Phi(X_k) = \Phi(X).$$

Setting

$$f(x) := \sup_j f_j(x), \quad x \in \mathbb{R}^n,$$

we obtain

$$f(x) = \lim_{j \to \infty} g_j(x)$$

and due to Theorem 16.81 (B. Levi)

$$\int_{\mathbb{R}^n} f(x) \mathrm{d}\mu(x) = \lim_{j \to \infty} \int_{\mathbb{R}^n} g_j(x) \mathrm{d}\mu(x) = M.$$

Our task is to show actually that

$$\Phi(X) = \int_X f(x) \mathrm{d}\mu(x), \quad X \subset \mathbb{R}^n.$$

In order to prove this we introduce a function of sets $\lambda$ as follows:

$$\lambda(X) := \Phi(X) - \int_X f(x) \mathrm{d}\mu(x).$$

This function of sets is nonnegative and absolutely continuous with respect to $\mu$. If $\lambda(X) \not\equiv 0$ then there is $\varepsilon_0 > 0$ and measurable set $A$ with $\mu(A) > 0$ such that

$$\varepsilon_0 \mu(X \cap A) \le \lambda(X \cap A)$$

for any measurable $X \subset \mathbb{R}^n$. Next, for the function $h(x) := f(x) + \varepsilon_0 \chi_A(x)$ we have

$$\int_X h(x)\mathrm{d}\mu(x) = \int_X f(x)\mathrm{d}\mu(x) + \varepsilon_0\mu(X \cap A)$$
$$\leq \int_X f(x)\mathrm{d}\mu(x) + \lambda(X \cap A)$$
$$\leq \int_X f(x)\mathrm{d}\mu(x) + \Phi(X \cap A) - \int_{X \cap A} f(x)\mathrm{d}\mu(x)$$
$$\leq \int_{X \setminus A} f(x)\mathrm{d}\mu(x) + \Phi(X \cap A) \leq \Phi(X).$$

This means that $h \in E$. On the other hand,

$$\int_{\mathbb{R}^n} h(x)\mathrm{d}\mu(x) = \int_{\mathbb{R}^n} f(x)\mathrm{d}\mu(x) + \varepsilon_0\mu(A) > M.$$

But this contradicts the definition of constant $M$. This shows that $\lambda \equiv 0$ and

$$\Phi(X) = \int_X f(x)\mathrm{d}\mu(x).$$

It remains to show that the function $f$ is unique up to $\mu$-equivalency. If there are two functions $f_1$ and $f_2$ such that

$$\int_X f_1(x)\mathrm{d}\mu(x) = \int_X f_2(x)\mathrm{d}\mu(x) = \Phi(X)$$

for any measurable $X \subset \mathbb{R}^n$ then for any $k \in \mathbb{N}$ and $l \in \mathbb{N}$ the sets

$$A_k := \{x \in X : f_2(x) - f_1(x) > 1/k\}$$

and

$$B_l := \{x \in X : f_1(x) - f_2(x) > 1/l\}$$

satisfy

$$\mu(A_k) \leq k \int_{A_k} (f_2(x) - f_1(x))\mathrm{d}\mu(x) = 0$$

and

$$\mu(B_l) \leq l \int_{B_l} (f_1(x) - f_2(x))\mathrm{d}\mu(x) = 0.$$

But

$$\{x \in X : f_1(x) \neq f_2(x)\} = \left(\bigcup_{k=1}^{\infty} A_k\right) \cup \left(\bigcup_{l=1}^{\infty} B_l\right)$$

implies that $\mu(\{x \in X : f_1(x) \neq f_2(x)\}) = 0$, i.e., $f_1 = f_2$ a.e. on $X$. Thus, the theorem is completely proved.

**Remark 16.117.** Let $\Phi$ be an arbitrary (in terms of sign) real-valued $\sigma$-additive function of sets on $\mathbb{R}^n$. Then there exists a measurable set $I^+ \subset \mathbb{R}^n$ such that

$$\Phi(X \cap I^+) > 0, \quad \Phi(X \cap (\mathbb{R}^n \setminus I^+)) < 0$$

for any measurable set $X \subset \mathbb{R}^n$. The decomposition

$$\mathbb{R}^n = I^+ \cup (\mathbb{R}^n \setminus I^+)$$

is called the *Hahn decomposition*.

**Exercise 16.118.**     1. Prove the Hahn decomposition and its uniqueness up to $\Phi$-equivalency.

2. Prove that if $\lambda \not\equiv 0$ is an absolutely continuous (with respect to Lebesgue measure $\mu$) function of sets then there is $\varepsilon_0 > 0$ and measurable set $A$ with $\mu(A) > 0$ such that

$$\varepsilon_0 \mu(X \cap A) \leq \lambda(X \cap A)$$

for any measurable set $X \subset \mathbb{R}^n$.

The latter exercise allows us to introduce two functions of sets defined on measurable sets $X \subset \mathbb{R}^n$ with $\mu(X) < \infty$ such that

$$\Phi^+(X) := \Phi(X \cap I^+), \quad \Phi^-(X) := \Phi(X \cap (\mathbb{R}^n \setminus I^+)), \quad \Phi = \Phi^+ - \Phi^-.$$

As a consequence of this representation we obtain that the Radon–Nikodym theorem is valid for an arbitrary (in terms of sign) absolutely continuous function of sets.

The Radon–Nikodym theorem can be effectively applied in the Riesz theory on the representation of linear continuous functionals in Lebesgue spaces $L^p$.

A mapping $L : L^p(X) \to \mathbb{R}, 1 \leq p \leq \infty, \mu(X) \leq \infty$, is called a *linear functional* if

$$L(\alpha_1 f_1 + \alpha_2 f_2) = \alpha_1 L(f_1) + \alpha_2 L(f_2)$$

for every $f_1, f_2 \in L^p(X)$ and $\alpha_1, \alpha_2 \in \mathbb{R}$. A linear functional $L$ is said to be *bounded* (*continuous*) if there is a constant $M \geq 0$ such that

$$|L(f)| \leq M \|f\|_{L^p(X)}$$

for any $f \in L^p(X)$. The *norm* of $L$ is the smallest $M$ for which the bound above holds, i.e.,

$$\|L\|_{L^p \to \mathbb{R}} := \inf\{M : |L(f)| \leq M \|f\|_{L^p(X)}\} \equiv \sup_{\|f\|_{L^p(X)} \leq 1} |L(f)|.$$

The linear functional $L$ is *continuous* if and only if $L$ is bounded, i.e., $\|L\| < \infty$.

**Theorem 16.119 (Riesz representation theorem in $L^p$).**   *Let $1 \leq p < \infty$. Then for every bounded linear functional $L : L^p(X) \to \mathbb{R}, X \subset \mathbb{R}^n, \mu(X) \leq \infty$, there is a unique function $g \in L^{p'}(X), 1/p + 1/p' = 1$ such that*

$$L(f) = \int_X f(x)g(x)\mathrm{d}\mu(x)$$

*for every $f \in L^p(X)$. Moreover, $\|L\|_{L^p \to \mathbb{R}} = \|g\|_{L^{p'}(X)}$.*

***Proof.*** We assume first that $\mu(X) < \infty$. For any measurable $A \subset X$ we define

$$\Phi(A) := L(\chi_A).$$

Since we are assuming that $\mu(X) < \infty$, we have $\chi_A \in L^p(X)$, and thus $\Phi(A)$ is well-defined. Moreover, $\Phi(A)$ is a real-valued nonnegative $\sigma$-additive function of sets which is absolutely continuous with respect to $\mu$. Indeed, let $A$ and $B$ be disjoint measurable sets. Then $\chi_{A \cup B} = \chi_A + \chi_B$ and therefore $\Phi(A \cup B) = \Phi(A) + \Phi(B)$. If $\{A_j\}_{j=1}^\infty$ is an infinite family of measurable and mutually disjoint sets then setting

$$A := \bigcup_{j=1}^\infty A_j, \quad B_k := \bigcup_{j=1}^k A_j$$

we have

$$\|\chi_A - \chi_{B_k}\|_{L^p(X)}^p = \int_X |\chi_A(x) - \chi_{B_k}(x)|^p \mathrm{d}\mu(x) = \mu(A \setminus B_k) \to 0$$

as $k \to \infty$. This means that $\chi_{B_k} \to \chi_A$ in $L^p(X)$ and by continuity of $L$ we have that

$$\lim_{k \to \infty} L(\chi_{B_k}) = L(\chi_A)$$

and consequently

$$\lim_{k \to \infty} \sum_{j=1}^k \Phi(A_j) = \Phi(A).$$

This shows that $\Phi$ is a $\sigma$-additive function of sets. The fact that $\Phi$ is absolutely continuous with respect to $\mu$ follows from the linearity of $L$ since if $\mu(A) = 0$ then $\chi_A = 0$ in $L^p(X)$ and therefore $\Phi(A) = L(\chi_A) = 0$. Applying Theorem 16.116 (Radon–Nikodym) we obtain that there exists $g \in L^1(X)$ such that

$$\Phi(A) = L(\chi_A) = \int_X \chi_A(x)g(x)\mathrm{d}\mu(x)$$

for every measurable set $A \subset X$. This proves the Riesz representation for characteristic functions. Therefore it holds for simple functions. Due to Theorem 16.111, every $f \in L^\infty(X)$ is a uniform limit of a sequence $\{f_j\}_{j=1}^\infty$ of simple functions and hence

$$\|f_j - f\|_{L^p(X)} \leq \|f_j - f\|_{L^\infty(X)} \, \mu(X) \to 0$$

and

$$|L(f_j) - L(f)| \leq \|L\|_{L^p \to \mathbb{R}} \|f_j - f\|_{L^p(X)} \to 0$$

as $j \to \infty$. On the other hand,

$$\left| \int_X f_j(x)g(x)\mathrm{d}\mu(x) - \int_X f(x)g(x)\mathrm{d}\mu(x) \right| \leq \int_X |f_j(x) - f(x)||g(x)|\mathrm{d}\mu(x)$$

$$\leq \|f_j - f\|_{L^\infty(X)} \int_X |g(x)|\mathrm{d}\mu(x) \to 0$$

as $j \to \infty$. It implies that if $f \in L^\infty(X)$ then

$$L(f) = \lim_{j \to \infty} L(f_j) = \lim_{j \to \infty} \int_X f_j(x)\mathrm{d}\mu(x) = \int_X f(x)g(x)\mathrm{d}\mu(x).$$

This shows that the Riesz representation theorem holds for every $f \in L^\infty(X)$. It also follows that the function $g$ belongs to $L^{p'}(X), 1 \leq p < \infty, 1/p + 1/p' = 1$, and

$$\|g\|_{L^{p'}(X)} \leq \|L\|_{L^p \to \mathbb{R}}.$$

Indeed, let first $1 < p < \infty$ and let

$$A_j := \{x \in X : |g(x)| \leq j\}, \quad f := \chi_{A_j}|g|^{p'-1} \operatorname{sgn} g.$$

Then $f \in L^\infty(X), |f|^p = |g|^{p'}$ on $A_j$ and

$$\int_{A_j} |g(x)|^{p'} \mathrm{d}\mu(x) = \int_{A_j} f(x)g(x)\mathrm{d}\mu(x) = L(f) \leq \|L\|_{L^p \to \mathbb{R}} \|f\|_{L^p(X)}$$

$$= \|L\|_{L^p \to \mathbb{R}} \|g\|_{L^{p'}(A_j)}^{p'/p}.$$

This implies that

$$\|g\|_{L^{p'}(A_j)}^{p'-p'/p} \leq \|L\|_{L^p(A_j)}$$

and letting $j \to \infty$ we get

$$\|g\|_{L^{p'}(X)} \leq \|L\|_{L^p \to \mathbb{R}}.$$

If now $p = 1$, i.e., $p' = \infty$, we introduce the set $A_j$ as follows:

$$A_j := \{x \in X : |g(x)| \geq \|L\|_{L^1 \to \mathbb{R}} + 1/j\}.$$

Then we have

$$\|L\|_{L^1 \to \mathbb{R}} \mu(A_j) = \|L\|_{L^1 \to \mathbb{R}} \|\chi_{A_j}\|_{L^1(X)} \geq |L(\chi_{A_j} \operatorname{sgn} g)|$$

$$= \left| \int_X \chi_{A_j}(x) g(x) \operatorname{sgn} g(x) \mathrm{d}\mu(x) \right| \geq (\|L\|_{L^1 \to \mathbb{R}} + 1/j) \mu(A_j)$$

for $j = 1, 2, \ldots$. This holds only if $\mu(A_j) = 0$. Thus,

$$\mu(\{x \in X : |g(x)| > \|L\|_{L^1 \to \mathbb{R}}\}) = \mu \left( \bigcup_{j=1}^{\infty} A_j \right) \leq \sum_{j=1}^{\infty} \mu(A_j) = 0,$$

i.e., $|g(x)| \leq \|L\|_{L^1 \to \mathbb{R}}$ a.e. on $X$ and

$$\|g\|_{L^\infty(X)} \leq \|L\|_{L^1 \to \mathbb{R}}.$$

Combining all these facts we conclude that $g \in L^{p'}(X), 1 \leq p < \infty$, and for every $f \in L^\infty(X)$ we have

$$L(f) = \int_X f(x) g(x) \mathrm{d}\mu(x),$$

where both sides of the equality are linear continuous functionals on $L^p(X)$ and they coincide on $L^\infty(X)$ which is dense in $L^p(X)$ since $\mu(X) < \infty$. This proves the Riesz representation theorem for $L^p(X), 1 \leq p < \infty, \mu(X) < \infty$, with the inequality

$$\|g\|_{L^{p'}(X)} \leq \|L\|_{L^p \to \mathbb{R}}.$$

We want to prove the equality in this inequality. Applying Hölder's inequality we get

$$|L(f)| \leq \|f\|_{L^p(X)} \|g\|_{L^{p'}(X)}.$$

Hence,

$$\|L\|_{L^p \to \mathbb{R}} \leq \|g\|_{L^{p'}(X)}$$

and the corresponding equality holds.

Now we consider the case $\mu(X) = \infty$. In this case $X$ can be represented as

$$X = \bigcup_{j=1}^{\infty} X_j,$$

where $X_j$ are measurable with $\mu(X_j) < \infty$. Let us define the function

$$w(x) := \sum_{j=1}^{\infty} w_j(x), \quad w_j(x) = \begin{cases} \frac{2^{-j}}{1+\mu(X_j)}, & x \in X_j, \\ 0, & x \in X \setminus X_j. \end{cases}$$

Then for all $x \in X$ it follows that $0 < w(x) < 1$ and $w \in L^1(X)$ since

$$0 < \int_X w(x)\mathrm{d}\mu(x) = \sum_{j=1}^{\infty} \int_{X_j} w(x)\mathrm{d}\mu(x) = \sum_{j=1}^{\infty} 2^{-j} \int_{X_j} \frac{\mathrm{d}\mu(x)}{1+\mu(X_j)}$$

$$= \sum_{j=1}^{\infty} 2^{-j} \frac{\mu(X_j)}{1+\mu(X_j)} < 1.$$

We define a function of sets as

$$\widetilde{\mu}(A) = \int_A w(x)\mathrm{d}\mu(x),$$

where $A \subset X$ is measurable. This function is a positive real-valued $\sigma$-additive absolutely continuous function of sets with $\widetilde{\mu}(A) < \infty$. We may consider this function as a new Lebesgue measure on $X \subset \mathbb{R}^n$. Next, let us consider a linear continuous functional $\widetilde{L}$ on $\widetilde{L}^p$ with respect to $\widetilde{\mu}, 1 \le p < \infty$, defined as

$$\widetilde{L}(\widetilde{f}) := L(w^{1/p}\widetilde{f}), \quad \widetilde{f} \in \widetilde{L}^p(X).$$

Repeating the previous proof of the Riesz representation but for functional $\widetilde{L}$ on $\widetilde{L}^p(X)$ we obtain that there is $\widetilde{g} \in \widetilde{L}^{p'}(X)$ such that

$$\widetilde{L}(\widetilde{f}) = \int_X \widetilde{f}(x)\widetilde{g}(x)\mathrm{d}\mu(x), \quad \widetilde{f} \in \widetilde{L}^p(X).$$

Setting $g(x) := w^{1/p'}(x)\widetilde{g}(x)$ for $1 < p < \infty$ and $g(x) := \widetilde{g}(x)$ for $p = 1$ we get

$$\left( \int_X |g(x)|^{p'}\mathrm{d}\mu(x) \right)^{1/p'} = \left( \int_X |\widetilde{g}(x)|^{p'} w(x)\mathrm{d}\mu(x) \right)^{1/p'}$$

$$= \left( \int_X |\widetilde{g}(x)|^{p'}\mathrm{d}\widetilde{\mu}(x) \right)^{1/p'} = \left\| \widetilde{L} \right\|_{\widetilde{L}^p \to \mathbb{R}} = \|L\|_{L^p \to \mathbb{R}}.$$

Finally, we have for every $f \in L^p(X)$ that

$$L(f) = \widetilde{L}(w^{-1/p}f) = \int_X w(x)^{-1/p}f(x)\widetilde{g}(x)\mathrm{d}\widetilde{\mu}(x)$$

$$= \int_X w(x)^{-1/p}f(x)w(x)^{-1/p'}g(x)\mathrm{d}\widetilde{\mu}(x) = \int_X f(x)g(x)\mathrm{d}\mu(x).$$

This finishes the proof.

**Remark 16.120.** Riesz representation theorem does not hold in $L^\infty(X)$. The reason is that not every linear continuous functional on $L^\infty(X)$ can be represented as the integral

$$\int_X f(x)g(x)\mathrm{d}\mu(x), \quad f \in L^\infty(X),$$

with some function $g \in L^1(X)$.

**Exercise 16.121.**     1. Construct an example which shows that the Riesz representation theorem fails for $L^\infty(X)$.

2. Prove that for every $g \in L^{p'}(X), 1/p + 1/p' = 1, 1 \le p \le \infty$, the functional

$$L(f) := \int_X f(x)g(x)\mathrm{d}\mu(x), \quad f \in L^p(X),$$

is a linear continuous functional on $L^p(X)$ with

$$\|L\|_{L^p \to \mathbb{R}} = \|g\|_{L^{p'}(X)}.$$

3. Prove that

$$\|f\|_{L^p(X)} = \sup_{\|g\|_{L^{p'}(X)} \le 1} \int_X f(x)g(x)\mathrm{d}\mu(x)$$

for $1 \le p < \infty$.

4. Let $L$ be a linear continuous functional on the space $C[a,b]$. Prove that there is a function $g \in V[a,b]$ such that

$$L(f) = \int_a^b f(x)\mathrm{d}g(x), \quad f \in C[a,b],$$

where the integral in the right-hand side is the Riemann–Stieltjes integral with respect to $g$. Prove also that

$$\|L\|_{C \to \mathbb{R}} = V_a^b(g).$$

5. Let $l^p, 1 \le p \le \infty$, denote the linear spaces defined as

$$l^p := \left\{ \{\alpha_j\}_{j=1}^\infty \subset \mathbb{R} : \sum_{j=1}^\infty |\alpha_j|^p < \infty \right\}, \quad \|\{\alpha_j\}_{j=1}^\infty\|_{l^p} = \left( \sum_{j=1}^\infty |\alpha_j|^p \right)^{1/p}$$

for $1 \le p < \infty$ and

$$l^\infty := \left\{ \{\alpha_j\}_{j=1}^\infty \subset \mathbb{R} : \sup_j |\alpha_j| < \infty \right\}, \quad \|\{\alpha_j\}_{j=1}^\infty\|_{l^\infty} = \sup_j |\alpha_j|.$$

Prove that any linear continuous functional $L$ in $l^p, 1 \le p < \infty$, has a form

$$L(\{\alpha_j\}_{j=1}^\infty) = \sum_{j=1}^\infty \alpha_j \beta_j,$$

where $\{\beta_j\}_{j=1}^\infty \subset l^{p'}$ and

$$\|L\|_{l^p \to \mathbb{R}} = \|\{\beta_j\}_{j=1}^\infty\|_{l^{p'}}.$$

## 16.6 ▪ Indefinite Lebesgue integral

This section is devoted mostly to the indefinite (with respect to upper or lower bounds) Lebesgue integral on the real line.

Let $f \in L^1[a, b]$. Then $f \in L^1[a, x]$ for any $x \in [a, b]$. Thus we may consider a new function

$$F(x) := \int_a^x f(t) \mathrm{d}\mu(t), \quad x \in [a, b].$$

If $f \geq 0$ then $F$ is a nondecreasing function. In the general case the function $F$ can be represented as the difference of two nondecreasing functions as

$$F(x) = \int_a^x f_+(t) \mathrm{d}\mu(t) - \int_a^x f_-(t) \mathrm{d}\mu(t), \quad x \in [a, b],$$

where we use the nonnegative functions $f_+ = (f + |f|)/2$ and $f_- = (|f| - f)/2$. This fact allows us to restrict the needed investigations to the case of nonnegative function $f$ and, respectively, to the case of nondecreasing function $F$.

We list some important properties of monotone functions:

1. Every monotone function on an interval $[a, b]$ is measurable and bounded and therefore belongs to $L^1[a, b]$.

2. Every monotone function has breakpoints only of the first kind and their number is at most countable (see Theorems 5.54 and 5.65), i.e., it is continuous a.e. on $[a, b]$.

3. Every monotone function which is continuous from the left can be uniquely represented as the sum of monotone continuous functions and the jump functions (see Exercise 5.66).

**Exercise 16.122.** Prove the latter three assertions.

The main fact concerning monotone functions is the following theorem.

**Theorem 16.123 (Lebesgue theorem of differentiability of monotone functions).** *Let $f$ : $[a, b] \to \mathbb{R}$ be monotone. Then $f$ has a finite derivative a.e. on $[a, b]$, i.e., $f$ is differentiable a.e. on $[a, b]$.*

*Proof.* Let us introduce the following four values which exist (but might be infinite) for any function $f$ at any point $x_0$:

$$\lambda_- := \varliminf_{\substack{x \to x_0 \\ x < x_0}} \frac{f(x) - f(x_0)}{x - x_0}, \quad \Lambda_- := \varlimsup_{\substack{x \to x_0 \\ x < x_0}} \frac{f(x) - f(x_0)}{x - x_0},$$

$$\lambda_+ := \varliminf_{\substack{x \to x_0 \\ x > x_0}} \frac{f(x) - f(x_0)}{x - x_0}, \quad \Lambda_+ := \varlimsup_{\substack{x \to x_0 \\ x > x_0}} \frac{f(x) - f(x_0)}{x - x_0}.$$

It is clear that always

$$\lambda_- \leq \Lambda_-, \quad \lambda_+ \leq \Lambda_+.$$

If $\lambda_- = \Lambda_-$ and $\lambda_+ = \Lambda_+$ then there exist the left and right derivatives of $f$ at $x_0$. Moreover, if

$$-\infty < \lambda_- = \Lambda_- = \lambda_+ = \Lambda_+ < \infty$$

then $f$ is differentiable at $x_0$. For proving the theorem we need to show that these equalities hold a.e. on $[a, b]$. In the proof of this result the following lemma of F. Riesz plays a very important role.

**Lemma 16.124 (Riesz).** *Let* $g : [a, b] \to \mathbb{R}$ *be continuous. Then the set of points* $\{x_0\}$ *invisible to the right, i.e., the set*

$$X_0 = \{x_0 \in [a, b] : \text{there is } \xi \in (x_0, b] \text{ such that } g(x_0) < g(\xi)\},$$

*is open. Moreover, this set is equal to*

$$X_0 = \bigcup_{j=1}^{\infty} (a_j, b_j), \quad (a_j, b_j) \cap (a_k, b_k) = \emptyset, j \neq k,$$

*and* $g(a_j) \leq g(b_j)$ *for* $j = 1, 2, \dots$ *. It may happen that the first interval is* $[a_1, b_1)$.

*Proof.* The fact that $X_0$ is open follows from the continuity of $g$ (see Theorem 5.49). Thus, $X_0$ can be represented as the union of open intervals (see Proposition 16.13) as

$$X_0 = \bigcup_{j=1}^{\infty} (a_j, b_j),$$

where $(a_j, b_j)$ are mutually disjoint. It may only happen that the first interval is equal to $[a_1, b_1)$ with $a_1 = a$. So it only remains to show that $g(a_j) \leq g(b_j)$ for $j = 1, 2, \dots$. Let us assume on the contrary that $g(a_j) > g(b_j)$ for some $j$. Then there is $x_0^{(j)} \in (a_j, b_j)$ with $g(x_0^{(j)}) > g(b_j)$ as well due to continuity of $g$. Let

$$x_0^* = \sup x_0^{(j)},$$

where the supremum is taken with respect to all such points and for which $g(x_0^*) = g(x_0^{(j)})$. Next, there is $\xi > x_0^*$ such that $g(\xi) > g(x_0^*)$ and $\xi \notin (a_j, b_j)$. But $\xi > b_j$ is impossible also since otherwise

$$g(b_j) < g(x_0^*) < g(\xi), \quad b_j \notin X_0,$$

and $b_j$ is not a point invisible to the right. This contradiction proves the lemma. $\blacksquare$

**Remark 16.125.** Similarly, a point $x_0 \in (a, b)$ is called *invisible to the left* if there is a point $\xi \in [a, b)$ such that $\xi < x_0$ with $g(\xi) > g(x_0)$. In that case the Riesz lemma is also valid with $g(a_j) \geq g(b_j), j = 1, 2, \dots$ (see the representation for $X_0$).

We will continue the proof of Lebesgue's theorem with continuous nondecreasing function $f$. In order to prove this theorem in that case it suffices to show that a.e. on $[a, b]$ it holds that

$$\Lambda_+ < \infty, \quad \lambda_- \geq \Lambda_+$$

since $\Lambda_- \leq \lambda_+$ for the nondecreasing function. Then we obtain the inequalities

$$\Lambda_+ \leq \lambda_- \leq \Lambda_- \leq \lambda_+ \leq \Lambda_+$$

which imply the needed equalities a.e. on $[a, b]$. We first show that $\Lambda_+ < \infty$ a.e. on $[a, b]$. Indeed, if on the contrary $\Lambda_+ = \infty$ at some point $x_0$ then for any $M > 0$ there exists $\xi > x_0$ such that

$$\frac{f(\xi) - f(x_0)}{\xi - x_0} > M,$$

i.e.,

$$f(\xi) - M\xi > f(x_0) - Mx_0.$$

In other words, the point $x_0$ is invisible to the right for the function $g(x) = f(x) - Mx$. By the Riesz lemma the set of all such points is open and for each $j = 1, 2, \ldots$ we have (see the representation for $X_0$)

$$g(a_j) \le g(b_j)$$

or

$$f(b_j) - f(a_j) \ge M(b_j - a_j).$$

It follows that

$$\sum_{j=1}^{\infty}(b_j - a_j) \le \sum_{j=1}^{\infty}\frac{f(b_j) - f(a_j)}{M} \le \frac{f(b) - f(a)}{M}.$$

Since $M$ is arbitrary (large), this inequality implies that the set of such points is of measure zero, i.e., $\Lambda_+ < \infty$ a.e. on $[a, b]$. The same technique can be applied to prove that $\lambda_- \ge \Lambda_+$ a.e. on $[a, b]$. Indeed, let $m$ and $M$ be two rational numbers with $0 < m < M < \infty$ and let $E_{mM}$ denote the set of all points $x \in [a, b]$ for which $\Lambda_+ > M$ and $\lambda_- < m$. It suffices to show that $\mu(E_{mM}) = 0$ since the set of points where $\lambda_- < \Lambda_+$ is represented as the union of not more than countable sets $E_{mM}$. We use the following lemma.

**Lemma 16.126.** *For any interval $(\alpha, \beta) \subset [a, b]$ it holds that*

$$\mu(E_{mM} \cap (\alpha, \beta)) \le \frac{m}{M}(\beta - \alpha).$$

*Proof.* Let $x \in (\alpha, \beta)$ and $\lambda_- < m$. Then there exists $\xi < x$ such that

$$\frac{f(\xi) - f(x)}{\xi - x} < m$$

or

$$f(\xi) - m\xi > f(x) - mx,$$

i.e., this $x$ is invisible to the left for the function $f(x) - mx$. By the Riesz lemma the set of all such $x$ is open and is represented as the union (not more than countable) of mutually disjoint open intervals $(\alpha_k, \beta_k)$ and

$$f(\beta_k) - f(\alpha_k) \le m(\beta_k - \alpha_k).$$

On each interval $(\alpha_k, \beta_k)$ consider the set of all points for which $\Lambda_+ > M$. Applying again the Riesz lemma we get that this set (as the set of points invisible to the right) is represented as the union of not more than countable mutually disjoint open intervals $(\alpha_k^{(j)}, \beta_k^{(j)}), j = 1, 2, \ldots$, with

$$\beta_k^{(j)} - \alpha_k^{(j)} \le \frac{1}{M}(f(\beta_k^{(j)}) - f(\alpha_k^{(j)})).$$

We conclude that the set $E_{mM} \cap (\alpha, \beta)$ is covered by the family of intervals $(\alpha_k^{(j)}, \beta_k^{(j)}), k = 1, 2, \ldots, j = 1, 2, \ldots$, such that

$$\sum_{k=1}^{\infty}\sum_{j=1}^{\infty}(\beta_k^{(j)} - \alpha_k^{(j)}) \le \frac{1}{M}\sum_{k,j=1}^{\infty}(f(\beta_k^{(j)}) - f(\alpha_k^{(j)})) \le \frac{m}{M}\sum_{k=1}^{\infty}(\beta_k - \alpha_k) \le \frac{m}{M}(\beta - \alpha).$$

Now we show that $\mu(E_{mM}) = 0$. Indeed, let $\mu(E_{mM}) = t$. Then for any $\varepsilon > 0$ there exists an open set $G = \cup_{l=1}^{\infty}(a_l, b_l)$, where $\{(a_l, b_l)\}_{l=1}^{\infty}$ are mutually disjoint such that

$$E_{mM} \subset G, \quad \sum_{l=1}^{\infty}(b_l - a_l) < t + \varepsilon.$$

Hence,

$$t = \mu(E_{mM}) \leq \frac{m}{M} \sum_{l=1}^{\infty} (b_l - a_l) < \frac{m}{M}(t + \varepsilon).$$

Due to the arbitrariness of $\varepsilon > 0$ we get that

$$t \leq \frac{m}{M} t, \quad 0 < \frac{m}{M} < 1,$$

This implies that $t = 0$. Thus Lemma 16.126 is proved for the nondecreasing continuous function. For monotone but not necessarily continuous functions we take into account that such functions have breakpoints only of the first kind. In that case the Riesz lemma might be generalized in terms of definition of the points $x$ invisible to the right as

$$\max(g(x_0 - 0), g(x_0), g(x_0 + 0)) < g(\xi).$$

For the nondecreasing function it reduces to the inequality

$$g(x_0 + 0) < g(\xi).$$

Lemma 16.126 and thus Theorem 16.123 are completely proved now.

**Corollary 16.127.** *Let $\{F_j\}_{j=1}^{\infty}$ be a sequence of nondecreasing functions on the interval $[a, b]$ and let the series*

$$\sum_{j=1}^{\infty} F_j(x) =: F(x)$$

*converge pointwise on the interval $[a, b]$. Then this series allows termwise differentiation a.e. on $[a, b]$ and*

$$F'(x) = \sum_{j=1}^{\infty} F_j'(x)$$

*a.e. on $[a, b]$.*

**Proof.** We may assume without loss of generality that $F_j(x) \geq 0$ and $F_j(a) = 0$ for all $j = 1, 2, \ldots$ (otherwise we can put $\widetilde{F}_j(x) := F_j(x) - F_j(a)$). Theorem 16.123 gives that $F_j'$ and $F'$ exist a.e. on $[a, b]$. Let $\xi \in [a, b]$ and let $x$ be such that the derivatives $F_j'(x)$ and $F'(x)$ exist. Then for any $N \in \mathbb{N}$ we have that

$$\sum_{j=1}^{N} \frac{F_j(\xi) - F_j(x)}{\xi - x} \leq \frac{F(\xi) - F(x)}{\xi - x}.$$

Letting $\xi \to x$ we obtain

$$\sum_{j=1}^{N} F_j'(x) \leq F'(x).$$

Since $F_j'(x) \geq 0$,

$$\sum_{j=1}^{\infty} F_j'(x) \leq F'(x).$$

Hence the series

$$\sum_{j=1}^{\infty} F_j'(x)$$

converges a.e. on $[a, b]$. It remains to show that actually we have equality in the latter inequality a.e. on $[a, b]$. Since $F(b) = \sum_{j=1}^{\infty} F_j(b)$, for any $k \in \mathbb{N}$ there is $N_k \in \mathbb{N}$ such that

$$0 \leq F(b) - \sum_{j=1}^{N_k} F_j(b) < 1/2^k.$$

Due to monotonicity of $F_j$ we obtain

$$0 \leq F(x) - \sum_{j=1}^{N_k} F_j(x) < 1/2^k$$

for all $x \in [a, b]$. This implies that the series

$$\sum_{k=1}^{\infty} \left( F(x) - \sum_{j=1}^{N_k} F_j(x) \right)$$

converges pointwise on $[a, b]$ (even uniformly). Thus, as proved above, this series allows termwise differentiation such that the series

$$\sum_{k=1}^{\infty} \left( F'(x) - \sum_{j=1}^{N_k} F_j'(x) \right)$$

converges a.e. on $[a, b]$. Using now the necessary condition of convergence of any series we may conclude that

$$\lim_{k \to \infty} \left( F'(x) - \sum_{j=1}^{N_k} F_j'(x) \right) = 0$$

or

$$F'(x) = \sum_{j=1}^{\infty} F_j'(x)$$

a.e. on $[a, b]$. This finishes the proof.

**Remark 16.128.** As a consequence of this theorem we obtain that the jump function (see Exercise 5.66) has a derivative which is equal to zero a.e.

The next nontrivial result concerns the differentiation of the indefinite Lebesgue integral as a function of the upper bound.

**Theorem 16.129 (Reconstruction of the integrand).** *Let $f \in L^1[a, b]$ be real-valued. Then*

$$\frac{\mathrm{d}}{\mathrm{d}x} \int_a^x f(t)\mathrm{d}\mu(t) = f(x)$$

*a.e. on $[a, b]$.*

**Proof.** Since

$$F(x) := \int_a^x f(t)\mathrm{d}\mu(t)$$

can be represented as the difference of two nondecreasing functions, Theorem 16.123 gives that $F'(x)$ exists a.e. on $[a, b]$. It remains only to show that $F'(x) = f(x)$ a.e. on $[a, b]$. Let us show first that $F'(x) \leq f(x)$ a.e. on $[a, b]$. If $f(x) < F'(x)$ then there are rational numbers $\alpha < \beta$ such that

$$f(x) < \alpha < \beta < F'(x).$$

Denoting by $E_{\alpha\beta}$ the set of all such values $x \in [a, b]$ we obtain that this set is measurable. Due to absolute continuity of the Lebesgue integral (see Theorem 16.66) for any $\varepsilon > 0$ there is $\delta > 0$ such that

$$\left| \int_X f(t)\mathrm{d}\mu(t) \right| < \varepsilon$$

for any measurable set $X \subset [a, b]$ with $\mu(X) < \delta$. For this $\delta > 0$ we may find an open set $G \subset [a, b]$ such that

$$E_{\alpha\beta} \subset G, \quad \mu(G) < \mu(E_{\alpha\beta}) + \delta$$

(see Theorem 16.16). If $x \in E_{\alpha\beta}$ then for all $\xi$ in the small neighborhood of $x$ and $\xi > x$ we have

$$F(\xi) - \beta\xi > F(x) - \beta x.$$

It means that $x$ is invisible to the right for the function $F(x) - \beta x$. By the Riesz lemma we may conclude that there exists an open set

$$S = \bigcup_{j=1}^{\infty} (a_j, b_j)$$

with mutually disjoint intervals such that

$$E_{\alpha\beta} \subset S \subset G, \quad F(b_j) - \beta b_j \geq F(a_j) - \beta a_j$$

or

$$\frac{1}{b_j - a_j} \int_{a_j}^{b_j} f(t)\mathrm{d}\mu(t) \geq \beta.$$

Summation over $j$ yields

$$\int_S f(t)\mathrm{d}\mu(t) \geq \beta\mu(S).$$

On the other hand

$$\int_S f(t)\mathrm{d}\mu(t) = \int_{E_{\alpha\beta}} f(t)\mathrm{d}\mu(t) + \int_{S \setminus E_{\alpha\beta}} f(t)\mathrm{d}\mu(t)$$
$$< \alpha\mu(E_{\alpha\beta}) + \varepsilon \leq \alpha\mu(S) + |\alpha|\delta + \varepsilon.$$

So

$$\mu(S) \leq \frac{\varepsilon + |\alpha|\delta}{\beta - \alpha}.$$

This implies that $\mu(S) = 0$ and therefore $\mu(E_{\alpha\beta}) = 0$ also and

$$f(x) \geq F'(x)$$

a.e. on $[a, b]$. The opposite inequality can be obtained by considering $-f$ instead of $f$. This proves the theorem.

We would like now to generalize the fundamental fact of Riemann integration, i.e., the Newton–Leibniz formula

$$\int_a^b F'(t)\mathrm{d}t = F(b) - F(a), \quad F' \in C[a,b],$$

to Lebesgue integration. To define the class $\{F\}$ of such functions we first show the following result.

**Theorem 16.130 (Integrability of the derivative of monotone function).** *Let $f : [a,b] \to \mathbb{R}$ be nondecreasing. Then $f' \in L^1[a,b]$ and*

$$\int_a^b f'(x)\mathrm{d}\mu(x) \le f(b) - f(a).$$

*Proof.* Let us consider the function

$$F_h(x) := \frac{f(x+h) - f(x)}{h}, \quad x, x+h \in [a,b], h \neq 0.$$

Since $f$ is nondecreasing on $[a,b]$, $f \in L^1[a,b]$ and therefore $F_h \in L^1[a,b]$ as well. Hence, we can write

$$\int_a^b F_h(x)\mathrm{d}\mu(x) = \frac{1}{h}\int_a^b f(x+h)\mathrm{d}\mu(x) - \frac{1}{h}\int_a^b f(x)\mathrm{d}\mu(x)$$

$$= \frac{1}{h}\int_b^{b+h} f(x)\mathrm{d}\mu(x) - \frac{1}{h}\int_a^{a+h} f(x)\mathrm{d}\mu(x),$$

where we have put $f(x) := f(a)$ for $x \le a$ and $f(x) := f(b)$ for $x \ge b$. This representation allows us to obtain

$$\lim_{h\to+0}\int_a^b F_h(x)\mathrm{d}\mu(x) = \lim_{h\to 0}\left(\frac{1}{h}\int_b^{b+h} f(x)\mathrm{d}\mu(x) - \frac{1}{h}\int_a^{a+h} f(x)\mathrm{d}\mu(x)\right)$$

$$= f(b) - f(a+0).$$

Applying now Fatou's lemma (Theorem 16.83) we get

$$\int_a^b f'(x)\mathrm{d}\mu(x) \le \lim_{h\to+0}\int_a^b F_h(x)\mathrm{d}\mu(x) = f(b) - f(a+0) \le f(b) - f(a).$$

It can be noted here that $f' \in L^1[a,b]$ follows also from Fatou's lemma. This concludes the proof.

**Example 16.131.** Consider the function

$$f(x) = \begin{cases} 0, & 0 \le x \le 1/2, \\ 1, & 1/2 < x \le 1. \end{cases}$$

Then $f'(x) = 0$ a.e. on $[0,1]$ and

$$\int_0^1 f'(x)\mathrm{d}\mu(x) = 0 < 1 = f(1) - f(0).$$

The latter example and theorem show that the class of all monotone functions is too wide for the Newton–Leibniz formula to hold.

**Exercise 16.132.** Let $f : [a, b] \to \mathbb{R}$ be monotone. Prove that

$$\int_a^b f'(t) \mathrm{d}\mu(t) = f(b) - f(a)$$

implies

$$\int_a^x f'(t) \mathrm{d}\mu(t) = f(x) - f(a)$$

a.e. on $[a, b]$.

**Definition 16.133.** *A function $f : [a, b] \to \mathbb{R}$ is called* absolutely continuous *on $[a, b]$ if for any $\varepsilon > 0$ there is $\delta > 0$ such that*

$$\sum_{j=1}^N |f(b_j) - f(a_j)| < \varepsilon$$

*for any family of mutually disjoint open intervals $\{(a_j, b_j)\}_{j=1}^N, N \leq \infty$, from $[a, b]$ with $\sum_{j=1}^N (b_j - a_j) < \delta$.*

It is clear that any absolutely continuous function is of bounded variation (see Definition 5.67) and uniformly continuous (see Definition 5.84). The converse is not true for either of these two statements. The collection of all absolutely continuous functions forms a linear subspace in the space of all functions of bounded variation. Therefore any real-valued absolutely continuous function can be represented as the difference of two nondecreasing functions (see Corollary 5.69).

The next theorem is probably the most important result of Lebesgue integration on the real line.

**Theorem 16.134 (Lebesgue theorem of reconstruction of absolutely continuous function).** *Let $F : [a, b] \to \mathbb{R}$ be absolutely continuous. Then $F' \in L^1[a, b]$ and*

$$\int_a^x F'(t) \mathrm{d}\mu(t) = F(x) - F(a)$$

*for any $x \in [a, b]$.*

**Proof.** Let us prove first that if $g \in L^1[a, b]$ then

$$G(x) := \int_a^x g(t) \mathrm{d}\mu(t)$$

is absolutely continuous. Let $\{(a_j, b_j)\}_{j=1}^N$ be a family of mutually disjoint open intervals from $[a, b]$. Then

$$\sum_{j=1}^N |G(b_j) - G(a_j)| = \sum_{j=1}^N \left| \int_{a_j}^{b_j} g(t) \mathrm{d}\mu(t) \right|$$

$$\leq \sum_{j=1}^N \int_{a_j}^{b_j} |g(t)| \, \mathrm{d}\mu(t) = \int_{\cup_{j=1}^N (a_j, b_j)} |g(t)| \, \mathrm{d}\mu(t).$$

Since the Lebesgue integral is absolutely continuous, for any $\varepsilon > 0$ there is $\delta > 0$ such that

$$\int_{\cup_{j=1}^N (a_j,b_j)} |g(t)| \, \mathrm{d}\mu(t) < \varepsilon$$

if $\sum_{j=1}^N (b_j - a_j) < \delta$.

We need also the following lemma, which has independent interest.

**Lemma 16.135.** *Let $f : [a,b] \to \mathbb{R}$ be nondecreasing. If $f' = 0$ a.e. on $[a,b]$ then $f \equiv constant$.*

**Proof.** The interval $[a,b]$ can be written as the union

$$[a,b] = \{x \in [a,b] : f'(x) = 0\} \cup Z,$$

where $\mu(Z) = 0$. Since $f$ is absolutely continuous, for any $\varepsilon > 0$ there is $\delta > 0$ such that Definition 16.133 is fulfilled. Let us cover the set $Z$ by a family $\{(a_j, b_j)\}_{j=1}^{\infty}$ of mutually disjoint intervals such that

$$\sum_{j=1}^{\infty} (b_j - a_j) < \delta.$$

By the choice of $\delta > 0$ we have

$$\sum_{j=1}^{\infty} |f(b_j) - f(a_j)| < \varepsilon.$$

This fact can be interpreted such that $\mu(f(Z)) = 0$, i.e., the image of $Z$ under the mapping $f$ has measure zero. Consider now any point $x_0 \in [a,b] \setminus Z$. Since $f'(x_0) = 0$, for $x > x_0$ and $x$ from a small neighborhood of $x_0$ we have

$$0 \le \frac{f(x) - f(x_0)}{x - x_0} < \varepsilon$$

or $0 \le f(x) - f(x_0) < \varepsilon(x - x_0)$. So $x_0$ is invisible to the right for the function $g(x) = \varepsilon x - f(x)$. By the Riesz lemma the set $[a,b] \setminus Z$ is contained in the family $\{(\alpha_k, \beta_k)\}_{k=1}^{\infty}$ of mutually disjoint intervals with

$$\varepsilon \beta_k - f(\beta_k) \ge \varepsilon \alpha_k - f(\alpha_k).$$

It follows that

$$\sum_{k=1}^{\infty} (f(\beta_k) - f(\alpha_k)) \le \varepsilon \sum_{k=1}^{\infty} (\beta_k - \alpha_k) \le \varepsilon(b - a).$$

In other words the image $f([a,b] \setminus Z)$ has measure zero. Hence $f(Z)$ and $f([a,b] \setminus Z)$ both have measure zero. But

$$f([a,b]) = f(Z) \cup f([a,b] \setminus Z) = [f(a), f(b)]$$

since $f$ is nondecreasing. Thus the length of this interval is equal to zero and therefore $f \equiv$ constant on $[a,b]$.

To end the proof of the theorem it suffices to consider the case when the function $F$ is nondecreasing. In that case the function

$$\Phi(x) := F(x) - \int_a^x F'(t) \mathrm{d}\mu(t)$$

is also nondecreasing (see Theorem 16.130). Moreover, $\Phi$ is absolutely continuous as the difference of two absolutely continuous functions and $\Phi'(x) = 0$ a.e. on $[a, b]$ (see Theorem 16.129). Hence the lemma above gives that $\Phi \equiv$ constant a.e. on $[a, b]$ and this constant is obviously equal to $F(a)$. This finishes the proof.

Since any function $f$ of bounded variation is equal to the sum of continuous function $v$ of bounded variation and the jump function $h$ such that

$$f(x) = v(x) + h(x), \quad x \in [a, b],$$

we have that $f'(x) = v'(x)$ a.e. on $[a, b]$. If we consider any continuous function $F$ of bounded variation then setting

$$\Psi(x) := \int_a^x F'(t)\mathrm{d}\mu(t)$$

we obtain that the difference

$$G(x) := F(x) - \Psi(x)$$

is also a continuous function of bounded variation which has the derivative

$$G'(x) = F'(x) - F'(x) = 0$$

a.e. on $[a, b]$. It does not follow from here that $G \equiv$ constant (compare with Theorem 16.134 and Lemma therein). The reason is that $F$ is not necessarily absolutely continuous.

**Definition 16.136.** *Let $G : [a, b] \to \mathbb{R}$ be continuous and of bounded variation. If $G' = 0$ a.e. on $[a, b]$ then $G$ is said to be* singular.

**Proposition 16.137.** *Every function $f : [a, b] \to \mathbb{R}$ of bounded variation can be represented as the sum*

$$f(x) = h(x) + \Psi(x) + G(x), \quad x \in [a, b],$$

*where $h$ is the jump function, $\Psi$ is absolutely continuous, and $G$ is singular.*

*Proof.* Since $f$ is of bounded variation,

$$f(x) = h(x) + v(x), \quad x \in [a, b],$$

where $h$ is the jump function and $v$ is a continuous function of bounded variation. In turn $v$ is equal to

$$v(x) = \int_a^x v'(t)\mathrm{d}\mu(t) + G(x), \quad x \in [a, b],$$

where

$$\Psi(x) = \int_a^x v'(t)\mathrm{d}\mu(t)$$

is absolutely continuous (see Theorem 16.134) and $G$ is singular (in general).

**Remark 16.138.** The latter proposition shows that

$$f'(x) = \Psi'(x)$$

a.e. on $[a, b]$, i.e., when integrating the derivative of a function $f$ of bounded variation one can recover not the function $f$ itself but only its absolutely continuous component $\Psi$. Two other components $h$ and $G$ disappear.

**Exercise 16.139.**     1. Prove that the representation from the latter proposition

$$f = h + \Psi + G$$

is unique if we require that any two functions of the three are equal to zero at the point $x = a$.

2. Prove that $f : [a, b] \to \mathbb{R}$ is absolutely continuous if and only if it transfers a set $X \subset [a, b]$ of measure zero to the set $Y := f(X)$ of measure zero also.

3. Let $f \in L^1[a, b]$. Prove that

$$V_a^b(F) = \int_a^b |f(t)| \mathrm{d}\mu(t),$$

where $F(x) = \int_a^x f(t) \mathrm{d}\mu(t)$.

4. Does the function

$$f(x) = \begin{cases} x^{3/2} \sin \frac{1}{x}, & x \in (0, 1], \\ 0, & x = 0, \end{cases}$$

satisfy Theorem 16.134? Justify your answer.

Absolutely continuous functions and linear continuous (bounded) functionals allow one to introduce generalized derivatives first introduced by S. L. Sobolev and then by L. Schwartz.

**Definition 16.140.** *Let $f : \mathbb{R} \to \mathbb{R}$ be* locally integrable, *i.e., $f \in L^1[a, b]$ for any finite interval $[a, b]$. Let*

$$L_{f_1}(\varphi) = - \int_{-\infty}^{\infty} f(x) \varphi'(x) \mathrm{d}\mu(x),$$

*where $L_{f_1}$ is a linear bounded functional defined for any $\varphi \in C_0^{\infty}(\mathbb{R})$, i.e., for any infinitely many times differentiable function of compact support. Then a function $f_1$, which defines the functional $L_{f_1}$ such that*

$$\int_{-\infty}^{\infty} f_1(x) \varphi(x) \mathrm{d}\mu(x) = L_{f_1}(\varphi),$$

*is called the* generalized derivative *of $f$.*

**Exercise 16.141.** Prove that

1. if $f$ is absolutely continuous then $f' = f_1$, where $f'$ is usual derivative,

2. if $f' = f_1$ then $f$ is equal a.e. to some absolutely continuous function,

3. if $f' = f_1$ and $f$ is continuous then $f$ is even absolutely continuous.

# Chapter 17

# Continuity in Banach spaces. Topological concepts

Most of the results in $\mathbb{R}^n$, $n \geq 1$, discussed earlier can be generalized to normed (Banach) spaces.

A linear space $X$ is called a *normed space* if there is a mapping

$$\|\cdot\| : X \to \mathbb{R}$$

such that $\|\cdot\|$ satisfies the conditions

1. for any $x \in X$ it follows that $\|x\| \geq 0$ and $\|x\| = 0$ if and only if $x = 0$,

2. for any $x \in X$ and for any $\lambda \in \mathbb{R}$ it follows that $\|\lambda x\| = |\lambda| \, \|x\|$,

3. for any $x, y \in X$ it follows that $\|x + y\| \leq \|x\| + \|y\|$ and this inequality is called the *triangle inequality*.

A linear space $X$ equipped with a norm $\|x\|$ is called a normed (linear) space.

A sequence $\{x_j\}_{j=1}^{\infty} \subset X$ is said to be convergent in $X$ if there exists $x \in X$ such that

$$\lim_{j \to \infty} \|x_j - x\| = 0.$$

A sequence $\{x_j\}_{j=1}^{\infty} \subset X$ is said to be a *Cauchy sequence* in $X$ if for any $\varepsilon > 0$ there exists $n_0 \in \mathbb{N}$ such that

$$\|x_j - x_k\| < \varepsilon$$

for all $j, k \geq n_0$.

**Definition 17.1.** *A normed space $X$ is called complete, or a* Banach space, *if every Cauchy sequence $\{x_j\}_{j=1}^{\infty} \subset X$ is convergent in $X$. A subset $Y$ of a Banach space $X$ is called closed if $\{x_j\}_{j=1}^{\infty} \subset X$ and $\lim_{j \to \infty} x_j = x$ imply $x \in Y$. A closed subset of a Banach space is also a Banach space.*

**Exercise 17.2.** Let $X$ be a normed space with norm $\|\cdot\|$ and let $\{x_j\}_{j=1}^{\infty} \subset X$ converge to $x \in X$. Prove that

$$\lim_{j \to \infty} \|x_j\| = \|x\|,$$

that is, the norm is continuous real-valued function.

**Exercise 17.3.** Let $\{x_j\}_{j=1}^{\infty}$ be a Cauchy sequence in a normed space $X$. Prove that $\{x_j\}_{j=1}^{\infty}$ is bounded, i.e., there is $M > 0$ such that $\|x_j\| \leq M$ for all $j \in \mathbb{N}$.

**Remark 17.4.**    1. A linear space $\mathbb{R}^n, n \geq 1$, is a Banach space with the Euclidean norm defined as

$$\|x\|_{\mathbb{R}^n} = \left( \sum_{j=1}^{n} |x_j|^2 \right)^{1/2}, \quad x = (x_1, x_2, \ldots, x_n) \in \mathbb{R}^n;$$

see Theorems 3.39 and 13.7.

2. A linear space $l^p, 1 \leq p \leq \infty$, of sequences $\{\alpha_j\}_{j=1}^{\infty} \subset \mathbb{R}$ (see Exercise 16.121) is a Banach space if the norm is defined as

$$\left\|\{\alpha_j\}_{j=1}^{\infty}\right\|_{l^p} = \left( \sum_{j=1}^{\infty} |\alpha_j|^p \right)^{1/p} < \infty, \quad 1 \leq p < \infty,$$

and

$$\left\|\{\alpha_j\}_{j=1}^{\infty}\right\|_{l^\infty} = \sup_j |\alpha_j|, \quad p = \infty.$$

3. A linear space $L^p(X), 1 \leq p \leq \infty, X \subset \mathbb{R}^n$, of measurable functions $f : X \to \mathbb{R}$ defined on measurable set $X$ is a Banach space if the norm is defined as

$$\|f\|_{L^p(X)} = \left( \int_X |f(x)|^p \mathrm{d}\mu(x) \right)^{1/p} < \infty, \quad 1 \leq p < \infty,$$

and

$$\|f\|_{L^\infty(X)} = \operatorname*{ess\,sup}_{x \in X} |f(x)| < \infty, \quad p = \infty,$$

where $\mu(x)$ is Lebesgue measure in $\mathbb{R}^n$ (see Theorems 16.97 and 16.107).

The set

$$B_R(x_0) = \{x \in X : \|x - x_0\| < R\}$$

is called the *open ball* of radius $R > 0$ and centered at $x_0 \in X$ in normed space $X$ and the set

$$S_R(x_0) = \{x \in X : \|x - x_0\| = R\}$$

is said to be the sphere of radius $R$ and centered at $x_0 \in X$. The set

$$\overline{B_R}(x_0) = B_R(x_0) \cup S_R(x_0)$$

is said to be the *closed ball*.

**Definition 17.5.** *Let $X$ be a normed space. A set $Y \subset X$ is said to be bounded in $X$ if there exists $M > 0$ such that $\|x\| \leq M$ for all $x \in Y$ and $Y$ is called* totally bounded *if for every $\varepsilon > 0$ there exists $m \in \mathbb{N}$ and points $x_1, x_2, \ldots, x_m \in Y$ with*

$$Y \subset \bigcup_{j=1}^{m} B_\varepsilon(x_j).$$

**Remark 17.6.** Each totally bounded set is bounded as the union of finitely many bounded balls. The converse is true for subsets of $\mathbb{R}^n$ with Euclidean norm but not in general. For example, in an infinite dimensional space $l^2$ the closed unit ball centered at $\{0\}$ would require an infinite number of balls of radius $\varepsilon < 1$ to cover points of the form $e_j = (0, 0, \ldots, 0, 1, 0, \ldots, 0), j = 1, 2, \ldots$, having 1 at the $j$ position.

**Definition 17.7.** *Let $X$ be a normed space. A point $x_0 \in Y \subset X$ is said to be an* internal point *of $Y$ if there is $B_\delta(x_0), \delta > 0$ such that $B_\delta(x_0) \subset Y$. A set $Y$ is said to be open in $X$ if any point $x \in Y$ is internal. The set of all internal points of $Y$ is denoted as* int $Y$.

**Definition 17.8.** *A point $x_0 \in Y \subset X$ is said to be a* limiting point *of $Y$ if for any $\delta > 0$, small enough, we have*

$$B'_\delta(x_0) \cap Y := \{x \in Y : 0 < \|x - x_0\| < \delta\} \cap Y \neq \emptyset.$$

*The set of all limiting points of $Y$ is denoted $Y'$ and $Y$ is said to be closed in $X$ if $Y' \subset Y$. The union $Y' \cup Y$ is called the* closure *of $Y$ and denoted by $\overline{Y} = Y' \cup Y$.*

**Exercise 17.9.** Define the boundary $\partial Y$ of $Y \subset X$. Prove that $\partial Y$ is closed in $X$ and $Y \setminus \partial Y$ is open. Hint: Use Definitions 12.23 and 12.24.

**Definition 17.10.** *A set $K$ of a normed space $X$ is said to be* compact *if for any open cover $\{G_\alpha\}_{\alpha \in I}$ of $K$, i.e.,*

$$K \subset \bigcup_{\alpha \in I} G_\alpha$$

*with each $G_\alpha$ open, there exists a finite subfamily $\{G_{\alpha_j}\}_{j=1}^m$ such that*

$$K \subset \bigcup_{j=1}^m G_{\alpha_j}, \quad \alpha_j \in I.$$

*A set $K$ is said to be* sequentially compact *if every sequence $\{x_j\}_{j=1}^\infty \subset K$ contains a subsequence which converges to some $x \in K$.*

**Theorem 17.11 (Heine–Borel theorem for normed spaces).** *Let $K$ be a subset of a normed space $X$. Then the following statements are equivalent:*

1. *$K$ is compact.*

2. *$K$ is sequentially compact.*

3. *$K$ is complete and totally bounded.*

*Proof.* The proof is almost the same as the proof of Theorem 13.10.

**Corollary 17.12.** *Every closed subset $Y$ of a compact set $K \subset X$ is compact.*

**Corollary 17.13.** *If $Y \subset X$ is totally bounded and complete then $Y$ contains a convergent sequence.*

**Remark 17.14.** Corollary 17.13 can be reformulated as follows: a set $Y$ in a normed space $X$ has the *Bolzano–Weierstrass property*, i.e., every sequence in $Y$ has a convergent subsequence in $Y$ if and only if $Y$ is compact in $X$.

**Definition 17.15.** *Let $X$ and $Y$ be normed spaces with norms $\|\cdot\|_X$ and $\|\cdot\|_Y$, respectively. A function $f : X \to Y$ is said to be* continuous *at $x_0 \in X$ if for every $\varepsilon > 0$ there is $\delta > 0$ such that for all $x \in X$ with $\|x - x_0\|_X < \delta$ it follows that $\|f(x) - f(x_0)\|_Y < \epsilon$, i.e.,*

$$\lim_{x \to x_0} f(x) = f(x_0).$$

*A function $f$ is said to be continuous on a subset $X_1 \subset X$ if it is continuous at every $x \in X_1$. A function $f$ is said to be* uniformly continuous *on $X_1 \subset X$ if for every $\varepsilon > 0$ there is $\delta > 0$ such that for $x', x'' \in X_1$ with $\|x' - x''\|_X < \delta$ it follows that $\|f(x') - f(x'')\|_Y < \varepsilon$.*

**Theorem 17.16 (Continuity in terms of preimages).** *Let $f : X \to Y$ be a function in the normed spaces $X$ and $Y$. The function $f$ is continuous on $X$ if and only if for every open set $G \subset Y$ its preimage*

$$f^{-1}(G) = \{x \in X : y = f(x), y \in G\}$$

*is open in $X$.*

***Proof.*** Let $f$ be continuous on $X$ on $X$, let $G \subset Y$ be open and let $x_0 \in f^{-1}(G)$. Since $G$ is open, there exists $\varepsilon > 0$ such that $B_\varepsilon(f(x_0)) \subset G$. Since $f$ is continuous, there exists $\delta > 0$ (for this $\varepsilon > 0$) with $\|f(x) - f(x_0)\|_Y < \varepsilon$ whenever $\|x - x_0\|_Y < \delta$. This means that for $x \in B_\delta(x_0)$ we have $f(x) \in B_\varepsilon(f(x_0)) \subset G$ and therefore $B_\delta(x_0) \subset f^{-1}(G)$. Hence $f^{-1}(G)$ is open.

Conversely, let $x_0 \in X$ and $\varepsilon > 0$. The neighborhood $B_\varepsilon(f(x_0))$ is open and by hypothesis its preimage $f^{-1}(B_\varepsilon(f(x_0)))$ is also open. Therefore there exists $\delta > 0$ with $B_\delta(x_0) \subset f^{-1}(B_\varepsilon(f(x_0)))$ so that $f(B_\delta(x_0)) \subset B_\varepsilon(f(x_0))$. But this fact is equivalent to $\|x - x_0\|_X < \delta$ implying $\|f(x) - f(x_0)\|_Y < \varepsilon$, i.e., $f$ is continuous.

**Remark 17.17.** The continuity of $f$ is not equivalent to the requirement that the image $f(U)$ of an open set $U \subset X$ is open in $Y$. An example of this is $f : \mathbb{R} \to \mathbb{R}, f(x) = |x|$. Here $f(-a, a) = [0, a), a > 0$, which is not open. But nevertheless the following theorem holds.

**Theorem 17.18 (Image of compact sets).** *Let $X$ and $Y$ be normed spaces, $K \subset X$ compact, and let $f : K \to Y$ be continuous. Then $f(K)$ is compact.*

***Proof.*** Let $\{U_\alpha\}_{\alpha \in I}$ be an open cover of $f(K)$. We set $G_\alpha := f^{-1}(U_\alpha), \alpha \in I$. By Theorem 17.16 we know that $G_\alpha$ is open. Moreover, the family $\{G_\alpha\}_{\alpha \in I}$ forms an open cover of $K$. Hence there exists a finite subcover $\{f^{-1}(G_{\alpha_j})\}_{j=1}^m$ of $K$. But then $f(K)$ is covered by the sets $\{f(U_{\alpha_j})\}_{j=1}^m \subset \{G_{\alpha_j}\}_{j=1}^m$. So, $\{U_{\alpha_j}\}_{j=1}^m$ is a finite subcover of $f(K)$. This proves the theorem.

**Corollary 17.19.** *If $f : K \subset X \to Y$ is continuous and $K$ is compact then $f(K)$ is totally bounded.*

We are now in position to formulate and prove the analogues of theorems for continuous functions in normed spaces.

**Theorem 17.20 (Arithmetic properties).**

1. *Let $X$ be a normed space and let $f, g : X \to \mathbb{R}$ be continuous. Then the functions*

$$f \pm g, \quad fg, \quad \max(f,g), \quad \min(f,g), \quad |f|$$

   *are continuous. If $g(x) \neq 0$ for all $x \in X$ then $f/g$ is continuous also.*

2. *Let $X, Y$ and $Z$ be normed spaces and let $f : X \to Y$ be continuous at $x_0 \in X$ and let $g : Y \to Z$ be continuous at $f(x_0) \in Y$. Then the superposition $\varphi = g \circ f$ is continuous at $x_0$.*

*Proof.* The proof is literally the same as the proof of Theorem 5.49.

**Theorem 17.21 (Continuity of uniformly convergent sequence of continuous functions).** *Let* $\{f_j\}_{j=1}^{\infty}, f_j : X \to Y$, *be a sequence of continuous functions in the normed spaces $X$ and $Y$. If $\{f_j\}_{j=1}^{\infty}$ converges uniformly to $f$ in $X$, i.e., for any $\varepsilon > 0$ there is $n_0 \in \mathbb{N}$ such that for all $x \in X$ and $j \geq n_0$ it follows that $\|f_j(x) - f(x)\| < \varepsilon$ then $f$ is also continuous on $X$.*

*Proof.* See Exercise 15.45.

**Theorem 17.22 (Weierstrass theorem for normed spaces).** *Let $K \subset X$ be compact in a normed space $X$ and let $f : X \to \mathbb{R}$ be continuous. Then $f$ assumes its maximum and minimum on $K$, i.e., there exist $x', x'' \in K$ such that $f(x') = \sup_{x \in K} f(x)$ and $f(x'') = \inf_{x \in K} f(x)$.*

*Proof.* We shall prove statement concerning maximum. Let $\{x_j\}_{j=1}^{\infty} \subset K$ be a sequence with

$$\lim_{j \to \infty} f(x_j) = \sup_{x \in K} f(x).$$

Let us note that this value is finite (see Theorem 17.18 and its corollary). Since $K$ is sequentially compact, the sequence $\{x_j\}_{j=1}^{\infty}$ converges after choosing a subsequence (if needed) to some $x' \in K$. Then continuity of $f$ implies that $f(x') = \lim_{j \to \infty} f(x_j) = \sup_{x \in K} f(x)$.

**Theorem 17.23 (Cantor's theorem for normed spaces).** *Let $K$ be compact in a normed space $X$. Let $Y$ be a normed space and let $f : K \to Y$ be continuous. Then $f$ is uniformly continuous on $K$.*

*Proof.* Let $\varepsilon > 0$. Then for every $x \in K$ there exists $\delta(x) > 0$ such that

$$f(B_{2\delta(x)}(x)) \subset B_{\varepsilon/2}(f(x)),$$

where the balls $B_{\delta(x)}$ and $B_{\varepsilon/2}$ are in normed spaces $X$ and $Y$, respectively. Next,

$$K \subset \bigcup_{x \in K} B_{\delta(x)}(x)$$

and since $K$ is compact then this open cover has a finite subcover, i.e., there exist $x_1, x_2, \ldots, x_m \in K$ such that

$$K \subset \bigcup_{j=1}^{m} B_{\delta(x_j)}(x_j).$$

Let $\delta = \min_{j=1,2,\ldots,m} \delta(x_j) > 0$. If $x', x'' \in K$ and $\|x' - x''\|_X < \delta$ then there exists $j_0 \in \{1, 2, \ldots, m\}$ with $x', x'' \in B_{2\delta}(x_{j_0})$. It implies that $f(x'), f(x'') \in B_{\varepsilon/2}(f(x_{j_0}))$ and therefore $\|f(x') - f(x'')\|_Y < \varepsilon$. This proves the theorem.

We want to consider linear maps (as a particular case of general mappings) between normed spaces, also called linear operators, and to apply them to the differentiability in normed spaces.

**Definition 17.24.** *Let $X$ and $Y$ be normed spaces and let $L : X \to Y$ be a* linear map, *i.e., a map for which*

$$L(\alpha x + \beta y) = \alpha L(x) + \beta L(y), \quad x, y \in X, \alpha, \beta \in \mathbb{R}.$$

*The map $L$ is called bounded if there exists $M \geq 0$ such that $\|L(x)\|_Y \leq M \|x\|_X$ for all $x \in X$.*

**Theorem 17.25 (Criterion of continuity for linear maps).** *Let $L : X \to Y$ be linear between normed spaces $X$ and $Y$. Then $L$ is continuous if and only if it is bounded.*

**Proof.** Let $L : X \to Y$ be bounded and let $\varepsilon > 0$. Then for $\delta = \varepsilon/M$ (assuming $M > 0$ since otherwise $L \equiv 0$) we have that for any $x', x'' \in X$ with $\|x' - x''\| < \delta$ it follows that

$$\|L(x') - L(x'')\|_Y = \|L(x' - x'')\|_Y \leq M \|x' - x''\|_X < \varepsilon.$$

Hence $L$ is even uniformly continuous.

Conversely, let $L : X \to Y$ be continuous. Since $L$ is, in particular, continuous at $\{0\}$, for $\varepsilon = 1$ there exists $\delta > 0$ such that $\|L(\xi)\|_Y < 1$ for all $\xi \in X$ with $\|\xi\|_X < \delta$. If we choose $M = 2/\delta > 0$ then for any $x \in X, x \neq 0$ and for $\xi = x/(M \|x\|_X)$ we have that $\|\xi\|_X < \delta$ (actually $\|\xi\|_X = \delta/2$) and $\|L(\xi)\|_Y < 1$. By the linearity of $L$ we get

$$\|L(x)\|_Y = \|M \|x\|_X L(\xi)\|_Y = M \|x\|_X \|L(\xi)\|_Y < M \|x\|_X.$$

This finishes the proof.

**Remark 17.26.** We showed even more than it was stated. Namely, $L$ is continuous at $\{0\}$ implies that it is bounded and this in turn implies that $L$ is uniformly continuous, i.e., the assumption that $L$ is linear is very essential here.

**Definition 17.27.** *Let $L : X \to Y$ be a continuous linear map between normed spaces. The norm $\|L\|_{X \to Y}$ of $L$ is defined by*

$$\|L\|_{X \to Y} = \sup_{\|x\|_X = 1} \|L(x)_Y\| = \sup_{\|x\|_X \leq 1} \|L(x)_Y\| = \sup_{x \neq 0} \frac{\|L(x)_Y\|}{\|x\|_X}.$$

**Exercise 17.28.** Prove the equivalence of these three definitions of the norm $\|L\|_{X \to Y}$.

**Definition 17.29.** *Let $X$ and $Y$ be normed spaces. We denote the space of all continuous linear maps $L : X \to Y$ by $B(X, Y)$ and equip it with the norm $\|\cdot\|_{X \to Y}$ from above.*

**Theorem 17.30 (Banach space of linear operators).** *Let $Y$ be a Banach space and let $X$ be a normed space. Then $B(X, Y)$ is a Banach space also.*

**Proof.** Let $\{L_j\}_{j=1}^{\infty} \subset B(X, Y)$ be a Cauchy sequence relative to $\|\cdot\|_{X \to Y}$, i.e., for any $\varepsilon > 0$ there exists $n_0 \in \mathbb{N}$ such that

$$\|L_k - L_j\|_{X \to Y} < \varepsilon$$

for any $k, j \geq n_0$. For any $x \in X$ and for any $k, j \geq n_0$ we have that

$$\|L_k(x) - L_j(x)\|_Y = \|(L_k - L_j)(x)\|_Y \leq \|L_k - L_j\|_{X \to Y} \|x\|_X < \varepsilon \|x\|_X.$$

Therefore, for each $x \in X$ the sequence $\{L_j(x)\}_{j=1}^{\infty}$ forms a Cauchy sequence in $Y$. Since $Y$ is a Banach space, this sequence has a limit which we shall denote by $L(x)$. This map $L$ is linear since for any $x, y \in X$ and $\alpha, \beta \in \mathbb{R}$, we have

$$\|L(\alpha x + \beta y) - \alpha L(x) - \beta L(y)\|_Y$$
$$\leq \|L(\alpha x + \beta y) - L_j(\alpha x + \beta y)\|_Y + \|\alpha L_j(x) - \alpha L(x)\|_Y + \|\beta L_j(x) - \beta L(x)\|_Y \to 0$$

as $j \to \infty$. Hence

$$L(\alpha x + \beta y) = \alpha L(x) + \beta L(y).$$

Moreover, $L_j$ also converges to $L$ in the norm of $B(X,Y)$. Indeed, let $\|x\|_X = 1$. Then

$$\|L(x) - L_j(x)\|_Y = \lim_{k \to \infty} \|L_k(x) - L_j(x)\|_Y \le \varepsilon,$$

i.e., $\sup_{\|x\|_X} \|L(x) - L_j(x)\|_Y \le \varepsilon$ for all $j \ge n_0$. In addition to this, $L$ is bounded due to

$$\|L(x)\|_Y \le \|(L - L_j)(x)\|_Y + \|L_j(x)\|_Y$$

if $j$ is fixed appropriately. Hence $L \in B(X,Y)$.

We insert here a very useful result about invertibility of linear maps between Banach spaces.

**Theorem 17.31 (Invertibility of linear maps).** *Let $L_0 : X \to Y$ be a bijective continuous linear map between Banach spaces $X$ and $Y$ with a continuous inverse $L_0^{-1}$. If $L \in B(X,Y)$ satisfies*

$$\|L - L_0\|_{X \to Y} < \|L_0^{-1}\|_{Y \to X}^{-1}$$

*then $L$ is also bijective with a continuous inverse.*

*Proof.* Since $L$ can be represented as

$$L = L_0(I - L_0^{-1}(L_0 - L)),$$

where $I$ is the identical operator in $X$, using the geometric series we have

$$L^{-1} = \left( \sum_{j=0}^{\infty} (L_0^{-1}(L_0 - L))^j \right) L_0^{-1}$$

if we can show that the latter series converges. Indeed, by the triangle inequality

$$\left\| \sum_{j=k}^{m} (L_0^{-1}(L_0 - L))^j \right\|_{X \to X} \le \sum_{j=k}^{m} \left\| (L_0^{-1}(L_0 - L))^j \right\|_{X \to X}$$

$$\le \sum_{j=k}^{m} \left( \|L_0^{-1}\|_{Y \to X} \|L_0 - L\|_{X \to Y} \right)^j \to 0$$

as $m, k \to \infty$ by hypothesis. This proves the theorem taking into account Theorem 17.30. $\qquad \blacksquare$

Linear maps allow us to introduce also the concept of differentiability for mappings between Banach spaces and get the elementary rules for differentiation.

**Definition 17.32.** *Let $X$ and $Y$ be Banach spaces, let $U \subset X$ be open, and let $f : U \to Y$ be a map. The map $f$ is said to be* differentiable *at $x_0 \in U$ if there is a continuous linear map $L : X \to Y$ such that*

$$\lim_{x \to x_0, x \ne x_0} \frac{\|f(x) - f(x_0) - L(x - x_0)\|_Y}{\|x - x_0\|_X} = 0.$$

*We denote $L = \partial f$ and say that $\partial f(x_0)$ is the* derivative *of $f$ at $x_0$. The map $f$ is said to be* differentiable in $U$ *if it is differentiable at every $x_0 \in U$.*

**Exercise 17.33.** Let $f$ be differentiable at $x_0 \in U$. Prove that $\partial f(x_0)$ is uniquely determined and $f$ is continuous at $x_0$.

**Exercise 17.34.** Let $f$ and $g$ be differentiable at $x_0 \in U$ and let $\alpha \in \mathbb{R}$. Prove that $f + g$ and $\alpha f$ are also differentiable at $x_0$ and

$$\partial(f + g)(x_0) = \partial f(x_0) + \partial g(x_0), \quad \partial(\alpha f)(x_0) = \alpha \partial f(x_0).$$

**Theorem 17.35 (Chain rule).** *Let $X$, $Y$, and $Z$ be Banach spaces. Let $U \subset X$ be open, $x_0 \in U$, and $f : U \to Y$ differentiable at $x_0$. Assume also that $\Omega \subset Y$ is open with $y_0 = f(x_0) \in \Omega$ and $g : \Omega \to Z$ is differentiable at $y_0$. Then the superposition $g \circ f$ is defined in an open neighborhood of $x_0$ and is differentiable at $x_0$ with*

$$\partial(g \circ f)(x_0) = \partial g(y_0)\partial f(x_0).$$

*Proof.* By Exercise 17.33 the map $f$ is continuous at $x_0$ and hence there exists an open ball $B_r(x_0) \subset U$ with $f(B_r(x_0)) \subset \Omega$. The function $g \circ f$ is then well-defined on $B_r(x_0)$. Now, for $x \in B_r(x_0)$ we have

$$\|g(f(x)) - g(f(x_0)) - \partial g(y_0)\partial f(x_0)(x - x_0)\|_Z$$
$$\leq \|g(f(x)) - g(f(x_0)) - \partial g(y_0)(f(x) - f(x_0))\|_Z$$
$$+ \|\partial g(y_0)(f(x) - f(x_0) - \partial f(x_0)(x - x_0))\|_Z.$$

For $\varepsilon > 0$ we choose $\eta > 0$ in such a way that for $\|y - y_0\|_Y < \eta$ we have

$$\|g(y) - g(y_0) - \partial g(y_0)(y - y_0)\|_Z \leq \frac{\varepsilon \|y - y_0\|_Y}{2(1 + \|\partial f(x_0)\|_Y)}.$$

This is possible since $g$ is differentiable at $y_0$. Next, we choose $\delta_1 > 0$ so that for $\|x - x_0\|_X < \delta_1$ we have

$$\|f(x) - f(x_0) - \partial f(x_0)(x - x_0)\|_Y \leq \frac{\varepsilon \|x - x_0\|_X}{2 \|\partial g(y_0)\|_Z}.$$

Finally, we choose $0 < \delta_2 < \frac{\eta}{1 + \|\partial f(x_0)\|_Y}$ in such a way that for $\|x - x_0\|_X < \delta_2$ we have

$$\|f(x) - f(x_0)\|_Y \leq (1 + \|\partial f(x_0)\|_Y) \|x - x_0\|_X.$$

This is possible since $f$ is differentiable at $x_0$. These choices guarantee that

$$\|f(x) - f(x_0)\|_Y < \eta.$$

We set $\delta = \min(\delta_1, \delta_2) > 0$. Then for $\|x - x_0\|_X < \delta$ we have, using the conditions above, that

$$\|g(f(x)) - g(f(x_0)) - \partial g(y_0)\partial f(x_0)(x - x_0)\|_Z \leq \varepsilon \|x - x_0\|_X.$$

As $\varepsilon > 0$ was arbitrary it follows that

$$\lim_{x \to x_0, x \neq x_0} \frac{\|g(f(x)) - g(f(x_0)) - \partial g(y_0)\partial f(x_0)(x - x_0)\|_Z}{\|x - x_0\|_X} = 0.$$

This proves the theorem.

**Exercise 17.36.** Let $X$ and $Y$ be Banach spaces and $x, y \in X$. Denote the line joining $x$ and $y$ as $S = \{x + t(y - x) : 0 \le t \le 1\}$. Assume that $U$ is an open neighborhood of $S$ and that $f : U \to Y$ is continuous and differentiable at every point of $S$ with

$$\|\partial f(z)\|_Y \le M, \quad z \in S.$$

Prove that

$$\|f(x) - f(y)\|_Y \le M \|x - y\|_X.$$

Hint: Consider the superposition

$$g(t) = f(x + t(y - x)), \quad t \in [0, 1].$$

**Exercise 17.37.** Let $f_p : \mathbb{R}^n \to \mathbb{R}$ be the map

$$f_p(x) = \left( \sum_{j=1}^{n} |x_j|^p \right)^{1/p}, \quad p = 1, 2.$$

Where are these functions differentiable? Calculate the derivatives whenever they exist.

There is a very efficient application of the abstract Banach fixed point theorem to nonlinear differential equations. Let us first formulate this theorem in Banach spaces (compare with Theorems 11.4 and 11.5).

**Theorem 17.38 (Banach fixed point theorem).** *Let $A$ be a closed subspace of a Banach space $X$ and let $F : A \to A$ satisfy*

$$\|F(x_1) - F(x_2)\|_X \le q \|x_1 - x_2\|_X$$

*for all $x_1, x_2 \in A$ and for fixed $0 \le q < 1$. This condition is called the* contraction principle. *Then there is a unique $\xi \in A$ such that $F(\xi) = \xi$.*

*Proof.* The proof is exactly the same as that of Theorem 11.4. One can only mention that the proof uses the fact that $A$ itself is a Banach space since it is a closed subspace of a Banach space.

**Remark 17.39.** If we have a family $F(x, \alpha)$ with parameter $\alpha$ where all $F(x, \alpha)$ fulfill the contraction principle with $0 \le q < 1$ independent on $\alpha$ then the solution $\xi = \xi(\alpha)$ of $F(\alpha, \xi) = \xi$ depends continuously on $\alpha$ which may vary in an open subset of some Banach space $X$.

**Exercise 17.40.** Let $F : A \to A$ be as in Theorem 17.38. Assume that for each $j = 1, 2, \ldots$ there exists $q_j$ such that

$$\left\| F^j(x_1) - F^j(x_2) \right\|_X \le q_j \|x_1 - x_2\|_X, \quad x_1, x_2 \in A.$$

Prove that if $\sum_{j=1}^{\infty} q_j < \infty$ then $F$ has a unique fixed point.

**Exercise 17.41.** Let $F : A \to A$ be as in Theorem 17.38. Assume that $X$ is compact Banach space. Prove that if

$$\|F(x_1) - F(x_2)\|_X < \|x_1 - x_2\|_X, \quad x_1, x_2 \in A,$$

then $F$ has a unique fixed point which can be obtained as the minimizer of $\|F(x) - x\|_X$ using the limit of any iterative sequence $x_j = F(x_{j-1}), j = 1, 2, \ldots$, with $x_0 \in A$.

**Applications of Banach fixed point theorem to nonlinear differential equations**   We
consider the nonlinear differential equation on the line

$$-u''(x) + \alpha(x)|u(x)|^2 u(x) = k^2 u(x), \quad x \in \mathbb{R},$$

where $\alpha \in L^1(\mathbb{R})$ and $k > 0$ is a spectral parameter (wave number). This type of equation can
be met in scattering theory. That's why we are looking for the special solutions in the form

$$u(x) = u_0(x) + u_{\text{sc}}(x), \quad u_0(x) = e^{ikx},$$

where $u_{\text{sc}}$ must satisfy the Sommerfeld radiation condition at infinity or

$$\lim_{r \to \infty} \left( \frac{\partial u_{\text{sc}}(x)}{\partial r} - i k u_{\text{sc}}(x) \right) = 0, \quad r = |x|.$$

Since $u_0''(x) = -k^2 u_0(x)$, one can show that $u_{\text{sc}}$ satisfies the equation

$$u_{\text{sc}}(x) = - \int_{-\infty}^{\infty} \frac{i e^{ik|x-y|}}{2k} \alpha(y)|u_0(y) + u_{\text{sc}}(y)|^2 (u_0(y) + u_{\text{sc}}(y)) dy,$$

where $\frac{i e^{ik|x|}}{2k}$ is the fundamental solution of the operator $-\frac{d^2}{dx^2} - k^2$ on the line. We can rewrite
this equation in the operator form

$$u_{\text{sc}}(x) = F(u_{\text{sc}})(x),$$

where the operator $F$ is defined by the right-hand side of the integral equation. Hence, the
existence of its solutions can be reduced to the question of the fixed points of $F$.

To apply the Banach fixed point theorem we consider the Banach space $X = L^\infty(\mathbb{R})$ (see
Theorem 16.107) and its closed subspace $A = \overline{B}_\rho(0) \subset L^\infty(\mathbb{R})$. First we find the conditions
which guarantee that $F : A \to A$, and second the conditions for contraction.

Indeed, if $\|v_{\text{sc}}\|_{L^\infty(\mathbb{R})} \le \rho$ then

$$|F(v_{\text{sc}})(x)| \le \frac{1}{2k} \int_{-\infty}^{\infty} |\alpha(y)|(1+\rho)^3 dy \le \frac{(1+\rho)^3}{2k} \|\alpha\|_{L^1(\mathbb{R})} \le \rho.$$

This implies that for given $\rho > 0$ the spectral parameter $k > 0$ must satisfy the condition

$$k \ge \frac{(1+\rho)^3}{2\rho} \|\alpha\|_{L^1(\mathbb{R})},$$

which guarantees that $F : A \to A$.

To satisfy the contraction principle we write

$$|F(u_{\text{sc}}^{(1)}) - F(u_{\text{sc}}^{(2)})|$$

$$\le \frac{1}{2k} \int_{-\infty}^{\infty} |\alpha(y)| \left| \left[ |u_0 + u_{\text{sc}}^{(1)}|^2 (u_0 + u_{\text{sc}}^{(1)}) - |u_0 + u_{\text{sc}}^{(2)}|^2 (u_0 + u_{\text{sc}}^{(2)}) \right] \right| dy$$

$$\le \frac{1}{2k} \int_{-\infty}^{\infty} |\alpha(y)|$$

$$\times \left( (1+\rho)^2 \left\| u_{\text{sc}}^{(1)} - u_{\text{sc}}^{(2)} \right\|_{L^\infty(\mathbb{R})} + (1+\rho) \left| |u_0 + u_{\text{sc}}^{(1)}|^2 - |u_0 + u_{\text{sc}}^{(2)}|^2 \right| \right) dy$$

$$\le \frac{(1+\rho)^2 \|\alpha\|_{L^1(\mathbb{R})} + 2(1+\rho)^2 \|\alpha\|_{L^1(\mathbb{R})}}{2k} \left\| u_{\text{sc}}^{(1)} - u_{\text{sc}}^{(2)} \right\|_{L^\infty(\mathbb{R})}.$$

Thus, the condition

$$k > \frac{3(1+\rho)^2}{2} \|\alpha\|_{L^1(\mathbb{R})}$$

ensures the contraction principle for $F$.

Finally, the conditions of the Banach fixed point theorem are fulfilled if $k > 0$ and $\rho > 0$ satisfy the conditions

$$k \geq \frac{(1+\rho)^3}{2\rho} \|\alpha\|_{L^1(\mathbb{R})}, \quad k > \frac{3(1+\rho)^2}{2} \|\alpha\|_{L^1(\mathbb{R})}.$$

If, for example, $\rho = 1$ then the condition

$$k > 6 \|\alpha\|_{L^1(\mathbb{R})}$$

provides existence and uniqueness of $u_{\mathrm{sc}}$ from the ball $\overline{B}_1(0) \subset L^\infty(\mathbb{R})$ and therefore the solution of the form $u(x) = u_0(x) + u_{\mathrm{sc}}(x)$ for the original nonlinear differential equation satisfies $\|u\|_{L^\infty(\mathbb{R})} \leq 2$. In addition, the solution $u(x)$ can be obtained in $L^\infty(\mathbb{R})$ as

$$u(x) = u_0(x) + \lim_{j \to \infty} u_j(x),$$

where the iteration sequence $u_j$ is defined by $u_j = F(u_{j-1}), j = 1, 2, \ldots$, with, for example, $u_0 = 0$.

# Bibliography

[1] T. APOSTOL *Mathematical Analysis*, 2nd ed., Addison-Wesley, Reading, MA, 1974. (Not cited)

[2] G. M. FIKHTENGOL'TS *The Fundamentals of Mathematical Analysis, Vols.* 1, 2, Pergamon Press, Oxford, UK, 1965. (Not cited)

[3] V. A. ILYIN AND È. G. POZNYAK *The Fundamentals of Mathematical Analysis Parts* 1, 2, MIR, Moscow, 1982 (in Russian). (Not cited)

[4] A. N. KOLMOGOROV AND S. V. FOMIN *Elements of the Theory of Functions and Functional Analysis*, Nauka, Moscow, 1981 (in Russian). (Cited on p. x)

[5] A. N. KOLMOGOROV AND S. V. FOMIN *Introductory Real Analysis*, 5th ed., Prentice-Hall, Englewood Cliffs, NJ, 1970. (Not cited)

[6] H. ROYDEN AND P. FITZPATRICK *Real Analysis*, 4th ed., Pearson Education Asia Limited and China Machine Press, 2010. (Not cited)

[7] W. RUDIN *Principles of Mathematical Analysis*, 3rd ed., Indian Edition, McGraw-Hill India, 2013. (Not cited)

[8] V. A. ZORICH *Mathematical Analysis* I, II, 2nd ed., Springer, Berlin, 2015, 2016. (Not cited)

# Index